GOLF COURSE GUIDE TO BRITAIN AND IRELAND

The Sunday Telegraph

GOLF COURSE GUIDE TO BRITAIN AND IRELAND

DONALD STEEL

CollinsWillow
An Imprint of HarperCollins*Publishers*

This edition published 1992 by
Collins Willow
an imprint of HarperCollins Publishers
London

First published 1968
Tenth revised edition 1992

©Sunday Telegraph 1992
©Maps, HarperCollins Publishers 1992

Cover photograph: Dromoland Castle

A CIP catalogue record for this book
is available from the British Library
ISBN 0-00-218411-7

This edition produced by
Robert MacDonald Publishing, London SW1

Typeset by Peter MacDonald, Twickenham
Printed in Great Britain by
Scotprint Ltd, Musselburgh, Scotland

CONTENTS

KEY TO THE MAPS

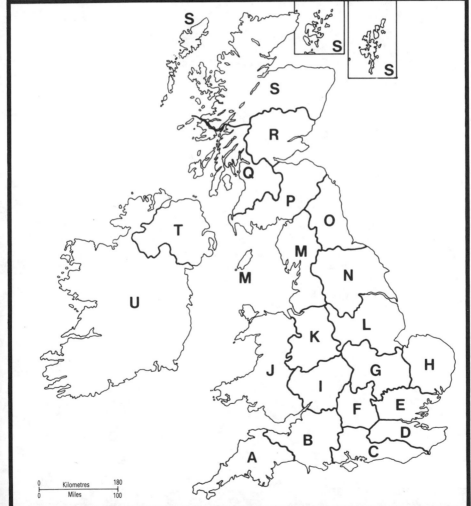

FOREWORD

Since the 9th edition of the Golf Course Guide was published in May 1990, more courses have been built and opened in Britain than in any two year period in the history of golf course architecture which became a recognised trade almost a hundred years ago. The last couple of years has seen a spate of Clubs celebrating centenaries and the next few years will see many more.

The 1890s marked a golden era but the 1990s will have generated a higher proportion of new golfers than any other age and there is absolutely no sign that demand has, or will, reach saturation point. Statistics are not always helpful and the predictions in the Royal and Ancient's "Demand for Golf" may have been counter productive. Last year, the English Golf Union reported that permission for something like 1200 new projects had been granted in England alone but this led to Local Authorities and Banks viewing matters with increasing suspicion, a situation exacerbated by the news that many ambitious developments were in financial trouble.

What is needed are new courses imaginatively designed, soundly built and sensibly priced. There is also a requirement for some more basic developments and short golfing academies to cater for beginners and the less ambitious although that will not satisfy everybody for long. Young golfers can become scratch golfers in three or four years and they will want to graduate from the "nursery slopes" as fast as possible. Academies — a new term in the context of golf — provide only temporary accommodation.

Multi-million pound enterprises have strictly limited appeal, even if some of their developers have not helped themselves or their causes by planning the wrong thing in the wrong place. It is undeniable that all decent new projects must ultimately cost more in terms of annual subscriptions and entrance fees than the average in established Clubs throughout Britain and Ireland. However, the cost of golf in these islands has always represented remarkably good value for money and this can only be preserved if architects do not try to create extravagant flights of fancy that only a handful can afford and fewer still can play successfully and thus enjoy.

Nothing has been more damaging than the absurd belief that a golf course can only be good if it possesses the label "championship", a trend that has resulted in many breaches of the trade descriptions act. Conferring a loose term to aid marketing is not necessarily any indication of quality but this Guide has always been an impartial directory of the courses available to those who consult it.

What matters far more is the range of choice and the freedom to play that exists. Nowhere else in the world can you find such variety of settings. The game is played in stately, sheltered parks, on wild and lonely moors, undulating downland, glorious heathland and on the ancient seaside links where golf began.

The Guide was first launched to make golfers aware of their good fortune and to help arouse the urge to explore. That remains the driving force and, whilst there beats in a few the heart of a champion, the pleasure derived from a sense of escape and a little health giving exercise in places of rare beauty is what keeps most of us going. Long may it continue.

Donald Steel
March 1992

INTRODUCTION

Several important changes have been made to the guide in this present edition. The most obvious is the introduction of colour into the maps, adding considerably to the ease with which courses can be located and identified. At the same time, the geographical organisation of the book has been radically altered; and, for the first time, a separate section devoted to a selection of driving ranges and other practice facilities has been included.

Organisation. The book is divided into 21 areas or county groupings, as opposed to the 28 used in previous editions. The areas have been chosen on the basis of golfing affinities and familiarity of use rather than cartographical convenience or bureaucratic definition. In particular, the purely administrative boundaries created by local government reorganisation have been ignored where they conflict with County Golf Union affiliations; thus the golf courses of Humberside have been reallocated to Lincolnshire and Yorkshire, those of the West Midlands to Warwickshire or Staffordshire, those of Avon to Gloucestershire and Somerset. Middlesex has been resurrected. This is not just in recognition of the fact that the new counties and metropolitan areas were little loved; it anticipates similar action on the part of the government itself.

As before, the areas are labelled alphabetically, from A to U. Each area has a map indicating the location of courses within it (see page 7 for a key to the county groupings and pages on which individual area maps are to be found). Within each section, courses are listed alphabetically, and numbered, and the combination of letter and number is used to identify each course in the overall index (page 308).

Course Information. For each golf course in the book, we have tried to provide the following information: the name; telephone number; address; travel directions to the course; a brief description of the type of course; the number of holes, length and Standard Scratch Score; the course architect and date of foundation if known; restrictions on visiting golfers — when they may play and whether reservations, club membership, handicap certificates are required, for example; green fees; whether parties or visiting societies are permitted and, if so, when; what catering and other facilities (for example swimming pools, tennis courts, putting greens or driving ranges) are available; and finally local hotels (particularly where golfing holidays can be arranged).

Where no information is given for a particular category — eg Societies or Catering — it can be assumed that the facilities are not available to visitors or don't exist.

Similarly, the absence of hotel information does not mean that there are no local hotels. On the contrary, details of accommodation facilities are normally only given where hotels are relatively scarce, or where specific attention is paid to the requirements of golfers or where there is a recommendation from the golf course concerned. In other cases, there will generally be an abundance of local hotels or of bed and breakfast accommodation, of which details can be found from one of the many guide books on the market, or from the local tourist board.

It should be noted that telephone numbers in the Republic of Ireland should be dialled in the same way as other international calls. The numbers given are those for use when telephoning from within Eire itself. From all other countries (including the UK) the area code (without the zero) should be prefixed with the international dialling code (010 353).

Green Fees. All the information in this book has been compiled with the help of club secretaries and was valid at the time of going to press (January 1992). However, many clubs set green fees for the coming year in the spring, and information may not have been available during the period of compilation of this book. Intending golfers would generally be wise to ring the golf course concerned to check before

Donald Steel
and
Co. Ltd.

International Golf Course Architects

Designs currently under construction
or completed in twelve countries

The Forum, Stirling Road, Chichester, West Sussex PO19 2EN
Telephone: (0243) 531901/532582
Fax: (0243) 532581
Telex: 86402 CHITYP G

Member of British Institute of Golf Course Architects

setting out. It should also be noted that some green fees are subject to VAT, in addition to the fees quoted, and that weekend rates often apply on public holidays also, even if this is not specifically stated in the Guide.

Green fees given for courses in Eire should be assumed to be in Irish pounds.

Abbreviations. In order to accommodate the considerable number of new courses in this edition, some abbreviations have been used. These should be self-evident:

G & CC = Golf and Country Club
LC = Leisure Centre
GC = Golf Centre or Golf Complex
WD = weekday(s) — Monday to Friday
WE = weekend(s) — Saturday, Sunday
BH = Bank (or Public) Holidays
GH = Guest House

Standard abbreviations are also used for months and days of the week.

Driving Ranges. Despite the considerable number of new golf courses, it still remains difficult (and often expensive) for the casual golfer in many areas to spend an hour or two improving his or her game. No doubt in response to this, a plethora of driving ranges and other types of practice facility have appeared. We have therefore included a selection of these at the end of the book (between pages 298 and 307). Space limitations have made it impossible to give more than the most basic information; however, it should be noted that the great majority offer P.G.A. professional golfing tuition, as well as club repair, club hire and, often, a full range of retail services.

Comments. The publishers of this Guide would welcome any information about courses that are not in the book — and indeed about any errors or alterations relating to the current contents, so that they can be incorporated in the next edition. Any comments and suggestions should be sent to: The Sunday Telegraph Golf Course Guide, PO Box 13, Wotton-under-Edge, Gloucestershire GL12 8JL, where they will be gratefully received.

A

CORNWALL, DEVON, CHANNEL ISLANDS

There is about the courses in this region an unmistakable air of holiday golf although it is thoroughly easy to appreciate how the members of Clubs heave a sigh of relief when the holidaymakers have gone for the year and they are left in peace.

For the historical contribution that its golfers have made to the game it is appropriate to start in Jersey, where Harry Vardon and Ted Ray were born, Vardon in a cottage on the edge of Royal Jersey's Links at Grouville. It is remarkable that of the tiny handful of British winners of the US Open two were born within a mile or so of each other on an island that represents a mere dot on the world map. Vardon, who did not take up the game until he was 21 and yet was Open champion four years later, forged his game on a course that begins along the shore of Grouville Bay under the watchful, distant eye of Mont Argeuil.

Elsewhere, particularly on the second nine, recent change has eliminated one or two architectural shortcomings but nothing compared to the new broom that has transformed La Moye, set on Jersey's exposed western headland. In less than 20 years, it has been turned from a test of sporting eccentricities into one which, given the aid of a stiff breeze, can have a field of top clan professionals at full stretch.

In that time, a winning score has risen by as much as 15 strokes over four rounds, but over the water on Guernsey there has been no such upheaval on the charming Royal Guernsey which has to shoulder and satisfy almost the entire golfing demand of the community.

Over on the mainland, St Mellion and Bodmin have boosted the courses in Cornwall, a county whose traditional delights surround West Cornwall at Lelant, Trevose and St Enodoc, the latter with a fine new clubhouse on land purchased from the Duchy in their centenary year in 1990.

Local interest in Devon was given a boost when their men's team won the English Counties championship for the first time in 1985, a tribute to the courses on which many were raised.

East Devon, a sort of elevated seaside Sunningdale, is the pick in the South, the Manor House at Moretonhampstead dominates the central heart while Saunton and Royal North Devon guard the northern coast with justifiable pride. Saunton, which has always been one of my favourite spots, boasts arguably the best pair of courses in Britain, the West upgraded a year or two back to rival its neighbour — a regular and deserved choice for championships.

Across the estuary at Westward Ho!, Royal North Devon is an ageless monument, the oldest seaside course in England although one where invasion of the sea is proving hard to repel. Nevertheless, ground that may appear plain from a distance comes compellingly to life as the holes penetrate land that is full of character down nearer the famous Pebble Ridge. No golfer with a grain of romance in his soul should pass it by, particularly as journeys to that part of the world have been made so much simpler by a new road from Tiverton and by a new bridge that crosses the estuary at Bideford.

A hearty word, too, for Yelverton on the edge of Dartmoor, north of Plymouth and for Thurlestone and Churston; and a welcome to a new complex on Woodbury Common near Budleigh Salterton which lends a nice, modern balance to a south western tip of Britain which has so many good things to offer.

A1 **Alderney**
☎(048 182) 2835
Routes des Carriers, Alderney,
Channel Islands
1 mile E of St Annes.
Undulating seaside course.
9 holes, 2528 yards, S.S.S.32;
double rounds for 18, S.S.S.65
Designed by Frank Pennink.
Visitors: welcome at all times,
except competition days.
Green Fee: on application.
Societies: catered for on weekdays
by arrangement and weekends for
special events.
Catering: bar foods served on
weekdays, Sun lunch, special parties
or lunches by arrangement.
Hotels: Bellevue; Sea View.

A2 **Axe Cliff**
☎(0297) 20499, 24371 Sec.
Squires Lane, Axmouth, Seaton,
Devon EX12 4AB
Through village of Axmouth, along
riverside, turn left just before
Axmouth bridge and straight up lane.
Coastal course one side, countryside
the other.
18 holes, 4867 yards, S.S.S.64
Founded 1892

Visitors: h/cap cert and membership
of recognised club required; own
clubs, no sharing; course closed until
11am Wed; with member only
12am-2pm Sat and 1-2pm Sun;
competitions Sun before 11.30am.
Green Fee: £10 WD, £12 WE & BH.
Societies: welcome, must book in
advance.
Catering: bar and catering.
Hotels: Shrubbery (Rousdon).

A3 **The Ballpark**
☎(0326) 572518
Wheal Dream, Wendron, Helston,
Cornwall
1.5 miles N of Helston on B3297
Redruth road.
18 holes, Par 3
Visitors: welcome any time.
Green Fee: on application
Catering: at Jolly Farmer.
Pitch & Putt, tennis, croquet, putting
green.

A4 **Bigbury**
☎(0548) 810207
Bigbury-on-Sea, Kingsbridge, Devon
TQ7 4BB
Take A379 Plymouth-Kingsbridge

road; turn right 2 miles from Modbury
at Harraton Cross, signposted
Bigbury-on-Sea; club is a further 5
miles from here.
Undulating seaside course.
18 holes, 6076 yards, S.S.S.69
Designed by J.H. Taylor.
Founded 1926
Visitors: welcome.
Green Fee: £20/day, £10 after 5pm.
Societies: welcome by
arrangement.
Catering: full facilities.
Hotels: Thurlestone; Cottage Hotel
(Hope Cove).

A5 **Bodmin G & CC**
☎(0208) 73600, 77325
Lostwithiel Rd, Bodmin, Cornwall
Between Bodmin and Lostwithiel, S
of A30.
Championship moorland/parkland
course.
18 holes, 6162 yards, Par 71
Designed by J. Hamilton Stutt.
Founded 1990
Visitors: welcome.
Green Fee: on application.
Societies: welcome.
Catering: full bar and restaurant.
Driving range.

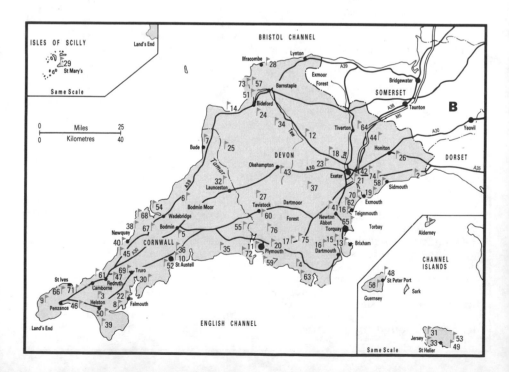

A6 **Bowood Park**
☎(0840) 21307
Valley Truckle, Lanteglos, Camelford, Cornwall PL32 7RT
On A39 S of Camelford.
Parkland course.
18 holes, 6692 yards, S.S.S.72
Opening summer 1992
Visitors: h/cap certs required, ring for starting times.
Green Fee: £20.
Societies: welcome.
Catering: full bar and restaurant facilities.
Practice ground.

A7 **Bude and N Cornwall**
☎(0288) 352006 Sec, 353176 catering, 353635 Pro.
Burn View, Bude, Cornwall EX23 8DA
A39, 1 minute from town centre.
Seaside links course.
18 holes, 6202 yards, S.S.S.70
Designed by Tom Dunn.
Founded 1891
Visitors: 1st tee reserved for members 8-9.30am, 12.30-2pm, 5-6.30pm; times may be booked in advance.
Green Fee: £20/day WD, £25/day WE & BH.
Societies: welcome; 1st tee can be reserved (Mon-Fri).
Catering: wide selection of meals available throughout the day.
Hotels: Camelot; Grosvenor; Falcon; Penarvor; Burn Court; Chough; Cliff; Langfield Manor; Stamford Hill.

A8 **Budock Vean**
☎(0326) 250288
Mawnan Smith, Falmouth, Cornwall TR11 5LG
On main road between Falmouth and Helston, 7 miles from Helston.
Undulating parkland course.
9 holes, 5222 yards, S.S.S.65

Designed by James Braid, D. Cook and P.H. Whiteside.
Founded 1932
Visitors: welcome any time.
Green Fee: on application
Societies: all year on application, except Sun.
Catering: snacks, lunch and table d'hôte or à la carte dinner.
Hotels: Budock Vean.

A9 **Cape Cornwall G & CC**
☎(0736) 788611
Cape Cornwall, St Just, Penzance, Cornwall TR19 7NL
A3071 to St Just-in-Penwith, left at memorial clock, 1 mile on left.
Coastal parkland course.
18 holes, 5665 yards, S.S.S.68
Founded May 1990
Visitors: welcome except Sat and Sun between 8am and 11.30am.
Green Fee: £14/round, £20/day WD; £16/round, £20/day WE & BH.
Societies: any time by arrangement.
Catering: full bar all week, lunch 12-2pm, dinner 7-10pm Thurs-Sat (winter), Tues-Sat (summer).
Heated pool, snooker, solarium, gym, sauna, practice area, putting green.

A10 **Carlyon Bay Hotel**
☎(072 681) 2304
Carlyon Bay, St Austell, Cornwall PL25 3RD
Main Plymouth-Truro road 1 mile W of St Blazey.
Clifftop/parkland course.
18 holes, 6463 yards, S.S.S.71
Designed by Hamilton Stutt.
Founded 1926
Visitors: h/cap certs required; ring for starting times (Par 4228).
Green Fee: on application
Societies: welcome, ring Par 4228.
Catering: full facilities.
Hotels: Carlyon Bay.

A11 **China Fleet CC**
☎(0752) 848668
Saltash, Cornwall PL12 6LJ
1 mile from Tamar Bridge, leave A38 before tunnel and follow signs.
Parkland course.
18 holes, 6551 yards, S.S.S.72
Designed by Martin Hawtree.
Founded June 1991
Visitors: by prior arrangement only; after 1st June 1992.
Green Fee: on application.
Societies: by arrangement with Sec (golf).
Catering: full facilities.
Hotels: accommodation available; off-peak packages.

A12 **Chulmleigh**
☎(0769) 80519
Leigh Rd, Chulmleigh, N Devon EX18 7BL
From Barnstaple follow "Tourist Route Exeter" signs; from Exeter follow A377 Crediton road, continue through Crediton, after approx 12 miles turn right into Chulmleigh.
Meadowland course.
18 holes, 1450 yards, S.S.S.54; winter (Dec-Mar), 9 holes, 2360 yards, S.S.S.56
Designed by J.W.D. Goodban OBE.
Founded 1976
Visitors: welcome.
Green Fee: £4.50/round (£3.75 jnrs), £7/2 rounds (£6 jnrs), £9/day (£8 jnrs).
Societies: welcome by prior arrangement.
Catering: light snacks, licensed bar.
Hotels: Thelbridge Cross Inn.

A13 **Churston**
☎(0803) 842751 Sec, 842894 Pro.
Churston, Nr Brixham, Devon TQ5 0LA
On A379 3 miles from Paignton.

Downland course overlooking Torbay.
18 holes, 6219 yards, S.S.S.70
Designed by H.S. Colt.
Founded 1890
Visitors: members of recognised golf clubs only; h/cap certs required.
Green Fee: on application.
Societies: by arrangement.
Catering: available each day during summer, opening hours depend on time of year.

A14 Clovelly G & CC
☎(0237) 431442, 431448
Woolsery, Bideford, Devon EX39 5RA
6 miles S of Clovelly off A39.
Parkland course.
9 holes (18 tees), 5648 yards, S.S.S.67
Designed by John Hepplewhite.
Founded 1987
Visitors: no restrictions except acceptable standard of golf.
Green Fee: £12 (18 holes) all week.
Societies: by prior arrangement
Catering: bar and restaurant.
Swimming, snooker, pool, tennis, fishing, children's play area.
Hotels: lodge accommodation available on site.

A15 Dainton Park
Totnes Rd, Ipplepen, Newton Abbot, Devon
On A381 Newton Abbot-Totnes road.
Parkland course.
18 holes, 6250 yards, S.S.S.70
Designed by Adrian Stiff.
Opening autumn 1992
Visitors: welcome at any time, pay-as-you-play.
Green Fee: £10 WD, £14 WE.
Societies: welcome.
Catering: full facilities.

A16 Dartmouth G & CC
☎(080 421) 650, (080421) 628 fax.
Blackawton, Totnes, Devon TQ9 7DG
Off A3122 between Totnes and Dartmouth, 5 miles W of Dartmouth.
Moorland/parkland course.
18 holes, 7012 yards, Par 72; 9 holes, 2614 yards, Par 33
Designed by Jeremy Pern.
Opening spring 1992
Visitors: requested to book starting times at the club and produce h/cap certs.
Green Fee: £27.
Societies: Mon-Fri, phone for confirmation of date, start times, fees etc.

Catering: bar meals, restaurant, lounge/spike bar; function room for 240.
Full leisure club facilities scheduled for summer 1992.
Hotels: Fingals (Dittisham).

A17 Dinnaton
☎(0752) 892512, 892452
Dinnaton Sporting and Country Club, Ivybridge, Devon PL21 9HU
At A38 Ivybridge follow Dinnaton Golf signs.
Parkland course.
9 hole Par 3, 2500 yards, S.S.S.48
Founded 1989
Visitors: welcome at all times.
Green Fee: £10.
Societies: welcome at all times by arrangment.
Catering: Club bar, coffee lounge, Haywain restaurant.
Floodlit driving range, badminton, squash, volleyball, solarium, sauna, multi-gym, tennis, snooker.
Hotels: phone above number for accommodation on site or (0626) 333678.

A18 Downes Crediton
☎(0363) 773025 Sec, 773991 clubhouse, 774464 Pro.
The Clubhouse, Hookway, Crediton, Devon EX17 3PT
Off A377 Exeter-Crediton road, 8 miles NW of Exeter; turn off at Crediton railway station (by Shell garage), then left at crossroads towards Hookway.
Parkland/meadowland course with water features.
18 holes, 5917 yards, S.S.S.68
Founded 1976
Visitors: welcome, phone Sec/Pro.
Green Fee: £16 WD, £22 WE & BH.
Societies: welcome Tues and Fri.
Catering: coffee, lunch, dinner.
Hotels: Rosemont; Fair Park GH.

A19 East Devon
☎(03954) 3370
North View Rd, Budleigh Salterton, Devon
5 miles E of Exmouth on A376.
Heathland/seaside course.
18 holes, 6214 yards, S.S.S.70
Founded 1902
Visitors: welcome with letter of intro.
Green Fee: £20.
Societies: by arrangement.
Catering: full facilities every day from 10am.

A20 Elfordleigh G & CC
☎(0752) 336428
Colebrook, Plympton, Plymouth, Devon PL7 5EB
Off A38, 5 miles NE of Plymouth, 2 miles from Marsh Mills roundabout.
Undulating parkland course.
9 holes (18 tees), 5773 yards, S.S.S.68
Designed by J.H. Taylor.
Founded 1932
Visitors: weekdays unrestricted, weekends phone first; h/cap cert required.
Green Fee: on application
Societies: Thurs, phone first.
Catering: full facilities.
Swimming, snooker, squash, tennis.
Hotels: Elfordleigh.

A21 Exeter G & CC
☎(0392) 874139
Countess Wear, Exeter, Devon EX2 7AE
Topsham road off Countess Wear roundabout.
Parkland course.
18 holes, 6009 yards, S.S.S.69
Designed by James Braid.
Founded 1929
Visitors: welcome on weekdays.
Green Fee: £20/day.
Societies: Thurs only by arrangement.
Catering: lunch and evening meals all week.
Tennis, snooker, squash, gym, indoor pool.
Hotels: Devon Motel and Countess Wear, Buckram Lodge.

A22 Falmouth
☎(0326) 311262, 40525 Sec, 316229 Pro.
Swanpool Road, Falmouth, Cornwall TR11 5BQ
0.5 mile W of Swanpool Beach, Falmouth, on road to Maenporth.
Seaside parkland course.
18 holes, 5680 yards, S.S.S.67
Founded 1928
Visitors: welcome.
Green Fee: £15/round, £20/day, £70/week; jnrs under 18 £8/round.
Societies: welcome by written application; 4 weeks notice required.
Catering: bar, lunch and tea daily, evening meals by arrangement.
Practice fields.
Hotels: Royal Duchy; St Michael's; Penmere Manor; Greenlawns; Meudon Vean; Park Grove; Falmouth: all offer reduced fees or free golf and golfing breaks/packages.

A23 Fingle Glen

☎(0647) 61817
Fingle Glen Golf and Leisure
Complex, Tedbourne St Mary, Nr
Exeter, Devon EX6 6AF
Public parkland course.
9 holes (18 from summer 1993),
2466 yards, S.S.S.63
Designed by W. Pile.
Founded July 1989
Visitors: welcome; tee reserved Sat
am.
Green Fee: £7 (9 holes), £12.50 (18
holes) WD; £9 (9 holes), £16.50 (18
holes) WE.
Societies: welcome, not weekends.
Catering: bar, lounge, restaurant,
10.00am-10.00pm.
Floodlit driving range, fishing by
arrangement.
Hotels: own 9-bed hotel; golfing
breaks/packages available.

A24 Great Torrington

☎(0805) 22229
Weare Trees, Torrington, Devon
EX38 7EZ
1 mile from Torrington on Weare
Giffard road.
Undulating commonland course.
9 holes, 4418 yards, S.S.S.62
Founded 1932
Visitors: welcome except Sun am.
Green Fee: £9 WD, £12 WE & BH.
Societies: by arrangement except
Sun am.
Catering: full meals by arrangement.
Hotels: Castle Hill.

A25 Holsworthy

☎(0409) 253177
Kilatree, Holsworthy, N Devon, EX22
6XU
1.5 miles W of Holsworthy on A3072
Bude road.
Parkland course.
18 holes, 6059 yards, S.S.S.69
Founded 1937
Visitors: welcome except Sun am.
Green Fee: £12 WD, £15 WE & BH.
Societies: welcome by
arrangement.
Catering: bar; dining facilities.
Hotels: Coles Mill; Court Barn
(Clawton).

A26 Honiton

☎(0404) 44422 Sec, 42943 Pro,
47167 bar and catering
Middlehills, Honiton, Devon EX14
8TR
2 miles S of Honiton on minor road
from town centre, past railway
station and up steep hill signposted
Northleigh and Seaton; caravans
should approach from A35.
Parkland course.
18 holes, 5931 yards, S.S.S.68
Founded 1896
Visitors: members of a recognised
golf club welcome any time except
prior reservation for competition.
Green Fee: £16/day WD, £20 WE &
BH.
Societies: limited number catered
for, usually on Thurs.
Catering: lunch, high tea and dinner,
except Sun.
Hotels: Deer Park, Honiton Motel;
private towing caravan park with
prior bookings during summer
months.

A27 Hurdwick

☎(0822) 612746
Tavistock Hamlets, Tavistock, Devon
PL19 8PZ
1 mile N of Tavistock on road to
Brentnor.
Parkland course.
18 holes, 4553 yards, S.S.S.62
Designed by Hawtree.
Founded Aug 1990
Visitors: welcome.
Green Fee: £14/round, £20/day WD;
£16/round, £25/day WE & BH.
Societies: Tues-Fri inclusive.
Catering: bar and bar snacks
available.
Hotels: Bedford (Tavistock); Castle
Inn (Lydford).

A28 Ilfracombe

☎(0271) 862176
Hele Bay, Ilfracombe, N Devon EX34
9RT
On A399 Ilfracombe to Combe Martin
road.
Undulating heathland course with
spectacular views over sea and
moors.
18 holes, 5857 yards, S.S.S.68
Founded 1892
Visitors: welcome; start sheets
May-Oct; golfing certification
required.
Green Fee: £16/day WD, £18/day
WE & BH; £70/5 day ticket (Mon-Fri).
Societies: welcome by arrangement
with Sec.
Catering: normal bar; full time
catering.
Pool tables.
Hotels: Collingdale, Darnley, Floyd,
Wembley, Abbeydale, Maranatha, St
Helier, Avalon, Seven Hills,
Woodlands.

A29 Isles of Scilly

☎(0720) 22692
St Mary's, Isles of Scilly, TR21 0NF
1.5 miles from Hugh Town in St
Mary's.
Moorland course.
9 holes, 5974 yards, S.S.S.69
Designed by Horace Hutchinson.
Founded 1904
Visitors: welcome Mon-Sat.
Green Fee: on application
Catering: available.

A30 Killiow

☎(0872) 70246
Killiow, Kea, Nr Truro, Cornwall TR3
6AG
Leave Truro on A39 Truro/Falmouth
road; turn right at 1st roundabout 3
miles from Truro, clearly signposted
thereafter.
Picturesque parkland course.
18 holes, 3542 yards, S.S.S.57
Founded 1987
Visitors: welcome at all times;
course restricted for members' use
until 10.30am weekends and Bank
Holidays; in main season advisable to
ring for availability.
Green Fee: £8.50/round WD,
£10.50/round WE.
Hotels: Hospitality Hotels (St Agnes).

A31 La Moye

☎(0534) 43401 Sec/Manager,
47166 Course Ranger.
La Moye, St Brelade, Jersey, Channel
Islands
From airport turn right at crossroads,
follow main road to main junction,
turn right at crossroads; club about 1
mile down road, private lane on right.
Links course.
18 holes, 6741 yards, S.S.S.72
Founded 1902
Visitors: welcome 9.30-11.30am,
2.30-4.00pm except competition
days; must have h/cap cert.
Green Fee: £30/round, £50/day (inc.
lunch).
Societies: on request.
Catering: full restaurant facilities.
Practice ground, indoor practice net.
Hotels: Atlantic; L'Horizon; Le Chalet
and others.

A32 Launceston

☎(0566) 773442
St Stephens, Launceston, Cornwall
PL15 8HF
1 mile N of Launceston on Bude road
(B3254).
Parkland course.

18 holes, 6407 yards, S.S.S.71
Designed by Hamilton Stutt.
Founded 1927
Visitors: weekdays by arrangement.
Green Fee: £20.
Societies: Mon-Fri by arrangement.
Catering: available by arrangement.
Hotels: White Hart.

A33 Les Mielles
☎(0534) 82787
The Mount, Valde la Mare, St Ouen's,
Jersey, Channel Islands
In the middle of St Ouen's Bay.
Public seaside course
12 holes, 4,200 yards, S.S.S.60
Founded 1976
Visitors: welcome.
Green Fee: £4.50/round WD,
£5/round WE.
Societies: welcome weekdays by
prior arrangement.
Catering: cafeteria.
Driving range.
Hotels: Lobster Pot; La Place.

A34 Libbaton
☎(0769) 60269, 60167 Pro.
High Bickington, Umberleigh, N
Devon EX37 9BS
On B3217 1 mile through High
Bickington towards Winkleigh,
adjacent to A377 Barnstaple-
Crediton road.
Parkland course.
18 holes, 6250 yards, S.S.S.68
Founded 1988
Visitors: welcome.
Green Fee: £12/round, £15/day WD;
£15/round, £18/day WE.
Societies: welcome Mon, Tues,
Wed, Fri; society package (golf and
food) £27.50 per head.
Catering: food all day, bar except
Sun when licensing laws apply.
Floodlit driving range, trout fishing.
Hotels: Bedford House; Northcote
Manor.

A35 Looe
☎(050 34) 239
Bin Down, Looe, Cornwall PL13 1PX
Midway between Liskeard and Looe.
Downland/parkland course.
18 holes, 5940 yards, S.S.S.68
Designed by Harry Vardon.
Founded 1934
Visitors: welcome 7 days per week.
Green Fee: £15/round, £24/day; 5
and 7 day tickets available.
Societies: welcome, arranged to suit
requirements.
Catering: bar open all day.

A36 Lostwithiel G & CC
☎(0208) 873550
Lower Polscoe, Lostwithiel, Cornwall
PL22 0HQ
On A390 12 miles W of Liskeard,
signposted.
Parkland course.
18 holes, 6098 yards, S.S.S.71
Designed by Stewart Wood R.I.B.A.
Founded 1991
Visitors: welcome with current
h/cap cert; booking advised for
starting time.
Green Fee: £15 WD, £20 WE.
Societies: most welcome, not
weekends or Bank Holidays.
Catering: bar and bar snacks all day;
restaurant evenings and Sun lunch.
Tennis.
Hotels: Lostwithiel G & CC on
course; golf inclusive bargain breaks
available.

A37 Manor House Hotel
☎(0647) 43055
Moretonhampstead, Newton Abbot,
Devon TQ13 8RE
12 miles from Exeter and Newton
Abbot on Princetown road.
Parkland course.
18 holes, 6016 yards, S.S.S.69
Designed by J.W. Abercrombie.
Founded 1934
Visitors: welcome by arrangement.
Green Fee: on application
Societies: catered for 7 days.
Catering: full facilities.
Hotels: Manor House.

A38 Merlin
☎(0841) 540222
Mawganporth, Newquay, TR8 4AD
Links type course.
9 holes, 2300 yards, S.S.S.32, (18
holes, 6,600 yards from autumn
1992)
Founded July 1991
Visitors: welcome any time.
Green Fee: £5.50 (9 holes), £8.50
(18 holes).
Societies: parties of 12 or more by
arrangement.
Catering: available in Merrymoor
Inn, Mawganporth (1 mile).
Hotels: White Lodge, golfing
packages available.

A39 Mullion
☎(0326) 240685 Sec, 240276
Clubhouse, 241176 Pro.
Cury, Helston, Cornwall TR12 7BP
5 miles from Helston on A3083
Lizard road.

Links and clifftop course.
18 holes, 6022 yards, S.S.S.69
Founded 1895
Visitors: welcome, h/cap required.
Green Fee: £16.50/day, £57.50/5
days.
Societies: welcome, green fee £12.
Catering: bar snacks, restaurant.
Hotels: Polurrian; Mullion Cove;
Mullion Holiday Park; Cornwallis.

A40 Newquay
☎(0637) 874354/874830
Tower Rd, Newquay, Cornwall TR7
1LT
From ring road down Tower Rd to
end, adjacent to Fistral beach.
Seaside course.
18 holes, 6136 yards, S.S.S.69
Designed by H.S. Colt.
Founded 1890
Visitors: welcome.
Green Fee: £16 WD, £20 WE.
Societies: catered for weekdays.
Catering: full facilities.
Tennis, snooker, gym.
Hotels: Bristol; Atlantic Headland.

A41 Newton Abbot (Stover)
☎(0626) 52460
Bovey Rd, Newton Abbot, S Devon
TQ12 6QQ
On A382 Newton Abbot-Bovey
Tracey road, N of Newton Abbot.
Parkland course.
18 holes, 5886 yards, S.S.S.68
Designed by James Braid
Founded 1931
Visitors: must be introduced or have
proof of membership of recognised
club.
Green Fee: £21/day.
Societies: Thurs only, minimum 24.
Catering: full catering daily from
11am.
Hotels: Edgemoor; Dolphin.

A42 Northbrook
☎(0392) 57436, fax (0392) 424285
Topsham Rd, Exeter, Devon EX2 6EU
From M5 junction 30 take A379; at
1st roundabout take 3rd exit onto
B3182 Topsham road, course 0.5
mile on left.
Public, wooded parkland course.
18 holes, 1078 yards, S.S.S.54
Founded 1968
Visitors: open to all.
Green Fee: £1.65/round (clubs
provided).
Catering: vending and
confectionery.

Saunton

Name the courses worthy of the Open championship if they were more strategically located, and Saunton would be top of many lists. A strange fact because in many ways Saunton's setting is its prime asset. It is hard to avoid sounding like a travel brochure when describing the vast, wide stretch of golden sand, the estuaries of the Taw and the Torridge, the botanic delights of the Burrows and the mountainous dunes that divide the golf from the sea. A keen eye quickly spots the Pebble Ridge and the links of Westward Ho! across the estuary, which are the oldest seaside links in England.

Bernard Darwin, in his wonderful book *The Golf Courses of the British Isles* published in 1910, describes a visit to Westward Ho! as a "reverent pilgrimage", blossoming forth into pages of ecstatic detail, but he glosses over Saunton in a few lines. "Saunton" he wrote "looks at first glance like a fine golf course". Nonetheless, he quoted Herbert Fowler as rating Saunton "almost, if not quite, as highly as Westward Ho!" and Harry Vardon as saying that he "would like to retire to Saunton and do nothing but play golf for pleasure".

In fairness to Darwin, Saunton had barely come of age when he wrote those words and I am sure that, had he had occasion to re-assess his judgements, he would have written a purple passage or two on the subject of Saunton. It was, after all, one of the very few seaside links laid out for the modern ball, which is why it has withstood the recent advancements in the manufacture of clubs and balls better than any.

As John Goodban's excellent history of the Club — *The First 90 Years* — relates, the changes that have been necessary were mostly caused by the upheaval of the Second World War. The clubhouse became the headquarters of the Coast Defence Unit and the courses a battle training school with the sandhills mined against invasion.

Three years earlier, Saunton reached a deserved peak of eminence by staging the English championship in which Frank Pennink beat Leonard Crawley in the final. Pre-war Saunton had two fine courses and an assured future.

After the war, Saunton rose phoenix-like from the ashes, although there was a period of uncertainty when its survival might have been said to be a 'close run thing'. Until 1960 the management of the Club was in the hands of its owners, the Christie Estate — also the owners of Glyndebourne — but the saviour of the old Old course was Ken Cotton.

He was able to restore most of it in 1950 with the only radical change being to the first two and last two holes. From a tee on a high ridge near the clubhouse, he made a new 1st hole which, with the addition of the new 2nd, stretched the first four holes (all par 4s) to nigh on a mile. However, one of the charms of Saunton is that two of its three short holes really are short. The 5th and the 13th are classic examples of how short holes need not be a long iron or a wood but still demand plenty of stout hitting.

Cotton's other amendment was to cut a gap in the hills at the 8th and to turn the 17th into a downhill short hole and the 18th into a fine par 4 which curves right-handed to a green outside the clubhouse windows.

A significant development came in 1974 with the opening of the new West course. Instead of the pre-war Old and New courses came the East and West and, following the decision in 1987 to remodel the greens on the West, there is no doubt that the two courses are as fine as any in Britain.

Saunton's demand for the best championships and other important events is illustrated by its selection for three English strokeplay championships, the 1984 St Andrews Trophy match between Great Britain, Ireland and the continent of Europe, countless county events and the alternate staging with Royal North Devon of the West of England strokeplay championship — inaugurated in 1968. Lovers of Saunton hope it will one day house the Amateur championship. It's glories are infinite.

A43 Okehampton

☎(0837) 52113
Okehampton, Devon EX20 1EF
A30 to Okehampton centre from
where club is clearly signposted.
Undulating moorland course.
18 holes, 5307 yards, S.S.S.67
Founded 1913
Visitors: welcome, no athletes'
shorts, ankle socks or denim.
Green Fee: on application
Societies: by prior arrangement.
Catering: available.

A44 Padbrook Park (Cullompton)

☎(0884) 38286
Padbrook Park, Cullompton, Devon
EX15 1RU
1 mile from M5 Junction 28.
Parkland course; pay-as-you-play.
9 holes (double tees), 6108 yards,
S.S.S.69; 9-hole Par 3.
Designed by Bob Sandow
Founded 1991
Visitors: welcome at all times.
Green Fee: £5 (9 holes), £8 (18
holes), WD; £7 (9 holes), £14 (18
holes) WE.
Societies: welcome by prior
arrangement.
Catering: full bar and catering all
day.
3-rink indoor bowling arena, tennis,
outdoor pool, fishing lake and nature
trail.
Hotels: can be arranged through
manager.

A45 Perranporth

☎(0872) 573701, 572454
Budnic Hill, Perranporth, Cornwall
TR6 0AB
A3075 from Newquay then B3285;
club is on fringe of town adjacent to
beach.
Links course.
18 holes, 6208 yards, S.S.S.71
Designed by James Braid.
Founded 1929
Visitors: welcome but ring before
arrival.
Green Fee: on application.
Societies: welcome.
Catering: resident Steward and
Stewardess.
Hotels: Beach Dunes; Dunsmore.

A46 Praa Sands

☎(0736) 763445
Germoe Crossroads, Praa Sands,
Penzance, Cornwall TR20 9TQ
7 miles E of Penzance on A394.

Scenic seaside parkland course.
9 holes, 4096 yards, S.S.S.60
Founded May 1971
Visitors: welcome 8.30am-11pm
any day except Fri after 5pm and Sun
am.
Green Fee: £11/round (£7 with
member).
Societies: welcome by prior
arrangement.
Catering: open all day for meals or
snacks.
Pool, darts.
Hotels: Tarbert; Mount Prospect;
Beachfield (Penzance).

A47 Radnor Golf Centre

☎(0209) 211059
Radnor Road, Redruth, Cornwall.
2 miles NE of Redruth, signposted
from A3047 – the old Redruth
by-pass and North Country Cross
route.
Public heathland type course created
on derelict land.
9 holes Par 3, 1326 yards.
Designed by Gordon Wallbank.
Founded 1988
Visitors: no restrictions but own
clubs required; phone first.
Green Fee: £4 (9 holes), £6 (18
holes).
Catering: bar, possibly light snacks
from 1992.
Driving range, indoor ski training
machine, snooker.

A48 Royal Guernsey

☎(0481) 47022
L'Ancresse Vale, Guernsey, Channel
Islands
3 miles from St Peter Port.
Seaside course.
18 holes, 6206 yards, S.S.S.70
Designed by Mackenzie Ross.
Founded 1890
Visitors: not after 12am Thurs and
Sat; not Sun: must produce h/cap
cert.
Green Fee: £20/round/day, (£13
with member).
Societies: small societies on
application between Oct and Mar.
Catering: morning coffee, afternoon
tea, lunch, evening meals Tues, Wed,
Thurs, Fri and Sat.
Hotels: Pembroke; L'Ancresse
Lodge.

A49 Royal Jersey

☎(0534) 54416, 51042 Sec,
Steward and Members
Grouville, Jersey, Channel Islands

4 miles E of St Helier on road to
Gorey.
Seaside course.
18 holes, 6059 yards, S.S.S.70
Founded 1878
Visitors: welcome weekdays after
10am, weekends and Bank Holidays
after 2.30pm (BST) or 12.30pm
(whites).
Green Fee: on application.
Societies: small parties only.
Catering: full facilities by prior
arrangement with Steward.
Hotels: Beachcomber; Grouville Bay.

A50 Royal Naval Air Station Culdrose

☎(0326) 574121 extn 2413/7543
RNAS Culdrose, Helston, Cornwall
TR12 8QY
2.5 miles from Helston on Lizard
road.
Part of military airfield; members
only.
9 holes (18 tees), S.S.S.71
Founded 1962
Visitors: through Sec or as guest of
member, daily play restricted to
weekends and leave periods.
Green Fee: £5

A51 Royal North Devon

☎(0237) 473817 Sec, 473824
Clubhouse
Westward Ho, Bideford, Devon EX39
1HD
From Northam village take the road
down Bone Hill past the P.O. keeping
left; clubhouse is visible as you come
down the hill.
Links course.
18 holes, 6449 yards, S.S.S.72
Designed by Tom Morris.
Founded 1864
Visitors: welcome; booking
required.
Green Fee: on application.
Societies: by booking.
Catering: full facilities.
Snooker.
Hotels: Culloden House; Durrant
House; Anchorage.

A52 St Austell

☎(0726) 74756 Sec, 72649
Clubhouse
Tregongeeves Lane, St Austell,
Cornwall PL26 7DS
On A390 St Austell-Truro road, 1 mile
W of St Austell; the Tregongeeves
Lane junction is clearly signposted
just below St Mewan school.
Heathland/parkland course.

18 holes, 5725 yards, S.S.S.68
Founded 1911
Visitors: welcome with reservation; must be club members and hold h/cap certs.
Green Fee: £15/round/day WD, £18 WE.
Societies: catered for weekdays by arrangement.
Catering: full service; hot meals, bar snacks daily; evening meals available, phone first.
Hotels: Cliff Head; Carlyon Bay.

A53 St Clements
☎(0534) 21938
Jersey Recreation Grounds Co Ltd, Graeve d'azette, St Clements, Jersey, Channel Islands JE2 6QN
Close to St Helier.
Meadowland course
9 holes, 2244 yards, Par 30
Founded 1913
Visitors: welcome; Sun not before 1pm, Mon (except Bank Holidays) not before 11am; advisable to ring in advance.
Green Fee: on application
Catering: buffet bar and restaurant. Tennis (16 courts), bowling, putting green etc.

A54 St Enodoc
☎(020 886) 3216
Rock, Wadebridge, Cornwall PL27 6LB
From Wadebridge take B3314 Port Isaac road for 3 miles and then turn left to Rock.
Links course.
Church Course, 18 holes, 6207 yards, S.S.S.70; Holywell Course, 18 holes, 4166 yards, S.S.S.61
Designed by James Braid.
Founded 1890
Visitors: h/cap cert required for Church course.

Green Fee: on application.
Societies: limited to out of holiday season.
Catering: full facilities available every day.
Hotels: St Enodoc; St Moritz; Bodare; Port Gaverne.

A55 St Mellion International
☎(0579) 50101; (0579) 50116 fax.
St Mellion, Saltash, Cornwall PL12 6SD
3 miles S of Callington on A388.
Parkland course.
Nicklaus course, 18 holes, 6626 yards, S.S.S.72; Old course, 18 holes, 5927 yards, S.S.S.68
Designed by Jack Nicklaus (International course), J. Hamilton Stutt (Old Course).
Founded 1976
Visitors: welcome.
Green Fee: on application.
Societies: welcome.
Catering: restaurant, coffee shop, grill room; banqueting, conferences. Swimming pool, sauna, solarium, mulitgym, badminton, tennis, snooker.
Hotels: St Mellion.

A56 St Pierre Park Hotel
☎(0481) 727039, 728282 hotel.
Rohais, St Peter Port, Guernsey, Channel Islands
1 mile W of St Peter Port on Rohais road.
Hilly course with water hazards.
9 holes, 1500 yards, S.S.S.48
Designed by Tony Jacklin.
Founded 1984
Visitors: welcome except during competitions (Sun am).
Green Fee: £9 (9 holes), £14 (18 holes) WD; £10 (9 holes), £16 (18 holes) WE.

Societies: by arrangement.
Catering: full facilities at St Pierre Park Hotel.
Driving range, indoor swimming pool, health suite, etc.
Hotels: St Pierre Park.

A57 Saunton
☎(0271) 812436
Saunton, Nr Braunton, N Devon EX33 1LG
On B3231 from Braunton to Croyde, 7 miles from Barnstaple.
Traditional links course.
East, 18 holes, 6703 yards, S.S.S.73; West, 18 holes, 6356 yards, S.S.S.71
Designed by Herbert Fowler (East Course), Frank Pennink (West Course).
Founded 1897
Visitors: must be members of clubs with h/cap certs.
Green Fee: £21.50/day Mon-Fri, £26.50/day WE & BH.
Societies: any time booked in advance.
Catering: full restaurant all day.
Hotels: Saunton Sands; Kittiwell House; Preston House.

A58 Sidmouth
☎(0395) 513451 Sec, 513023 Club, 516407 Pro.
Cotmaton Road, Peak Hill, Sidmouth, Devon EX10 8SX
Take Exeter Station Rd to Woodlands Hotel, then turn right on Cotmaton Rd.
Undulating parkland course.
18 holes, 5800 yards, S.S.S.64
Founded Oct 1889
Visitors: welcome by arrangement with Sec.
Green Fee: £12 WD, £15 WE.
Societies: by arrangement.
Catering: no catering Mon; all-day bar Sat.

A59 Staddon Heights
☎(0752) 402475
Staddon Heights, Plymstock,
Plymouth, Devon PL9 9SP
Leave Plymouth city on the
Plymstock road; clubhouse is 5 miles
S of city near Royal Navy aerial
towers.
Seaside course.
18 holes, 5861 yards, S.S.S.68
Founded 1895
Visitors: welcome weekdays with
h/cap cert.
Green Fee: £15 WD, £20 WE & BH.
Societies: weekdays.
Catering: every day.
Hotels: Highlands.

A60 Tavistock
☎(0822) 612049 Clubhouse,
612344 Sec.
Down Rd, Tavistock, Devon PL19
9AQ
Take the Whitchurch road, turning
into Down Rd, and onto Whitchurch
Down.
Moorland course.
18 holes, 6250 yards, S.S.S.70
Founded 1890
Visitors: welcome, telephone in
advance.
Green Fee: £15 WD, £20 WE & BH.
Societies: by arrangement.
Catering: lunch, bar snacks, evening
meals.
Hotels: Bedford; Moorland Links;
Arundel Arms.

A61 Tehidy Park
☎(0209) 842208
Nr Camborne, Cornwall TR14 0HH
Off A302, 2 miles NE of Camborne on
the Portreath road.
Parkland course.
18 holes, 6241 yards, S.S.S.70
Founded 1922
Visitors: h/cap cert required.
Green Fee: £17/round, £22/day WD;
£22/round, £28/day WE & BH.
Societies: weekdays only.
Catering: full range bar snacks, à la
carte restaurant mornings and
evenings.
Snooker.
Hotels: Penventon; Glenfeadon; Old
Shire Inn; Tyacks.

A62 Teignmouth
☎(0626) 774194
Exeter Rd, Teignmouth, Devon TQ14
9NY
2 miles from Teignmouth on Haldon
Moor.

Moorland course.
18 holes, 6142 yards, S.S.S.69
Designed by Dr Alister Mackenzie.
Founded 1924
Visitors: must be members of a club
and have h/cap cert.
Green Fee: £20 WD, £23 WE.
Societies: by appointment, not
weekends or Wed.
Catering: full service every day.
Hotels: London; Venn Farm.

A63 Thurlestone
☎(0548) 560405
Thurlestone, Nr Kingsbridge, S
Devon TQ7 3NZ
Take Thurlestone turning from A379
Plymouth-Salcombe road; club
situated 4 miles S of Kingsbridge.
Downland course.
18 holes, 6337 yards, S.S.S.70
Founded 1897
Visitors: must produce a current
h/cap cert from recognised club.
Green Fee: £20/day, any day.
Societies: not catered for.
Catering: full facilities available all
day.
12 tennis courts (3 hard, 9 grass).
Hotels: Thurlestone.

A64 Tiverton
☎(0884) 252187
Post Hill, Tiverton, Devon EX16 4NE
5 miles from junction 27 on M5
towards Tiverton on A373; take 1st
exit left on dual carriageway through
Samford Peverell to Halberton.
Parkland/meadowland course.
18 holes, 6263 yards, S.S.S.71
Designed by James Braid.
Founded 1931
Visitors: letter of intro. or h/cap cert
required; no visitors Wed pm,
weekends or Bank Holidays, or
during Championship, Club and Open
meetings.
Green Fee: £20 WD, £26 WE.
Societies: no, unless already a
standard fixture.
Catering: lunch, teas available.
Hotels: Tiverton; Green Headland;
Hartnoll.

A65 Torquay
☎(0803) 314591
Petitor Rd, St Marychurch, Torquay,
Devon TQ1 4QF
N of Torquay on A379 Teignmouth
road, on outskirts of town.
Parkland course.
18 holes, 6192 yards, S.S.S.69
Founded 1910

Visitors: h/cap certs required.
Green Fee: £20 WD, £25 WE & BH.
Societies: by arrangement.
Catering: except Mon.

A66 Tregenna Castle Hotel
☎(0736) 795254
St Ives, Cornwall TR26 2DE
In grounds of Tregenna Castle Hotel,
signposted to left just before St Ives
on A3074 from Hayle.
Parkland course
18 holes, 3549 yards, S.S.S.57
Founded 1982
Visitors: welcome; ring for tee
times.
Green Fee: £9/day WD, £10/day WE
& BH.
Societies: welcome by prior
arrangement.
Catering: full bar and restaurant
facilities at hotel.
Tennis, squash, badminton,
swimming etc.
Hotels: Tregenna Castle.

A67 Treloy
☎(0637) 878554
Newquay, Cornwall TR7 4JN
On A3059 St Columb Major-
Newquay road, 3 miles from
Newquay.
Public heathland/parkland course.
9 holes, 2143 yards, S.S.S.31
Designed by M.R.M. Sandow
Founded 1991
Visitors: welcome.
Green Fee: £7.50 9 holes, £11.50 18
holes.
Societies: welcome.
Hotels: Barrowfield, Hotel California
(Newquay); White Lodge, Tredragon
(Mawgan Porth).

A68 Trevose Country Club
☎(0841) 520208
Constantine Bay, Padstow, Cornwall
PL28 8JB
4 miles W of Padstow off B3276.
Seaside links course.
18 holes, 6608 yards, S.S.S.71; 9
holes, 1357 yards, Par 29
Designed by H.S. Colt.
Founded 1925
Visitors: welcome; 3 and 4 ball
matches restricted; phone first.
Green Fee: on application
Societies: any time except
July-Sept.
Catering: all meals, good restaurant.
Swimming pool, tennis courts.
Hotels: Treglos; own self-catering
accommodation available.

TREVOSE
GOLF AND COUNTRY CLUB
Constantine Bay, Padstow, Cornwall
Padstow (0841) 520208

- Championship Golf Course of 18 holes. S.S.S. 71. Fully automatic watering on all greens.
- 9 hole Short Course.
- Excellently appointed Club House with Restaurant providing full catering and air conditioning throughout.
- Accommodation in very superior chalets, bungalows, flats and dormy suites. Midweek bookings are encouraged.
- 3 Hard Tennis Courts.

- Heated swimming pool open from mid May to mid September.
- In addition to membership for Golf and Tennis, social membership of the Club is also available with full use of the Club House, Putting Greens and Sports Room.
- Six glorious sandy bays within about a mile of the Club House, with pool, open sea and surf bathing, and an open coast line for walks.
- Professional G. Alliss.

A69 **Truro**
☎(0872) 78684
Treliske, Truro, Cornwall TR1 3LG
From Truro follow A390 to Redruth, after 2 miles turn right at small roundabout; course signposted.
Undulating parkland course.
18 holes, 5357 yards, S.S.S.66
Designed by Colt, Alison & Morrison.
Founded 1937
Visitors: welcome, phone to ascertain any tee reservations.
Green Fee: £16/day/round WD, £21 WE & BH, (half price with member).
Societies: welcome except weekends and Tues.
Catering: full bar and restaurant facilities every day.
Snooker.
Hotels: special arrangements with Hospitality Hotels.

A70 **Warren**
☎(0626) 862255
Dawlish Warren, Dawlish, Devon EX7 0NF
Take A379 from Exeter to Dawlish Warren.
Links course.
18 holes, 5968 yards, S.S.S.69
Founded 1892
Visitors: welcome with h/cap certs.
Green Fee: £17 WD, £20 WE.

Societies: weekdays by arrangement with Sec.
Catering: bar snacks and meals all week.
Hotels: Langstone Cliff; Dawlish Warren.

A71 **West Cornwall**
☎(0736) 753401 Sec, 753177 Pro, 753319 Members
Lelant, St Ives, Cornwall TR26 3DZ
A30 to Hayle, then A3074 to St Ives.
Seaside links course.
18 holes, 5884 yards, S.S.S.68
Founded Dec 1889
Visitors: welcome; h/cap cert required.
Green Fee: £18/round.
Societies: on application to Sec.
Catering: lunch and dinner daily except Mon.
Snooker.
Hotels: Badger Inn (Lelant); Boskerris (Carbis Bay).

A72 **Whitsand Bay Hotel**
☎(0503) 30276
Portwrinkle, Crafthole, Torpoint, Cornwall PL11 3BY
On B3247, 6 miles off A38 from Plymouth.
Clifftop course.

18 holes, 5800 yards, S.S.S.69
Designed by William Fernie of Troon.
Founded 1905
Visitors: welcome; h/cap cert required.
Green Fee: £13 WD, £16 WE.
Societies: welcome all year by arrangement.
Catering: full facilities, 2 bars, 3 restaurants.
Indoor swimming pool, sauna, solarium etc.
Hotels: Whitsand Bay; special golf rates for residents.

A73 **Willingcott G & CC**
☎(0271) 870070, 870077
Woolacombe, N Devon EX34 7HN
2 miles S of Woolacombe in Ossaborough.
Heathland/moorland course.
9 holes, 2945 yards, Par 35
Designed by David Rice.
Opening autumn 1992.
Visitors: please phone for details of visitor requirements, society meetings, green fees etc.
Catering: bars, restaurants.
Full leisure complex with all amenities.
Driving range, practice facilities.
Hotels: accommodation on site; golfing breaks/packages available.

A74 Woodbury Park Golf & Country Club
☎(0395) 33382
Management Office, Woodbury Salterton, Nr Exeter, Devon EX5 1EL
From M5 junction 30 take A3052 Sidmouth road, turn right onto B3180, after approx 1 mile turn right to Woodbury Salterton, then immediately turn right to course.
Part municipal parkland course, some heathland.
18 holes (private), 6680 yards, S.S.S.73; 9 holes (public), 2350 yards, Par 33.
Designed by J. Hamilton Stutt
Founded 1992
Visitors: h/cap cert required for 18 hole course; all welcome on 9 hole.
Green Fee: 18 hole course, £25 (still to be finalised); 9 hole course, municipal rates.
Societies: by arrangement.
Catering: limited at present.

A75 Wrangaton
☎(0364) 73229
Wrangaton, South Brent, S Devon TQ10 9HJ
Turn off A38 between South Brent and Bittaford at Wrangaton P.O.
Moorland/parkland course.
18 holes, 6041 yards, S.S.S.69
Designed by Donald Steel.
Founded 1895
Visitors: welcome; h/cap cert or proof of competence required.
Green Fee: £15/day WD, £20/day WE & BH.
Societies: welcome Tues and Thurs only.
Catering: bar and catering facilities daily.
Hotels: The Coaching House; Glazebrook.

A76 Yelverton
☎(0822) 852824
Golf Links Rd, Yelverton, Devon PL20 6BN
8 miles N of Plymouth and 5 miles S of Tavistock on A386.
Moorland course.
18 holes, 6293 yards, S.S.S.70
Designed by Herbert Fowler.
Founded 1904
Visitors: accredited golfers welcome; h/cap cert required.
Green Fee: on application.
Societies: welcome by arrangement.
Catering: daily.
Hotels: Manor House; Moorland Links.

B

SOMERSET, DORSET, WILTSHIRE, SOUTH AVON

Some of the most enjoyable golf in Britain can be found around Bournemouth, an area rich in natural heathland characterised by heather, gorse, pines and silver birch. Ferndown, Parkstone and Broadstone are the pick, although Isle of Purbeck is the best from a scenic point of view. Both Queen's Park and Meyrick Park also feature some of the finest public facilities in the country and, as a result, are highly popular.

Dorset, like the rest of southern England, has seen its share of new developments in recent years, one course opening its doors this Summer being Dudsbury at Longham which has a splendid clubhouse position looking down on the River Stour. Converted from farmland and boasting lakes, well established trees and pleasant contours, it fills an obvious need in an area where the demand is great. Slightly more remote are the settings of Sherborne in the midst of rural splendour and Lyme Regis on its clifftop perch close to the border with Devon. However, both of them typify the variety that exists on British courses.

Wiltshire is among our smaller counties in golfing terms, although Marlborough and High Post deserve mention, together with Broome Manor at Swindon which is certainly among the busiest courses. A public complex, it operates a booking system to cater for the enormous demand. But the one true championship course in Dorset, Wiltshire, Somerset and Avon is Burnham and Berrow, looking out on the Bristol Channel and the coastline of Wales.

Its dunes used to be among the most mountainous, the arrangement of the holes taking somewhat eccentric benefit of them, until modern amendments ironed out a few quirks and kinks. Burnham's most recent changes surrounded the loss of the Church hole and the old 13th which is now a housing estate. In consequence, the 14th is a short hole in the opposite direction but, for all its undoubted challenge, Burnham and Berrow is unchanging in its appeal.

Weston-super-Mare is worth a visit, one memory of my first acquaintance of it thirty years ago being the comparison of one hole with the Road Hole at St Andrews. In spite of the persuasiveness of my guide, I remained unconvinced but that is no criticism of a course whose original design was by Tom Dunn, one of the early professionals who was among the first to turn his hand to golf course architecture.

There is nothing really outstanding in the region of Bristol or Bath but pleasant rounds await at Long Ashton, Bristol & Clifton, Knowle, and, in the Gloucestershire area, Lansdown and Tracy Park. Mendip, north of Shepton Mallett, displays the best of Frank Pennink's art.

Crossing over into Wiltshire again, North Wilts represents some of the finest elements of downland golf while the courses of Salisbury and South Wiltshire rub shoulders with Salisbury racecourse. Chippenham — extended from twelve holes — has been greatly improved and Shrivenham Park keeps a welcome for all.

B1 The Ashley Wood

☎(0258) 452253 Sec, 480379 Pro.
Wimborne Rd, Blandford, Dorset
DT11 9HN
From Blandford 1 mile S along B3082
Wimborne road.
Undulating meadowland course.
9 holes, 6227 yards, S.S.S.70
Founded 1896
Visitors: welcome except Tues am,
weekends am, competition and
match days; golf club membership or
h/cap cert required.
Green Fee: £17 (18 holes) WD (£10
with member), £21 WE & BH (£12
with member).
Societies: by arrangement with Sec.
Catering: Stewardess welcomes
applications.
Hotels: Crown (Blandford Forum).

B2 Bath

☎(0225) 425182
Sham Castle, North Rd, Bath, Avon
BA2 6JG
Take A36 Bath to Warminster road,
turn up North Rd, club is about 800
yards on left, 1.5 miles SE of Bath.
Downland course.
18 holes, 6369 yards, S.S.S.70
Founded 1880
Visitors: must have h/cap; welcome
weekdays and weekends, subject to
course availability.
Green Fee: £21 WD, £25 WE.
Societies: catered for Wed and Fri.
Catering: daily; bar snacks Thurs.
Hotels: Bath; Beaufort; Dukes; Spa.

B3 Blue Circle

☎(0373) 822481
Trowbridge Rd, Westbury, Wilts
Parkland course; part of Blue Circle
Works Sports Complex.
9 holes, 5500-6000 yards, S.S.S.66
Visitors: with member only, or on
county card system.
Green Fee: £6/day WD, £10/day WE.
Societies: by arrangement.
Catering: by arrangement.

B4 Bournemouth & Meyrick Park

☎(0202) 290307
Central Drive, Meyrick Park,
Bournemouth BH2 6LH
In centre of Bournemouth.
Public parkland course, very
picturesque.
18 holes, 5663 yards, S.S.S.68
Founded 1890
Visitors: welcome any time;
advisable to book previous day.

Green Fee: £10.40/round.
Societies: welcome by prior
arrangement.
Catering: café. Squash.

B5 Bowood G & CC

☎(0249) 822228, 822218 fax.
Bowood House, Calne, Wilts SN11
9PQ
Follow signs off M4 and A4 to
Bowood House.
Public course in Grade 1 parkland.
18 holes, 7317 yards, S.S.S.74 (from
Championship tees)
Designed by Dave Thomas
Founded May 1992
Visitors: open to anyone with proof
of h/cap.
Green Fee: £25/round, £40/day WD;
£40/round, £65/day WE.
Societies: weekdays.
Catering: private dining room,
restaurant, lounge bar.
Driving range, tennis.
Hotels: serviced house on course
(sleeps 8), free golf; apply for details.

B6 Bradford-on-Avon

☎(0225) 868268
Avon Close, Trowbridge Rd,
Bradford-on-Avon, Wilts
From Bradford towards Trowbridge,
on left near Police Station.
Parkland course alongside River
Avon.
9 holes, 2109 metres, S.S.S.61
Founded June 1991
Visitors: welcome, not Sat/Sun am.
Green Fee: £6 (9 holes), £10 (18
holes).
Catering: clubhouse due for
completion mid-summer 1992.
Hotels: Lea Park.

B7 Brean

☎(0278) 751570
Coast Rd, Brean, Burnham-on-Sea,
Somerset TA8 2RF
Leave M5 at junction 22, follow signs
for Brean Leisure Park, course 4
miles N of Burnham, 6 miles M5.
Level moorland course.
18 holes, 5714 yards, S.S.S.68
Founded 1975
Visitors: members of other golf
clubs welcome, not Sat or Sun am.
Green Fee: £10 WD, £15 WE.
Societies: welcome weekdays with
prior notice.
Catering: bar and snacks, meals
arranged in adjacent Leisure Centre.
Hotels: Dunston House, Queens;
caravan park (touring/static) on site.

B8 Bridport and West Dorset

☎(0308) 22597 Members, 421095
Sec.
East Cliff, West Bay, Bridport, Dorset
DT6 4EP
Off A35, 1.5 miles S of Bridport on
B3157.
Seaside clifftop course.
18 holes, 5246 yards, S.S.S.66
Designed by G.S.P. Salmon.
Founded 1891
Visitors: welcome.
Green Fee: on application
Societies: as arranged.
Catering: full, plus licensed bar.
Hotels: Haddon House.

B9 Brinkworth

☎(066 641) 277
Longmans Farm, Brinkworth,
Chippenham, Wilts SN15 5DG
Between Swindon and Malmesbury
on B4042.
Meadowland course.
18 holes, c. 6000 yards, S.S.S.69
Founded 1984
Visitors: welcome any time.
Green Fee: on application
Societies: by arrangement.
Catering: available.

B10 Bristol & Clifton

☎(0275) 393474
Beggar Bush Lane, Failand, Nr
Clifton, Bristol BS8 3TH
Junction 19 off M5, 4 miles along
A369 to Bristol turn right at traffic
lights, then further 1.5 miles.
Parkland course.
18 holes, 6294 yards, S.S.S.70
Founded 1891
Visitors: welcome weekdays with
club h/cap cert; weekends with
member only.
Green Fee: £25 WD, £30 WE.
Societies: by arrangement, not
weekends.
Catering: normal golf club catering.
Hotels: Redwood Lodge; Beggar
Bush Land; Failand.

B11 Broadstone

☎(0202) 692595
Wentworth Drive, Broadstone, Dorset
Off A349 half-way between
Wimborne and Poole.
Heathland course.
18 holes, 6151 yards, S.S.S.70
Designed by G. Dunn & H.S. Colt.
Founded 1898
Visitors: weekdays after 9.30 am.
Green Fee: WD £18/round, £22/day.

Societies: weekdays only by prior arrangement.
Catering: full facilities by prior arrangement.
Hotels: King's Head; Fairlight.

B12 Broome Manor

☎(0793) 532403
Piper's Way, Swindon, Wilts SN3 1RG
2 miles from M4 junction 15 to Swindon; follow signs for Golf Complex.
Public parkland course.
18 holes, 6359 yards, S.S.S.70;
9 holes, 2745 yards, S.S.S.67
Designed by Hawtree & Son.
Founded 1976
Visitors: welcome; booking system in operation (course very busy throughout the year).
Green Fee: 18 holes, £7.50 WD, £8 WE & BH; 9 holes, £4.30 WD, £4.60 WE & BH.
Societies: welcome Mon-Thurs only.
Catering: full facilities all week. Driving range.
Hotels: Holiday Inn; Crest; Goddard Arms.

B13 Bulbury Woods

☎(092 945) 574
Halls Rd, Lytchett Matravers, Nr Poole, Dorset BH16 6EP
Off Poole-Bere Regis road.
Parkland course.
18 holes, 6020 yards, S.S.S.68
Designed by J. Sharkey.
Founded 1989
Visitors: welcome.
Green Fee: £15/round, £25/day WD; £18/round, £30/day WE.
Societies: welcome Mon-Fri.
Catering: full catering and bar. Practice ground.

B14 Burnham & Berrow

☎(0278) 785760
St Christopher's Way, Burnham-on-Sea, Somerset TA8 2PE
M5 junction 22, 1 mile N of Burnham.
Seaside links, championship course.
18 holes, 6327 yards, S.S.S.72;
9 holes, 6332 yards, S.S.S.70
Founded 1890
Visitors: must be members of recognised club with h/caps of 22 or under (ladies 30) for championship course; book in advance.

Green Fee: £26 WD, £36 WE; 9-hole course, £8/day.
Societies: as for visitors.
Catering: daily 11am-6pm; breakfast/dinner by prior booking.
Hotels: Dormy House at club, golf incl. prices; Cloisters; Batch Farm.

B15 Came Down

☎(0305) 813494
Came Down, Dorchester, Dorset DT2 8NR
2 miles S of Dorchester off A354.
Undulating downland course.
18 holes, 6224 yards, S.S.S.71
Designed by J.H. Taylor.
Founded 1905
Visitors: welcome; restricted weekends.
Green Fee: on application
Societies: by appointment Wed.
Catering: full facilities.

B16 Castle Combe

☎(0249) 782982, 782992 fax
Castle Combe, Wilts SN14 7PL
Off B4039 to N of Castle Combe village.

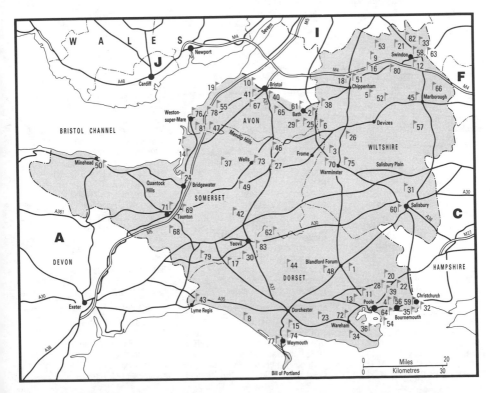

Members (shareholders) club.
18 holes, 6210 yards, Par 71
Designed by P. Alliss & C. Clark.
Founded 1992
Visitors: none.

B17 **Chedington Court**
☎(0935) 891413
South Perrott, Beaminster, Dorset
DT8 3HU
0.5 mile E of South Perrott on A356
Crewkerne-Dorchester road.
Parkland course.
9 holes, 3542 yards, Par 72
Founded 1991
Visitors: welcome; proper dress
required.
Green Fee: 9 holes, £8.50 WD,
£9.50 WE; 18 holes, £14 WD, £16.50
WE.
Societies: by arrangement.
Catering: no bar; limited
refreshments available.
Hotels: Chedington Court (0935
891265), bargain breaks all year.

B18 **Chippenham**
☎(0249) 652040 Sec.
Malmesbury Rd, Chippenham, Wilts
SN15 5LT
Junction 17 off M4, 1 mile from town
centre on A429.
Meadowland course.
18 holes, 5540 yards, S.S.S.67
Founded 1896
Visitors: welcome with restrictions,
must have proof of h/cap.
Green Fee: £20 WD, £25 WE.
Societies: welcome weekdays only.
Catering: lunch, limited catering Mon
Hotels: Old Bell (Malmesbury).

B19 **Clevedon**
☎(0272) 874057 Sec, 874704 Pro,
873140 Steward
Castle Rd, Clevedon, Avon BS21 7AA
M5 junction 19, follow signs to
Clevedon; on outskirts of town turn
right into Holly Lane, right at top of
hill into private lane to club and castle.
Undulating parkland course.
18 holes, 5887 yards, S.S.S.69
Designed by Sandy Herd.
Founded 1894
Visitors: every day, not Wed am;
must be playing members of a golf
club and must produce h/cap certs.
Green Fee: £20 WD, £30 WE & BH.
Societies: Tues only, not Bank
Holidays.
Catering: every day except Mon.
Snooker.
Hotels: Walton Park.

B20 **Crane Valley**
☎(0202) 814088
West Farm, Romford, Verwood,
Dorset BH31 6LE
From A31 take B3081 signposted
Verwood, course is on left hand side
on northern outskirts of Verwood.
Parkland course, part public.
18 holes, 6450 yards, S.S.S.71;
9 holes (public), 2100 yards, Par 33.
Designed by Donald Steel.
Opening summer 1992
Visitors: members of recognised
clubs with h/cap certs on 18 hole
course; all welcome on 9 hole course.
Green Fee: phone for details.
Societies: by appointment.
Catering: full restaurant and bar,
spikes bar and snacks. Driving range.

B21 **Cricklade Hotel & CC**
☎(0793) 750751
Common Hill, Cricklade, Wilts SN6
6HA
B4040 Cricklade-Malmesbury road,
15 mins from M4 junctions 15/16.
Parkland course.
9 holes, 1830 yards, S.S.S.62
Designed by Ian Bolt.
Opening May 1992
Visitors: welcome Mon-Fri.
Green Fee: on application.
Societies: welcome.
Catering: full; à la carte restaurant.
Indoor swimming pool, snooker,
tennis, health and fitness facilities.
Hotels: Cricklade.

B22 **Dudsbury**
☎(0202) 593499
Christchurch Rd, Ferndown, Dorset
BH22 8ST
From A31 at Ferndown take A348 for
c. 2 miles, then left down B3073,
entrance on right after c. 500 yards.
Parkland course.
18 holes, 6200 yards, S.S.S.71; 5
hole Academy course.
Designed by Donald Steel.
Founded April 1992
Visitors: details of visitor
requirements and fees not available
at time of going to press; phone for
information.
Catering: Spike bar, lounge bar,
restaurant, function suite.

B23 **East Dorset**
☎(0929) 472244 Sec, 472272 shop
Hyde, Wareham, Dorset BH20 7NT
A352 from Wareham (by-pass), take
1st junction right past Worgret Manor
Hotel, enter Puddletown Rd, Worgret

Heath, after 3-4 miles turn right at
Hyde junction, 300 yards to club.
Parkland course, part in
rhododendron woodland.
16 holes until July 1992; 18 hole
championship course and 9 hole
woodland course thereafter.
Designed by Martin Hawtree.
Founded 1978
Visitors: welcome subject to
availability; prior reservation.
Green Fee: £14/round, £17/day WD;
£17/round, £21/day WE.
Societies: welcome on application.
Catering: full bar and restaurant.
Driving range.

B24 **Enmore Park**
☎(0278) 671481
Enmore, Bridgwater, Somerset TA5
2AN
3 miles W of Bridgwater on Durleigh
road.
Undulating parkland course.
18 holes, 6241 yards, S.S.S.71
Designed by A.R. Bradbeer.
Founded 1932
Visitors: weekdays, check
weekends.
Green Fee: £18/round, £25/day WD;
£25/round, £30/day WE & BH.
Societies: Mon, Tues, Thurs.
Catering: available, restricted
catering Mon.
Hotels: Walnut Tree (N Petherton).

B25 **Entry Hill**
☎(0225) 834248
Entry Hill, Bath, Avon BA2 5NA
A367 Wells road from city centre,
fork left into Entry Hill Rd after 1 mile;
course is about 0.5 mile on right.
Compact, hilly parkland course
(private club playing public course).
9 holes, 2103 yards, S.S.S.61
Founded 1985
Visitors: no restrictions but
pre-booking up to 7 days in advance
essential for weekends, Bank
Holidays and peak periods.
Green Fee: £6.40/18 holes, £4/9
holes WD; £7.20/18 holes, £4.50/9
holes WE.
Societies: weekdays by
arrangement with Pro.
Hotels: Bear.

B26 **Erlestoke Sands**
Erlestoke, Devizes, Wiltshire
On B3098 midway between
Westbury and Devizes.
Parkland course.
18 holes, 6649 yards, S.S.S.72

Designed by Adrian Stiff.
Opening in 1992
Visitors: welcome.
Green Fee: £10 WD, £14 WE.
Societies: weekdays only.
Catering: full facilities.
14-acre practice ground.

B27 Farrington
☎(0761) 241274
Marsh Lane, Farrington Gurney,
Bristol BS18 5TS
On A37/A39 from Bath and Bristol
towards Wells.
Undulating downland course.
9 holes (18 from May 1993), 1440
yards, S.S.S.27
Designed by Jonathan Gaunt
Opening July 1992
Visitors: welcome, advance booking
required; no jeans.
Green Fee: £5.50/round.
Catering: temporary clubhouse.
Driving range.

B28 Ferndown
☎(0202) 874602
119 Golf Links Rd, Ferndown, Dorset
BH22 8BU
A31 to Trickett's Cross and A348 to
Ferndown.
Heathland links course.
Old Course, 18 holes, 6442 yards,
S.S.S.71; New Course, 9 holes, 5604
yards, S.S.S.68
Designed by Harold Hilton (Old).
Founded 1913
Visitors: prior permission, h/cap cert
required; limited weekends.
Green Fee: Old, £30 WD, £35 WE;
New, £20 WD, £25 WE.
Societies: Tues and Fri only.
Catering: full facilities all week.
Hotels: Coach House Motel; Dormy;
Bridge House.

B29 Fosseway CC
☎(0761) 412214, 418357 fax.
Charlton Lane, Midsomer Norton,
Bath, Somerset BA3 4BD
Off A367 10 miles S of Bath, through
Radstock, left at Charlton roundabout.
Parkland course.
9 holes, 4246 yards, S.S.S.61
Founded 1971
Visitors: members only on Sat to
12am, Sun to 2pm, Wed after 5pm.
Green Fee: £10 WD and Sun pm,
£15 Sat pm & BH.
Catering: full facilities; restaurant,
bar meals; conferences, banqueting.
Swimming, bowls, squash, snooker.
Hotels: Centurion (part of complex).

B30 Halstock
☎(0935) 891689
Halstock Golf Enterprises, Common
Lane, Halstock, Nr Yeovil, Somerset
BA22 9SF
300 yards from centre of Halstock
village
18 holes, 4351 yards, S.S.S.63
Founded 1988
Visitors: welcome.
Green Fee: £9/round WD, £10/round
WE.
Societies: by arrangement.
Catering: limited at present.

B31 High Post
☎(072 273) 356
Great Durnford, Salisbury, Wilts SP4
6AT
Half-way between Salisbury and
Amesbury on the A345.
Downland course.
18 holes, 6267 yards, S.S.S.70
Founded 1922
Visitors: unrestricted weekdays,
h/cap cert required weekends.
Green Fee: £20/round, £25/day WD;
£25/round WE & BH.
Societies: catered for weekdays.
Catering: full catering facilities.
Hotels: The Inn; High Post.

B32 Highcliffe Castle
☎(0425) 272210
107 Lymington Rd, Highcliffe on Sea,
Dorset BH23 4LA
A35 to Hinton Admiral, follow
signpost to Highcliffe, approx 1 mile;
on A337 3 miles E of Christchurch.
Seaside course.
18 holes, 4732 yards, S.S.S.63
Founded 1913
Visitors: welcome if member of
recognised golf club.
Green Fee: £16.50 WD, £25 WE &
BH.
Societies: Tues only.
Catering: bar and restaurant.
Hotels: Avonmouth; Waterford
Lodge.

B33 Highworth
☎(0793) 766014
Highworth Community Golf Centre,
Swindon Rd, Highworth, Wilts SN6
7SJ
A361 Swindon-Highworth road, in
village.
Public, undulating downland course.
9 holes, 3230 yards, S.S.S.35
Designed by Boro' of Thamesdown.
Founded 1990
Visitors: welcome.

Green Fee: £4.30 WD, £4.60 WE.
Societies: welcome.
9 hole Pitch & Putt, practice ground.
Hotels: Blunsdon House; Jesmond
House.

B34 Hyde House CC
Head Office (081) 940 7782
Forest Lodge, Hyde, Nr Wareham,
Dorset
Woodland/parkland courses with
river and lakes.
New 18 holes, 6230 yards, S.S.S.72;
Old 18 holes, 6450 yards, S.S.S.72
Designed by J. Hamilton Stutt & Chris
Reynard.
Visitors: no casual visitors, bookings
only through head office for golf and
multi-adventure activities.
Green Fee: on application.
Societies: welcome at all times.

B35 Iford Bridge
☎(0202) 473817
Iford Bridge Sports Centre, Barrack
Rd, Iford, Christchurch, Dorset BH23
2BA
Off A35 between Bournemouth and
Christchurch, then signposted.
Public parkland/meadowland course
next to River Stour.
9 holes, 4852 yards, S.S.S.68
Founded 1977
Visitors: welcome.
Green Fee: municipal rates.
Societies: apply to local Council.
Catering: bar facilities and snacks.
Driving range, tennis, bowling.
Hotels: Christchurch Information
Centre (471780) for bargain breaks.

B36 Isle of Purbeck
☎(092 944) 361
Studland, Dorset BH19 3AB
By ferry from Sandbanks or by road
through Wareham, left onto B3351
signposted Studland at Corfe Castle.
Undulating heathland course.
Purbeck Course, 18 holes, 6248
yards, S.S.S.71; Dene Course, 9
holes, 2022 yards, S.S.S.30
Designed by H.S. Colt.
Founded August 1892
Visitors: welcome; h/cap cert
required for Purbeck Course.
Green Fee: Purbeck Course,
£20.50/round, £27.50/day WD;
£25.50/round, £32.50/day WE; Dene
Course, £8.50/day WD, £10/day WE.
Societies: by arrangement.
Catering: lunch and evening meals
except Mon.
Hotels: Knoll House; Pines.

B37 Isle of Wedmore
☎(0934) 712452
Lineage, Lascots Hill, Wedmore,
Somerset BS28 4QT
1st right past church in Wedmore,
0.5 mile on right.
Parkland course.
18 holes, 5900 yards, S.S.S.69
Designed by Terry Murray.
Opening July 1992
Visitors: welcome, usual standards
of dress, no jeans T-shirts etc.
Green Fee: £10/round WD,
£14/round WE.
Societies: flexible, phone and
discuss.
Catering: bar and dining room.

B38 Kingsdown
☎(0225) 742530
Kingsdown, Corsham, Wilts SN14
9BS
Turn off A4 onto A363, left at Crown
Inn 250 yards, uphill for 2 miles.
Heathland course.
18 holes, 6445 yards, S.S.S.71
Founded 1880
Visitors: welcome with h/caps, not
weekends.
Green Fee: £22 WD.
Societies: by arrangement with Sec.
Catering: dining room meals or bar
snacks.
Hotels: Beaufort (Bath); Conigre
Farm (Melksham); Park Lane Motel
(Corsham).

B39 Knighton Heath
☎(0202) 572633
Francis Ave, Bournemouth, Dorset
B11 8NX
On main A348 Poole-Ringwood road,
junction with A3049 at Wallisdown
roundabout.
Heathland course.
18 holes, 6120 yards, S.S.S.69
Founded 1976
Visitors: after 9.30am weekdays,
not weekends or Bank Holidays.
Green Fee: on application.
Societies: weekdays by prior
arrangement.
Catering: lunch daily except Mon.
Hotels: Bridge House (Longham).

B40 Knowle
☎(0272) 770660
Fairway, Brislington, Bristol BS4 5DF
3 miles S of city centre on the A4 to
junction with West Town Lane,
entrance on left 800 yards along
West Town Lane.
Parkland course.

18 holes, 6016 yards, S.S.S.69
Designed by Hawtree & J.H. Taylor.
Founded 1905
Visitors: welcome weekdays,
weekends by special arrangement;
h/cap certs required.
Green Fee: £20.50/round,
£25.50/day WD; £25.50/round,
£30.50/day WE.
Societies: Thurs only.
Catering: lunch daily, evening meals
by arrangement.
Hotels: Grange (Keynsham).

B41 Long Ashton
☎(0275) 392316
Long Ashton, Bristol BS18 9DW
Leave M5 at junction 19, take A369
to Bristol, turn right into B3129 at
traffic lights and then left onto
B3128; club is 0.5 mile on right.
Undulating moorland/parkland
course.
18 holes, 6051 yards, S.S.S.70
Designed by Hawtree & Taylor.
Founded 1893
Visitors: must have official club
h/cap.
Green Fee: £20 WD, £28 WE.
Societies: by arrangement.
Catering: full facilities daily until
6pm; evening meal by arrangement.
Hotels: Redwood Lodge.

B42 Long Sutton
☎(0458) 241017
Long Load, Nr Langport, Somerset
TA10 9JU
Take Langport road from A303, after
3 miles turn left into Long Sutton,
course 1 mile on left.
Parkland course.
18 holes, 6148 yards, S.S.S.69
Designed by Patrick Dawson.
Founded Sept 1991
Visitors: pay-as-you-play course,
tees must be booked at weekends.
Green Fee: £12/round WD, £16 WE.
Societies: by prior arrangement.
Catering: bar and restaurant from
autumn 1992.
Driving range.
Hotels: arranged through Sec.

B43 Lyme Regis
☎(0297) 442963, 442043 Catering
Timber Hill, Lyme Regis, Dorset DT7
3HQ
Off A3052 Charmouth road 1 mile E
of town.
Undulating meadowland course.
18 holes, 6220 yards, S.S.S.70
Founded 1893

Visitors: welcome, must have h/cap
cert or proof of membership of
recognised club; restrictions on
Thurs and Sun.
Green Fee: £21/day WD (£17 after
2pm), £21/day WE.
Societies: apply for booking; Tues,
Wed and Fri.
Catering: full à la carte, hot and cold
snacks all day.
Hotels: Alexander; Bay; Buena Vista;
Devon; Fairwater Head; Tudor
House; The Cedars (Axminster);
White House (Charmouth); all offer
reduced green fees.

B44 Lyons Gate
☎(03005) 239
Lyons Gate Farm, Lyons Gate,
Dorchester DT2 7AZ
3 miles N of Cerne Abbas on A352
Sherborne-Dorchester road.
Wooded farmland course.
9 holes, 2000 yards, S.S.S.60
Designed by Ken Abel.
Founded 1991
Visitors: welcome.
Green Fee: £4.50 (9 holes), £7.50
(18 holes).
Societies: enquiries welcome.
Catering: light refreshments;
clubhouse under construction.
Practice nets.

B45 Marlborough
☎(0672) 512147
The Common, Marlborough, Wilts
SN8 1DU
0.75 mile from town centre on A345
to Swindon.
Downland course.
18 holes, 6505 yards, S.S.S.71
Founded 1888
Visitors: welcome weekdays and
weekends on non-competition days,
ring in advance; h/cap certs required.
Green Fee: £19/round, £28/day WD;
£40/round WE.
Societies: with prior booking,
weekdays only.
Catering: full facilities all week.
Hotels: Castle & Ball; Ivy House.

B46 Mendip
☎(0749) 840570 Sec, 840793 Pro.
Gurney Slade, Bath, Somerset BA3
4UT
3 miles N of Shepton Mallet off A37.
Undulating downland course.
18 holes, 6330 yards, S.S.S.70
Designed by H. Vardon with an
extension by F. Pennink.
Founded 1908

Visitors: with member only at weekends unless member of affiliated club; phone Pro to check availability.
Green Fee: £17/round, £25 day WD; £30/day WE.
Societies: welcome Mon-Fri.
Catering: full facilities every day.
Hotels: White Hart.

B47 Mendip Spring

☎(0934) 853337
Honeyhall Lane, Congresbury, Avon BS19 5JT
From M5 junction 21 take A370 towards Bristol, turn right in Congresbury onto B3133.
Parkland course with hill views.
Brinsea, 18 holes, 6500 yards, S.S.S.72; Lakeside, 9 holes, 2,300 yards
Designed by Terry Murray.
Founded 1991
Visitors: starting times may be reserved.
Green Fee: Brinsea £20/day WD, £30 WE; Lakeside, £10/day WD, £15 WE.
Societies: apply to director of golf.
Catering: bar and restaurant.
Extensive leisure facilities, driving range, swimming pool, health club.

B48 Mid-Dorset

☎(0258) 861386, 861184 Pro, 860656 Fax
Belchalwell, Blandford Forum, Dorset DT11 0EG
9 miles SW of Blandford between Okeford Fitzpaine and Ibberton.
Parkland course.
18 holes, 6503 yards
Designed by Project Golf (D.W. Asthill).
Founded 1990
Visitors: all welcome.
Green Fee: £20/day WD, £25/day WE & BH.
Societies: welcome by prior arrangement.
Catering: lunches, tea, evening meals, 7-day bar open all day.
Large practice facilities.
Hotels: Swan (Sturminster Newton); Anvil (Pimperne Blandford).

B49 Millfield School

Nr Glastonbury, Somerset
1 mile SE of Butleigh.
Parkland course.
9 holes, 4516 yards, S.S.S.62
Founded 1970
Visitors: members and guests only.

B50 Minehead & West Somerset

☎(0643) 2057
The Warren, Minehead, Somerset TA24 5SJ
E end of sea front.
Links course.
18 holes, 6130 yards, S.S.S.69
Designed by Johnny Alan.
Founded 1882
Visitors: welcome.
Green Fee: £19.50 WD, £23 WE & BH.
Societies: welcome on written application.
Catering: by prior arrangement with Steward/Stewardess; snacks always available.
Hotels: Wyncott; York; Northfield; Marshfield.

B51 Monkton Park Par 3

☎(0249) 653928
Monkton Park, Chippenham, Wilts SN15 3PE
Into Chippenham, past railway station, turn right.
Parkland course.
9 holes, Par 3 (longest hole 175 yards)
Designed by M. Dawson.
Founded 1965
Visitors: welcome.
Green Fee: on application
Catering: refreshments available.

B52 North Wilts

☎(038 086) 627
Bishops Cannings, Devizes, Wilts SN10 2LP
1 mile from A4 E of Calne.
Downland course.
18 holes, 6484 yards, S.S.S.71
Founded 1890
Visitors: welcome.
Green Fee: £18 WD, £25 WE.
Societies: welcome by prior arrangement.
Catering: full facilities available.
Hotels: Bear (Devizes); Lansdowne Strand (Calne).

B53 Oaksey Park

☎(06667) 7995
Oaksey, Nr Malmesbury, Wilts SN16 9SB
Off A419 between Swindon and Cirencester, W of Cotswold Water Park.
Public parkland course.
9 holes, 2904 yards, S.S.S.68
Designed by Chapman & Warren.
Founded 1991

Visitors: welcome.
Green Fee: £10/day WD, £15/day WE; low season £6 and £10.
Societies: welcome.
Catering: full facilities.
Driving range, practice ground, clay pigeon shoot, rare breeds, children's play area, archery, hot air ballooning.
Hotels: Oaksey Park Country Cottages Hotel (10 farm cottages).

B54 Parkstone

☎(0202) 707138
Links Rd, Parkstone, Poole, Dorset BH14 9JU
A35 Bournemouth-Poole road, turn S at St Osmond's Church.
Undulating heathland course.
18 holes, 6250 yards, S.S.S.70
Designed by Willie Park and James Braid.
Founded 1910
Visitors: welcome weekdays (book in advance); h/cap certs required.
Green Fee: £24/round, £32/day WD; £30/round, £40/day WE & BH.
Societies: catered for on weekdays.
Catering: lunch available every day.

B55 Puxton Park

☎(0934) 823328
Woodspring Golf & Leisure Park, Puxton, Nr Weston-Super-Mare, Avon BS24 6TA
2 miles E of M5 junction 21 on A370 Bristol-Weston road.
Moorland course.
18 holes, Par 72
Designed by R. Hemmingway & Partner.
Opening Aug 1992
Visitors: ring for details of visitor restrictions, society meetings, catering etc.

B56 Queen's Park (Boscombe)

☎(0202) 302611, 36198 (Boscombe GC)
Queen's Park West Drive, Bournemouth, Dorset BH8 9BY
From Ringwood, take Wessex Way (A338), leave by 1st junction, turn right at roundabout and right again into Queens Park West Drive.
Undulating public parkland course
18 holes, 6505 yards, S.S.S.72
Founded 1906
Visitors: welcome any time.
Green Fee: £10.40 (£12)/round.
Societies: by prior arrangement.
Catering: bar and restaurant facilities.

B57 RAF Upavon
☎(0980) 630787 Club Manager
York Rd, Upavon, Pewsey, Wilts SN9 6BQ
2 miles SE of Upavon village on A342.
Undulating downland course.
9 holes, 5116 metres, S.S.S.67
Visitors: welcome on weekdays and with member at weekends.
Green Fee: £12/day WD, £15/day WE; fees must be paid at RAF Guardroom.
Societies: welcome on weekdays, maximum 32.
Catering: by special arrangement.
Hotels: Antelope.

B58 RMCS Shrivenham
☎(0793) 785725
RMCS Shrivenham, Swindon, Wilts SN6 8LA
In grounds of Royal Military College of Science on A420 1 mile NE of Shrivenham.
Parkland course
9 holes, 2603 yards, S.S.S.66
Founded 1953
Visitors: restricted access; with member only; entry to grounds must be arranged with Manager.
Green Fee: £6 WD, £8 WE.
Societies: limited access weekdays.

B59 Riversmeet
☎(0202) 473912, 477987
Two Riversmeet Leisure Centre, Stony Lane South, Christchurch, Dorset BH23 1HW
Left at mini-roundabout at end of Christchurch High St, on to crossroads, right to Leisure Centre.
Picturesque public seaside course.
18 holes, 1455 metres, Par 3
Visitors: welcome any time.
Green Fee: £3.60/round.
Catering: bar and restaurant.
Squash, badminton, swimming pool, gym etc.

B60 Salisbury & South Wiltshire
☎(0722) 742645 Sec, 742929 Pro.
Netherhampton, Salisbury, Wilts SP2 8PR
On A3094 2 miles from Salisbury and from Wilton.
Parkland course.
18 holes, 6528 yards, S.S.S.71; 9 hole course.
Designed by J.H. Taylor.
Founded 1888
Visitors: welcome; h/cap cert required weekends.

Green Fee: £20.50 WD, £29 WE & BH.
Societies: welcome by arrangement.
Catering: full bar and catering. Snooker.
Hotels: Rose & Crown (Salisbury); Pembroke Arms (Wilton).

B61 Saltford
☎(0225) 873513
Golf Club Lane, Saltford, Bristol BS18 3AA
Off A4 between Bath and Bristol.
Meadowland course.
18 holes, 6081 yards, S.S.S.69
Founded 1904
Visitors: welcome; h/cap cert required.
Green Fee: £18.50/round, £22.50 2 rounds.
Societies: Mon and Thurs by arrangement.
Catering: meals served daily. Snooker.
Hotels: Grange (Keynsham); Crown; Tunnel House.

B62 Sherborne
☎(0963) 814431
Higher Clatcombe, Sherborne, Dorset DT9 4RN
1 mile N of Sherborne off B3145 to Wincanton.
Parkland course.
18 holes, 5758 yards, S.S.S.68
Designed by James Braid.
Founded 1894
Visitors: weekdays and weekends dependent on Club Diary.
Green Fee: £18 WD, £23 WE & BH.
Societies: Tues and Wed by arrangement.
Catering: comprehensive range of facilities available.
Hotels: Post House; Half Moon.

B63 Shrivenham Park
☎(0793) 783853
Pennyhooks, Shrivenham, Swindon, Wilts SN6 8HH
A420 Swindon-Oxford road 6 miles from Swindon, leave by-pass for Shrivenham; on E edge of village.
Public undulating parkland course.
18 holes, 6000 yards, S.S.S.70
Visitors: welcome, pay-as-you-play.
Green Fee: £9/round, £15.50/day WD; £12/round, £18.50/day WE; reductions for jnrs & OAPs.
Societies: at all times.
Catering: full bar and restaurant. Pitch & Putt course.

B64 Solent Meads Par 3
☎(0202) 420795
Rolls Drive, Nr Hengistbury Head, Bournemouth, Dorset
In Selfridge Avenue, off Broadway at Hengistbury Head.
Public seaside course.
18 holes, Par 3, 2235 yards
Visitors: welcome at all times.
Green Fee: municipal rates.
Catering: light refreshments, café. Driving range.

B65 Stockwood Vale
☎(0272) 866505
Stockwood Lane, Keynsham, Bristol BS18 2ER
In Stockwood Lane off A4.
Public, undulating parkland course.
9 holes, 4020 yards, S.S.S.61
Designed by J. Wade & M. Ramsay.
Founded 1991
Visitors: no restrictions; proper dress required; tee times bookable 7 days in advance.
Green Fee: 9 holes, £4.50 WD, £5.50 WE; 18 holes, £9 WD, £11 WE.
Societies: by prior arrangement.
Catering: clubhouse opening 1992. Driving range.
Hotels: The Grange.

B66 Swindon
☎(067 284) 327
Ogbourne St George, Marlborough, Wilts SN18 1TB
Junction 15 off M4, on A345 to Marlborough.
Undulating downland course.
18 holes, 6226 yards, S.S.S.70
Designed by Taylor, Hawtree and Cotton.
Founded 1929
Visitors: welcome on weekdays.
Green Fee: on application.
Societies: weekdays.
Catering: restaurant, bar snacks.

B67 Tall Pines
☎(0275) 472076
Cooks Bridle Path, Downside, Backwell, Bristol BS19 3DJ
0.5 mile N of Bristol Airport.
Public parkland course.
18 holes, 4800 yards, S.S.S.62
Designed by Terry Murray.
Founded 1990
Visitors: Welcome, booking at weekends only.
Green Fee: £10 WD, £12.50 WE.
Societies: Mon-Fri.
Catering: bar and restaurant.
Hotels: Towns Talk.

Sherborne

Sherborne belongs to that category of courses that provides the right degree of testing quality, without in any way impairing the enjoyment of a round in an incomparable setting — views, on a good day, across two or three counties. Taking the road up the hill out of a town famous for its abbey and its schools, you reach the club down a narrow country lane. Before the club's founding in 1894, the whole area was part of the fertile agricultural plain that surrounds it, but the second nine in particular covers some gently rolling land of which Harry Colt would certainly have approved. He believed that undulations and hummocks are of great value through the green as they provide difficult stances and lies, without which no golf course can be deemed to be perfect.

Judged from the first six holes, Sherborne suggests a non-stop assault with woods and long irons. The first nine is, in fact, more than 800 yards longer than the second, though that does not necessarily mean that the second nine is any easier in relation to par. What it does mean is that the first six holes, including three par 5s, hold the key to a good score, the 1st and 3rd being notable par 4s.

It is easy enough though to have your card in tatters almost before you have started. There is plenty of scope for going out of bounds with an opening drive to a fairway which tapers cleverly to ensure that the further you hit the ball, the straighter you have to be. Control is essential too with the second shot to the 2nd, doglegging round the practice ground, while the 3rd and 4th, running up and back, are two of the best.

The 5th is the first of an excellent batch of short holes which vary in length and character, as all good short holes should, the 5th being perhaps the finest and the 7th the most daunting. In between, the par 5 6th demands a well positioned drive to allow a flat stance for what is most likely to be a long second; and the second, too, requires both care and thought in order to leave the easiest pitch when the pin is tucked away at the back of the green.

Nothing less than the most truly-hit tee shot will suffice at the 7th but there is a little respite at the 8th and 9th which epitomises the compact nature of the layout on a limited acreage. It accommodates one more hole, the third par 3, before crossing back and passing the clubhouse and on down the excellent 459 yard 11th where the sloping terrain demands that, to hold both fairway and green, there is a very definite, if narrow, line to adopt.

It is from the tee that the full panorama of the view unfolds, an unmistakable slice of England at its greenest and best. There are other chances to stand and stare but not until the business in hand is complete and the ridge up the 18th fairway has been safely scaled.

In the meantime, the tiny 12th is not to be taken lightly. It is an admirable illustration that short holes don't have to be 200 yards to give a sense of achievement at hitting the green; and, though of modest length also, the 13th and 14th, one up and one back down again, permit little room for error in judging the pitches comprising the second shots.

The 15th has much in common with the 7th, a tee shot with the emphasis on carry, while the drive at the 16th must be well flighted to clear the trees guarding the wooded menace on the right. It may be wiser to take the safer line to the left and to rub shoulders with those turning back up the 17th with its hopes of a birdie. But, by now, thoughts are on negotiating the final slope to the 18th.

This is done preferably with a drive and crisp iron but, for those flagging physically and in spirit, the sight of the clubhouse has the same effect as an oasis in the desert and it's no mirage. It has splendid reviving powers and if, on reflection, your golf is best forgotten, look not on the dark side. A further glimpse at the scenic splendour will promptly persuade you that it has been amply worthwhile.

B68 Taunton & Pickeridge
☎(082 342) 240
Corfe, Taunton, Somerset TA3 7BY
B3170, 4 miles S of Taunton, through
Corfe village, then 1st left.
Undulating course.
18 holes, 5927 yards, S.S.S.68
Founded 1892
Visitors: welcome weekdays by
arrangement, h/cap cert required.
Green Fee: on application
Societies: weekdays except Tues.
Catering: full facilities.

B69 Taunton Vale
☎(0823) 412220 Manager, 412880
Pro/reservations.
Creech Heathfield, Taunton,
Somerset TA3 5EY
Just off A361 at junction with A38,
exits 24 or 25 from M5.
Part public parkland course.
18 holes, 6000 yards, Par 70; 9
holes, 2000 yards, Par 32
Designed by John Pyne.
Founded July 1991
Visitors: welcome, appropriate
dress and etiquette.
Green Fee: 18 holes, £12 WD, £15
WE; 9 holes, £6 WD, £7.50 WE.
Societies: welcome weekdays.
Catering: full bar and catering in
clubhouse.
Extensive golf practice area.
Hotels: Walnut Tree (N Petherton –
Best Western packages); Post House,
County, Castle (Taunton).

B70 Thoulstone Park
☎(0373) 832825, 832821 fax.
Chapmanslade, Nr Westbury, Wilts
BA13 4AQ
2.5 miles W of Warminster on A36.
Parkland course, spectacular views.
18 holes, 6384 yards, S.S.S.71
Designed by J.R. Hartley.
Founded Oct 1991
Visitors: welcome; h/cap cert or
proof of playing ability required.
Green Fee: £17.50 WD, £25 WE.
Societies: welcome weekdays;
special arrangements for weekends,
contact Director of Golf.
Catering: Restaurants, bars;
conferences, function rooms, offices.
Driving range, squash, swimming,
gymnasium etc.

B71 Vivary
☎(0823) 289274, 333872
Taunton, Somerset
In centre of Taunton.
Municipal parkland course.

18 holes, 4620 yards, S.S.S.63
Designed by Herbert Fowler.
Founded 1930s
Visitors: welcome.
Green Fee: on application.
Societies: welcome weekdays only.
Catering: available.
Hotels: County; Castle; Corner
House.

B72 Wareham
☎(0929) 554147
Sandford Rd, Wareham, Dorset BH20
4DH
On A351 near railway station, 8 miles
from Poole.
Undulating parkland/heathland
course with fine views.
18 holes, 5352 yards, S.S.S.68
Founded 1926
Visitors: welcome 9.30am to 5pm
Mon-Fri, phone in advance; h/cap
certs required.
Green Fee: £15/round, £20/day.
Societies: by arrangement.
Catering: full bar and catering.
Hotels: Springfield.

B73 Wells (Somerset)
☎(0749) 675005, 679059 Pro.
East Horrington Rd, Wells, Somerset
BA5 3DS
1.5 miles from city centre off B3139.
Meadowland/parkland course.
18 holes, 5354 yards, S.S.S.66
Founded 1893
Visitors: welcome, current h/cap
card required weekends; no visitors
before 9.30am weekends.
Green Fee: £14.50/round,
£17.50/day WD; £18.50/round,
£22/day WE & BH.
Societies: welcome with advance
booking, weekdays only.
Catering: bar, midday and evening
meals available 7 days.
Hotels: Caravan facilities adjacent.

B74 Wessex Golf Centre
☎(0305) 784737
Radipole Lane, Weymouth, Dorset
Behind Weymouth football ground.
9 holes, Par 3
Visitors: welcome any time.
Green Fee: £2.90/round.
Driving range.

B75 West Wilts
☎(0985) 212702
Elm Hill, Warminster, Wilts BA12 0AU
A350 towards Westbury, on edge of
town.

Downland course.
18 holes, 5709 yards, S.S.S.68
Designed by J.H. Taylor.
Founded 1891
Visitors: welcome with h/cap cert.
Green Fee: £20 WD, £30 WE.
Societies: accepted Wed/Thurs/Fri.
Catering: available.
Hotels: The Bell.

B76 Weston-super-Mare
☎(0934) 626968 Office, 633360
Pro.
Uphill Rd North, Weston-super-Mare,
Avon BS23 4NQ
M5 or A370 from Bristol.
Seaside links course.
18 holes, 6225 yards, S.S.S.70
Designed by T. Dunn.
Founded July 1892
Visitors: welcome, h/cap cert
required at weekends and Bank
Holidays.
Green Fee: £20 WD, £28 WE & BH.
Societies: by arrangement.
Catering: bar and restaurant, snacks
and meals daily.
Snooker.
Hotels: Grand Atlantic; Beachlands;
Arosfa; Rozel.

B77 Weymouth
☎(0305) 773981
Links Rd, Weymouth, Dorset DT4 0PF
From Dorchester take A354, at
Wessex roundabout take Town
Centre exit, signposted at next exit.
Seaside/parkland course.
18 holes, 6009 yards, S.S.S.69
Designed originally by James Braid;
redesigned by J. Hamilton Stutt.
Founded 1905
Visitors: welcome with h/cap cert or
proof of club membership.
Green Fee: £16 WD, £22 WE & BH.
Societies: Tues and Thurs by
arrangement.
Catering: full bar and restaurant.
Practice area.
Hotels: Moonfleet Manor, weekday
packages.

B78 The Willows
☎(0934) 823328
Woodspring Golf & Leisure Park,
Puxton, Nr Weston-Super-Mare,
Avon BS24 6TA
2 miles E of M5 junction 21 on A370
Bristol-Weston road.
Moorland course.
18 holes, 6559 yards, Par 72
Designed by R. Hemmingway &
Partner.

Founded 1991
Visitors: welcome.
Green Fee: £8 WD, £10 WE.
Catering: full facilities.

B79 Windwhistle

☎(0460) 30231, (0460) 30055 fax.
Windwhistle, Cricket St Thomas, Nr
Chard, Somerset TA20 4DG
On N side of A30 5 miles from
Crewkerne, 3 miles from Chard,
opposite wildlife park; follow signs
from M25 junction 25.
Downland/parkland course.
18 holes, 6500 yards, S.S.S.71; 9
holes, 3200 yards.
Designed by J.H. Taylor (1932),
Leonard Fisher (1992).
Founded 1932
Visitors: welcome but advisable to
phone first.
Green Fee: on application.
Societies: welcome by appointment,
phone for information.
Catering: comprehensive catering
facilities.
International standard squash
courts.
Hotels: information on request.

B80 Wootton Bassett

☎(0793) 849999
Wootton Basset, Swindon, Wilts SN4
7PB
Parkland course with 10 large lakes.
18 holes, 6,600 yards, SSS73

Designed by Peter Alliss and Clive
Clark.
Founded April 1992
Visitors: phone for availability.
Green Fee: £20.
Societies: phone for availability.
Catering: full bar and restaurant
facilities.

B81 Worlebury

☎(0934) 623214
Monks Hill, Worlebury,
Weston-super-Mare, Avon BS22 9SX
2 miles from M5 at top of hill (off
A370); 2 miles from centre of
Weston-super-Mare.
Seaside meadowland course.
18 holes, 5921 yards, S.S.S.69
Designed by W. Hawtree & Son.
Founded 1908
Visitors: welcome on weekdays.
Green Fee: £16 WD (£11 with
member), £16 with member WE.
Societies: catered for on weekdays.
Catering: snacks, lunch and evening
meals available.
Snooker.
Hotels: Grand Atlantic; Beachlands;
Commodore; Royal Pier; Berni Royal;
Rozel; Old Colonial; Queenswood.

B82 Wrag Barn G & CC

☎(0793) 764533 Sec, 766027 Pro.
Shrivenham Road, Sevenhampton,
Nr Highworth, Wilts SN6 7QA
10 miles from M4 Junction 15; take

A419 towards Cirencester, right at
3rd roundabout (A361) to Highworth,
then right on B4000 to Shrivenham,
course is 0.5 mile on right.
Undulating, scenic, parkland course.
18 holes, 6548 yards, S.S.S.71
Designed by Hawtree & Sons.
Founded July 1990
Visitors: welcome; some restrictions
at weekends, advisable to ring Pro.
Green Fee: £12/round WD,
£20/round WE & BH
Societies: by arrangement with Sec.
Catering: full bar and restaurant
facilities; catering for companies,
parties, receptions.
Hotels: Blunsden House Hotel &
Leisure Centre (Blunsden).

B83 Yeovil

☎(0935) 22965 Sec, 75949
Clubhouse, 73763 Pro.
Sherborne Rd, Yeovil, Somerset
BA21 5BW
1 mile E of Yeovil on A30 Yeovil to
Sherborne road.
Undulating parkland course.
18 holes, 6144 yards, S.S.S.69
Designed by Fowler & Alison.
Founded 1919
Visitors: welcome weekdays;
weekends with h/caps only; ring in
advance.
Green Fee: on application
Societies: by arrangement, not
weekends.
Catering: full except Mon.

C

HAMPSHIRE, SUSSEX, ISLE OF WIGHT

The connoisseur, making his way east from Brokenhurst Manor in the New Forest to Rye on the East Sussex border with Kent, passes through as good and varied a golfing tapestry as could be imagined — a veritable Aladdin's Cave. Compared with other parts of the country, the volume of courses is none too dense but any shortcomings in quantity are more than absorbed by quality.

For the purposes of playing qualification at county level, Hampshire embraces the Channel Islands, the Isle of Wight and Hayling Island, the latter a links, or part links, which Tom Simpson rated enormously highly. I also remember Henry Longhurst singing its praises and I can join in the chorus but Hampshire's inland gems are North Hants and Fleet, Blackmoor and Liphook — all extensions of the rich seam of heather, gorse and silver birch country which starts with Wentworth and Sunningdale in the east and continues down through Swinley Forest and Camberley Heath.

Liphook, straddling the busy A3 and involving one or two mad dashes to cross it, has had strong naval connections in view of its proximity to Portsmouth but it has remained essentially a refuge for the Club golfer in spite of being able to test the best.

Hockley and Royal Winchester typify downland golf at its best, while Stoneham at Southampton is more in the mould of Liphook. Sussex, too, is full of variety with something for everyone. West Sussex at Pulborough is a particular favourite, ideal for any occasion and giving the chance of a good score with its five short holes although, like Rye, the par of 68 can be tantalisingly elusive.

Straight hitting has more merit than unharnessed power, for the heather is punishing but the unique charms of Rye centre more on a battle with the winds that sweep off the sea or across the exposed and chilly reaches of ancient Romney Marsh.

There is a charm about Rye that never varies or fades. Expectation begins with departure from the ancient town and its cobbled streets and heightens as the road to Camber twists and turns through fields of grazing sheep. The character of the golf is distinctive in the range of shots it demands, the ability to flight the ball and gauge how it will run on landing being infinitely more valuable than memorising yardage charts and clubbing by numbers.

Rye is a monument to the links style of British golf but the new East Sussex National is the opposite, an expensive machine-shaped exercise in creating a new landscape. There are those who prefer it to courses which preserve nature rather than fighting it, and nowhere is that aspect better seen than at Royal Ashdown Forest or Crowborough which run hither and thither across the Sussex Downs, Ashdown Forest notably without bunkers.

Goodwood is another from whose highest points scenic splendour unfurls, a contrast to its neighbour, the Goodwood Park Hotel Golf and Country Club which occupies a large part of the grounds of Goodwood House. Bognor Regis, Selsey and Littlehampton lie a few miles to the south while Chichester Golf Centre is a recently opened venture at Hunston — ideal for those wishing to learn the ropes.

Worthing, Brighton and Eastbourne are well served while Cooden Beach has a host of admirers, along with a particular favourite in Seaford, another downland course overlooking the Channel.

C1 Aldershaw
☎(0424) 870898
Sedlescombe, E Sussex TN33 0SD
On main A21 near Sedlescombe.
Parkland course.
18 holes, 6400 yards, S.S.S.71
Founded 1991
Visitors: Mon-Fri on production of
current h/cap cert.
Green Fee: £25 (£10 with member).
Societies: on application.
Catering: bar and snacks.
Driving range.
Hotels: Brickwall.

C2 Alresford
☎(0962) 733746
Tichborne Down, Alresford, Hants
SO24 0PN
1 mile S of A31 Winchester-Alton
road, 2 miles N of A272
Winchester-Petersfield road.
Undulating parkland course.
12 holes, 6066 yards, S.S.S.69
Designed by Cotton Pennink
Associates.
Founded 16 Nov 1890
Visitors: welcome; not before 12am
weekends and Bank Holidays.
Green Fee: £15/round (18 holes),
£22/day WD; £30/round WE & BH
(reductions with member).
Societies: Thurs only.
Catering: full catering every day
except Mon.
Hotels: Swan; Bell.

C3 Alton
☎(0420) 82042
Old Odiham Rd, Alton, Hants GU34
4BU
2 miles N of Alton on A32 turn right at
Golden Pot public house, 1st right
again, 0.5 mile on right.
Undulating parkland course.
9 holes, 5744 yards, S.S.S.68
Founded 1908
Visitors: welcome Mon-Fri;
weekends 18 h/cap or with member.
Green Fee: £11/round, £16/day WD;
£16/round, £20/day WE & BH.
Societies: by prior arrangement
weekdays.
Catering: bar.
Hotels: Alton House; Swan.

C4 Ampfield Par 3
☎(0794) 68480, 68750 Pro.
Winchester Rd, Ampfield, Romsey,
Hants SO51 9BQ
On A31 2.5 miles W of Hursley
village, next door to White Horse
public house.

Parkland course.
18 holes, 2478 yards, S.S.S.53
Designed by Henry Cotton MBE.
Founded 1963
Visitors: welcome but advisable to
telephone first; h/cap cert required
weekends and Bank Holidays.
Green Fee: on application.
Societies: small societies welcome
weekdays by prior arrangement.
Catering: light lunch (not Tues),
snacks and society dinners by prior
arrangement.
Hotels: Potters Heron (Ampfield);
White Horse (Romsey).

C5 Andover
☎(0264) 358040 Sec, 323980
Members, 324151 Pro.
Winchester Rd, Andover, Hants SP10
2EF
Just off A303 on Andover by-pass,
entrance to club about 500 yards
after leaving A303 on A3057.
Undulating parkland course.
9 holes, 5933 yards, S.S.S.68
Founded 1907
Visitors: welcome.
Green Fee: £11 (£7 with member)
WD, £22 (£11 with member) WE; full
day £16.50 (£10 with member) WD.
Societies: welcome weekdays.
Catering: snacks, lunch, evening
meal except Tues.
Hotels: Danebury; White Hart.

C6 Army
☎(0252) 540638 Sec, 541104 Club,
547232 Pro.
Laffans Rd, Aldershot, Hants GU11
2HF
Access from Eelmoor Bridge off A323
Aldershot-Fleet road.
Heathland course.
18 holes, 6550 yards, S.S.S.71
Designed by Frank Pennink.
Founded 1883
Visitors: with member only, any
time.
Green Fee: on application.
Societies: Mon, Thurs only.
Catering: available 9am to 5pm.
Hotels: Queens

C7 Ashdown Forest Hotel
☎(0342 82) 4866
Chapel Lane, Forest Row, E Sussex
RH18 5BB
3 miles S of East Grinstead on A22 in
village of Forest Row, E on B2110;
Chapel Lane 4th on right.
Heathland/woodland course.
18 holes, 5510 yards, S.S.S.67

Designed by Horace Hutchinson
(1930s); Henry Luff (1965).
Founded 1985 (Anderida Golfers).
Visitors: welcome but advisable to
check, particularly at weekends.
Green Fee: on application.
Societies: catered for 7 days.
Catering: full restaurant service and
bar snacks 7 days. Banqueting
facilities up to 100.
Hotels: Ashdown Forest.

C8 Avisford Park
☎(0243) 554611
Avisford Park Country Hotel,
Walberton, Arundel, W Sussex BN18
0LS
On A27 4 miles W of Arundel, 6 miles
E of Chichester.
Parkland course.
9 holes, 3009 yards, S.S.S.35
Visitors: welcome, pay-as-you-play.
Green Fee: winter, £10/day WD,
£12/day WE; summer, £12/day WD,
£15/day WE.
Societies: any time.
Catering: bar and restaurant.
Tennis, swimming, squash, etc.
Hotels: own hotel on site; subsidised
golf for resdents.

C9 Barton-on-Sea
☎(0425) 615308 Sec, 611210 Pro,
610189 Members, 639092 Steward
Marine Drive, Barton-on-Sea, New
Milton, Hants BH25 7DY
Off A337 at the extreme E end of
Marine Drive at Barton.
Seaside course.
18 holes, 5565 yards, S.S.S.67 (27
holes from 1993)
Designed by H.S. Colt.
Founded 1898
Visitors: welcome weekdays after
8.30am and weekends and Bank
Holidays after 11.15am; advisable to
ring to ascertain programme for day.
Green Fee: £18/round WD, £21 WE
& BH.
Societies: societies 12 and over
accepted Wed and Fri.
Catering: snacks and teas, evening
meals for societies by arrangement.
Hotels: Chewton Glen; Old
Coastguard; Passford House.

C10 Basingstoke
☎(0256) 465990
Kempshott Park, Basingstoke, Hants
RG23 7LL
On A30 3 miles W of Basingstoke, M3
junction 7.
Parkland course.

18 holes, 6284 yards, S.S.S.70
Designed by James Braid.
Founded 1928
Visitors: weekdays with h/cap cert,
weekends with member.
Green Fee: on application.
Societies: welcome Wed and Thurs.
Catering: full every day except Mon.
Hotels: Tudor Lodge.

C11 **Basingstoke District Hospitals**
☎(0256) 20347
Aldermarston Rd, Basingstoke,
Hants RG24 9ND
2 miles from Basingstoke in
Basingstoke Hospital grounds;
situated between A339 Basingstoke-
Newbury road and A340
Basingstoke-Aldermarston road.
Parkland course.
9 holes (18 tees), 5462 yards,
S.S.S.67
Founded 1971
Visitors: welcome except Wed pm;
restrictions at weekends during
competitions.
Green Fee: £9 WD, £11.50 WE; £4
OAPs and Jnrs.
Societies: Mon-Fri, not Wed.
Catering: bar.

C12 **Basingstoke Golf Centre**
☎(0256) 50054
Worting Rd, West Ham, Basingstoke,
Hants RG23 0TY
M3 junction 7; 0.5 mile from
Basingstoke town centre in
Basingstoke Leisure Park.
Public parkland course.
9 holes Par 3, 908 yards.
Visitors: welcome.
Green Fee: £2.50/round.
Driving range.

C13 **Bishopswood**
☎(0734) 815213
Bishopswood Lane, Tadley,
Basingstoke, Hants RG26 6AT
6 miles N of Basingstoke, off A340.
Public parkland course.
9 holes, 6474 yards, S.S.S.71
Designed by Blake and Phillips.
Founded 1976
Visitors: welcome by prior booking
only.
Green Fee: £7.15 (9 holes), £12.25
(18 holes).
Societies: weekdays by
arrangement.
Catering: bar snacks and restaurant.
Driving range.

C14 **Blackmoor**
☎(0420) 472775
Golf Lane, Whitehill, Bordon, Hants
GU35 9EH
Off A325 between Farnham and
Petersfield, turn into Firgrove Rd at
Whitehill crossroads.
Parkland/heathland course.
18 holes, 6213 yards, S.S.S.70
Designed by H.S. Colt.
Founded 1913
Visitors: welcome weekdays with
h/cap cert.
Green Fee: £33 (£16.50 with
member)/day, £25 (£12.50 with
member) after 12am or 1pm in
summer; not WE.
Societies: Wed, Thurs and Fri.
Catering: full, available every day.
Hotels: Silver Birch (Greatham).

C15 **Bognor Regis**
☎(0243) 821929
Downview Rd, Felpham, Bognor
Regis, W Sussex PO22 8JD
A259 Littlehampton-Bognor road,
from Bognor Regis to traffic lights,
turn left, clubhouse 0.5 mile at end of
road.
Parkland course
18 holes, 6238 yards, S.S.S.70

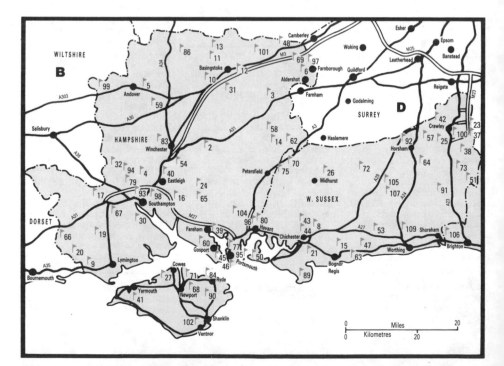

Designed by James Braid.
Founded 1 Jan 1892
Visitors: welcome with h/cap cert, weekends April-Oct with member only.
Green Fee: on application
Societies: welcome by arrangement only.
Catering: meals by arrangement.

C16 Botley Park Hotel CC
☎(0489) 780888, 789242 fax.
Winchester Road, Boorley Green, Botley, Hants SO3 2UA
NW of Botley on B3354 Winchester road, within easy reach of M27 junction 7, or M3/A33.
Parkland course.
18 holes, 6026 yards, S.S.S.70
Designed by Charles Potterton.
Founded Feb 1990
Visitors: phone bookings required; also h/cap cert.
Green Fee: £23 WD.
Societies: catered for on Wed and Thurs.
Catering: full restaurant facilities, bars and bar snacks; banqueting service.
Driving range, indoor swimming pool, squash, tennis, croquet, snooker, petanque, sauna etc.
Hotels: own hotel in complex.

C17 Bramshaw
☎(0703) 813433
Brook, Lyndhurst, Hants SO4 7HE
Exit from M27 (Cadnam) at junction 1, take B3078 for 1 mile, club on right behind Bell Inn.
Manor course, parkland; Forest course, undulating.

Manor, 18 holes, 6233 yards, S.S.S.70; Forest, 18 holes, 5774 yards, S.S.S.69
Founded 1880
Visitors: not weekends unless playing with member or Bell Inn resident.
Green Fee: £26/day.
Societies: welcome weekdays, bookings only.
Catering: full catering.
Hotels: Bell Inn within Golf Complex (golf inclusive breaks available with reserved tee times).

C18 Brighton & Hove
☎(0273) 556482
Dyke Rd, Brighton, E Sussex BN1 8YJ
N of Brighton centre, 2.5 miles up Dyke Rd on left hand side.
Downland course.
9 holes, 5722 yards, S.S.S.68
Founded 1887
Visitors: welcome; not before 12am Wed, 10am Fri, 12am Sun.
Green Fee: on application.
Societies: catered for weekdays by arrangement.
Catering: full service available; Snooker.
Hotels: Old Ship.

C19 Brokenhurst Manor
☎(0590) 23332 Sec, 23092 Pro.
Sway Rd, Brokenhurst, Hants SO42 7SG
A337 to Brockenhurst, then B3055 S from village centre, course 1 mile on right hand side.
Gently undulating forest/parkland course.
18 holes, 6222 yards, S.S.S.70

Designed by H.S. Colt, with recent alterations by J. Hamilton Stutt.
Founded 1919
Visitors: phone booking in advance; must have current h/cap cert.
Green Fee: £25/round, £30/day WD; £35/round WE & BH.
Societies: Thurs; book in with Sec.
Catering: bar and meals every day.
Hotels: information on request.

C20 Burley
☎(042 53) 2431
Cott Lane, Burley, Ringwood, Hants BH24 4BB
Leave A31 Ringwood-Cadnam road at Picket Post, through Burley Street and Burley; club at top of hill, 400 yards from village centre on Lymington road.
Undulating heathland course.
9 holes, 6149 yards, S.S.S.69
Founded 1905
Visitors: welcome with h/cap cert and required standard of dress; not Wed until 1.30pm (Ladies Day); members only most Sat, some Sun.
Green Fee: £10/day (£5 with member).
Catering: bar and catering available lunch time most days.
Hotels: Moorhill House; Burley Manor; White Buck; Toad Hall.

C21 Chichester Golf Centre
☎(0243) 533833
Hoe Farm, Hunston, Chichester, W Sussex PO20 6AX
3 miles S of A27 on B2145 to Selsey, through village of Hunston on left hand side.
Public course with membership; parkland with water on 7 holes.
18 holes, 6177 yards, S.S.S.69; 9-hole Par 3, 825 yards.
Designed by Philip Sanders
Founded August 1990
Visitors: welcome (no h/cap required); advisable to ring in advance; strict dress code on 18-hole course.
Green Fee: £12 WD, £16.50 WE: Par 3, £3.50 WD, £4.50 WE (inc. clubs and ball).
Societies: Welcome Mon-Fri; contact General Manager.
Catering: Temporary facilities; club house opening Autumn 1992.
Driving range.
Hotels: Golfing holidays and mini-golfing breaks at Hunston Mill and Millside Cottage Hotel; full, half or self-catering available.

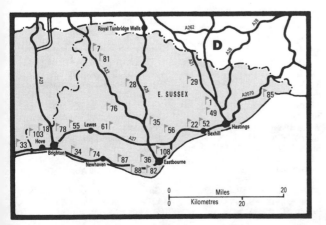

C22 Cooden Beach

☎(042 43) 2040
Cooden Sea Rd, Nr Bexhill-on-Sea,
E Sussex TN39 4TR
A259 Eastbourne-Hastings road,
follow Cooden Beach sign at Little
Common roundabout.
Seaside course.
18 holes, 6450 yards, S.S.S.71
Designed by Herbert Fowler.
Founded 1912
Visitors: h/cap certs required; prior
arrangement preferred.
Green Fee: £21 WD, £26 WE and BH.
Societies: Mon, Thurs, Fri by
arrangement.
Catering: full services available.
Hotels: Cooden Resort.

C23 Copthorne

☎(0342) 712508
Borers Arms Rd, Copthorne, Crawley,
W Sussex RH10 3LL
On A264, 4 miles E of Crawley; 2
miles E of exit 10 from M23.
Heathland course.
18 holes, 6505 yards, S.S.S.71
Designed by James Braid.
Founded 1892
Visitors: welcome weekdays and
afternoons at weekends.
Green Fee: £25/round, £32/day WD;
£40/round WE after 1pm.
Societies: Thurs and Fri.
Catering: lunch Mon-Fri and Sun.
Hotels: Copthorne.

C24 Corhampton

☎(0489) 877279
Sheeps Pond Lane, Droxford,
Southampton, Hants SO3 1QZ
Right off A32 at Corhampton on
B3135 for 1 mile.
Downland course.
18 holes, 6088 yards, S.S.S.69
Founded 1891
Visitors: welcome weekdays, with
member at weekends.
Green Fee: £20/round, £32/day WD.
Societies: welcome Mon and Thurs.
Catering: lunch, tea, dinners except
Tues.
Hotels: Little Uplands Country Guest
House; Coach House Motel.

C25 Cottesmore

☎(0293) 28256
Bucham Hill, Pease Pottage,
Crawley, Sussex RH11 9AT
M23 exit to Pease Pottage, 1 mile
down Horsham road from Pease
Pottage, on right.
Undulating meadowland course.

Old, 18 holes, 6100 yards, S.S.S.70;
New, 18 holes, 5400 yards, S.S.S.68
Designed by M.D. Rogerson.
Founded 1974
Visitors: welcome.
Green Fee: on application
Societies: weekdays only; weekend
breaks in club accommodation.
Catering: full bar and restaurant
facilities.
Hotels: accommodation at club.

C26 Cowdray Park

☎(0730) 813599 Sec.
Midhurst, W Sussex GU29 0BB
Situated about 1 mile E of Midhurst
on A272.
Parkland course.
18 holes, 5972 yards, S.S.S.70
Founded 1920
Visitors: welcome.
Green Fee: on application.
Societies: catered for Mon, Wed,
Thurs.
Catering: bar snacks daily, evening
meals by arrangement.
Hotels: Angel; Spread Eagle.

C27 Cowes

☎(0983) 292303
Crossfield Ave, Cowes, PO31 8HN
Make for Cowes High School; course
is at far end of school playing field.
Parkland course.
9 holes, 2967 yards, S.S.S.68
Founded 1908
Visitors: welcome by arrangement;
not before 11.30am Sun or
10.30am-3pm Thurs.
Green Fee: on application.
Societies: by prior application to
Sec.
Catering: bar snacks 11.30am-1pm
except Sun, summer only.
Hotels: Fountain; New Holmwood.

C28 Crowborough Beacon

☎(0892) 661511
Beacon Rd, Crowborough, E Sussex
TN6 1UJ
8 miles S of Tunbridge Wells on A26.
Heathland course.
18 holes, 6318 yards, S.S.S.70
Founded 1895
Visitors: weekdays; h/cap cert or
letter of intro. required.
Green Fee: £22.50/round, £34/day
WD; £16.50/round with county card.
Societies: Mon, Tues, Wed by prior
arrangement with Sec.
Catering: for up to 60; breakfast
available by prior arrangement.
Hotels: Winston Manor.

C29 Dale Hill

☎(0580) 200112, 201090 Pro.
Ticehurst, Wadhurst, E Sussex TN5
7DQ
Turn off A21 at Flimwell, on B2087
towards Ticehurst.
Parkland/woodland course.
18 holes, 6055 yards, S.S.S.69
Founded 1972
Visitors: welcome; telephone Pro to
obtain tee time.
Green Fee: £17/day WD, £24 WE.
Societies: booking form obtained
from Sec.
Catering: full facilities all week;
breakfast if ordered in advance.
Hotels: Dale Hill, special golf breaks
and packages.

C30 Dibden

☎(0703) 207508 Bookings, 845596
shop
Main Rd, Dibden, Southampton,
Hants SO4 5TB
Turn off A326 at Dibden roundabout,
course 0.5 mile on right hand side.
Public parkland course.
18 holes, 6206 yards, S.S.S.70; 9
holes, Par 27
Designed by Hamilton Stutt.
Founded 1974
Visitors: welcome, no restrictions.
Green Fee: £3.60 WD, £5.30 WE.
Societies: by arrangement with Pro.
Catering: full facilities available.

C31 Dummer

Dummer, Hants
Parkland course.
18 holes, Par 72
Designed by Peter Alliss and Clive
Clark.
Visitors: course opening April 1992;
write for details.
Green Fee: £20.
Societies: write for details.
Catering: full facilities.

C32 Dunwood Manor

☎(0794) 40549
Shootash Hill, Romsey, Hants SO51
0GF
Off A27 Romsey-Salisbury road, after
2 miles turn right at Shootash cross
roads into Danes Rd, club is on left.
Undulating parkland course.
18 holes, 6004 yards, S.S.S.69
Founded 1972
Visitors: welcome weekdays by
arrangement.
Green Fee: £20/round, £25/day WD;
£30/round WE & BH.
Societies: by arrangement.

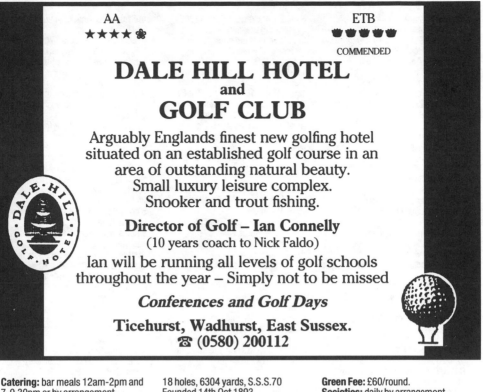
Catering: bar meals 12am-2pm and 7-9.30pm or by arrangement. Snooker and pool table.
Hotels: Moat House; White Horse.

C33 Dyke
☎(0273) 857296
Dyke Rd, Brighton, E Sussex BN1 8YJ
5 miles N of Brighton between A23 and A27.
Downland course.
18 holes, 6588 yards, S.S.S.71
Founded 1906
Visitors: welcome by appointment.
Green Fee: £21/round, £31/day WD; £31/round WE & BH.
Societies: full day inc. meals £45.
Catering: licensed bar, restaurant. Snooker.
Hotels: Old Ship (Brighton).

C34 East Brighton
☎(0273) 604838
Roedean Rd, Brighton, E Sussex BN2 5RA
Follow A259 from Brighton towards Newhaven, then signs for Marina; over 1st set of traffic lights; club 50 metres on left.
Seaside course.

18 holes, 6304 yards, S.S.S.70
Founded 14th Oct 1893
Visitors: welcome on weekdays, weekends by appointment; h/cap cert required.
Green Fee: £21/day WD, £30/day WE.
Societies: by arrangement Tues pm, Thurs, Fri.
Catering: full bar, lunch/tea except Mon, evening meals by arrangement. Snooker.
Hotels: Old Ship (golfing packages); Grand; Metropolis; Hospitality Inn.

C35 East Sussex National
☎(0825) 841217, 75577
Little Horsted, Uckfield, East Sussex TN22 5TS
2 miles S of Uckfield on A22.
Part (18 holes) public course:
England's "Augusta" – bent grass tees, fairways and greens.
East, 18 holes, 7081 yards, S.S.S.74
West, 18 holes, 7154 yards, S.S.S.74
National Academy, 3 holes, 1155 yards, S.S.S.12
Designed by Bob Cupp.
Founded 1989
Visitors: welcome; reservations advised.

Green Fee: £60/round.
Societies: daily by arrangement.
Catering: bar and restaurant.
Academy of Golf Teaching Centre; 2 double ended practice ranges; chipping, pitching, putting greens.
Hotels: Horsted Place Hotel on site (golfers' privileges).

C36 Eastbourne Downs
☎(0323) 20827
East Dean Rd, Eastbourne, E Sussex BN20 8ES
On A259 W of Eastbourne.
Downland course.
18 holes, 6635 yards, S.S.S.72
Designed by J.H. Taylor.
Founded 1907
Visitors: welcome.
Green Fee: £20/day.
Societies: welcome.
Catering: Tues-Sun.
Hotels: Queens; Princes; Lansdowne; Wish Tower.

C37 Effingham Park
☎(0342) 716528
West Park Rd, Copthorne, W Sussex RH10 3EU
From M23 junction 10 onto A264.

Parkland course.
9 holes, 1749 yards, S.S.S.30
Founded 1980
Visitors: welcome, not before 1pm
Sat/Sun, not after 4pm Tues.
Green Fee: £8 (9 holes), £11.50 (18
holes) WD; £9/£13.50 WE.
Societies: on application.
Catering: 2 restaurants, club bar.
Leisure Club – swimming, sauna,
gym etc.
Hotels: Effingham Park; Copthorne
(American Express weekend break).

C38 Fairway
☎(0293) 521706
Horsham Rd, Pease Pottage,
Crawley, W Sussex RH11 8AL
S of Crawley off A23.
Public, flat parkland course.
9 holes, 1864 yards, S.S.S.57
Visitors: welcome.
Green Fee: £8 (18 holes) WD,
£10.50 WE.
Societies: welcome
Catering: available.
Driving range.
Hotels: The George (Crawley).

C39 Fleetlands
☎(0705) 822351 extn 44384 Sec.
R.N.A.Y. Fleetlands, Gosport, Hants
PO13 0AW
Off A32 2 miles S of Fareham.
9 holes, 4775 yards, S.S.S.63
Founded 1963
Visitors: with members only.
Green Fee: on application.
Societies: by appointment.
Catering: bar.

C40 Fleming Park
☎(0703) 612797 Pro, 612692
catering
Magpie Lane, Eastleigh, Hants SO5
PLH
A27/M27, turn off at Eastleigh sign, 1
mile to course.
Parkland course.
18 holes, 4402 yards, S.S.S.62
Designed by Charles Lawrie.
Founded 1973
Visitors: welcome, phone in
advance.
Green Fee: on application
Societies: apply to Pro.
Catering: bar snacks and meals.

C41 Freshwater Bay
☎(0983) 752955
Afton Down, Freshwater Bay, Isle of
Wight PO40 9TZ

3 miles from Yarmouth on A3055
overlooking Freshwater Bay.
Seaside downland course.
18 holes, 5379 yards, S.S.S.68
Founded 1893
Visitors: welcome after 9.30am on
weekdays and 10am on Sun.
Green Fee: £16 WD, £20 WE & BH.
Societies: welcome at times shown
for visitors; max 30; all bookings
must be confirmed in writing.
Catering: lunch and snacks;
licensed bar.
Hotels: Albion; Country Garden;
Farringford; Saunders.

C42 Gatwick Manor Hotel
☎(0293) 26301
London Rd, Lowfield Heath, Nr
Crawley, W Sussex
0.75 miles S of Gatwick Airport on
A23.
Refurbished parkland course.
9 holes, 1118 yards, Par 28
Designed by Patrick Tallack.
Visitors: welcome; priority to guests
of Hotel.
Green Fee: on application
Societies: societies and Company
days welcome by prior arrangement.
Catering: 2 bars and 2 restaurants.
Hotels: Gatwick Manor.

C43 Goodwood
☎(0243) 774968
Goodwood, Chichester, W Sussex
PO18 0PN
On A286 5 miles N of Chichester.
Downland/parkland course.
18 holes, 6318 yards, S.S.S.70
Designed by James Braid.
Founded 1891
Visitors: not before 10am weekends
and holidays; book in at Pro shop.
Green Fee: £25 WD, £35 WE.
Societies: Wed, Thurs; essential to
book early.
Catering: full catering by booking
except Mon. Snooker table.
Hotels: Goodwood Park; Chichester
Resort; Dolphin & Anchor.

C44 Goodwood Park Hotel Golf & Country Club
☎(0243) 775987
Goodwood, Nr Chichester, W Sussex
PO20 0QB
A27-M27 E of Chichester, in the
grounds of Goodwood House.
Parkland course.
18 holes, 6525 yards, S.S.S.72
Designed by Donald Steel.
Founded 1989

Visitors: welcome with h/cap cert
and correct attire.
Green Fee: £16/round WD,
£25/round WE (no day tickets).
Societies: welcome by arrangement
Tues-Thurs.
Catering: full catering and bar
facilities, inc. private rooms.
Tennis, swimming, squash, snooker,
gym, sauna etc.
Hotels: Goodwood Park (golf and
leisure breaks available).

C45 Gosport & Stokes Bay
☎(0705) 527941 Sec, 581625 Club
Fort Rd, Haslar, Gosport, Hants PO12
2AT
S on A32 from Fareham, E to Haslar.
Links course.
9 holes, 5856 yards, S.S.S.68
Founded 1885
Visitors: welcome except Sun am.
Green Fee: £10 WD, £16 WE.
Societies: by arrangement.
Catering: bar snacks, meals by
arrangement.
Hotels: Anglesey.

C46 Great Salterns
☎(0705) 664549, 699519
Portsmouth Golf Centre, Eastern Rd,
Portsmouth PO3 6QB
2 miles from A27 on A2030 into
Southsea.
Public seaside/parkland course.
18 holes, 5600 yards, S.S.S.68
Founded 1914
Visitors: welcome, booking system
7 days.
Green Fee: £8.20 summer, £6.15
winter.
Societies: welcome by prior
arrangement.
Catering: at Farmhouse pub
adjacent to course.
Driving range.
Hotels: Hilton; Inn Lodge next to
Farmhouse.

C47 Ham Manor
☎(0903) 783288
Angmering, W Sussex BN16 4JE
3 miles E of Littlehampton.
Gently undulating parkland course.
18 holes, 6216 yards, S.S.S.70
Designed by H.S. Colt.
Founded 1936
Visitors: welcome after 8.45am by
arrangement; h/cap certs required.
Green Fee: on application
Societies: by arrangement.
Catering: lunch except Mon.
Snooker.

C48 Hartley Wintney

☎(025 126) 4211 Sec, 3779 Pro, 2214 Club
London Rd, Hartley Wintney, Hants RG27 8PT
On A30 8 miles NE of Basingstoke.
Parkland course.
9 holes, 6096 yards, S.S.S.69
Founded 1891
Visitors: weekdays; Bank Holidays and weekends with member only; restrictions on Wed.
Green Fee: £15/round, £22/day.
Societies: Tues and Thurs only.
Catering: snacks and meals 6 days.
Hotels: Lismoyne; Lamb.

C49 Hastings

☎(0424) 852981
Battle Rd, St Leonards-on-Sea, E Sussex TN38 0TA
A2100 from Battle to Hastings, 3 miles NW of Hastings.
Public undulating parkland course.
18 holes, 6284 yards, S.S.S.71
Designed by Frank Pennink.
Founded 1973
Visitors: no restrictions; tee booking system.
Green Fee: on application.
Societies: welcome Mon-Fri.
Catering: full facilities.
Driving range
Hotels: Beauport Park.

C50 Hayling

☎(0705) 464446 Sec, 464491 Pro, 463712 Steward
Ferry Rd, Hayling Island, Hants PO11 0BX
5 miles S of Havant off M27 to A3023, situated at W end of seafront.
Seaside course
18 holes, 6489 yards, S.S.S.71
Designed by Tom Simpson.
Founded 1883
Visitors: private club h/cap cert required and letter of intro. from Home Club appreciated.
Green Fee: £22/day, £30 WE (by prior arrangement).
Societies: Tues and Wed only by prior arrangement.
Catering: not Mon.
Hotels: Post House; Rook Hollow.

C51 Haywards Heath

☎(0444) 414866
High Beech Lane, Haywards Heath, W Sussex RH16 1SL
2 miles NE of Haywards Heath, follow B2112 towards Lindfield, then left towards Ardingly into Summerhill Lane; High Beech Lane is 4th on left.
Parkland course.
18 holes, 6206 yards, S.S.S.70
Founded 1922
Visitors: welcome subject to tee reservations.
Green Fee: on application
Societies: Wed and Thurs only.
Catering: bar, lunch, evening catering by arrangement.

C52 Highwoods

☎(0424) 212625 Sec, 212770 Pro.
Ellerslie Lane, Bexhill-on-Sea, E Sussex TN39 4LJ
Off A259 from Eastbourne/Hastings, 2 miles from Bexhill; from Battle A269 via Ninfield, turn right in Sidley.
18 holes, 6218 yards, S.S.S.70
Designed by J.H. Taylor
Founded 1925
Visitors: welcome with h/cap cert; no visitors Sun before 12am unless with member.
Green Fee: £20/round/day WD, £25 WE & BH.
Societies: by arrangement.
Catering: lunch by arrangement, snacks, tea.
Hotels: Cooden Resort; White Friars.

C53 Hill Barn

☎(0903) 37301
Hill Barn Lane, Worthing, Sussex BN14 9QE
N of Worthing off London & Edinburgh Building Soc roundabout on A27, take exit directly before Brighton exit, signposted.
Municipal downland course.
18 holes, 6224 yards, S.S.S.70
Designed by Hawtree & Son.
Founded 1935
Visitors: welcome, no restrictions.
Green Fee: £9.50/round WD, £11/round WE & BH.
Societies: weekdays only; min 20.
Catering: breakfasts, snacks, hot meals available all day.
Hotels: Beach; Ardington & Chatsworth.

C54 Hockley

☎(0962) 713165, 714572 Steward, 713678 Pro.
Twyford, Winchester, Hants SO21 1PL
2 miles S of Winchester on A335 Twyford road.
Downland course
18 holes, 6279 yards, S.S.S.70
Designed by James Braid.
Founded 1915
Visitors: welcome weekdays, and at weekends with member or by arrangement with Secretary.
Green Fee: on application.
Societies: not Mon.
Catering: snacks, lunch and evening meals; other requirements contact Steward.
Hotels: Wessex (Winchester).

C55 Hollingbury Park

☎(0273) 552010
Ditchling Rd, Brighton, Sussex BN1 7HS
1 mile from Brighton, astride the Downs between A23 London Rd and A27 Lewes Rd.
Public undulating downland course.
18 holes, 6502 yards, S.S.S.71
Designed by J. Braid and J.H. Taylor
Founded 1908
Visitors: welcome anytime.
Green Fee: municipal rates.
Societies: weekdays only.
Catering: full restaurant facilities open 7 days.
Hotels: Old Ship; Preston Resort.

C56 Horam Park

☎(04353) 3477, 3677 fax.
Chiddingly Rd, Horam, E Sussex TN21 0JJ
0.5 mile S of Horam on road to Chiddingly; Horam is 13 miles N of Eastbourne on A267.
Parkland course with lakes.
9 holes, 2911 yards, S.S.S.68
Designed by Glen Johnson.
Founded 1985
Visitors: welcome, ring for bookings.
Green Fee: ring for details.
Societies: ring for brochure.
Catering: carvery, bar meals.
Driving range.
Hotels: Boship Farm (Hailsham).

C57 Ifield G & CC

☎(0293) 520222
Rusper Rd, Ifield, Crawley, W Sussex RH11 0LN
M23 Crawley junction; follow signs to Brighton and A23; after 3 roundabouts take right turning; left into Ifield Drive, 2nd right after shops, 1st left into Rusper Rd 0.5 mile then signposted.
Parkland course.
18 holes, 6314 yards, S.S.S.70
Designed by Bernard Darwin; constructed by F. Hawtry and J.H. Taylor.
Founded 1927

Visitors: welcome weekdays only or with member at weekends.
Green Fee: £25/round/day, £18 after 1pm.
Societies: welcome Mon, Tues pm, Wed pm, Thurs.
Catering: full facilities all week.

C58 Kingsley

☎(0420) 476118
Main Road, Kingsley, Nr Bordon, Hants GU35 9NG
Off A325 Farnham-Petersfield road, 3 miles E of Bordon.
Public parkland course.
9 holes, 1797 yards, S.S.S.27
Founded May 1990
Visitors: welcome, booking on Sun only.
Green Fee: £3 Mon-Sat, £7 Sun (18 holes only).
Catering: bar and snacks available. Dome Tennis Centre, indoor bowls (opening 1992).
Hotels: Merrie Monks Motel (Bucks Horn Oak); Alton House (Alton).

C59 Leckford & Longstock

☎(0264) 810710
Leckford, Stockbridge, Hants
2.5 miles N of Stockbridge on Andover road.
Downland course
9 holes, 3251 yards, S.S.S.71
Designed by John Morrison.
Visitors: invitation only.
Green Fee: on application

C60 Lee-on-the-Solent

☎(0705) 551170 Manager, 550207 Members, 551181 Pro.
Brune Lane, Lee-on-the-Solent, Hants PO13 9PB
3 miles due S of M27 junction 9.
Heathland course.
18 holes, 5959 yards, S.S.S.69
Founded 1905
Visitors: welcome on weekdays; h/cap cert required.
Green Fee: £18/round/day WD, £20 WE.
Societies: Thurs, book in advance.
Catering: Mon-Fri.
Hotels: Belle Vue.

C61 Lewes

☎(0273) 473245
Chapel Hill, Lewes, Sussex
On A27 Lewes-Eastbourne road opposite junction of Cliffe High St and South St.

Downland course.
18 holes, 5951 yards, S.S.S.69
Founded 1896
Visitors: welcome weekdays; weekends after 10.30am; Sat restricted 12am-2pm.
Green Fee: on application
Societies: by arrangement.
Catering: full facilities.

C62 Liphook

☎(0428) 723271 Pro, 723785 Sec
Wheatsheaf Enclosure, Liphook, Hants GU30 7EH
1 mile S of Liphook off A3.
Heath/heatherland course.
18 holes, 6250 yards, S.S.S.70
Designed by Arthur Croome.
Founded 1921
Visitors: h/cap cert required; phone in advance; not before 2pm Sun & Bank Holidays.
Green Fee: £22.50/round, £31/day WD; £31/round, £41/day Sat; £36/round Sun & BH.
Societies: Wed, Thurs & Fri, min 16, max 28.
Catering: bar and bar snacks daily; 3 course lunch and dinner available.
Hotels: Links; Angel.

C63 Littlehampton

☎(0903) 717170
170 Rope Walk, Riverside, Littlehampton, W Sussex BN17 5DL
From Littlehampton take Bognor Regis road; take 1st left after bridge over river, marked To Golf Club.
Seaside links course.
18 holes, 6244 yards, S.S.S.70
Founded 1898
Visitors: welcome 7 days; after 12am weekends.
Green Fee: £22 WD, £30 WE.
Societies: not weekends.
Catering: full catering facilities daily.
Hotels: Bailiff's Court; Beach.

C64 Mannings Heath

☎(0403) 210228
Goldings Lane, Mannings Heath, Horsham, W Sussex RH13 6JU
3 miles SE of Horsham on A281; 4 miles from M25, exit at Pease Pottage or Handcross.
Undulating parkland course.
18 holes, 6404 yards, S.S.S.71
Founded 1908
Visitors: welcome by prior arrangement.
Green Fee: £18/round WD, £25/round WE.
Societies: weekdays.

Catering: daily on application.
Hotels: King's Head; Cisswood House; South Lodge.

C65 Meon Valley Hotel G & CC

☎(0329) 833455
Sandy Lane, Shedfield, Southampton SO3 2HQ
On A334 8 miles E of Southampton between Botley and Wickham.
Parkland courses.
Meon course, 18 holes, 6519 yards, S.S.S.71; Valley course, 9 holes, 2714 yards, S.S.S.68
Designed by Hamilton Stutt.
Founded 1978
Visitors: welcome with h/cap cert.
Green Fee: Meon course, £22/round WD, £30/round WE & BH; Valley course, £10/round WD, £15/round WE & BH.
Societies: by arrangement, residents only at weekends.
Catering: meals and snacks. Squash, tennis, snooker, indoor swimming pool etc (residents only).
Hotels: Meon Valley (residential golf packages available).

C66 Moors Valley

☎(0425) 479776
Moors Valley Country Park, Horton Rd, Nr Ringwood, Hants.
A31 through Ringwood, right at roundabout signposted Ashley Heath, 2 miles on right; course inside Country Park.
Public parkland course.
9 holes (18 by spring 1992), 2755 yards, Par 35
Designed by Martin Hawtree.
Founded Oct 1989
Visitors: no restrictions.
Green Fee: £6.50 (18 holes) WD, £8.45 WE; reductions for jnrs.
Societies: apply to Golf Director.
Catering: at visitor centre in Park.

C67 New Forest

☎(0703) 282752 Office, 282450 Pro shop
Southampton Rd, Lyndhurst, Hants SO43 7BU
On A35 Southampton-Bournemouth road between Ashurst and Lyndhurst.
Heathland course.
18 holes, 5742 yards, S.S.S.68
Designed by Peter Swann.
Founded 1888
Visitors: from 8.30am Mon-Fri, from 10am Sat, from 1.30pm Sun.

Liphook

For most golfers charm is a more important quality in a course than challenge. Liphook is the type which combines the two in equal measure. 6207 yards is not long these days but matching the par of 70 is another matter when the heather and trees, the hallmark of the best Surrey and Hampshire courses, place such a premium on controlled shot-making.

You certainly appreciate the lovely setting rather more if you keep straight, the countryside possessing more normal contouring than the valleys, plateaux and gulleys that characterise the land surrounding the Devil's Punchbowl at Hindhead just up the Portsmouth Road, and in terms of golf course architecture, Liphook has rightly been hailed as an example for the connoisseur.

My late senior partner, Ken Cotton, was always singing its praises but the remarkable part of the story is that its designer, A.C. Croome, was first and foremost a schoolmaster. Liphook was the only new course for which he was entirely responsible. Jack Neville keeps him notable company in this regard, Neville's lone masterpiece being Pebble Beach. It was ill health rather than lack of demand that prevented Croome pursuing the final chapter of a working life that had more variety than most.

In addition to being a housemaster at Radley College, he wrote about cricket and golf for several newspapers, both games at which he excelled himself. He was founder member of the Oxford and Cambridge Golfing Society donating the Croome Shield for annual competition among College pairs at the President's Putter, and was a regular competitor in the Amateur and other championships.

It was J.F. Abercromby, the designer of Addington, among others, who persuaded him to join forces in the firm of Fowler, Abercromby, Simpson and Croome — as elite a quartet as anyone could muster. At first, Croome's role was mainly administrative, but inside every golfer is a golf course architect clamouring to get out, and Liphook was the ultimate expression of Croome's talents.

No clubhouse gets a better view of its 1st and 18th holes, the work of John Morrison who wanted to provide a fine, long short hole to get players moving, but, apart from the difficulty of the opening tee shot, Liphook is quick to let golfers know what is expected of them. There are three par 4s of well over 400 yards in the first six holes, the 4th, High View, being particularly demanding. It leads to the first crossing of the busy road and on to the first of three par 5s where thorn trees feature in the drive.

The 6th, with its little grassy hollow behind the green, doubles back on the 5th, the attractive short 7th starting the section of 10 holes on the other side of the railway. The railway is not the feature it is on some courses although the 7th and 8th run roughly parallel to it. The 9th, 438 yards, another demanding 4, prompts a long uphill second over a road and a heathery dell but the 10th offers a more inviting drive even if a ditch lurks on the approach to the green.

A large central bunker dominates the short 11th in a visual sense, the 12th, Forest Mere, completing the long par 4s and always with a victim or two. A nice downhill drive and a slightly uphill second give the longer hitters a chance of a birdie at the 13th, and, for those negotiating the dogleg successfully, a good pitch can do the same at the 14th.

Then it is a deep breath and a mad dash to the 15th where the drive takes us up over a steep ridge with the temptation to cut off more than is good for us. The 16th is the reverse of the 15th, a quarry and the corner of a wood awaiting any poorly struck or mis-directed second. The walk to the 17th is a last reminder of the Portsmouth Road which explains in part the club's traditionally strong links with the Navy; the 17th's tee shot across a diagonal, corrugated bank of gorse and heather makes the fifth and last short hole difficult to judge, enhancing Liphook's reputation that it's not just nautical men who are all at sea.

Green Fee: £12/round/day WD, £15 WE & BH.
Societies: Tues, Wed & Thurs; to be booked and confirmed in advance.
Catering: bar from 11am Mon-Sat, 12am-3pm Sun; snacks and meals 11.30am-4pm Mon-Sat.
Hotels: Crown; Lyndhurst Park; Carey's Manor.

C68 Newport
☎(0983) 525076
St George's Down, Newport, Isle of Wight PO30 3BA
A3056 Newport-Sandown road 0.5 mile from Newport.
Undulating parkland course.
9 holes, 5704 yards, S.S.S.68
Designed by Guy Hunt.
Founded 1896
Visitors: welcome except Sat and Sun am.
Green Fee: £10 WD, £12 WE, half price with member.
Societies: welcome; bar catering available.
Catering: bar meals on request to Stewardess before round.

C69 North Hants
☎(0252) 616443, 811627 fax
Minley Rd, Fleet, Hants GU13 8RE
0.5 mile N of Fleet Station on B3013.
Heathland course.
18 holes, 6257 yards, S.S.S.70
Designed by James Braid.
Founded 1904
Visitors: by prior arrangement with Sec; letter of intro. and h/cap cert required.
Green Fee: on application.
Societies: Tues and Wed.
Catering: lunch, tea, dinner; pre-booking required.

C70 Old Thorns
☎(0428) 724555
London Kosaido Co Ltd, Old Thorns, Longmoor Rd, Liphook, Hants GU30 7PE
On A3 into Liphook, at mini-roundabout take B2131 for 1 mile until sign on left to London Kosaido GC; turn up lane and go to end.
Public parkland course.
18 holes, 6115 yards, S.S.S.71
Designed by Commander John Harris, adapted by Peter Alliss and Dave Thomas
Founded 1982
Visitors: welcome.
Green Fee: £22/round, £35/day WD; £32 WE.

Societies: weekdays, min 12, £49 per person inc 2 rounds of golf, morning coffee, ploughman's lunch, evening meal.
Catering: full à la carte menu and Japanese restaurant.
Driving range, putting green, swimming, sauna, tennis etc.
Hotels: Old Thorns.

C71 Osborne
☎(0983) 295421
Osborne, East Cowes, Isle of Wight PO32 6JX
A3052 Newport to East Cowes road, in grounds of Osborne House.
Parkland course.
9 holes, 6304 yards, S.S.S.70
Founded 1903
Visitors: not before 12am Sat & Sun or 1.30pm Tues.
Green Fee: £15 WD, £15 WE.
Societies: by arrangement.
Catering: limited, by arrangement.
Hotels: Padmore House, Crossway; Clarence House.

C72 Osiers Farm
☎(0798) 44097
Petworth, W Sussex GU28 9LX
2.5 miles N of Petworth on A283 Guildford road.
Public course over farmland, hedges, trees etc.
9 holes, 5220 yards, S.S.S.64
Designed by Chris Duncton.
Founded 1991
Visitors: welcome at any time.
Green Fee: £5 for 9 holes, £7 for 18 holes; reductions for jnrs and OAPs.
Societies: as required, not Sun, Bank Holidays or Sat am.
Catering: light refreshments.
Driving range.
Hotels: B&B on course; Angel, Mason's Arms (Petworth).

C73 Paxhill Park
☎(0444) 484467
East Mascalls Lane, Lindfield, W Sussex RH16 2QN
Parkland course.
18 holes, 6174 yards, S.S.S.68
Designed by Patrick Tallack.
Founded Oct 1990
Visitors: welcome; restricted after 12am weekends.
Green Fee: £15/round, £25/day WD; £20/round, £25/day WE.
Societies: daily; weekends, pm only.
Catering: full restaurant and bar facilities; banqueting.
Hotels: Birch (Haywards Heath).

C74 Peacehaven
☎(0273) 514049
Brighton Rd, Newhaven, E Sussex BN9 9UH
On A259 1 mile W of Newhaven.
Undulating downland course.
9 holes, 5007 yards, S.S.S.65
Founded 1895
Visitors: welcome weekdays, after 11.30am weekends and Bank Holidays.
Green Fee: on application
Societies: catered for Mon-Fri.
Catering: available.

C75 Petersfield
☎(0730) 62386 Sec and fax, 67732 Pro.
Heath Rd, Petersfield, Hants GU31 4EJ
Turn off A3 to E at town centre (Red Lion), clubhouse 1 mile past lakes.
Heathland/parkland course.
18 holes, 5649 yards, S.S.S.67
Founded 1892
Visitors: welcome weekdays, weekends after 12am.
Green Fee: £15/round, £20/day WD; £20/round, £25/day WE.
Societies: Wed, Thurs and Fri (no evening catering).
Catering: bar and dining area; lunch available Tues-Sat; evening meals by prior booking.
Hotels: Concorde; Red Lion.

C76 Piltdown
☎(082 572) 2033, 2389 Pro.
Piltdown, Uckfield, E Sussex TN22 3XB
1 mile W of Maresfield off A272 signposted Isfield.
Undulating gorse and heather.
18 holes, 6059 yards, S.S.S.69
Designed by J. Rowe, G.M. Dodd, Frank Pennink.
Founded 1904
Visitors: not before 9.30am (2pm Sun); various restrictions, essential to phone; h/cap cert or letter of intro. required; jacket and tie in clubhouse.
Green Fee: £27.50/round/day.
Societies: by arrangement Mon, Wed and Fri only.
Catering: bar snacks and full catering daily, phone (082572) 4112.
Hotels: Roebuck; Maiden's Head; Horsted Place.

C77 Portsmouth
☎(0705) 372210
Crookhorn Lane, Widley, Portsmouth, Hants PO7 5QL

On the hills overlooking Portsmouth Harbour on N of the city, within 1 mile of both A3 and A3M.
Municipal parkland course.
18 holes, 6200 yards, S.S.S.70
Founded 1926
Visitors: welcome.
Green Fee: £8.20.
Societies: please arrange weekdays.
Catering: full facilities available.
Hotels: Bear; Corner House.

C78 Pyecombe
☎(079 18) 5372
Clayton Hill, Pyecombe, Sussex BN45 7FF
On A273, 0.5 mile from junction with A23 at Pyecombe, 5 to 6 miles N of Brighton.
Downland course.
18 holes, 6234 yards, S.S.S.70
Founded 1894
Visitors: weekdays after 9.15am; Sat after 2pm; Sun after 3pm.
Green Fee: £16 WD, £25 WE.
Societies: catered for Mon, Tues pm, Wed, Thurs.
Catering: full services available.

C79 Romsey
☎(0703) 734637 Manager, 732218 Steward
Romsey Rd, Nursling, Southampton, Hants SO1 9XW
2 miles SE of Romsey on A3057 Southampton road; near M27/M271 junction 3.
Wooded parkland course.
18 holes, 5851 yards, S.S.S.68
Designed by Charles Lawrie.
Founded 1925
Visitors: welcome Mon-Fri.
Green Fee: £18.50/round, £22.50/day.
Societies: Mon, Tues and Thurs.
Catering: full licensed bar, full restaurant facilities.
Hotels: White Horse (Romsey).

C80 Rowlands Castle
☎(0705) 412784
Links Lane, Rowlands Castle, Hants PO9 6AE
7 miles S of Petersfield; leave A3(M) junction Havant/Rowlands Castle.
Parkland course.
18 holes, 6381 yards, S.S.S.70
Founded 1902
Visitors: welcome weekdays; not Sat; restricted numbers Sun, advisable to ring.
Green Fee: £22/round/day WD; £25 Sun and BH.

Societies: catered for Tues and Thurs, details on application.
Catering: until 6pm except Mon.
Hotels: Brookfield; Bear; Fountain Inn (Rowlands Castle).

C81 Royal Ashdown Forest
☎(0342) 822018, 822247 Pro shop
Chapel Lane, Forest Row, East Grinstead, E Sussex RH18 5LR
A22 East Grinstead-Eastbourne road, 4.5 miles S of East Grinstead turn left in Forest Row opposite church onto B2110, after 0.5 mile turn right into Chapel Lane, top of hill turn left, over heath to clubhouse.
Undulating moorland course with views over forest.
18 holes, 6477 yards, S.S.S.71
Founded 1888
Visitors: welcome, restricted weekends, Bank Holidays; advisable to phone beforehand.
Green Fee: £31 WD, £36 WE.
Societies: Wed-Fri normal catering; Mon limited catering.
Catering: lunch, tea; casual visitors requested to book in advance or before teeing off.
Hotels: Ashdown Forest; Chequers.

C82 Royal Eastbourne
☎(0323) 29738 Sec.
Paradise Drive, Eastbourne, Sussex BN20 8BP
0.5 mile from Town Hall.
Parkland/downland course.
18 holes, 6109 yards, S.S.S.69;
9 holes, 4294 yards, S.S.S.61
Founded 1887
Visitors: h/cap cert required for 18 hole course, advisable to telephone 3-4 days in advance.
Green Fee: on application.
Societies: by arrangement.
Catering: full facilities daily.
Snooker.
Hotels: Grand; Lansdowne.

C83 Royal Winchester
☎(0962) 852462
Sarum Rd, Winchester, Hants SO22 5QE
Leave Winchester on Romsey road.
Downland course.
18 holes, 6218 yards, S.S.S.70
Designed by H.S. Colt and A.P. Taylor.
Founded 1888
Visitors: weekdays, h/cap cert required.
Green Fee: £25/round/day.
Societies: Mon, Tues, Wed.

Catering: every day except Thurs; liaise with Steward.
Hotels: Royal; Wessex.

C84 Ryde
☎(0983) 614809
Binstead Rd, Ryde, Isle of Wight PO33 3NF
Main Ryde-Newport road.
Parkland course.
9 holes, 5200 yards, S.S.S.66
Founded 1921
Visitors: not Wed pm, Sun am.
Green Fee: on application
Catering: meals and snacks.

C85 Rye
☎(0797) 225241
Camber, Rye, E Sussex TN31 7QS
A259 from Rye towards Folkestone, turn right after 0.5 mile at signpost Camber, course 3 miles on right.
Links course.
18 holes, 6310 yards, S.S.S.71;
9 holes, 6141 yards, S.S.S.70
Designed by H.S. Colt.
Founded 1894
Visitors: only introduced by member.
Green Fee: £26/round, £39/day WD.
Catering: lunch daily except Tues.
Hotels: George; Mermaid; Broomhill Lodge; Playden Oasts; Hope Anchor; Top of the Hill; Queens Head.

C86 Sandford Springs
☎(0635) 297881/2/3, 298065 fax
Wolverton, Nr Basingstoke, Hants RG26 5RT
On A339 between Basingstoke and Newbury.
Picturesque parkland course overlooking 5 counties.
18 holes, 6064 yards, S.S.S.70
Designed by Hawtree & Son.
Founded 1988
Visitors: welcome weekdays; booking system in operation.
Green Fee: £21/round, £30/day.
Societies: weekday society and company days; occasional weekends available.
Catering: full bar and restaurant facilities; parties, wedding receptions, business rooms etc.
Hotels: Hilton National (Basingstoke and Newbury), special rates agreed.

C87 Seaford
☎(0323) 892442
East Blatchington, Seaford, E Sussex BN25 2JD
Off A259 N of Seaford.

Downland course.
18 holes, 6241 yards, S.S.S.70
Designed by J.H. Taylor.
Founded 1887
Visitors: welcome weekdays after
9.30am; telephone first.
Green Fee: on application.
Societies: welcome after 9.30am by
prior arrangement.
Catering: breakfast, lunch, tea and
dinner available.
Hotels: Dormy House on course.

C88 Seaford Head
☎(0323) 894843 Sec, 890139 Pro.
Southdown Rd, Seaford, E Sussex
BN25 4JS
S of A259, 12 miles from Brighton.
Public seaside course.
18 holes, 5812 yards, S.S.S.68
Founded 1907
Visitors: welcome at all times.
Green Fee: on application
Societies: welcome.
Catering: light snacks.

C89 Selsey
☎(0243) 602203
Golf Links Lane, Selsey, Chichester,
W Sussex PO20 9DR
On B2145 7 miles S of Chichester.
Seaside course.
9 holes, 5932 yards, S.S.S.68
Founded 1909
Visitors: welcome if member of
recognised club.
Green Fee: on application
Societies: small societies welcome.
Catering: lunches and snacks
available.

C90 Shanklin & Sandown
☎(0983) 403217
The Fairway, Lake, Sandown, Isle of
Wight PO36 9PR
On A3055 to Lake, down The
Fairway.
Heathland course.
18 holes, 6068 yards, S.S.S.69
Designed by Dr. J. Cowper, James
Braid.
Founded 1900
Visitors: members of affiliated clubs
only with h/cap certs; after 1pm
weekends.
Green Fee: £21/round, £25/day WD;
£25/round/day WE; £16.50 after
3pm; half price for jnrs.
Societies: by arrangement, 20-40
players.
Catering: facilities available all week
from 10am all day; usual Sun bar
hours.

C91 Singing Hills Golf Course
☎(0273) 835353, 835444 fax.
Albourne, E Sussex
Adjacent to A23 at Albourne.
Downland courses; Lake 3rd is exact
replica of 17th at Sawgrass USA.
3 x 9 holes played in 3 different
combinations of 18; Lake/River,
Lake/Valley, River/Valley;
6200-6300 yards, S.S.S.71
Designed by Richard Hurd (Sandow).
Founded Easter 1992
Visitors: pay-as-you-play;
computerised booking; h/cap certs
or membership of recognised club
required.
Green Fee: £20/round (includes £4
voucher for bar/restaurant).
Societies: welcome by prior
arrangement; special facilties for
company days.
Catering: 2 bars, 2 restaurants,
conference facilities in Pavilion.
Extensive practice facilities.
Hotels: Hickstead Resort.

C92 Slinfold Park G & CC
☎(0403) 791154
Stane Street, Slinfold, Horsham,
W Sussex RH13 7RE
A281 S of junction with A29.
Wooded parkland course.
18 holes, 6450 yards, Par 71; 9 hole
course (pay-as-you-play).
Designed by John Fortune.
Founded 1928
Visitors: welcome.
Green Fee: on application.
Societies: apply for details.
Catering: full facilities.
Driving range, putting green, practice
ground.
Hotels: Random Hall.

C93 Southampton
☎(0703) 767996, 768407 Pro.
Golf Course Rd, Bassett,
Southampton, Hants
N end of city, off Bassett Ave, halfway
between Chilworth roundabout and
Winchester Rd roundabout.
Municipal parkland course.
18 holes, 5683 meters, S.S.S.70;
9 holes, 2185 meters.
Founded 1935
Visitors: welcome.
Green Fee: on application.
Societies: by arrangement with
Council Municipal Golf Course
Manager.
Catering: breakfast, lunch, bar
snacks available.
Hotels: Albany (Bassett).

C94 Southampton Manor Course
☎(0703) 740544
Manor Farm, Botley Rd, Chilworth,
Southampton, Hants SO1 7JE
On A27 between Southampton and
Romsey.
Public parkland course.
9 holes, 2362 yards, S.S.S.32
Founded 1989
Visitors: pay-as-you-play with
advance booking system, only 12
players per hour allowed.
Green Fee: £5/round WD,
£7.50/round WE.
Societies: by arrangement.
Catering: light refreshments; full
catering by arrangement.
Driving range.
Hotels: Hilton, Crest.

C95 Southsea
☎(0705) 830009
The Mansion, Great Salterns, Eastern
Rd, Portsmouth, PO3 6QB
2 miles off M27/A27/A3 on E road
into Portsmouth.
Municipal meadowland course.
18 holes, 5800 metres, S.S.S.68
Founded 1935
Visitors: welcome.
Green Fee: £9/round.
Societies: by arrangement with
Portsmouth City Council.
Catering: available in adjacent
Farmhouse public house.
Driving range at Portsmouth Golf
Centre.

C96 Southwick Park
☎(0705) 380131
Pinsley Drive, Southwick, Fareham,
Hants PO17 6EL
A333 7 miles N of Portsmouth, follow
signs to HMS Dryad.
Parkland course.
18 holes, 5855 yards, S.S.S.68
Designed by Charles Lawrie.
Founded 1977
Visitors: weekdays, weekends
guest of member.
Green Fee: £14
Societies: welcome Tues.
Catering: available.
Hotels: Holiday Inn (Cosham).

C97 Southwood
☎(0252) 548700
Ively Rd, Cove, Farnborough, Hants
GU14 0LJ
1 mile W of A325 Farnborough.
Public parkland course.
18 holes, 5553 yards, S.S.S.67

Designed by Hawtree & Son.
Founded 1977
Visitors: welcome, bookable at all times.
Green Fee: on application.
Societies: weekdays only.
Catering: bar snacks, tea and lunch.
Hotels: Lakeside International.

C98 **Stoneham**

☎(0703) 768151, 769272 Sec.
Bassett Green Rd, Bassett,
Southampton, Hants SO2 3NE
From A33 turn left at Chilworth
roundabout, 0.5 mile on left side of
A27; from M27 exit 5 follow signs to
Southampton then Bassett.
Heather and peat parkland course.
18 holes, 6310 yards, S.S.S.70
Designed by Willie Park.
Founded 1908
Visitors: any time tee is available;
restricted weekends.
Green Fee: £25/round/day WD,
£27.50/round/day WE.
Societies: Mon, Thurs, Fri by
arrangement.
Catering: full in daytime, bar
11.30am-10pm; evening meals by
arrangement.
Hotels: Wessex; Northlands; Crest;
Post House; Hilton.

C99 **Tidworth Garrison**

☎(0980) 42301 Sec, 42321 Club,
42393 Pro.
Bulford Rd, Tidworth, Hants SP9 7AF
A388 to Tidworth, then 1 mile along
Bulford Rd from bus station.
Downland course.
18 holes, 6075 yards, S.S.S.69
Founded 1908
Visitors: welcome by arrangement.
Green Fee: £18/day WD, £23 WE.
Societies: Tues, Thurs, Fri.
Catering: hot and cold meals daily
except Mon when sandwiches only.
Hotels: Antrobus Arms; George.

C100 **Tilgate Forest**

☎(0293) 530103
Titmus Drive, Tilgate, Crawley,
W Sussex RH10 5EY
M23, junction Pease Pottage, follow
main road to Crawley, at 1st
roundabout turn right, follow signs.
Public parkland course.
18 holes, 6359 yards, S.S.S.70;
9 holes, 1350 yards.
Designed by Huggett and Coles.
Founded 1983
Visitors: welcome.
Green Fee: £8.20 WD, £11.55 WE.

Societies: Mon-Thurs.
Catering: restaurant and bar all day.
Driving range.

C101 **Tylney Park**

☎(0256) 762079
Rotherwick, Basingstoke, Hants
Off A30 at Nately Scures, follow signs
for Rotherwick; approx 1.5 miles.
Parkland course.
18 holes, 6138 yards, S.S.S.70
Designed by W. Wiltshire.
Visitors: welcome; h/cap cert
required.
Green Fee: £16 WD (£8 with
member), £28 WE (£8.50 with
member).
Societies: welcome Mon to Fri.
Catering: meals served.
Hotels: Tylney Hall; Raven (Hook).

C102 **Ventnor**

☎(0983) 853326, 853198 Sec.
Steephill Down Rd, Ventnor, Isle of
Wight
A3055 to Ventnor, course on downs
above at Upper Ventnor.
Undulating downland course.
9 holes, 5752 yards, S.S.S.68
Founded 1892
Visitors: welcome except 12am-
3.30pm Fri, not before 1pm Sun.
Green Fee: £12.
Societies: not Sun am, catering by
arrangement.
Catering: snacks at bar.
Pool table.
Hotels: Eversly; Bonchurch Manor.

C103 **Waterhall**

☎(0273) 508658
Off Devils Dyke Rd, Brighton, E
Sussex BN1 8YN
W of the town, 5 miles from centre,
towards Devil's Dyke.
Hilly downland course.
18 holes, 5775 yards, S.S.S.68
Founded 1923
Visitors: welcome.
Green Fee: £10.50/round, £15/day
WD; £13/round WE & BH.
Societies: weekdays except Tues by
prior arrangement with Sec.
Catering: available daily during
summer; limited in winter.

C104 **Waterlooville**

☎(0705) 263388
Cherry-Tree Ave, Cowplain,
Waterlooville, Hants PO8 8BD
Off A3 in Cowplain, 5 miles N of
Portsmouth.

18 holes, 6647 yards, S.S.S.72
Designed by Henry Cotton.
Founded 1907
Visitors: welcome Mon to Fri.
Green Fee: on application.
Societies: Thurs only.
Catering: 10am to 5pm daily.
Hotels: Post House; Bear.

C105 **West Chiltington**

☎(0798) 813574 Sec, 812115 Pro
shop, 812631 Fax.
Broadford Bridge Road, West
Chiltington, W Sussex RH20 2YA
Turn left off A283 1 mile E of
Pulborough; from West Chiltington
village take Broadford Bridge Rd
opposite Queen's Head public house.
Public course with limited
membership; gently undulating
parkland.
18 holes, 5890 yards, S.S.S.69;
9-hole Par 3.
Designed by Brian Barnes
Founded July 1988
Visitors: welcome at all times.
Green Fee: 18 holes, £13 WD, £18
WE; 9 holes, £5 WD, £7.50 WE.
Societies: by prior arrangement.
Catering: full bar and catering.
Driving range, putting green.
Hotels: The Mill House (Ashington).

C106 **West Hove**

☎(0273) 419738, 413494
Church Farm, Hangleton, Hove,
Sussex.
New course and clubhouse off new
by-pass.
Undulating downland course.
18 holes, 6266 yards, S.S.S.74
Founded 1910
Visitors: weekdays, weekends pm
on application.
Green Fee: on application.
Societies: catered for weekdays.
Catering: available daily.
Snooker.
Hotels: Old Ship (Brighton).

C107 **West Sussex**

☎(079 82) 2563
Pulborough, West Sussex RH20 2EN
1.5 miles E of Pulborough on A283.
Heathland course.
18 holes, 6221 yards, S.S.S.70
Designed by Sir Guy Campbell, Major
C.K. Hutcheson.
Founded 1931
Visitors: welcome weekdays only
except Tues (members only) with
letter of intro. and h/cap cert.
Green Fee: on application.

Societies: Wed and Thurs.
Catering: lunch and tea.
Hotels: Abingworth Hall; The Roundabout.

C108 Willingdon
☎(0323) 410981
Southdown Rd, Eastbourne, E
Sussex BN20 9AA
0.5 mile N of Eastbourne off A22.
Downland course.
18 holes, 6049 yards, S.S.S.69
Designed by J.H. Taylor, modernised
by Dr Mackenzie 1925.

Founded 1898
Visitors: welcome weekdays.
Green Fee: £22/1/2 rounds WD, £25
Sat and Bank Holidays.
Societies: catered for on weekdays
only.
Catering: available by prior
arrangement.
Hotels: Grand; Queens; Lansdown.

C109 Worthing
☎(0903) 60801
Links Rd, Worthing, W Sussex BN14
9QZ

At top of hill on A27 0.25 mile E of
Offington roundabout at junction with
A24 London road.
Downland course.
Lower, 18 holes, 6519 yards,
S.S.S.72; Upper, 18 holes, 5243
yards, S.S.S.66
Designed by H.S. Colt.
Founded 1906
Visitors: by prior arrangement with
Sec.
Green Fee: on application
Societies: welcome weekdays
except Tues.
Catering: lunch served except Mon.

D

SURREY, KENT, SOUTH LONDON

Whatever geological quirk of fate decreed that Surrey should possess so much ground so utterly perfect for golf, the fact remains that lovers of inland courses regard it as their idea of paradise. Where else in the world (with the exception perhaps of Melbourne) is there such a cluster of absolutely first class places to play — most portraying the virtues of the pine, heather and silver birch country.

Until Woking was founded in 1893 "by a few mad barristers", the game around London had largely been confined to public commons and muddy parks but, within the space of a few years, a whole new dimension opened up introducing names now familiar the world over. Sunningdale, Walton Heath, Worplesdon, New Zealand, West Hill, West Byfleet and St George's Hill were all in existence by the time of the Great War. West Hill owes its creation to a woman, Mrs Geoffrey Lubbock, who grew tired of being unable to play anywhere on Sunday and enlisted the aid of Willie Park and Jack White, Open champion in 1904, to pioneer a Club which forms part of the famous trinity of W's with Worplesdon and Woking.

Everyone has his or her own particular favourite in Surrey although even the worst would be looked upon with envy in other areas of Britain. Their nearness to London and to Heathrow Airport, the pleasant nature of the challenge they offer and the fact that a number have 36 holes, make them enormously popular with visitors and visiting Societies.

Today, Wentworth, not founded until 1924, features prominently on the list, their Edinburgh course, opened in 1990, adding considerably to an already established reputation but the county map is festooned with famous names — Royal Wimbledon, Coombe Hill, Addington, Hankley Common, Camberley Heath, Farnham, Burhill and Effingham. Hoebridge has boosted the public amenities

while, at the other end of the scale, Wisley was opened last year funded by the sort of expensive debenture scheme more common in America and Japan.

Royal Mid-Surrey, on the edge of Kew Gardens and celebrating its centenary in 1992, is the standard-bearer of Surrey's relatively scarce parkland golf but, as if to illustrate how quickly soil conditions change, Kent enjoys none of the heather courses so widespread in Surrey.

Its focal point is centred firmly on the coastal links of Royal St George's, Royal Cinque Ports and Princes; and, to a slightly lesser degree, on Littlestone between Folkestone and Rye. Royal St George's modern importance is as the only Open championship venue south of Lancashire but Royal Cinque Ports, another Club to celebrate its centenary in 1992, and Princes share the distinction of housing Opens of long ago.

North Foreland is a course within easy reach of Sandwich and one used for the Open championship qualifying rounds but the Medway coastline has courses in most of its towns while, in addition to Canterbury, that city also has Broome Park, opened in 1979. A more recent addition is Tudor Park Hotel Golf and Country Club, a stone's throw from the more senior Leeds Castle which has just undergone something of a facelift.

Nearer London is the popular public course at Beckenham Place Park, and a word for Cobtree Manor near Maidstone and Edenbridge, which, if a member's Club, keeps an open door to visitors.

Knole Park and Wildernesse are highly respected names as well as excellent courses around Sevenoaks; West Kent, Rochester and Cobham, and Langley Park come in the same category along with Sundridge Park at Bromley which has two courses — established Clubs in a county in which West Malling, Poult Wood, Cranbrook and Cherry Lodge are others to have appeared in the last twenty-five years.

D1 The Addington
☎(081) 777 6057
205 Shirley Church Rd, Croydon,
Surrey CR50 5AB
2.5 miles from East Croydon Station.
Heathland course.
18 holes, 6243 yards, S.S.S.71
Designed by J.F. Abercromby.
Founded 1914
Visitors: welcome weekdays; h/cap
cert required.
Green Fee: on application
Societies: weekdays; advance
booking.
Catering: meals served.

D2 Addington Court
☎(081) 657 0281/2/3
Featherbed Lane, Croydon, Surrey
CR0 9AA
Undulating public heathland course
Championship, 18 holes, 5577
yards, S.S.S.67; Falconwood, 18
holes, 5513 yards, S.S.S.66; 9 holes,
1812 yards.
Designed by F. Hawtree Snr.
Founded 1931
Visitors: welcome.
Green Fee: Championship £11,
Falconwood £10, 9 hole course, £6.
Societies: welcome by prior
application.
Catering: full catering facilities.
18 hole Pitch & Putt, £1.50.
Hotels: Holiday Inn; Selsdon Park.

D3 Addington Palace
☎(081) 654 3061
Gravel Hill, Addington Park, Croydon,
Surrey CR0 5BB
2 miles from East Croydon station.
Parkland course
18 holes, 6262 yards, S.S.S.71
Founded 1923
Visitors: welcome weekdays; with
member weekends.
Green Fee: on application
Societies: Tues, Wed, Fri, Thurs pm.
Catering: snacks and meals except
Mon.

D4 Aquarius
☎(081) 693 1626
Marmora Rd, Honor Oak, London
SE22 0RY
Off Forest Hill Rd.
Set around a reservoir.
9 holes, 5034 yards, S.S.S.65
Founded 1912
Visitors: welcome with member
only.
Green Fee: £10/round/day.
Catering: restaurant Sat/Sun only.

D5 Ashford (Kent)
☎(0233) 622655
Sandyhurst Lane, Ashford, Kent
TN25 4NT
Off A20, 1.5 miles W of Ashford.
Parkland course.
18 holes, 6246 yards, S.S.S.70
Designed by C.K. Cotton.
Founded 1924
Visitors: welcome any day except
before 11am weekends and Bank
Holidays; h/cap certs required.
Green Fee: £22/day WD, £36/day
WE & BH.
Societies: Tues and Thurs by
arrangement.
Catering: full facilities; functions,
banquets etc.
Hotels: Eastwell Manor; The Croft.

D6 Austin Lodge
☎(0322) 863000, 862406 fax.
Eynsford, Nr Swanley, Kent DA4 0HU
Via M25 junction 3 and A20, then
A225 to Eynsford station, past station
along cul-de-sac to course.
Peaceful countryside course.
18 holes, 6590 yards, S.S.S.72
Designed by Peter Bevan & Mike
Walsh.
Founded July 1991
Visitors: by telephone booking.
Green Fee: £20/round.
Societies: welcome, bookings
required.
Catering: light meals and bar all day.
Golf academy.

D7 Banstead Downs
☎(081) 642 2284
Burdon Lane, Belmont, Sutton,
Surrey SM2 7DD
100 yards E of junction of A217 and
B2230.
Downland course
18 holes, 6169 yards, S.S.S.69
Founded 1890
Visitors: welcome with letter of
intro. Mon-Fri; Bank Holidays, Sat,
Sun am, with member only.
Green Fee: on application.
Societies: by arrangement.
Catering: 11am-6pm, dinner by
arrangement.
Hotels: Thatched House (Cheam);
Drift Bridge (Epsom).

D8 Barnehurst
☎(0322) 523746
Mayplace Rd East, Barnehurst, Kent
DA7 6JU
To Bexleyheath Clock Tower then on
to Mayplace Rd East, golf club on left.

Moorland course.
9 holes, 5320 yards, S.S.S.66
Founded 1903
Visitors: welcome Mon, Wed and Fri.
Green Fee: on application.
Catering: bar snacks served; lunch
can be arranged with Stewardess.
Hotels: Crest (Bexley).

D9 Barrow Hills
☎(0932) 848117
Longcross, Chertsey, Surrey KT16
0DS
4 miles W of Chertsey.
Parkland course.
18 holes, 3090 yards, S.S.S.53
Founded 1970
Visitors: with member only.

D10 Bearsted
☎(0622) 38198
Ware St, Bearsted, Kent ME14 4PQ
Off M20 at A249; turn right at lights,
left at roundabout, bear left at
mini-roundabout, straight on under
bridge; course 400 yards on left.
Parkland course.
18 holes, 6278 yards, S.S.S.70
Designed by Golf Landscapes.
Founded 1895
Visitors: must be member of bona
fide club with current h/cap; not
weekends unless with member;
advisable to phone.
Green Fee: £20/round, £28/day.
Societies: Tues-Fri by arrangement
with Sec.
Catering: bar, restaurant, snacks;
business lunches by arrangement.
Hotels: Country Court; Tudor Park
Hotel G & CC; Great Danes.

D11 Beckenham Place Park
☎(081) 650 2292
Beckenham Hill Rd, Beckenham,
Kent BR3 2BP
1 mile from Catford towards
Bromley, right at Homebase.
Public parkland course.
18 holes, 5722 yards, S.S.S.68
Founded 1932
Visitors: welcome.
Green Fee: on application
Catering: meals and snacks.

D12 Betchworth Park
☎(0306) 882052
Reigate Rd, Dorking, Surrey RH4 1NZ
1 mile E of Dorking on A25 to
Reigate, entrance opposite
horticultural gardens.
Parkland course

18 holes, 6266 yards, S.S.S.70
Designed by H. Colt.
Founded 1913
Visitors: Mon, Thurs, and Tues and
Wed pm; restricted Fri and Sun pm.
Green Fee: £28/day WD, £39 WE.
Societies: Mon and Tues.
Catering: lunch and tea available.
Hotels: Burford Bridge; White Horse;
Travellodge.

D13 **Bexleyheath**
☎(081) 303 6951
Mount Rd, Bexleyheath, Kent DA6
8JS

1 mile from station, off Upton Rd.
Undulating course.
9 holes, 5239 yards, S.S.S.66
Founded 1907
Visitors: welcome 8am-4pm
Mon-Fri.
Green Fee: £15, £7.50 with member.
Societies: by arrangement.
Catering: lunch, snacks and evening
meals, except Mon.
Hotels: Crest (Bexley).

D14 **Bramley**
☎(0483) 892696 Sec, 893042
Steward, 893685 Pro.

Bramley, Nr Guildford, Surrey GU5
0AL
4 miles S of Guildford on A281
Guildford-Horsham road, between
the villages of Shalford and Bramley.
Parkland course.
18 holes, 5966 yards, S.S.S.69
Designed by Charles Mayo,
redesigned by James Braid.
Founded 1913
Visitors: welcome Mon-Fri; guests
of members only at weekends.
Green Fee: £20.50/round,
£25.50/day.
Societies: Mon-Fri by prior
arrangement with Sec.

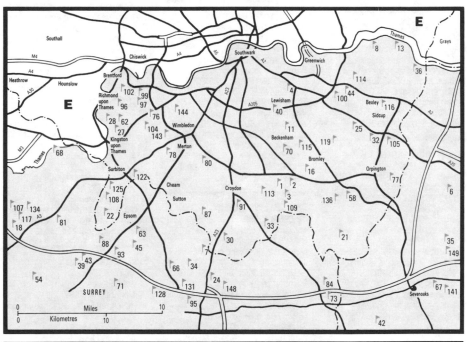

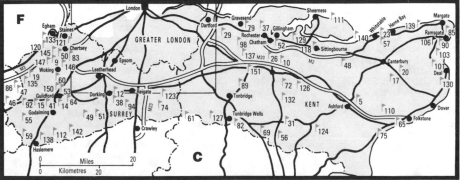

Catering: bar snacks and grill daily.
Hotels: Bramley Grange.

D15 Broadwater Park
☎(0483) 429955
Guildford Road, Farncombe, Nr Godalming, Surrey GU7 3BU
Public parkland course.
9 holes Par 3, 1323 yards.
Designed by K.D. Milton.
Founded 1989
Visitors: no restrictions.
Green Fee: 9 holes £3.25 WD, £3.75 WE; 18 holes £5.75 WD, £6.75 WE.
Societies: welcome weekdays.
Catering: bar, snacks. Driving range.

D16 Bromley
☎(081) 462 7014
Magpie Hall Lane, Bromley, BR2 8JF
A21 2 miles S of Bromley.
Public parkland course.
9 holes, 2507 yards, S.S.S.69
Visitors: welcome.
Green Fee: on application.
Societies: welcome.
Catering: snacks available.

D17 Broome Park CC
☎(0227) 831701
Barham, Canterbury, Kent CT4 6QX
Off M2 onto A2 then Folkestone road A260, 700 yards on right hand side.
Parkland course.
18 holes, 6610 yards, S.S.S.72
Designed by Donald Steel.
Founded 1979
Visitors: weekdays with h/cap cert; start times to be booked in advance.
Green Fee: on application.
Societies: Mon-Fri.
Catering: 2 bars, 2 restaurants daily. Tennis, snooker, banqueting.
Hotels: Woodpeckers Country.

D18 Burhill
☎(0932) 227345
Walton-on-Thames, Surrey KT12 4BL
Off A3 on A245 towards Byfleet, right into Seven Hills Rd and again into Burwood Rd, entrance 2nd on right.
Parkland course
18 holes, 6224 yards, S.S.S.70
Designed by Willie Park.
Founded 1907
Visitors: weekdays by arrangement, h/cap cert required.
Green Fee: on application.
Societies: catered for weekdays.
Catering: lunch, snacks except Mon. Squash, badminton.
Hotels: Oatlands Park (Weybridge).

D19 Camberley Heath
☎(0276) 23258
Golf Drive, Camberley, Surrey GU15 1JG
On A325 to Camberley; M3 exit 4, follow signs to Bagshot and Frimley.
Undulating heathland course.
18 holes, 6402 yards, S.S.S.71
Designed by H. S. Colt.
Founded 1913
Visitors: welcome, must have h/cap cert from recognised golf club and should telephone for tee reservation.
Green Fee: on application.
Societies: by arrangement.
Catering: meals and snacks served.

D20 Canterbury
☎(0227) 453532
Scotland Hills, Canterbury, Kent CT1 1TW
A257 1 mile from Canterbury.
Parkland course.
18 holes, 6249 yards, S.S.S.70
Designed by H.S. Colt.
Founded 1927
Visitors: welcome on weekdays.
Green Fee: £21/round, £29/day WD; £29/round (after 3pm) Sat and Sun.
Societies: Tues, Thurs only.
Catering: full menu Mon-Sat.
Hotels: Ebury; Canterbury; Abbots Barton.

D21 Cherry Lodge
☎(0959) 72550 office, 72989 Pro.
Jail Lane, Biggin Hill, Kent TN16 3AX
Off A233 by RAF Biggin Hill.
Undulating downland course.
18 holes, 6652 yards, S.S.S.72
Designed by John Day.
Founded 1969
Visitors: welcome Mon-Fri only by arrangement.
Green Fee: on application.
Societies: Mon-Fri, min 18; full catering facilities by prior booking.
Catering: à la carte restaurant Mon-Sat, Sun lunches, 2 bars. Banqueting.
Hotels: Kings Arms; Bromley Court.

D22 Chessington
☎(081) 391 0948
Garrison Lane, Chessington, Surrey KT9 2LW
Opposite Chessington South station, very near to Chessington zoo.
Public parkland course.
9 holes, 1400 yards, S.S.S.26
Designed by Patrick Tallack PGA.
Founded 1983
Visitors: welcome.

Green Fee: £3.10/9 holes WD, £3.75 WE.
Societies: welcome.
Catering: full catering facilities. Driving range.
Hotels: Seven Hills; Oatlands Park.

D23 Chestfield
☎(0227) 794411
103 Chestfield Rd, Whitstable, Kent CT5 3LU
0.5 mile S of Thanet Way at Swalecliffe/Chestfield roundabout.
Parkland/seaside course.
18 holes, 6181 yards, S.S.S.70
Founded 1925
Visitors: must have current h/cap cert; not weekends or Bank Holidays.
Green Fee: on application.
Societies: by arrangement Mon, Tues, Wed and Fri.
Catering: full facilities.
Hotels: Marine; Hotel St George.

D24 Chipstead
☎(0737) 555781
How Lane, Coulsden, Surrey CR3 3PR
Follow signs to Chipstead from A217.
Undulating parkland course.
18 holes, 5454 yards, S.S.S.67
Founded 1906
Visitors: welcome weekdays.
Green Fee: £25/day, £20 after 2pm, (£10 with member).
Societies: catered for on weekdays
Catering: lunch served except Mon; prior booking required.

D25 Chislehurst
☎(081) 467 2782
Camden Place, Camden Park Rd, Chislehurst, Kent BR7 5HJ
0.5 mile from Chislehurst station, on A222 to Bromley.
Parkland course.
18 holes, 5128 yards, S.S.S.65
Founded 1894
Visitors: welcome weekdays only.
Green Fee: £25 WD (£10 with member).
Societies: by arrangement with Sec.
Catering: lunch each day.
Hotels: Bromley Court.

D26 Cobtree Manor Park
☎(0622) 753276
Chatham Rd, Maidstone, Kent ME14 3AZ
Take A229 from M20.
Municipal parkland course.
18 holes, 5701 yards, S.S.S.68
Designed by F. Hawtree.

Founded 1984
Visitors: welcome.
Green Fee: £7.50 WD, £13.25 WE.
Societies: on application.
Catering: available.

D27 Coombe Hill
☎(081) 942 2284
Golf Club Drive, Kingston, KT2 7DG
0.25 mile W of A3 on A238.
Parkland course.
18 holes, 6286 yards, S.S.S.71
Designed by J.F. Abercromby.
Founded 1911
Visitors: by appointment only.
Green Fee: £45 WD only.
Societies: welcome weekdays.
Catering: lunches served every day.

D28 Coombe Wood
☎(081) 942 0388
George Rd, Kingston Hill, KT2 7NS
1 mile N of Kingston-on-Thames, off
Kingston Hill.
Parkland course.
18 holes, 5210 yards, S.S.S.66
Designed by T. Williamson.
Founded 1904
Visitors: weekdays only.
Green Fee: on application.
Societies: welcome Wed, Thurs, Fri.
Catering: available.
Hotels: Kingston Lodge (adjacent).

D29 Corinthian
☎(0474) 707559
Gay Dawn Farm, Fawkham,
Longfield, Kent DA3 8LZ
4 miles S of Dartford Tunnel, E of
Brands Hatch along Fawkham road.
Parkland course, artificial greens.
9 holes, 3118 yards, S.S.S.35
Founded 1987
Visitors: unrestricted weekdays, pm
only weekends and Bank Holidays.
Green Fee: £10/day.
Societies: by arrangement with Sec.
Catering: bar evenings, and Sat/Sun
lunch.
Tennis, squash, sauna, gymnasium.

D30 Coulsdon Court
☎(081) 668 0414 or 660 0468
Coulsdon Rd, Coulsdon, Surrey CR3
2LL
Just off A23, 2 miles S of Croydon, 2
miles N of M25 and M23.
Public parkland course.
18 holes, 6037 yards, S.S.S.69
Designed by H.S. Buck.
Founded 1926
Visitors: welcome.

Green Fee: on application
Societies: welcome.
Catering: full facilities.

D31 Cranbrook
☎(0580) 712833
Benenden Rd, Cranbrook, Kent TN17
4AL
Take A262 Ashford/Cranbrook
turning off A21 just N of
Lamberhurst; right at Bull public
house in Sissinghurst, over
crossroads (1.5 miles), 1 mile on left.
Heavily wooded parkland course.
18 holes, 6351 yards, S.S.S.70
Designed by John D. Harris.
Founded 1969
Visitors: welcome weekdays,
weekends with member only; h/cap
cert required.
Green Fee: £25 WD.
Societies: on application; specialists
in company golf days.
Catering: full bar and restaurant.
Hotels: Willesley; Kennel Holt; Tudor
Court.

D32 Cray Valley
☎(0689) 839677 Sec, 837909 Pro
shop, 831927 Clubhouse
Sandy Lane, St Paul's Cray,
Orpington, Kent BR5 3HY
A20 to Ruxley roundabout, junction
with A233.
Undulating meadowland course.
18 holes, 5624 yards, S.S.S.67;
9 hole Beginner's course.
Designed by Golf Centres Ltd.
Founded 1972
Visitors: weekdays unlimited,
weekends restricted.
Green Fee: £10 WD, £15.50 WE.
Societies: not weekends.
Catering: telephone above.

D33 Croham Hurst
☎(081) 657 5581, 657 7705 Pro.
Croham Rd, South Croydon, CR2 7HJ
1 mile from S Croyden; from M25 exit
6 N onto A22, take B270 to
Warlingham at roundabout, then
B269 to Selsdon; left at lights into
Farley Rd, club 1.75 miles on left.
Parkland course.
18 holes, 6286 yards, S.S.S.70
Designed by Hawtree & Sons.
Founded 1911
Visitors: h/cap cert required; with
member only at weekends.
Green Fee: £33/round/day.
Societies: Wed, Thurs, Fri.
Catering: full catering every day
10am-6pm; banqueting.

D34 Cuddington
☎(081) 393 0952
Banstead Rd, Banstead, Surrey SM7
1RD
200 yards from Banstead station.
Parkland course.
18 holes, 6352 yards, S.S.S.70
Designed by H.S. Colt.
Founded 1929
Visitors: welcome by appointment.
Green Fee: on application.
Societies: Thurs only.
Catering: available weekdays by
appointment.
Hotels: Driftbridge; Picard Motel.

D35 Darenth Valley
☎(09592) 2944 Steward, 2922 Pro.
Station Rd, Shoreham, Kent TN14 7SA
Along A225 Sevenoaks-Dartford
road, 4 miles N of Sevenoaks.
Public meadowland course.
18 holes, 6356 yards, S.S.S.71
Founded 1973 by M.F.C. Cross.
Visitors: welcome; bookings daily.
Green Fee: £8.70/round WD,
£11.30/round WE & BH.
Societies: welcome, prices on
application to the Steward.
Catering: bar meals, society
catering, functions (100).
Hotels: Royal Oak (Sevenoaks).

D36 Dartford
☎(0322) 226455
Dartford Heath, Dartford, Kent DA1
2TN
On Dartford Heath, 2 miles from
Dartford town centre.
Heathland course.
18 holes, 5914 yards, S.S.S.68
Founded 1897
Visitors: welcome weekdays if
member of recognised club, at
weekends only with member; h/cap
certs required.
Green Fee: £25.50 (£12.50 with
member).
Societies: Mon and Fri, booked well
in advance.
Catering: full restaurant service.
Hotels: Royal Bull; Victoria.

D37 Deangate Ridge
☎(0634) 251180
Hoo, Rochester, Kent ME3 8RZ
A228 from Rochester to Isle of Grain,
then road signposted to Deangate
Ridge, 4 miles NE of Rochester.
Municipal parkland course.
18 holes, 6300 yards, S.S.S.70
Designed by Hawtree & Sons.
Founded 1972

Visitors: welcome any time, bookings essential weekends.
Green Fee: on application.
Societies: welcome.
Catering: lunch and dinner served, bookings essential weekends.
Hotels: Inn on the Lake (on A2).

D38 **Dorking**
☎(0306) 886917, 885914
Chart Park, Dorking, Surrey RH5 4BX
A24 0.5 mile S of Dorking between A25 and N Holmwood roundabouts.
Undulating parkland course.
9 holes (18 tees), 5163 yards, S.S.S.65
Designed by James Braid.
Founded 1897
Visitors: welcome weekdays, members only weekends and Bank Holidays; Ladies' Day Wed am.
Green Fee: £16/day WD.
Societies: by arrangement.
Catering: full meals and snacks except Mon.
Hotels: Burford Bridge; White Horse.

D39 **Drift**
☎(04865) 4641
The Drift, East Horsley, Surrey KT24 5HD
Turn off A3 onto B2039 East Horsley road, club 2 miles on left, signposted.
Woodland course.
18 holes, 6414 yards, S.S.S.71
Founded 1975
Visitors: welcome weekdays only.
Green Fee: £26.
Societies: welcome weekdays except Tues am.
Catering: bar and restaurant.

D40 **Dulwich & Sydenham Hill**
☎(081) 693 3961
Grange Lane, College Rd, London SE21 7LH
Off S Circular road at Dulwich College and College Rd.
Parkland course.
18 holes, 6051 yards, S.S.S.69
Founded 1894
Visitors: welcome weekdays only by prior booking.
Green Fee: £25/round.
Societies: Mon-Fri by arrangement.
Catering: lunch daily, dinner by arrangement.
Hotels: Queens (Crystal Palace).

D41 **Dunsfold Aerodrome**
☎(0483) 272121 Sec

British Aerospace, Dunsfold Aerodrome, Nr Godalming, Surrey GU8 4BS
12 miles S of Guildford on A281.
Parkland course.
9 holes, 6036 yards, S.S.S.69
Founded 1965
Visitors: with member only.
Green Fee: £2/day.
Societies: from British Aerospace.
Catering: bar, snacks.

D42 **Edenbridge G & CC**
☎(0732) 865097
Crouch House Rd, Edenbridge, Kent TN8 5LQ
Travelling N through Edenbridge High St, turn left into Stangrove Rd (30 yards before railway station), at end of road turn right, course is short distance on left.
Undulating meadowland course.
Old, 18 holes, 6635 yards, S.S.S.71; New, 18 holes, 5763 yards, S.S.S.67; 9 hole Beginner's Course, Par 31
Founded 1975
Visitors: welcome, members only on Old Course weekends.
Green Fee: Old, £15/round WD, £18/round WE & BH; New, £12/round WD, £15/round WE; Beginner's Course £3/round.
Societies: weekdays only.
Catering: lunch, bar snacks daily.
Driving range.
Hotels: Oxted (East Grinstead).

D43 **Effingham**
☎(0372) 452203
Guildford Rd, Effingham, Surrey KT24 5PZ
On A246 8 miles E of Guildford.
Downland course.
18 holes, 6488 yards, S.S.S.71
Designed by H.S. Colt.
Founded 1927
Visitors: Mon-Fri by arrangement.
Green Fee: £27.50/day, £22.50 after 2pm.
Societies: Wed, Thurs and Fri.
Catering: lunch, tea, evening meal, snacks etc.
Tennis, squash, snooker (must be accompanied by member).
Hotels: Thatchers; Preston Cross.

D44 **Eltham Warren**
☎(081) 850 1166, 850 4477
Bexley Rd, Eltham, London SE9 2PE
Continuation of Eltham High St, 0.5 mile E.
Parkland course.
9 holes, 5840 yards, S.S.S.68

Founded 1890
Visitors: weekdays only; must be member of recognised club.
Green Fee: £25/day.
Societies: welcome weekdays.
Catering: bar snacks; full catering by arrangement except Mon and Fri. Snooker.
Hotels: Crest Hotel (Bexley).

D45 **Epsom**
☎(0372) 721666 Sec, 741867 Pro.
Longdown Lane South, Epsom, Surrey KT17 4JR
0.5 mile S of Epsom Downs Station.
Downland course.
18 holes, 5118 yards, S.S.S.65
Founded 1889
Visitors: welcome weekdays from 8am, except Tues from 12.30pm; bookings Sat and from 12am Sun.
Green Fee: on application.
Societies: Wed and Fri on written application, min 12, max 40.
Catering: meals and snacks.
Hotels: Drift Bridge; Chalk Lane.

D46 **Farnham**
☎(025 18) 2109
The Sands, Farnham, Surrey GU10 1PX
1 mile E of Farnham on A31, turning to The Sands signposted.
Parkland/heathland course.
18 holes, 6313 yards, S.S.S.70
Founded 1896
Visitors: welcome weekdays with h/cap cert; guests of members only at weekends.
Green Fee: on application.
Societies: welcome by arrangement Wed and Thurs.
Catering: full catering on request.
Hotels: Hogs Back; Bush; Bishops Table.

D47 **Farnham Park**
☎(0252) 715216
Folly Hill, Farnham, Surrey
0.75 mile N of Farnham, next to castle in Farnham Park.
Public Par 3 parkland course.
9 holes, 1161 yards, S.S.S.54
Designed by Henry Cotton.
Founded 1963
Visitors: welcome at all times; weekends and Bank Holidays booking only.
Green Fee: £2.90 WD, £3.70 WE; reductions jnrs and OAPs.
Catering: hot or cold snacks as required.
Hotels: The Bush (Farnham).

D48 **Faversham**
☎(079 589) 561
Belmont Park, Faversham, Kent
ME13 0HB
Leave M2 at junction 6, A251 to
Faversham, then A2 to Sittingbourne
for 0.5 mile, turn left at Brogdale Rd,
and follow signs.
Parkland course.
18 holes, 6021 yards, S.S.S.69
Founded 1902
Visitors: only with member
weekends and public holidays.
Green Fee: £21/round, £28/day WD;
£22/round, £30/day (with member)
WE.
Societies: Wed and Fri only, £23 per
round, £30 per day.
Catering: by arrangement with
Steward.
Hotels: Ship.

D49 **Fernfell G & CC**
☎(0483) 268855
Barhatch Lane, Cranleigh, Surrey
GU6 7NG
Take A281 out of Guildford; 1 mile
through Cranleigh take Ewhurst road,
then Shere turn into Barhatch Road/
Barhatch Lane.
Parkland course.
18 holes, 5561 yards, S.S.S.68
Founded 1985
Visitors: welcome weekdays.
Green Fee: £20/round.
Societies: welcome weekdays.
Catering: bar, restaurant, snacks.
Tennis, snooker, outdoor swimming
pool; banqueting.
Hotels: Post House; Bramley Grange.

D50 **Foxhills**
☎(0932) 872050, 874762 fax.
Stonehill Rd, Ottershaw, Surrey KT16
0EL
Off A320 at Otter public house, turn
right and right again into Foxhills Rd;
1 mile from M25 exit 11.
Heathland course.
Chertsey, 18 holes, 6658 yards,
S.S.S.71; Longcross, 18 holes, 6406
yards, S.S.S.71; 9 hole Par 3
Designed by F. Hawtree.
Founded 1973
Visitors: welcome Mon-Fri, after
12am weekends.
Green Fee: £40/round, £50/day.
Societies: only by appointment.
Catering: 3 restaurants plus bars.
Tennis (10 courts), squash (4), indoor
and outdoor pools, gym, health suite,
snooker, banqueting, clay shoot,
archery.
Hotels: 16 suites on the complex.

D51 **Gatton Manor**
☎(030 679) 555
Ockley, Dorking, Surrey RH5 5PQ
A29 1.5 miles SW of Ockley.
Undulating parkland course.
18 holes, 6145-6902 yards,
S.S.S.69-73
Designed by D.B. & D.G. Heath.
Founded 1969
Visitors: welcome except Sun am.
Green Fee: on application
Societies: weekdays.
Catering: meals and snacks.
Hotels: Gatton Manor.

D52 **Gillingham**
☎(0634) 53017 Sec, 55862 Pro,
50999 bar.
Woodlands Rd, Gillingham, Kent ME7
2AP
On A2 at Gillingham, about 2 miles
from M2 turn off to Gillingham.
Meadowland course.
18 holes, 5863 yards, S.S.S.68
Designed by James Braid.
Founded 1908
Visitors: must be member of another
club or hold current h/cap cert; only
with member weekends.
Green Fee: £18/round/day WD;
£8/round, £12/day with member WD
and WE.
Societies: any day except Thurs;
must be 24 or over Mon/Tues.
Catering: Wed-Sun lunch and
evening meals.
Hotels: Park Hotel.

D53 **Goal Farm Par 3**
☎(048 67) 3183, 3205
Gole Rd, Pirbright, Surrey GU24 0PZ
1 mile from Brookwood station off
A322 towards Pirbright
9 holes Par 3, 1273 yards
Founded 1977
Visitors: welcome, not Thurs am or
Sat.
Green Fee: £2.75/9 holes.
Catering: bar and bar snacks.

D54 **Guildford**
☎(0483) 63941
High Path Rd, Merrow, Guildford,
Surrey GU1 2HI
2 miles E of Guildford on A246.
Downland course.
18 holes, 6080 yards, S.S.S.70
Designed by James Braid.
Founded 1886
Visitors: welcome on weekdays,
weekends with member only.
Green Fee: on application.
Societies: welcome by arrangement.

Catering: bar snacks, restaurant by
arrangement.
Hotels: Angel; White Horse;
Clavadel.

D55 **Hankley Common**
☎(025 125) 2493
Tilford Rd, Tilford, Farnham, Surrey
GU10 2DD
4 miles SE of Farnham, take road to
Hindhead over railway crossing, fork
right to Tilford.
Heathland course.
18 holes, 6403 yards, S.S.S.71
Designed by James Braid
Founded 1895
Visitors: welcome weekdays, by
arrangement with Sec weekends;
h/cap cert required.
Green Fee: on application
Societies: Tues and Wed.
Catering: always available.

D56 **Hawkhurst**
☎(0580) 752396
High St, Hawkhurst, Cranbrook, Kent
TN18 4JS
On A268, 2 miles from A21 at
Flimwell, 0.5 mile from junction with
A229.
Undulating parkland course.
9 holes, 5791 yards, S.S.S.68
Designed by Rex Baldock.
Founded 1968
Visitors: welcome; only with
member weekends.
Green Fee: £18/day.
Societies: on application; mostly Fri.
Catering: by arrangement.
Hotels: Royal Oak.

D57 **Herne Bay**
☎(0227) 373964
Eddington, Herne Bay, Kent CT6 7PG
Take Thanet Way to Herne Bay, near
railway station.
Parkland course.
18 holes, 5403 yards, S.S.S.66
Founded 1920
Visitors: welcome, some restrictions
weekends and Bank Holidays.
Green Fee: on application
Societies: welcome any time.
Catering: full facilities, full meals by
prior arrangement.

D58 **High Elms**
☎(0689) 858175
High Elms Rd, Downe, Kent
5 miles out of Bromley off the A21 to
Sevenoaks.
Public parkland course.

18 holes, 5626 yards, S.S.S.69
Designed by Fred Hawtree
Founded 1969
Visitors: welcome.
Green Fee: £8.50/round.
Societies: weekdays only.
Catering: full meals and snacks.
Hotels: Bromley Court.

D59 Hindhead
☎(and fax) (0428) 604614
Churt Rd, Hindhead, Surrey GU26 6HX
1.5 miles N of Hindhead on A287
towards Farnham.
Heathland course.
18 holes, 6349 yards, S.S.S.70
Founded 1904
Visitors: welcome weekdays,
weekends by appointment; h/cap
cert required.
Green Fee: £25/round, £33/day WD;
£40 WE.
Societies: Wed and Thurs only.
Catering: bar, restaurant, snack bar.
Snooker.
Hotels: Devil's Punch Bowl; Pride of
the Valley (Churt).

D60 Hoebridge
☎(0483) 722611
Old Woking Rd, Old Woking, Surrey
GU22 8JH
On B382 Old Woking road between
Old Woking and West Byfleet.
Public meadowland course.
Main, 18 holes, 6587 yards,
S.S.S.71; Par 3, 18 holes, 2296
yards; Intermediate, 9 holes, 2294
yards, Par 33
Designed by John Jacobs.
Founded 1982
Visitors: welcome any time, must
book at weekends.
Green Fee: £12/round Main,
£6/round Par 3, £6.75/round
Intermediate.
Societies: not at weekends.
Catering: 8-10am breakfast, 12am-
2.30pm lunch, 7-9.30pm dinner.
12 snooker tables.
Hotels: Post House (Guildford); Hilton
International (Cobham).

D61 Holtye
☎(0342) 850635, 850576 Sec.
Holtye Common, Cowden,
Edenbridge, Kent TN8 7ED
On A264 between East Grinstead and
Tunbridge Wells, 5 miles from East
Grinstead.
Heathland course.
9 holes, 5300 yards, S.S.S.66
Founded 1893

Visitors: welcome weekdays;
restricted Thurs am and weekends
am; telephone first.
Green Fee: on application.
Societies: main day Tues, smaller
parties possible Fri.
Catering: hot snacks every lunch
time, meals by prior arrangement.
Hotels: White Horse Inn (adjacent).

D62 Home Park
☎(081) 977 2423 Office, 977 2658
Pro Shop, 977 4414 fax.
Hampton Wick, Richmond-upon-
Thames, Surrey KT1 4AS
From Kingston over Kingston Bridge,
left at roundabout, 50 yards on left
through iron gates at Old Kings Head
public house, straight road to club.
Parkland course in park of Hampton
Court Palace.
18 holes, 6598 yards, S.S.S.71
Founded 1895
Visitors: welcome.
Green Fee: £10.50/£16.50 WD
(£5/£10 with member), £18/£28 WE
(£10/£20 with member).
Societies: weekdays.
Catering: lunches and bar snacks
served; dinner bookings taken.
Hotels: Lion Gate.

D63 Horton Park CC
☎(081) 393 8400 office, 394 2626
shop
Hook Road, Epsom, Surrey KT19 8QG
Off Hook Rd through Epsom to
Chessington.
Public parkland course.
18 holes, 5208 yards, Par 70
Founded 1987
Visitors: welcome; proper golf
shoes, no jeans
Green Fee: £10.25/round WD,
£13/round WE.
Societies: welcome weekdays only.
Catering: 2 bars, restaurant,
function suite.
Hotels: Travel Inn (Chessington).

D64 Hurtmore
☎(0483) 426492
Hurtmore Rd, Hurtmore, Godalming,
Surrey GU7 2RN
Off A3, 3 mile S of Guildford.
Parkland course, 7 lakes.
18 holes, 5500 yards, S.S.S.69
Designed by Peter Alliss, Clive Clark.
Founded 1990
Visitors: welcome; pay-as-you-play
on booking system.
Green Fee: £18/round WD,
£22/round WE.

Societies: weekdays only.
Catering: restaurant, 2 bars.
Putting green, small practice area.

D65 Hythe Imperial
☎(0303) 267554 Sec.
Princes Parade, Hythe, Kent CT21 6AE
Turn off M20 to Hythe, to E end of
seafront.
Seaside course.
9 holes, 5533 yards, S.S.S.67
Founded 1950
Visitors: welcome with h/cap cert.
Green Fee: £15 WD, £25 WE.
Societies: by arrangement.
Catering: hotel; hotel/club bar.
Hotels: Hythe Imperial; Stade Court.

D66 Kingswood (Surrey)
☎(0737) 832188
Sandy Lane, Kingswood, Surrey
KT20 6NE
4 miles S of Sutton on A217, M25
junction 8.
Parkland course.
18 holes, 6821 yards, S.S.S.73
Designed by James Braid.
Founded 1928
Visitors: welcome if space available.
Green Fee: £28/round WD,
£40/round WE.
Societies: welcome weekdays.
Catering: full restaurant facilities.
Hotels: Bridge; Heathside.

D67 Knole Park
☎(0732) 452150
Seal Hollow Rd, Sevenoaks, Kent
TN15 0HJ
From M25 onto A21 Hastings road,
after 1 mile bear left onto A25
Maidstone road; at 2nd set of lights
turn right into Seal Hollow Rd, club
1.25 miles on left.
Parkland course.
18 holes, 6249 yards, S.S.S.70
Designed by J.A. Abercrombie.
Founded 1924
Visitors: weekdays only by
appointment; h/cap certs required.
Green Fee: £25.50/round, £36/2
rounds.
Societies: Tues, Thurs, Fri by
appointment only; 2 only per week.
Catering: lunch, tea, dinner.
Squash, snooker.
Hotels: Sevenoaks Park; Royal Oak.

D68 Laleham
☎(0932) 564211, 562877 Pro
Laleham Reach, Chertsey, Surrey
KT16 8RP

LEEDS CASTLE GOLF COURSE

'. . . there is nothing to compare with the delightful surroundings of Leeds Castle . . .'
(Donald Steel: The Golf Course Guide)

A round of golf at Leeds Castle offers some unforgettable golfing memories.

You'll find yourself playing alongside the moat, lining up tee shots against the Castle battlements and pausing to watch the black swans and wildfowl which inhabit the 500 acres of parkland.

This 9 hole, 2880 yard course was re-designed by Neil Coles and is open the year round for everyone to enjoy.

The golf Professional, Chris Miller, offers coaching, equipment advice and club and trolley hire, from the Golf Centre.

Golf societies and groups are welcomed and residential golf weekends can be organised.

Please call for further details or reservations. Booking is essential.

Leeds Castle Golf Course, nr. Maidstone, Kent.   Tel (0622)880467

A320 between Staines and Chertsey, opposite Thorpe Water Park.
Meadowland course.
18 holes, 6203 yards, S.S.S.70
Founded 1907
Visitors: welcome weekdays only before 4.30pm.
Green Fee: on application
Societies: Mon, Tues, Wed only; to play in 3 balls.
Catering: full facilities.

D69 Lamberhurst
☎(0892) 890241
Church Rd, Lamberhurst, Kent TN3 8DT
Entrance from A21 on outskirts of Lamberhurst village to N.
Undulating parkland course.
18 holes, 6277 yards, S.S.S.70
Designed by Frank Pennink.
Founded 1920
Visitors: welcome any day; after 12am weekends and Bank Holidays unless accompanied by member.
Green Fee: £25/day WD, £30/day WE & BH.
Societies: catered for on Tues, Wed and Thurs only.
Catering: lunch, dinner and snacks.
Hotels: Star and Eagle (Goudhurst).

D70 Langley Park
☎(081) 658 6849 or 650 1663 Pro.
Barnfield Wood Rd, Beckenham, Kent BR3 2SZ
At lights near Bromley South station turn into Westmoreland Rd, clubhouse 1.75 miles on left.
Gently undulating parkland course.
18 holes, 6488 yards, S.S.S.71
Designed by J.H. Taylor
Founded 1910
Visitors: not at weekends; telephone Pro for bookings.
Green Fee: £30/round or day.
Societies: Wed only.
Catering: full facilities every day.
Hotels: Bromley Court.

D71 Leatherhead
☎(0372) 843966
Kingston Rd, Leatherhead, Surrey KT22 0DP
M25 junction 9, take A243 towards London, entrance 500 yards.
Parkland course.
18 holes, 6107 yards, S.S.S.69
Founded 1903
Visitors: welcome by appointment.
Green Fee: £32.50/round, £37.50/2 rounds WD; £45/round WE.
Societies: welcome, not weekends.

Catering: restaurant, brasserie, bar.
Hotels: Woodlands Park (Oxshott).

D72 Leeds Castle
☎(0622) 880467, 765400 ext 4329
Leeds Castle, Maidstone, Kent ME17 1PL
On A20 from Maidstone towards Ashford, signposted to Leeds Castle.
Public parkland course.
9 holes, 2880 yards, Par 34
Designed by Neil Coles (4 holes, 1988)
Founded 1928
Visitors: bookings taken (9 holes only) 6 days in advance; correct dress, no denim jeans.
Green Fee: £8.50 (9 holes); £6 jnrs, disabled, OAPs.
Societies: and company bookings weekdays only.
Catering: Park Gate Inn, in car park.
Practice nets, putting green.
Hotels: Great Danes.

D73 Limpsfield Chart
☎(0883) 723405
Limpsfield, Oxted, Surrey RH8 0SL
On A25 between Oxted and Westerham, over traffic lights 300 yards on right, E of Oxted.

Heathland course.
9 holes, 5718 yards, S.S.S.68
Founded 1889
Visitors: welcome Mon, Tues, Wed
and Fri.
Green Fee: £17/round/day.
Societies: can be arranged.
Catering: meals served.
Hotels: Kings Arms; White Hart;
Hoskins Arms.

D74 **Lingfield Park**
☎(0342) 834602
Racecourse Road, Lingfield, Surrey
RH7 6PQ
M25 Junction 6; through Lingfield
village towards Edenbridge; course
is on left next to racecourse before
railway bridge.
Parkland course.
18 holes, 6500 yards, S.S.S.72
Founded May 1987
Visitors: welcome Mon-Fri;
weekends after 1pm.
Green Fee: £20/round, £30/day WD;
£30/round WE.
Societies: welcome by arrangement
with Manager.
Catering: full bar facilities, bar
snacks; other by arrangement.
Driving range.
Hotels: Copthorne; Effingham Park.

D75 **Littlestone**
☎(0679) 63355 Sec, 62310
Clubhouse, 62231 Pro.
St Andrews Rd, Littlestone, New
Romney, Kent TN28 8RB
A20 to Ashford, B2070 to New
Romney, 1.5 miles from New
Romney.
Seaside links course; 18-hole course
private, 9-hole course public.
18 holes, 6417 yards, S.S.S.71; 9
holes, 1998 yards, S.S.S.32
Designed by Laidlaw Purvis.
Founded 1888
Visitors: 18-hole course, weekdays
only; max h/cap 20 (Men), 30
(Ladies); advance booking required:
9-hole course, no restrictions.
Green Fee: on application
Societies: weekdays by
arrangement with Sec.
Catering: bar and restaurant.

D76 **London Scottish**
☎(081) 788 0135, 789 7517 Sec.
Windmill Enclosure, Wimbledon
Common, London SW19 5NQ
1 mile from Putney Station (S.R.).
Parkland course.
18 holes, 5436 yards, S.S.S.67

Founded 1865
Visitors: welcome weekdays, except
Bank Holidays; must wear red upper
garment.
Green Fee: on application.
Societies: all year; not weekends or
Mon.
Catering: lunch served, evening
meals if ordered, except Mon.

D77 **Lullingstone Park**
☎(0959) 34542 Pro, 34517 catering.
Park Gate, Chelsfield, Orpington, Kent
A20 to Swanley, then B258 Daltons
Rd to Park Gate.
Municipal parkland course.
18 holes, 6674 yards, S.S.S.72;
9 holes, 2432 yards
Designed by Fred Hawtree
Founded 1923
Visitors: welcome.
Green Fee: on application
Societies: by arrangement.
Catering: meals by arrangement.

D78 **Malden**
☎(081) 942 0654 Sec, 942 6009 Pro.
Traps Lane, New Malden, Surrey KT3
4RS
0.5 mile from New Malden station,
near A3 between Wimbledon and
Kingston.
Parkland course.
18 holes, 6201 yards, S.S.S.70
Founded 1926
Visitors: weekdays unrestricted,
weekends restricted.
Green Fee: on application to Pro.
Societies: Wed, Thurs, Fri.
Catering: all week.

D79 **Mid-Kent**
☎(0474) 568035
Singlewell Rd, Gravesend, Kent DA11
7RB
A2 S of Gravesend, turn off at
Tollgate Moathouse Hotel.
Parkland course.
18 holes, 6206 yards, S.S.S.70
Designed by Frank Pennink.
Founded 1909
Visitors: weekdays, weekends with
member.
Green Fee: on application
Societies: Tues only.
Catering: lunch except Mon, dinner
by arrangement.

D80 **Mitcham**
☎(081) 648 1508
Carshalton Rd, Mitcham Junction,
Surrey CR4 4HN

A237 off A23, by Mitcham Junction
station.
Meadowland course.
18 holes, 5935 yards, S.S.S.68
Founded 1886
Visitors: weekdays, restrictions
weekends.
Green Fee: on application
Societies: Tues and Thurs only.
Catering: full catering facilities
available.

D81 **Moore Place (Esher)**
☎(0372) 463533
Portsmouth Rd, Esher, Surrey KT10
9LN
On A3 Portsmouth road, 0.5 mile
from centre of Esher towards
Cobham.
Public undulating parkland course.
9 holes, 3512 yards, S.S.S.58
Designed by H. Vardon.
Reformed 1977
Visitors: welcome.
Green Fee: on application.
Societies: phone for information.
Catering: lunch and evening meals.
Hotels: Ladbrokes Seven Hills.

D82 **Nevill**
☎(0892) 525818
Benhall Mill Rd, Tunbridge Wells,
Kent TN2 5JW
Turn into Forest Rd from A267 out of
Tunbridge Wells.
Parkland/heathland course.
18 holes, 6336 yards, S.S.S.70
Designed by C.K. Cotton
Founded 1914
Visitors: accepted with h/cap cert.
Green Fee: £28/day (£14 with
member) WD, £17.50/day with
member only WE.
Societies: Wed, Thurs only.
Catering: 7 days a week.
Hotels: Spa; Calverley.

D83 **New Zealand GC**
☎(0932) 345049
Woodham Lane, Woodham,
Addlestone, Surrey KT15 3QD
At junction of Woodham Lane and
Sheerwater Rd in West Byfleet.
Parkland course.
18 holes, 6012 yards, S.S.S.69
Designed by Muir-Fergusson.
Founded 1895
Visitors: by arrangement.
Green Fee: on application.
Societies: weekdays only, by
arrangement.
Catering: bar and restaurant (no
evening meals).

D84 North Downs
☎(0883) 652057, 653298, 653004
Northdown Rd, Woldingham,
Caterham, Surrey CR3 7AA
Woldingham road at roundabout on
A22 at N end of Caterham bypass.
Undulating course.
18 holes, 5787 yards, S.S.S.68
Founded 1899
Visitors: welcome weekdays.
Green Fee: on application
Societies: catered for weekdays.
Catering: bar lunch except Mon.

D85 North Foreland
☎(0843) 62140 Sec, 69628 Pro.
Convent Rd, Broadstairs, Kent CT10
3PU
A28 from Canterbury, or
A2/M2/A299 from London to
Kingsgate via Broadstairs, course 1.5
miles from Broadstairs station.
Seaside/clifftop course.
18 holes, 6382 yards, S.S.S.71;
Short Course, 18 holes, 1752 yards,
Par 54
Designed by Fowler and Simpson.
Founded 1903
Visitors: main course by prior
booking, h/cap cert required; short
course unrestricted.
Green Fee: main course, £18/round,
£26/day, £26/round WE; short
course £5/round.
Societies: Wed and Fri.
Catering: available; functions.
Tennis.
Hotels: Castle Keep; Fayreness;
Castlemere; Rothsay; Ann Marie;
Hotel Lancaster.

D86 Oak Park (Crondall)
☎(0252) 850880, 850066 Pro.
Heath Lane, Crondall, Nr Farnham,
Surrey GU10 5PB
Off A287 Farnham-Odiham road 3
miles SE of M3 junction 5.
Gently undulating parkland course.
18 holes, 6437 yards, S.S.S.71
Designed by Patrick Dawson.
Founded 1984
Visitors: welcome; tee reservations
at weekends and public holidays.
Green Fee: £15/round, £22 WE &
BH.
Societies: welcome every day by
reservation.
Catering: bar, bar snacks, à la carte
restaurant (closed Sun/Mon
evenings).
Conference and banqueting facilities,
driving range.
Hotels: Bush (Farnham), THF Golfing
Breaks.

D87 Oaks Sports Centre
☎(081) 643 8363
Woodmansterne Rd, Carshalton,
Surrey SM5 4AN
On B2032 past Carshalton Beeches
station, Oaks Sports Centre
signposted N of A2022, half way
between A217 and A237.
Public meadowland course.
18 holes, 5975 yards, S.S.S.69;
9 holes, 1590 yards, S.S.S.28
Designed by Alphagreen.
Founded 1972
Visitors: welcome (public course).
Green Fee: 18 hole £8 WD, £10 WE;
9 hole £4 WD, £4.90 WE.
Societies: by arrangement.
Catering: refreshments all day,
public bar open normal pub hours.
Driving range, 5 squash courts,
sauna, solarium.
Hotels: Greyhound (Carshalton).

D88 Pachesham Park
☎(0372) 843453
Oaklawn Road, Leatherhead, Surrey
KT22 0BT
From M25 junction 9 towards Esher
on A244.
Parkland course.
9 holes, 1752 yards, S.S.S.56
Founded June 1991
Visitors: welcome.
Green Fee: £6.50 WD, £7.50 WE.
Societies: welcome.
Catering: bar and restaurant.
Driving range, putting green, practice
bunker.

D89 Poult Wood
☎(0732) 364039
Higham Lane, Tonbridge, Kent
2 miles N of Tonbridge off A227.
Public parkland course.
18 holes, 5569 yards, S.S.S.67
Designed by Fred Hawtree.
Founded 1974
Visitors: welcome, book in advance
if registered at golf shop.
Green Fee: £7 WD (jnrs/OAP £4),
£10.50 WE.
Societies: weekdays (18 holes)
£9.50; day tickets £19.
Catering: bar, restaurant, spikes
café, small meeting room.
4 squash courts.
Hotels: Rose & Crown; Chequers;
Leavers Manor; Langley.

D90 Prince's
☎(0304) 611118, 613797 Pro.
Sandwich Bay, Sandwich, Kent CT13
9QB

4 miles from Sandwich railway
station via St George's Rd and
Sandown Rd.
Traditional links course.
3 x 9-hole interconnecting loops, 3
combinations of 18 holes,
6500-7000 yards, S.S.S.72/71/71
Designed by Sir Guy Campbell &
John Morrison.
Founded 1904
Visitors: welcome, h/cap cert
required; no jeans.
Green Fee: £26.50/round, £29/day
WD; £31/round, £34/day Sat and BH;
£31/round, £39/day Sun; special
reduced rates Nov-April.
Societies: by arrangement, no
restrictions.
Catering: full bar and restaurant;
banqueting.
Driving range, snooker, pool.
Hotels: Bell, golf/accomodation
packages on request.

D91 Purley Downs
☎(081) 657 8347 Sec.
106 Purley Downs Rd, Purley, Surrey
CR2 0RB
3 miles S of Croydon on A235, fork
left onto Purley Downs Rd.
Downland course.
18 holes, 6212 yards, S.S.S.70
Founded 1894
Visitors: weekdays only; must have
h/cap cert.
Green Fee: £25 WD.
Societies: Mon, Thurs, some Fri.
Catering: 19th (informal), lounge
bar, dining room.

D92 Puttenham
☎(0483) 810498
Heath Rd, Puttenham, Guildford,
Surrey GU3 1AL
Just off A31, Farnham to Guildford
road (Hog's Back), 4 miles W of
Guildford.
Heathland course.
18 holes, 6214 yards, S.S.S.70
Founded 1894
Visitors: welcome weekdays only;
accomplished players only.
Green Fee: £25.50/day.
Societies: Wed, Thurs only.
Catering: full facilities available.
Hotels: Hog's Back.

D93 RAC Country Club
☎(0372) 276311
Woodcote Park, Epsom, Surrey KT18
7EW
A24, 1.75 miles from Epsom.
Parkland courses.

Coronation, 18 holes, 5474 yards, S.S.S.67; Old, 18 holes, 6702 yards, S.S.S.72
Founded 1913
Visitors: no.
Green Fee: on request.
Societies: on request.
Catering: full services available.
Hotels: Chalk Lane.

D94 **Redhill & Reigate**

☎(0737) 240777 Sec, 244626
Clubhouse, 244433 Pro.
Clarence Lodge, Pendleton Rd, Redhill, Surrey RH1 6LB
1 mile S of Reigate (A217), at traffic lights turn left (A2044), after 0.25 mile turn left into Pendleton Rd.
Moorland course.
18 holes, 5261 yards, S.S.S.66
Designed by James Braid.
Founded 1887
Visitors: welcome Mon-Fri; Sat and Sun after 11am; not Sun June-Sept.
Green Fee: on application
Societies: Wed and Thurs only.
Catering: bar snacks; meals if booked.

D95 **Reigate Heath**

☎(0737) 242610
Reigate Heath, Reigate, Surrey RH2 8QR
0.5 mile S of A25 to W of Reigate.
Heathland course.
9 holes, 5554 yards, S.S.S.67
Founded 1895
Visitors: welcome weekdays, but telephone first.
Green Fee: on application.
Societies: Wed and Thurs by arrangement.
Catering: full facilities daily except Mon.
Hotels: Reigate Manor; Cranleigh.

D96 **Richmond**

☎(081) 940 4351/1463
Sudbrook Park, Richmond, Surrey TW10 7AS
On A307 1 mile S of Richmond, look for Sudbrook Lane on left.
Parkland course.
18 holes, 5965 yards, S.S.S.69
Founded 1891
Visitors: welcome on weekdays by prior arrangement.
Green Fee: £32.
Societies: welcome Tues, Thurs and Fri.
Catering: bar snacks and lunches available every day.
Hotels: Petersham; Richmond Gate.

D97 **Richmond Park**

☎(081) 876 3205, 1795
Roehampton Gate, Richmond Park, London SW15 5JR
Just inside Roehampton Gate in Richmond Park.
Public parkland course
18 holes, 5909 yards, S.S.S.70;
18 holes, 5940 yards, S.S.S.68
Designed by Hawtree & Sons
Founded 1923
Visitors: welcome, dawn to dusk depending on Park Gate opening hours; must wear golf shoes; booking system at weekends.
Green Fee: on application.
Societies: welcome weekdays.
Catering: pavilion café.

D98 **Rochester & Cobham**

☎(0474 82) 3411
Park Pale by Rochester, Kent ME2 3UL
Situated on A2, turn left onto B2009 and follow signs to clubhouse.
Undulating parkland course.
18 holes, 6467 yards, S.S.S.71
Founded 1891
Visitors: weekdays unaccompanied h/cap cert required; weekends with member before 5pm.
Green Fee: £26/round, £36/day.
Societies: Tues and Thurs.
Catering: details on request.
Hotels: Inn on the Lake; Tollgate Motel.

D99 **Roehampton**

☎(081) 876 1621
Roehampton Lane, London SW15 5LR
Off A306 at end of Roehampton Lane.
Parkland course.
18 holes, 6046 yards, S.S.S.69
Founded 1901
Visitors: with member only.
Green Fee: £13 WD, £18 WE.
Societies: limited 32 players, must be introduced by a member.
Catering: full 7 day service.
Tennis, croquet, bowls, snooker, squash, indoor/outdoor pools complex.

D100 **Royal Blackheath**

☎(081) 850 1795
Court Rd, Eltham, London SE9 5AF
By road; 8 miles from central London, club entrance is 400 yards on left side of Court Rd after leaving Eltham High St; by rail; 5 minutes walk from Mottingham station.
Parkland course with Georgian clubhouse.
18 holes, 6209 yards, S.S.S.70

Designed by James Braid.
Founded 1608
Visitors: welcome, h/cap cert required.
Green Fee: £36/day.
Societies: welcome Tues-Fri, April-Oct.
Catering: dining room, bar.
Museum of Golf.
Hotels: Clarendon; Yardley Court (Eltham).

D101 **Royal Cinque Ports**

☎(0304) 374007
Golf Rd, Deal, Kent CT14 6RF
Follow coast road through Deal to end, turn left onto Godwyn Rd, at end turn right onto Golf Rd to club.
Seaside links course.
Medal, 18 holes, 6407 yards, S.S.S.71
Designed by Tom Dunn, Guy Campbell.
Founded 1892
Visitors: welcome weekdays, reservations required; must be members of recognised golf club and have h/cap below 20 (Men), 28 (Ladies); 2 ball play only.
Green Fee: £35/day/round before 1pm, £25 after 1pm.
Societies: by arrangement weekdays.
Catering: full facilities; jacket and tie required.
Hotels: Royal, Kings Head, Chequers (Deal); Bell (Sandwich).

D102 **Royal Mid-Surrey**

☎(081) 940 1894
Old Deer Park, Richmond, Surrey TW9 2SB
On A316, 300 yards before Richmond roundabout heading into London.
Parkland courses.
Inner, 18 holes, 5544 yards, S.S.S.68; Outer, 18 holes, 6343 yards, S.S.S.70
Designed by J.H. Taylor.
Founded 1892
Visitors: weekdays with letter of intro. from own club, membership or h/cap cert, or playing with member; weekends and Bank Holidays members' guests only.
Green Fee: £41/round WD.
Societies: recognised societies welcome if previously arranged with Sec.
Catering: lunch served except Mon, snack lunch served every day.
Hotels: Richmond Hill; Richmond Gate; Quinn's; Bishops.

Royal Cinq Ports, Deal

Nowhere in Britain, indeed nowhere in the world, do three Open championship courses lie in such close proximity as Prince's, Sandwich and Deal. You can chip a ball from Prince's to Sandwich and you could almost drive a ball from Sandwich onto the furthest reaches of Deal if it were not for the line of buildings that once included the late lamented Guildford Hotel.

Nowadays only Sandwich, reinstated in 1981, meets all the demands imposed by a modern Open, the old version of Prince's being largely demolished during the last war; but no course has remained more untouched by the years than Deal or, to give it its proper title, the Royal Cinque Ports G.C.

The sea has done its best on three occasions to sweep it away, large areas being devastated by floods swept in on angry tides, The most recent invasion was 1978 but it resulted in a gigantic exercise to strengthen the sea wall which is now thought to be man enough to repulse everything the elements might throw at it.

Like many champsionship links, Deal was no doubt more formidable in the days of the gutty ball and hickory shafts, the hummocky nature of the ground on many of the fairways being considerably easier to negotiate with a steel shaft and modern ball.

Its last Open was in 1920 when George Duncan profited from Abe Mitchell's spectacular collapse on the final day, but the tournament that keeps Deal in the forefront of the public eye is the Haford Hewitt whose participating legions descent every April to put themselves through a process of friendly torture.

The drama invariably unfolds on the 18th and 19th and, for that reason, they are the best remembered holes. The 1st is innocent enough as a first hole in spite of the stream in front of the green, and the chance of driving out of bounds or of burying a hook in the clumps of rushes. However, as the 19th, its cloak is far more sinister. The fairway seems to shrink in width and the stream casts some hypnotic power over those who seem to have all strangth and coordination drained from their hands.

The 2nd, a stern two-shooter, is the sort of hole you could only find on a British seaside links, a label even more applicable to the 3rd. There are two or three enormous hollows between twin sandhills and the green.

The 4th, Sandy Parlour, is the first of three short holes which make as good a set as you will find, each calling for a different shot with a different club in a different direction. David Blair thought enormously highly of them and was very much what one might term a Deal man, as was Leonard Crawley. Their shotmaking powers were well suited to controlling the ball in moderate winds that for ordinary folk made the fives many and the fours few.

From the 2nd to the 7th, you get used to the wind from the same quarter except for the pitch to the 6th — a stroke that catches many by surprise. First time players on the course never expect to find the green where it is.

The 9th, 10th and 11th are excellent fours, running largely at right angles to the rest of the holes particularly the finish which is easy or difficult according to the wind. The 12th is another old-fashioned shaped green while the 16th and 17th also have their own distinctive contours. The 16th, in fact, is perched up like a gun turret, the steep, guardian bank frequently killing off a long second seeking a birdie four.

On the 17th the problem for the second shot is finding a predictable landing area but at the 18th the only recommended way of hitting a flat, plateau green is carrying the shot all the way. Here again, the stream crossing the fairway claims its haul of balls although there is less excuse for causing a ripple than on the 1st. Bernard Darwin wrote, many moons ago, that Deal consists of plenty of "fine, straight-ahead, long-hitting golf". It still does.

D103 **Royal St George's**
☎(0304) 613090 Sec, 615236 Pro
Sandwich, Kent CT13 9PB
1 mile from Sandwich to Sandwich
Bay, turn left at district sign of Worth.
Links course.
18 holes, 6903 yards, S.S.S.74
Designed by Dr Laidlaw Purvis.
Founded 23 May 1887
Visitors: Mon-Fri only.
Green Fee: £33/round, £47/day.
Societies: details on request.
Catering: bar, restaurant, snack bar;
dinner by arrangement for parties.
Hotels: Bell; St Crispin Inn (Worth).

D104 **Royal Wimbledon**
☎(081) 946 2125
29 Camp Rd, Wimbledon, SW19 4UW
0.75 mile W of War Memorial in
Wimbledon village.
Parkland course.
18 holes, 6300 yards, S.S.S.70
Founded 1865
Visitors: none.
Societies: Wed, Thurs only.

D105 **Ruxley**
☎(0689) 871490
Sandy Lane, St Paul's Cray,
Orpington, Kent BR5 3HY
A20 to Ruxley roundabout, into
Sandy Lane.
Undulating parkland course.
18 holes, 4964 yards, S.S.S.65
Founded 1973
Visitors: welcome weekdays from
7am, weekends after 11.30am.
Green Fee: £9 WD, £13 WE.
Societies: welcome.
Catering: breakfasts and lunch
daily; evening meals by
arrangement.
Driving range.
Hotels: Crest (Bexley).

D106 **St Augustine's**
☎(0843) 590333 Sec, 590222 Pro.
Cottington Rd, Cliffsend, Ramsgate,
Kent CT12 5JN
Entrance at railway bridge on B2048
off Ramsgate-Sandwich road.
Parkland course.
18 holes, 5138 yards, S.S.S.65
Designed by Tom Vardon.
Founded 1907
Visitors: welcome with h/cap cert
weekdays and after 10.30am
weekends.
Green Fee: on application
Societies: weekdays except Mon;
prior booking essential.
Catering: available.

D107 **St George's Hill**
☎(0932) 842406
St George's Hill, Weybridge, Surrey
KT13 0NL
B374 from station towards Cobham,
0.5 mile on left.
Heathland course.
3 x 9 hole courses, 3 combinations of
18; 6569 yards, S.S.S.71; 6097
yards, S.S.S.69; 6210 yards,
S.S.S.70
Designed by H.S. Colt.
Founded 1913
Visitors: welcome Wed-Fri only
(Mon members and guests only,
Tues Ladies Day), must book tee time
in advance.
Green Fee: £30/round, £40/day.
Societies: catered for Wed-Fri.
Catering: full restaurant lunch and
bar snacks served.

D108 **Sandown Golf Centre**
☎(0372) 463340, 465921
More Lane, Esher, Surrey KT10 8AN
About 1 mile from Esher station, in
centre of Sandown Park racecourse,
off Portsmouth road; follow brown
signs to Sandown Park Leisure
Centre.
Public parkland course.
9 holes, 5656 yards, S.S.S.67;
9 holes Par 3
Designed by John Jacobs.
Founded 1967
Visitors: welcome at any time;
booking at weekends.
Green Fee: main course, £4.80 WD,
£6 WE; Par 3, £3.20 WD, £4 WE.
Societies: by arrangement.
Catering: available.
Driving range, 9-hole Pitch & Putt.
Hotels: Hilton National (Cobham).

D109 **Selsdon Park Hotel**
☎(081) 657 8811, 651 6171 fax.
Sanderstead, South Croydon, Surrey
CR2 8YA
B274 from Croydon, A2022 at
Selsdon.
Parkland course.
18 holes, 6402 yards, S.S.S.71
Designed by J.H. Taylor.
Founded 1930
Visitors: welcome, contact Pro at 1st
tee.
Green Fee: £20/round, £30/day WD;
£25/round (£20 after 4pm) Sat;
£30/round (£25 after 4pm) Sun.
Societies: welcome by prior
arrangement.
Catering: full service available.
Hotels: Selsdon Park.

D110 **Sene Valley**
☎(0303) 268514
Sene, Folkestone, Kent
Club signposted from A20 between
Ashford and Folkestone.
Undulating downland course.
18 holes, 6320 yards, S.S.S.70
Designed by Henry Cotton.
Founded 1888
Visitors: welcome but advisable to
telephone to check availability.
Green Fee: on application.
Societies: welcome by arrangement
with Manager.
Catering: daily except Mon.
Hotels: Imperial (Hythe); Burlington.

D111 **Sheerness**
☎(0795) 662585
Power Station Rd, Sheerness, Kent
ME12 3AE
9 miles from Sittingbourne on A249.
Seaside course.
18 holes, 6460 yards, S.S.S.71
Founded 1906
Visitors: welcome weekdays,
weekends with member.
Green Fee: £15 WD.
Societies: welcome Tues-Thurs.
Catering: except Mon.
Hotels: Royal; Abbey (Minster).

D112 **Shillinglee Park**
☎(0428) 653237, 644391 fax.
Chiddingfold, Godalming, Surrey GU8
4TA
Off A283, 2 miles S of Chiddingfold.
Public undulating parkland course.
9 holes, 2500 yards, S.S.S.63
Designed by Roger Mace.
Founded 1980
Visitors: welcome, advisable to
book; telephone bookings accepted.
Green Fee: £7.50 (9 holes), £13.50
(18 holes), £16.50/day WD; £8.50 (9
holes), £16 (18 holes), £19/day WE;
reductions for jnrs and OAPs.
Societies: and company golf days
welcome.
Catering: bar and restaurant
facilities available daily from
8.30am-6pm (3pm Sun); evening
meals and parties by arrangement.
Pitch & Putt, £3 unlimited play.
Hotels: Lythe Hill; Crown Inn.

D113 **Shirley Park**
☎(081) 654 1143
194 Addiscombe Rd, Croydon,
Surrey CR0 7LB
On A232 approx 1 mile E of East
Croydon station, near Shirley.
Parkland course.

18 holes, 6210 yards, S.S.S.70
Founded 1914
Visitors: welcome 9.30-12am,
1.30-4pm weekdays; with member
only weekends.
Green Fee: £26/day/round.
Societies: hald-day pm, Mon, Thurs,
Fri.
Catering: breakfast, snack lunch
and afternoon tea daily; banqueting,
functions (sponsored by member).
Hotels: Croydon Court; Holiday Inn;
Briarley.

D114 **Shooters Hill**
☎(081) 854 6368
Lowood, Eaglesfield Rd, London
SE18 3DA
Off A207.
Very hilly parkland/woodland course.
18 holes, 5736 yards, S.S.S.68
Founded 1903
Visitors: weekdays only with
recognised golf club h/cap.
Green Fee: £22/round, £27/day.
Societies: Tues and Thurs only; £24
per round, £30 per day.
Catering: after 10.30am daily.
Hotels: Clarendon (Blackheath).

D115 **Shortlands**
☎(081) 460 2471
Meadow Road, Shortlands, Kent BR2
0PB
9 holes, 5261, S.S.S.66
Founded 1894
Visitors: only with member.
Catering: bar and catering for
members and guests.

D116 **Sidcup**
☎(081) 300 2150
7 Hurst Rd, Sidcup, Kent DA15 9AE
A222 off A2, 400 yards N of Sidcup
railway station.
Parkland course.
9 holes, 5722 yards, S.S.S.68
Designed by James Braid and H.
Myrtle.
Founded 1891
Visitors: welcome, with member
only weekends; h/cap certs required;
smart casual dress except after 7pm.
Green Fee: £16/round/day.
Societies: welcome.
Catering: bar and restaurant
facilities except Mon. Snooker.

D117 **Silvermere**
☎(0932) 867275
Redhill Rd, Cobham, Surrey KT11
1EF

At junction 10 of M25 and A3 take
B366 to Byfleet; Silvermere is 0.5
mile on right.
Woodland/parkland/meadowland
course.
18 holes, 6333 yards, S.S.S.71
Founded 1976
Visitors: welcome, book 7 days in
advance; members only Sat/Sun am.
Green Fee: £14 WD, £18.50 WE.
Societies: weekdays only, £47 full
day including dinner.
Catering: full facilities from 8am.
Hotels: Hilton National.

D118 **Sittingbourne & Milton Regis**
☎(0795) 842261
Wormdale, Newington,
Sittingbourne, Kent ME9 7PX
1 mile N of exit 5 off M2 on A249.
Undulating course.
18 holes, 6121 yards, S.S.S.69
Designed by Harry Hunter.
Founded 1929
Visitors: welcome weekdays with
letter of intro. or h/cap cert.
Green Fee: £18.50 (18 holes),
£30.50 (36 holes).
Societies: catered for Tues, Thurs.
Catering: Tues to Sat.
Hotels: Coniston (Sittingbourne).

D119 **Sundridge Park**
☎(081) 460 0278
Garden Rd, Bromley, Kent BR1 3NE
5 minutes walk from Sundridge Park
station.
Parkland courses.
East, 18 holes, 6467 yards, S.S.S.71;
West, 18 holes, 6007 yards, S.S.S.69
Designed by James Braid and Jack
Randall.
Founded 1902
Visitors: welcome weekdays only;
official club h/cap required.
Green Fee: £34/day.
Societies: on application.
Catering: full facilities daily.
Hotels: Bromley Court; Bromley
Continental.

D120 **Sunningdale**
☎(0344) 21681
Ridgemount Rd, Sunningdale, Surrey
SL5 9RW
Ridgemount Rd is 50 yards W of
Sunningdale railway station crossing
on the A30.
Heathland courses.
Old, 18 holes, 6341 yards, S.S.S.70;
New, 18 holes, 6676 yards, S.S.S.72
Designed by Willie Park.

Founded 1901
Visitors: weekdays by arrangement.
Green Fee: £95/day.
Societies: Tues, Wed, Thurs by
arrangement.
Catering: full facilities except Mon.
Hotels: Berystede; Runnymede.

D121 **Sunningdale Ladies**
☎(0344) 20507
Cross Rd, Sunningdale, Surrey SL5
9RX
2nd turning left on A30 going W from
Sunningdale level crossing.
Heathland course
18 holes, 3622 yards, S.S.S.60
Designed by Edward Villiers.
Founded 1902
Visitors: welcome, phone first.
Green Fee: on application
Societies: catered for, Ladies only.
Catering: lunch and tea except Sun.

D122 **Surbiton**
☎(081) 398 3101
Woodstock Lane, Chessington,
Surrey KT9 1UG
From A3 westbound, take
Esher/Chessington fly off, turn left to
Claygate, club 400 yards on right.
Parkland course.
18 holes, 6211 yards, S.S.S.70
Founded 1896
Visitors: welcome weekdays only;
h/cap certs required; members'
guests only at weekends.
Green Fee: £27/round, £40.50/day.
Societies: Mon and Fri only.
Catering: full facilities.
Hotels: Haven (Esher).

D123 **Tandridge**
☎(0883) 712274
Oxted, Surrey RH8 9NQ
Off A25 by Oxted, 2 miles E of
Godstone; junction 6 from M25.
Parkland course.
18 holes, 6260 yards, S.S.S.70
Founded 1923
Visitors: welcome on Mon, Wed and
Thurs only, unless with member;
prior arrangement essential.
Green Fee: on application.
Societies: Mon, Wed and Thurs.
Catering: lunch daily except Tues.
Hotels: Hoskins Arms.

D124 **Tenterden**
☎(058 06) 3987
Woodchurch Rd, Tenterden, Kent
TN30 7DR
1 mile E of Tenterden on B2067.

Undulating parkland course.
18 holes, 6030 yards, S.S.S.69
Founded 1905
Visitors: welcome except Sat, Sun and Bank Holidays.
Green Fee: £18.
Societies: by arrangement.
Catering: light meals served, other catering by arrangement.
Hotels: Vine Inn; White Lion; Little Silver Country Hotel.

D125 **Thames Ditton & Esher**
☎(081) 398 1551
Scilly Isles, Portsmouth Rd, Esher, Surrey
Off A3 by Scilly Isles roundabout (0.25 mile from Sandown Park Race Course).
Parkland course.
9 holes, 5606 yards, S.S.S.65
Founded 1892
Visitors: welcome, Sun after 2pm.
Green Fee: on application
Societies: max 32 booked with Sec.
Catering: snacks, buffet for societies.

D126 **Tudor Park CC**
☎(0622) 34334
Ashford Rd, Bearstead, Maidstone, Kent ME14 4NR
Follow A20 Ashford road, on right, 3 miles from Maidstone centre.
Parkland course.
18 holes, 6041 yards, S.S.S.69.
Designed by Donald Steel.
Founded 1988
Visitors: welcome with h/cap cert.
Green Fee: on application
Societies: weekdays by prior arrangement.
Catering: full facilities.
Leisure club and conference facilities.
Hotels: Tudor Park Hotel.

D127 **Tunbridge Wells**
☎(0892) 523034
Langton Rd, Tunbridge Wells, Kent
Behind Marchants Garage next to Spa Hotel.
Undulating parkland course.
9 holes, 4560 yards, S.S.S.62
Founded 1889
Visitors: welcome weekdays only; h/cap cert required.
Green Fee: on application to Pro.
Societies: by arrangement with Sec.
Catering: 11am-3pm daily; evenings by arrangement.
Hotels: Spa; Wellington; Royal Wells.

D128 **Tyrrells Wood**
☎(0372) 376025
Tyrrells Wood, Leatherhead, Surrey KT22 8QP
Exit 9 from M25, follow A24 to Dorking, past AA caravan site, next turn left to Tyrrells Wood, signposted.
Undulating parkland course.
18 holes, 6234 yards, S.S.S.70
Designed by James Braid.
Founded 1922
Visitors: welcome weekdays and Sun pm by prior appointment; h/cap certs.
Green Fee: on application.
Societies: welcome, enquiries to manager.
Catering: available all day.
Hotels: Burford Bridge, White Horse.

D129 **Upchurch River Valley**
☎(0634) 360626
Oak Lane, Upchurch, Sittingbourne, Kent ME9 7AY
From M2 junction 4 take A278 Gillingham road, right at 3rd roundabout onto A2 to Rainham, course 2.5 miles on left.
Public moorland/seaside type course.
18 holes, 6160 yards, S.S.S.69;
9 holes Par 3, 1596 yards.
Designed by David Smart.
Founded June 1991.
Visitors: no restrictions, bookings available daily.
Green Fee: 18 holes, £9.20 WD, £12.30 WE; 9 holes, £5.50 WD, £6.50 WE; reductions jnrs and OAPs.
Societies: Mon-Fri, min 12, no max.
Catering: Rivers restaurant, full à la carte, Sun lunches.
Driving range, golfers only swimming pool.

D130 **Walmer & Kingsdown**
☎(0304) 373256
The Leas, Kingsdown, Deal, Kent CT14 8ER
Off A258, 2.5 miles S of Deal; signposted at Ringwould village.
Undulating meadowland course.
18 holes, 6451 yards, S.S.S.71
Designed by James Braid
Founded 1909
Visitors: welcome weekdays and after 12am weekends and Bank Holidays; must produce h/cap cert.
Green Fee: £20/round/day WD, £22 WE & BH.
Societies: by arrangement weekdays only.

Catering: full bar and restaurant facilities.
Hotels: Royal; Clarendon; Guildford House; Dover Moat House.

D131 **Walton Heath**
☎(0737) 812380
Tadworth, Surrey KT20 7TP
Leave M25 at exit 8, follow A217 towards London, turn left onto B2032, turning for golf club about 1 mile on right.
Heathland course.
Old, 18 holes, 6883 yards, S.S.S.73;
New, 18 holes, 6659 yards, S.S.S.72
Designed by Herbert Fowler.
Founded 1904
Visitors: welcome weekdays with letter of intro. and prior arrangement.
Green Fee: £50, £42 after 11.30am.
Societies: by arrangement.
Catering: full restaurant facilities.
Hotels: Copthorne; Burford Bridge.

D132 **Weald of Kent**
☎(0622) 890866
Maidstone Road, Headcorn, Kent TN27 9PJ
On A274 5 miles S of Maidstone.
Parkland course.
18 holes, 6169 yards, S.S.S.69
Designed by John Millen.
Founded 1991
Visitors: welcome.
Green Fee: £13.50 WD, £16 WE (pay as you play).
Societies: welcome except Sun.
Catering: full facilities all day; conferences, banqueting.
Shooting, fishing, riding.
Hotels: Shant (East Sutton).

D133 **Wentworth**
☎(0344) 842201
Wentworth Drive, Virginia Water, Surrey GU25 4LS
On the A30 between Egham and Sunningdale.
Heathland courses.
West, 18 holes, 6945 yards, S.S.S.74; East, 18 holes, 6176 yards, S.S.S.70; Edinburgh, 18 holes, 6979 yards, S.S.S.73; 9 holes, 1902 yards, S.S.S.30
Designed by H.S. Colt (East and West); J.R.M. Jacobs (Edinburgh).
Founded 1924
Visitors: weekdays only with prior booking.
Green Fee: West £80/round, East £55/round, Edinburgh £65/round.
Societies: Mon-Fri, limited to 50 max per course.

Catering: breakfast, lunch, dinner and banqueting.
Tennis: outdoor heated pool.
Hotels: Pennyhill Park; Royal Berkshire; Runnymede.

D134 **West Byfleet**
☎(0932) 343433 Sec, 345230 Club, 346584 Pro.
Sheerwater Rd, West Byfleet, Surrey KT14 6AA
Exit 10 from M25 on to A245 to about 0.75 mile W of West Byfleet.
Heathland/parkland course.
18 holes, 6211 yards, S.S.S.70
Designed by Cuthbert Butchart.
Founded 1904
Visitors: welcome weekdays only.
Green Fee: on application.
Societies: by arrangement on Tues and Wed only.
Catering: snacks, lunch and tea served; evening meals by arrangement; lunch only on Sun.
Hotels: Northfleet (Woking); Hilton International (Cobham).

D135 **West Hill**
☎(048 67) 4365
Bagshot Rd, Brookwood, Surrey GU24 0BH
On A322 Guildford-Bagshot road, club entrance next to railway bridge at Brookwood.
Heathland course.
18 holes, 6368 yards, S.S.S.70
Designed by Willie Park and Jack White.
Founded 1909
Visitors: Mon-Fri only.
Green Fee: £29/round, £39/day.
Societies: Mon-Fri, apply to Sec.
Catering: full facilities available.
Hotels: Worplesdon Place; Northfleet (Woking).

D136 **West Kent**
☎(0689) 851323
West Hill, Downe, Orpington, Kent BR6 7JJ
A21 to Orpington, head for Downe village.
Parkland/downland course.
18 holes, 6399 yards, S.S.S.70
Founded 1919
Visitors: welcome weekdays with letter from Sec or h/cap cert; phone in advance.
Green Fee: £22/round, £33/day.
Societies: by arrangement Tues, Wed, Thurs.
Catering: full facilities.
Hotels: Bromley Continental.

D137 **West Malling**
☎(0732) 844785 Sec, 844795 enquiries, 844022 Pro.
London Rd, Addington, Maidstone, Kent
A20 from London, turn left at Greenaway Hotel, 8 miles NW of Maidstone.
Parkland course.
Spitfire Course, 18 holes, 6142 yards, Par 70; Hurricane Course, 18 holes, 6011 yards, Par 70
Founded 1974
Visitors: welcome weekdays; after 12am weekends.
Green Fee: £16/round, £25/day; £20/round WE after 12am.
Societies: welcome by prior arrangement.
Catering: full facilities.
Hotels: Larkfield; Trusthouse Forte.

D138 **West Surrey**
☎(0483) 421275
Enton Green, Godalming, Surrey GU8 5AF
1.5 miles from Milford traffic lights on A2, 0.5 mile from Milford station.
Parkland course.
18 holes, 6247 yards, S.S.S.70
Designed by Herbert Fowler.
Founded 1909
Visitors: welcome preferably by arrangement to avoid reservations or restrictions (including weekends); collar and tie in dining room.
Green Fee: £32 all day WD, £40 (1 or 2 rounds) WE.
Societies: normally Wed (pm), Thurs and Fri by arrangement.
Catering: full restaurant facilities available by arrangement.
Hotels: Inn on the Lake; Pride of the Valley.

D139 **Westgate & Birchington**
☎(0843) 31115
176 Canterbury Rd, Westgate-on-Sea, Kent CT8 8LT
A27, 0.25 mile from Westgate station.
Seaside links course.
18 holes, 4926 yards, S.S.S.64
Founded 1892
Visitors: welcome if members of recognised clubs.
Green Fee: £12 WD, £15 WE & BH.
Societies: welcome by arrangement.
Catering: full facilities by arrangement.
Hotels: Edgewater; Ivyside; Rothesay (Broadstairs).

D140 **Whitstable & Seasalter**
☎(0227) 272020
Collingwood Rd, Whitstable, Kent CT5 1EB
From A299 Thanet Way turn off at Long Reach roundabout, drive down Borstal Hill, under railway bridge, take 2nd left into Nelson Rd and 2nd left again along unmade road.
Seaside links course.
18 holes, 5276 yards, S.S.S.63
Founded 1910
Visitors: welcome weekdays; weekends only with member.
Green Fee: £15 (£7.50 with member).
Catering: bar snacks.
Hotels: Marine.

D141 **Wildernesse**
☎(0732) 61199
Seal, Sevenoaks, Kent TN15 0JE
Off A25 in Seal village.
Rolling parkland course.
18 holes, 6205 yards, S.S.S.72
Designed by W. Park.
Founded 1890
Visitors: letter of intro. required.
Green Fee: £25/round, £35/day.
Societies: Mon and Thurs.
Catering: bar and restaurant.
Hotels: Post House; Royal Oak; Sevenoaks Park.

D142 **Wildwood**
☎(0403) 753255
Horsham Rd, Alfold, Surrey GU6 8JE
On A281, 10 miles S of Guildford, 10 miles NW of Horsham.
Wooded parkland course.
18 holes, 6770 yards, S.S.S.72
Designed by Hawtree & Co.
Opening summer 1992
Visitors: Mon-Fri with h/cap cert, weekends with member only.
Green Fee: about £40/day.
Societies: ring for details.
Catering: temporary facilities.
Teaching Academy; driving range, health and leisure facilities under development.
Hotels: Random Hall, golfing packages available.

D143 **Wimbledon Common**
☎(081) 946 7571 Sec, 946 0294 Pro.
Camp Rd, Wimbledon Common, London SW19 4UW
1 mile NW of War Memorial, past Fox & Grapes on right in Camp Rd.
Moorland course.

18 holes, 5438 yards, S.S.S.66
Designed by Tom and Willie Dunn.
Founded 1908
Visitors: welcome weekdays.
Green Fee: £13.50/round, £20/day.
Societies: accepted if sponsored by
club members only.
Catering: light meals available.

D144 **Wimbledon Park**
☎(081) 946 1002
Home Park Rd, Wimbledon Park,
London SW19 7HR
250 yards from Wimbledon Park
station (District Line).
Parkland course.
18 holes, 5465 yards, S.S.S.67
Founded 1899
Visitors: with h/cap cert or letter of
intro. from club; only after 3pm
weekends.
Green Fee: £25/day WD, £25/round
WE.
Societies: usually Tues and Thurs.
Catering: full facilities available
excluding Mon.
Hotels: Canizaro Park.

D145 **Windlemere**
☎(0276) 858727
Windlesham Rd, West End, Woking,
Surrey GU24 9QL
Take A322 from Bagshot towards
Guildford; turn left on A319 towards
Chobham; course is on left opposite
the Gordon Boys' School.
Gently undulating public parkland
course.
9 holes, 2673 yards, S.S.S.34
Designed by Clive D. Smith.
Founded 1978
Visitors: open to public on payment
of green fees.
Green Fee: £6 (9 holes), £10 (18
holes) WD; £7.50, £13 WE;
reductions for jnrs and OAPs.
Societies: as arranged with Pro at
club.
Catering: bar snacks always
available.
Driving range, pool tables.

D146 **The Wisley**
☎(0483) 211022
Mill Lane, Ripley, Nr Woking, Surrey
GU23 6QU

From M25 junction 10 take A3 to
Guildford, off at exit marked Ockham,
Send and Ripley, 3rd exit from
roundabout, 1st left into Mill Lane;
signs to club.
Parkland course (members only).
3 x 9 holes; Church, 3355 yards;
Garden 3385 yards; Mill, 3473 yards;
any combination gives 18 hole
course, S.S.S.73
Designed by Robert Trent Jones Jr.
Founded Jan 1990
Visitors: with member only.
Green Fee: £32.
Catering: bar, restaurant.

D147 **Woking**
☎(0483) 760053
Pond Rd, Hook Heath, Woking,
Surrey GU22 0JZ
Just S of 1st road bridge over
railway, W of Woking station
(Woking-Brookwood line), take
Hollybank Rd; then immediately right
into Golf Club Rd and right at end to
clubhouse; avoid Woking town
centre.
Heathland course.
18 holes, 6322 yards, S.S.S.70
Designed by Tom Dunn.
Founded 1893
Visitors: book in advance; not
weekends and public holidays.
Green Fee: £28/round, £42/day WD.
Societies: welcome if booked in
advance.
Catering: lunch available every day
if ordered in advance.
Hotels: Mayford Manor; Glen Court.

D148 **Woodcote Park**
☎(081) 668 2788 Sec.
Bridle Way, Meadow Hill, Coulsden,
Surrey CR5 2QQ
At far end of Meadow Hill, off
Smitham Bottom Lane, Purley, main
road from Wallington to Coulsden;
A23 nearest A road.
Slightly undulating parkland
course.
18 holes, 6624 yards, S.S.S.71
Founded 1912
Visitors: welcome on weekdays with
h/cap cert.
Green Fee: £19/round, £25/day.
Societies: weekdays by
arrangement.

Catering: bar snacks, à la carte
menu daily.
Snooker.
Hotels: The Aerodrome (Croydon).

D149 **Woodlands Manor**
☎(09592) 3806
Tinkerpot Lane, Sevenoaks, Kent
TN15 6AB
Off A225, 4 miles NE of Sevenoaks.
Undulating parkland course.
18 holes, 5858 yards, S.S.S.68
Founded 1928
Visitors: welcome weekdays; after
1pm weekends, with h/cap cert.
Green Fee: on application
Societies: welcome.
Catering: meals served.

D150 **Worplesdon**
☎(0483) 472277 Sec.
Heath House Rd, Woking, Surrey
GU22 0RA
Leave Guildford on A322 to Bagshot,
after 4 miles turn right into Heath
House Rd.
Heathland course.
18 holes, 6422 yards, S.S.S.71
Designed by J.F. Abercromby.
Founded 1908
Visitors: welcome with introduction
from Club Sec; weekdays only.
Green Fee: £35/round, £45/day.
Societies: Mon, Wed, Thurs, Fri by
arrangement.
Catering: bar every day, lunch
served except Tues.

D151 **Wrotham Heath**
☎(0732) 884800
Seven Mile Lane, Comp, Sevenoaks,
Kent TN15 8QZ
Off A20 near junction with A25.
Undulating parkland course.
9 holes (18 tees), 5823 yards,
S.S.S.68
Founded 1906
Visitors: welcome weekdays only
with h/cap cert; weekends if playing
with member.
Green Fee: £20/round, £30/day (£10
with member).
Societies: Fri only.
Catering: full catering facilities by
arrangement with Steward.
Hotels: Post House.

E

HERTFORDSHIRE, ESSEX, MIDDLESEX, NORTH LONDON

Essex has seen a significant number of new courses in the last couple of years and even more applications for permission to build. It is a big county but the greatest demand lies around the fringe of London where the supply of land is scarcer. West Essex, Romford, Ilford, Wanstead and Chigwell are all bastions of suburbia while public facilities are exemplified by Hainault Forest, Chingford and Belhus Park (Thurrock), but the increasing sense of freedom that the country brings is reflected in the character of the golf.

Clacton-on-Sea, Frinton and Quietwaters remind travellers how far Essex's limits extend from the sound of Bow Bells, but the best of the county's golf focuses on Chelmsford, Thorndon Park and Orsett. Thorpe Hall at Southend has the proud boast of having for years been the home Club of Michael Bonallack; and a word for Skips, newly extended and renamed Stapleford Abbots, and Channels, both less than 20 years old.

Neighbouring Hertfordshire is more densely populated with golf courses, even if the majority of them are in the south. Most are parkland in character although two of the exceptions are undoubtedly among the best. Ashridge and Berkhamsted enjoy a lofty perch on a ridge of the Chilterns, Ashridge where Henry Cotton was once the professional and Berkhamsted, a course on a delightful common famous for the absence of sand bunkers.

In common with many Clubs which started life in an exposed, open environment, Berkhampsted is now much more enclosed, making accuracy from the tee a definite prerequisite of good scoring. It is rightly popular. The northern boundary of Hertfordshire is marked by Royston on undulating heathland on which little has changed in a hundred years. The Club's annual fixture with Cambridge is the University's oldest in continuous existence.

Letchworth and Knebworth are divided by the Great North Road which also took land from Welwyn Garden City, the course on which Nick Faldo's talents were shaped. It highlights what can be achieved on a limited acreage. Nearer to London, Sandy Lodge, Hadley Wood, Porters Park, Brookmans Park and Moor Park (with its 36-holes) are among the best known.

There are South Herts, Mid-Herts, East Herts and West Herts with a worthy mention for Verulam and Batchwood Hall on opposite sides of St Albans. Elstree offers a variety of facilities, particularly for beginners and, at the other end of the scale, is the new Hanbury Manor. Brickendon Grange, even if now 25 years old, is more modern than most, and there are two courses at Harpenden.

The Middlesex courses, as you might expect, are altogether more confined although wonderful oases nevertheless for the city dweller. From planes approaching Heathrow, it is all too apparent how great are their land values. So too further north, where Enfield, Crews Hill and Bush Hill Park, once out in the countryside, are close to the border with Hertfordshire.

Middlesex, county champions for the first time in 1989, won the title again last year and have been indebted for some time to several fine golfers from Ealing. Ricky Willison, who won the 1981 English championship, later turned professional. Ealing fronts the A40 Western Avenue, a stone's throw from Sudbury and West Middlesex. Highgate, Hampstead and Hendon form as tight a cluster but Ashford Manor and Fulwell, almost into Surrey, are perhaps Middlesex's finest, along with Northwood.

E1 Abbey View
☎(0727) 41973
Holywell Hill, Westminster Lodge, St Albans, Herts
In centre of St Albans.
Public parkland course.
9 holes, 2162 yards
Designed by Jimmy Thomson.
Founded 1990
Visitors: open to public at all times.
Green Fee: £3.30/round (£2.75 Jnrs).

E2 Abridge G & CC
☎(04028) 396
Epping Lane, Stapleford Tawney, Essex RM4 1ST
M11 from London exit 5 via Abridge; from the N, M11 exit 7 via Epping.
Parkland course.
18 holes, 6070 yards, S.S.S.72
Designed by Henry Cotton.
Founded 1964
Visitors: weekdays only; h/cap cert required.
Green Fee: on application.
Societies: Mon and Wed.
Catering: every day except Fri (no evening meals).
Hotels: Post House, Epping.

E3 Airlinks
☎(081) 561 1418
Southall Lane, Hounslow, Middx TW5 9PE
Off M4 at junction 3 onto A312 and A4020; next to David Lloyd Tennis Centre.
Public meadowland/parkland course.
18 holes, 5885 yards, S.S.S.69
Designed by P. Alliss.
Founded 1984
Visitors: welcome, some restrictions at weekends.
Green Fee: on application.
Societies: welcome Mon-Fri; fees by negotiation.
Catering: licensed bar, snacks, hot and cold meals.
Driving range.
Hotels: London Airport hotels in vicinity.

E4 Aldenham G & CC
☎(0923) 853929
Church Lane, Aldenham, Nr Watford, Herts WD2 8AL
Leave M1 at junction 5, take A41 towards S Watford, turn left at 1st roundabout towards Radlett, club 0.25 mile.
Parkland course.
18 holes, 6445 yards, S.S.S.71; 9 holes, 2500 yards, S.S.S.29
Founded 1975
Visitors: welcome weekdays, after 1pm weekends.
Green Fee: £18/round WD, £25 WE.
Societies: Mon-Fri by arrangement.
Catering: snack bar, restaurant.
Hotels: London Hilton; Spiders Web.

E5 Arkley
☎(081) 449 0394
Rowley Green Rd, Barnet, Herts EN5 3HL
Off A1 at Stirling Corner to A411; signposted at Rowley Lane on left.
Parkland course.
2 x 9 holes, 6045 yards, S.S.S.69
Designed by James Braid.
Founded 1909
Visitors: weekdays restricted; weekends with member; (Tues Ladies Day).
Green Fee: £20/round/day.
Societies: Wed, Thurs, Fri, max 40.
Catering: meals daily except Mon.
Hotels: Elstree Moat House.

E6 Ashford Manor
☎(0784) 257687
Fordbridge Rd, Ashford, Middx TW15 3RT
Staines by-pass A308, 2 miles E of Staines.
Parkland course.
18 holes, 6343 yards, S.S.S.70
Founded 1898
Visitors: must be member of recognised golf club; weekends only by prior arrangement.
Green Fee: on application
Societies: weekdays.
Catering: available.

E7 Ashridge
☎(044 284) 2244
Little Gaddesden, Berkhamsted, Herts HA4 1LY
A41 to Berkhamsted, turn right at Northchurch on B4506.
Parkland course.
18 holes, 6508 yards, S.S.S.71
Designed by Sir Guy Campbell, Colonel Hotchkin and Cecil Hutchinson.
Founded 1932
Visitors: phone Sec for booking.
Green Fee: on application.
Societies: phone Sec for booking.
Catering: morning coffee, lunch, afternoon tea, sandwiches always available.
Hotels: Bell Inn.

E8 Ballards Gore
☎(0702) 258917 Sec, 258924 Pro.
Gore Rd, Canewdon, Rochford, Essex SS4 2DA
From London via A127 to Southend Airport, through Rochford onto Great Stambridge road; course 1.5 miles from Rochford centre.
Parkland course.
18 holes, 7062 yards, S.S.S.74
Designed by D. and J.J. Caton.
Founded 26 July 1980
Visitors: welcome weekdays; weekends guest of member only, after 12.30pm summer, 11.30am winter.
Green Fee: £20 WD.
Societies: weekdays by arrangement with Sec.
Catering: bar and restaurant facilities; private functions.
Hotels: Renouf.

E9 Basildon
☎(0268) 533297
Clay Hill Lane, Basildon, Essex SS16 5HL
On A176 off A13 or A127, Kingswood roundabout, Sparrows Herne.
Public undulating parkland course.
18 holes, 6122 yards, S.S.S.69
Designed by Cottons.
Founded 1967
Visitors: welcome at all times, booking weekends.
Green Fee: £7.50/round WD, £14.50 WE.
Societies: weekdays.
Catering: full facilities.
Hotels: Crest; Campinile.

E10 Batchwood Hall
☎(0727) 833349 Sec, 52101 Pro, 44250 reservations.
Batchwood Drive, St Albans, Herts AL3 5XA
NW corner of town; 5 miles S of M1 junction 9.
Public parkland course.
18 holes, 6463 yards, S.S.S.71
Designed by J.H. Taylor.
Founded 1935
Visitors: welcome only with reservation; not 6.30-10am Sat/Sun.
Green Fee: £8 WD, £10 WE.
Catering: bar and coffee; no food.
Tennis, squash.

E11 Belfairs (Southend-on-Sea)
☎(0702) 525345 Starter, 526911 Club members
Clubhouse, Eastwood Rd North, Leigh-on-Sea, Essex SS9 4LR

4.5 miles from Southend centre; Eastwood Rd links A127 and A13. Private club, public course; parkland front 9, heavily wooded back 9. 18 holes, 5871 yards, S.S.S.68 Designed by A.J. Colt. Founded 1926
Visitors: unrestricted but bookings Thurs am, weekends and holidays.
Green Fee: £10 WD, £15 WE and BH.
Catering: public restaurant.

E12 **Belhus Park (Thurrock)**
☎(0708) 854260

South Ockendon, Essex RM15 4QR A13 to Avely. Public parkland course. 18 holes, 5439 yards, S.S.S.68 Designed by Frank Pennink. Founded 1972
Visitors: bookings at course weekdays, by telephone weekends (booking card required).
Green Fee: £10.25, discount for local residents.
Societies: by arrangement; telephone manager.
Catering: bar and restaurant. Driving range, squash, swimming pool, leisure centre.

E13 **Bentley**
☎(0277) 373179
Ongar Rd, Brentwood, Essex CM15 9SS
4 miles N of Brentwood on A128. Parkland course. 18 holes, 6709 yards, S.S.S.72 Designed by Alec Swann. Founded 1972
Visitors: welcome Mon-Fri with letter of intro. or h/cap cert.
Green Fee: £18.50/round, £24/day.
Societies: weekdays by booking.
Catering: snacks all day, lunch; evening meals by arrangement.
Hotels: Post House.

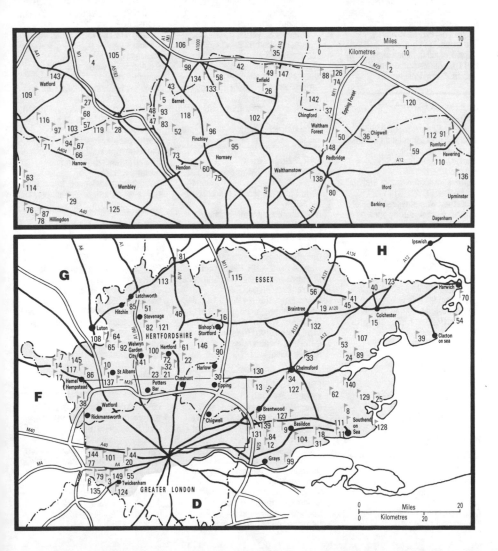

E14 Berkhamsted
☎(0442) 863730
The Common, Berkhamsted, Herts
HP4 2QB
Exit 8 off M1 to Hemel Hempstead, at
roundabout take Leighton Buzzard
road; after about 3 miles take Potten
End turn and follow road to club.
Heathland course.
18 holes, 6605 yards, S.S.S.72
Designed by G.H. Gowring (1890/2
Founder), 1912 C.J. Gilbert with
advice from Harry Colt, 1927
extension advice from James Braid.
Founded 1890
Visitors: welcome, must be member
of a golf club with h/cap; not before
12.30pm Tues, not before 11.30am
Sat, Sun and Bank Holidays.
Green Fee: on application.
Societies: Wed and Fri.
Catering: full facilities except Mon
and Tues (limited catering).
Hotels: Swan; Post House.

E15 Birch Grove
☎(0206) 34276
Layer Rd, Colchester CO2 0HS
2 miles S of Colchester on B1026.
Meadowland course.
9 holes, 4108 yards, S.S.S.60
Founded 1970
Visitors: welcome except Sun am.
Green Fee: £9 WD, £11 WE & BH.
Societies: weekdays catering for 60.
Catering: meals during opening
hours; parties by prior arrangement.

E16 Bishop's Stortford
☎(0279) 654715
Dunmow Rd, Bishop's Stortford,
Herts CM23 5HP
Exit 8 from M11, follow signs to town
centre/hospital, course is on left next
to Nag's Head on E edge of town.
Parkland course.
18 holes, 6440 yards, S.S.S.71
Founded 1912
Visitors: weekdays only; weekends
with member.
Green Fee: £21.
Societies: by appointment
weekdays only.
Catering: lunch and dinner by
appointment; bar meals to 9.30pm.
Hotels: Foxley; Post House.

E17 Boxmoor
☎(0442) 242434
18 Box Lane, Hemel Hempstead,
Herts HP3 0DH
0.75 mile from Hemel Hempstead
station on A41.
Undulating parkland course.
9 holes, 4854 yards, S.S.S.64
Founded 1890
Visitors: welcome weekdays, not
Sun; suitable attire and golf shoes
must be worn.
Green Fee: £10/round WD, £15 WE.
Societies: welcome, 4 weeks notice.
Catering: limited service. Pool.

E18 Boyce Hill
☎(0268) 793625
Vicarage Hill, South Benfleet, Essex
SS7 1PD
7 miles W of Southend-on-Sea; A127
to Rayleigh Weir (3 miles to course);
A13 to Victoria House Corner (1 mile).
Undulating parkland course.
18 holes, 5882 yards, S.S.S.68
Designed by James Braid.
Founded 1922
Visitors: welcome weekdays;
weekends with member.
Green Fee: £25/round, £30/day.
Societies: Thurs only.
Catering: service throughout the
day.
Hotels: Crest; Airport.

E19 Braintree
☎(0376) 24117 Members, 46079
Sec, 43465 Pro.
Kings Lane, Stisted, Braintree, Essex
CM7 8DA
A120 eastbound after Braintree
bypass, 1st left, 1 mile signposted.
Parkland course.
18 holes, 6122 yards, S.S.S.69
Designed by Hawtree and Son.
Founded 1891 (1971 at present site).
Visitors: welcome except Sun; h/cap
cert required Fri and Sat.
Green Fee: £24/day WD (£14/day
with member); £40/day WE & BH.
Societies: welcome by arrangement
Mon, Wed, Thurs (Tues Ladies Day).
Catering: meals served.
Hotels: White Hart.

E20 Brent Valley
☎(081) 567 4230
Church Rd, Hanwell, London W7 3BE
A4020 Uxbridge Rd, Hanwell, on to
Church Rd by Brent Lodge Animal
Centre.
Public meadowland course.
18 holes, 5440 yards, S.S.S.66
Designed by P. Alliss and D. Thomas
Founded 1938
Visitors: welcome 7 days.
Green Fee: on application.
Societies: organised via the Pro.
Catering: restaurant from 8am.

E21 Brickendon Grange
☎(099 286) 258/228/218
Brickendon, Nr Hertford, Herts SG13
8PD
3 miles S of Hertford near Bayford
station.
Undulating parkland course.
18 holes, 6315 yards, S.S.S.70
Designed by C.K. Cotton.
Founded 1968
Visitors: welcome weekdays.
Green Fee: on application.
Societies: welcome weekdays.
Catering: snack lunch served.

E22 Briggens House Hotel
☎(0279) 793742 Pro, 792416 Hotel
Stanstead Abbots, Ware, Herts
Just off A414 between St Albans and
Harlow.
Parkland course.
9 holes, 5800 yards, S.S.S.72
Founded 1988
Visitors: welcome, not Sun am;
usual dress rules apply.
Green Fee: £5.50 (9 holes), £10 (18
holes) WD; £8 (9 holes), £14.50 (18
holes) WE.
Societies: apply to Pro.
Catering: full facilities.
Putting green, croquet, tennis,
swimming pool.
Hotels: Briggens House, free golf for
residents, golfing weekends/breaks.

E23 Brookmans Park
☎(0707) 52487
Golf Club Rd, Hatfield, Herts AL9 7AT
Off Hatfield Rd, A1000 1 mile N of
Potters Bar, 3 miles S of Hatfield.
Parkland course.
18 holes, 6454 yards, S.S.S.71
Founded 1930
Visitors: weekdays except Tues; with
member and h/cap cert weekends.
Green Fee: £25/round, £30/day.
Societies: accepted Wed, Thurs.
Catering: snacks at lunchtime;
evening meals for societies only.
Hotels: Brookmans Park; Crest.

E24 Bunsay Downs
☎(024 541) 2648, 2369 members
Little Baddow Rd, Woodham Walter,
Nr Maldon, Essex CM9 6RW
Leave A414 at Danbury (signposted
Woodham Walter), course 0.5 mile to
W of village.
Public, gently undulating
meadowland course.
9 holes, 2913 yards, S.S.S.68;
9 holes Par 3, 1319 yards
Founded 1982

Visitors: welcome.
Green Fee: £6 (9 holes), £8 (18 holes) WD; £6.50 (9 holes), £8.50 (18 holes) WE.
Societies: welcome.
Catering: breakfast, lunch, evening meal, 10am (8am weekends) - 10pm.
Driving range, petanque.

E25 Burnham-on-Crouch
☎(0621) 782282
Ferry Rd, Creeksea, Burnham-on-Crouch, Essex CM0 8PQ
Turn right off B1010 2 miles after Althorne at 40mph limit for Burnham.
Undulating meadowland course.
9 holes, 5918 yards, S.S.S.68
Founded 1923
Visitors: welcome; start 9.30am-2pm; not Thurs am, weekends or Bank Holidays; proof of h/cap or club membership required.
Green Fee: £16/day.
Societies: catered for Tues.
Catering: bar snacks available; evening meals by arrangement.
Hotels: White Hart.

E26 Bush Hill Park
☎(081) 360 5738
Bush Hill, Winchmore Hill, London N21 2BU
0.5 mile S of Enfield town.
Parkland course.
18 holes, 5809 yards, S.S.S.68
Founded 1895
Visitors: welcome weekdays.
Green Fee: £25/round, £30/day.
Societies: on application, not Wed.
Catering: bar snacks, full restaurant.
Hotels: Oak Lodge; Royal Chase.

E27 Bushey G & CC
☎(081) 950 2283
High St, Bushey, Herts WD2 1BJ
On A411 1.5 miles from M1/A411 junction.
Parkland course.
9 holes, 3000 yards, S.S.S.69
Designed by Donald Steel.
Founded 1980
Visitors: weekdays before 6pm; weekends and Bank Holidays after 2pm; no visitors Wed.
Green Fee: £8 (9 holes), £15 (18 holes) WD; £10 (9 holes), £20 (18 holes) WE.
Societies: max 36-40 by arrangement, not Wed.
Catering: meals served; functions.
Driving range, health club, squash.
Hotels: Ladbrokes; Spiders Web; Hilton National.

E28 Bushey Hall
☎(0923) 225802
Bushey Hall Drive, Bushey, Herts WD2 2EP
1 mile SE of Watford.
Undulating parkland course.
18 holes, 6099 yards, S.S.S.69
Founded 1886
Visitors: welcome weekdays with h/cap cert.
Green Fee: £18/round, £25/day.
Societies: weekdays except Wed and Fri.
Catering: full catering service.

E29 C & L Golf & CC
☎(081) 845 5662/3/4, 841 5515 fax.
Junction of West End Road & A40, Northolt, Middlesex UB5 6RD
A40 from London; opposite Northolt Airport.
Parkland course.
9 holes, 4438 yards, S.S.S.62
Designed by Patrick Tallack.
Founded Jan 1991
Visitors: public days Mon, Wed, Fri; no jeans or T-shirts; golf shoes only.
Green Fee: public, £5 for 9 holes, £10 for 18 holes.
Societies: any day during the week; very competitive rates.
Catering: main bar, restaurant; banqueting hall.
Tennis, snooker, bowls, squash and health and fitness facilities.

E30 Canons Brook
☎(0279) 421482
Elizabeth Way, Harlow, Essex CM19 5BE
M11 to Harlow, Edinburgh Way then Elizabeth Way.
Parkland course.
18 holes, 6745 yards, S.S.S.73
Designed by Sir Henry Cotton.
Founded 1963
Visitors: welcome weekdays.
Green Fee: £22.50/round/day.
Societies: welcome weekdays.
Catering: lunch, dinners except Sun.
Hotels: Churchgate; Moat House.

E31 Castle Point
☎(0268) 510830
Waterside Farm, Somnes Ave, Canvey Island, Essex SS8 8BH
A13 to Southend, A130 to Canvey Island at Sadler's Farm roundabout, over Waterside Farm roundabout to Somnes Ave, course on left.
Public seaside links course.
18 holes, 5627 yards, S.S.S.69
Designed by Golf Landscapes.

Founded June 1988
Visitors: welcome, no restrictions.
Green Fee: £9 WD, £12 WE.
Societies: on request in advance.
Catering: bar and restaurant.
Driving range.
Hotels: Crest (Basildon).

E32 Chadwell Springs
☎(0920) 463647
Hertford Rd, Ware, Herts SG12 9LE
On A119 half way between Hertford and Ware.
Parkland course.
9 holes, 3209 yards, S.S.S.71
Designed by J.H. Taylor.
Founded 1975
Visitors: welcome weekdays, guests of member only weekends.
Green Fee: WD £14 (18 holes), £18/day; WE with member £10/day.
Societies: welcome on weekdays.
Catering: lunchtime food served.
Hotels: Salisbury Arms; Moat House.

E33 Channels
☎(0245) 440005
Belsteads Farm Lane, Little Waltham, Chelmsford, Essex CM3 3PT
2 miles NE of Chelmsford on A130.
Undulating course on restored gravel workings, lakes and wildlife.
18 holes, 5927 yards, S.S.S.69
Designed by Henry Cotton & Assoc.
Founded 1974
Visitors: welcome weekdays only.
Green Fee: on application.
Societies: weekdays only.
Catering: excellent table d'hôte, à la carte. Restored Essex barn available for weddings and corporate days.
Hotels: County; South Lodge.

E34 Chelmsford
☎(0245) 256483
Widford Rd, Chelmsford, Essex CM2 9AP
A1016 to Wood St roundabout, Chelmsford, turn right (from London) and right again.
Undulating parkland course.
18 holes, 5944 yards, S.S.S.68
Founded 1893
Visitors: welcome weekdays if members of recognised club; weekends with member only.
Green Fee: on application.
Societies: limited number by arrangement; Wed, Thurs only.
Catering: lunch except Mon, dinners Fri, Sat only, bar snacks daily.
Hotels: South Lodge.

E35 Cheshunt
☎(0992) 24009 booking, 29777 club
Park Lane, Cheshunt, Herts EN7 6QD
From M25 exit 25 towards Hertford,
left at 2nd lights to mini-roundabout,
turn right then signposted.
Municipal parkland course.
18 holes, 6608 yards, S.S.S.71
Founded 1976
Visitors: welcome weekdays and by
arrangement at weekends.
Green Fee: £6.30 (£3.10 OAPs) WD,
£7.70 WE.
Societies: any time by arrangement.
Catering: cafeteria service all day.

E36 Chigwell
☎(081) 500 2059
High Rd, Chigwell, Essex IG7 5BH
On A113, 13.5 miles NE of London.
Undulating parkland course.
18 holes, 6279 yards, S.S.S.70
Founded 1925
Visitors: by prior appointment;
weekdays only unless with member.
Green Fee: £25/round, £30/day.
Societies: Mon, Wed and Thurs;
early booking essential.
Catering: bar and catering facilities.
Hotels: Prince Regent; Roebuck.

E37 Chingford
☎(081) 529 5708, 529 2195 (Royal
Epping Forest GC)
Bury Rd, Chingford, London E4
Off Station Rd, 300 yards S of
Chingford station.
Public parkland course.
18 holes, 6432 yards, S.S.S.70
Designed by James Braid.
Founded 1888
Visitors: welcome, red outer
garment must be worn.
Green Fee: £6.20 WD, £9 WE.
Societies: by appointment.
Catering: snacks, no bar.

E38 Chorleywood
☎(0923) 282009
Common Rd, Chorleywood, Herts
WD3 5LN
0.5 mile from Chorleywood station
near Sportsman Hotel.
Well-wooded heathland course on
common land.
9 holes, 5676 yards, S.S.S.67
Founded 1890
Visitors: welcome weekdays except
Tues and Thurs am.
Green Fee: £12 WD.
Societies: small societies, limited.
Catering: bar and catering; snooker.
Hotels: The Sportsman.

E39 Clacton-on-Sea
☎(0255) 421919
West Rd, Clacton-on-Sea, Essex
CO15 1AJ
On A133 16 miles from Colchester, 1
mile W of pier next to old Butlins
Holiday Camp.
Undulating seaside course.
18 holes, 6494 yards, S.S.S.71
Designed by Jack White.
Founded 1892
Visitors: weekdays subject to
availability; Sat am, Sun pm and
Bank Holidays on application; h/cap
certs required at all times.
Green Fee: £15/round, £23/day WD;
£23 WE & BH.
Societies: by prior arrangement with
Sec.
Catering: full except Mon.
Hotels: Royal; Glengarry.

E40 Colchester
☎(0206) 853396 Sec, 852946
Clubhouse
Braiswick, Colchester, Essex CO4
5AU
0.75 mile up Bergholt Rd from
Colchester North station.
Parkland course.
18 holes, 6319 yards, S.S.S.70
Designed by James Braid.
Founded 1907
Visitors: welcome weekdays,
weekends only with member.
Green Fee: £22/day.
Societies: weekdays by
arrangement.
Catering: available.
Hotels: Marks Tey Motel; George;
Mill.

E41 Colne Valley (Essex)
☎(0787) 224233, 224452 fax.
Station Road, Earls Colne, Essex CO6
2LT
Leave A12 at Colchester, take A604
for 8 miles through Earls Colne
village, Station Rd is 1st on right.
Parkland course in the Colne valley,
river and 6 lakes.
18 holes, 6272 yards, S.S.S.70
Designed by Howard Swan.
Founded May 1990
Visitors: welcome weekdays and
after 10am weekends and Bank
Holidays.
Green Fee: £16/round WD,
£20/round WE.
Societies: welcome weekdays by
arrangement.
Catering: limited, temporary
clubhouse; ploughman's,
sandwiches and licensed bar.

E42 Crews Hill
☎(081) 363 6674
Cattlegate Rd, Crews Hill, Enfield,
Middx EN2 8AZ
Off A1005 Enfield to Potters Bar road
into East Lodge Lane, turn right into
Cattlegate Rd.
Parkland course.
18 holes, 6230 yards, S.S.S.70
Founded 1921
Visitors: must be members of
recognised club; weekends and
Bank Holidays only with member.
Green Fee: on application
Societies: advance booking.
Catering: lunch except Mon.

E43 Dyrham Park
☎(081) 440 3361
Galley Lane, Barnet, Herts.
2 miles outside Barnet near Arkley,
off A1 and M25.
Parkland course.
18 holes, 6369 yards, S.S.S.70
Designed by C.K. Cotton.
Founded 1963
Visitors: only as guest of member or
member of Golf Society.
Green Fee: £15 WD, £23 WE.
Societies: Wed only; two rounds
golf, light lunch and dinner or lunch
and afternoon tea.
Catering: full restaurant facilities.
Hotels: Crest (Bignalls Corner).

E44 Ealing
☎(081) 997 0937
Perivale Rd, Greenford, Middx UB6
8SS
Off A40 W opposite Hoover factory.
Parkland course.
18 holes, 6216 yards, S.S.S.77
Founded 1898
Visitors: welcome weekdays only.
Green Fee: £30 (£15 with member).
Societies: Mon, Wed and Thurs only.
Catering: bar snacks, lunches every
day; evening meal by arrangement.
Hotels: Caernarvon; Kempton
House; Bridge (Greenford).

E45 Earls Colne G & CC
☎(0787) 224466
Earls Colne, Nr Colchester, Essex
CO6 2NS
On B1024 Earls Colne-Coggeshall
road, 4 miles N of A12, 1 mile S of
A604.
Landscaped and tree-planted course
on converted farmland.
18 hole championship course, 6842
yards, Par 73; 9 holes, Par 30; 4 hole
Academy course for tuition.

Designed by Reg Plumbridge.
Founded 1991
Visitors: welcome.
Green Fee: £15/round (£10 OAPs)
WD, £18/round WE.
Societies: welcome.
Catering: full bar and restaurant.
Driving range; leisure, health and
beauty facilities, flying school,
business and conference facilities.
Hotels: Marks Tey; Anchor; White
Hart (Coggeshall).

E46 **East Herts**
☎(0920) 821978 Sec
Hamels Park, Buntingford, Herts SG9
9NA
A10 between Buntingford and Ware,
just N of Puckeridge roundabout.
Parkland course.
18 holes, 6449 yards, S.S.S.71
Founded 1898
Visitors: Mon-Fri only; h/cap cert
required.
Green Fee: £23/round, £30/day.
Societies: larger Mon and Fri;
restricted to 20 other times.
Catering: facilities available.
Hotels: Vintage Corner Motel.

E47 **Edgewarebury**
☎(081) 958 3571
Edgeware Way, Edgeware, Middx
HA8
On A41 between Edgeware and
Elstree.
Par 3 Pitch & Putt course.
9 holes, 1045 yards, Par 27
Founded 1946
Visitors: welcome 9am until dusk;
no booking necessary.
Green Fee: £3 (9 holes), club hire £1.

E48 **Elstree**
☎(081) 953 6115 Sec, 207 5680 Pro.
Watling St, Elstree, Herts WD6 3AA
Between Elstree Studios and Elstree
Flying Club on A5183 Radlett road;
30 mins from Central London, near
M1 junction 5.
Parkland course.
18 holes, 6100 yards, S.S.S.71
Designed by Donald Steel.
Founded Aug 1984
Visitors: welcome weekdays, after
2pm weekends and Bank Holidays.
Green Fee: £30/day WD, £40 WE
after 2pm.
Societies: welcome weekdays by
arrangement.
Catering: full facilities all day.
Driving range.
Hotels: Spiders Web; Hilton.

E49 **Enfield**
☎(081) 363 3970, 342 0381 fax.
Old Park Rd South, Enfield, Middx
EN2 7DA
1 mile NE of Enfield, near Enfield
Chase railway station.
Parkland course.
18 holes, 6154 yards, S.S.S.70
Designed by James Braid.
Founded 1893
Visitors: welcome weekdays (except
Bank Holidays); 24 hours notice, with
h/cap and if member of another club.
Green Fee: on application.
Societies: Mon, Wed and Fri,
excluding Bank Holidays.
Catering: meals available every day.
Hotels: Royal Chase; The Enfield.

E50 **Fairlop Waters**
☎(081) 500 9911
Forest Rd, Barkingside, Ilford, Essex
IG6 3JA
Signposted from M11 and along A12;
near Fairlop underground station.
Public heathland course.
18 holes, 6018 yards, S.S.S.69;
9 hole Par 3, 1167 yards
Designed by John Jacobs Golf.
Founded Jan 1988
Visitors: tidy dress required.
Green Fee: £6.50 WD, £9 WE.
Societies: weekdays by
arrangement.
Catering: bar, Daltons American
Diner, 2 banqueting suites.
Driving range, sailing, children's play
area, country park.

E51 **The Family Golf Centre**
☎(0462) 482929
Jack's Hill, Graveley, Herts SG4 7EQ
Just off junction 8 or 9 of A1(M),
approx 1.5 miles along B197 N of
village of Graveley.
Inland links/ downland course.
Chesfield Downs, 18 holes, 6630
yards, S.S.S.72; Lannock Links, 9
holes Par 3, 975 yards, S.S.S.27
Designed by Jonathan Gaunt.
Founded Jan 1991
Visitors: pay-as-you-play; advance
booking system to reserve tee-off
times, 1 week's notice preferred.
Green Fee: Chesfield Downs, £11
(£10 with member) WD, £20 (£15
with member) WE; Lannock Links, £3
WD, £4 WE.
Societies: by arrangement.
Catering: "19th Hole" bar and bistro;
coffee shop. Driving range.
Hotels: Novotel (Knebworth Park,
Stevenage); special rates available.

E52 **Finchley**
☎(081) 346 2436
Nether Court, Frith Lane, Mill Hill,
London NW7 1PU
Near junction of A1 and A41, Mill Hill
East underground 5 min walk.
Parkland course.
18 holes, 6411 yards, S.S.S.71
Designed by James Braid.
Founded 1929
Visitors: welcome weekdays, pm
weekends.
Green Fee: on application.
Societies: Wed and Fri.
Catering: every day except Mon.
Hotels: Hendon Hall.

E53 **Forrester Park**
☎(0621) 891406
Beckingham Rd, Great Totham, Nr
Maldon, Essex CM9 8EA
3 miles E of Maldon on B1022.
Parkland course.
18 holes, 6073 yards, S.S.S.69
Designed by D.A.H. Everett & T.R.
Forrester-Muir.
Founded 1975
Visitors: to look like golfers, not
before 12.30pm Sat, Sun.
Green Fee: £12/round WD,
£17/round WE on request.
Societies: with prior reservation
Mon, Thurs, Fri.
Catering: bar 8am until dark, snacks
8am-6pm daily; lunch 10.30am-2pm
Mon-Sat; party dinners on request.
4 all-weather tennis courts,
banqueting/conferences for 80.

E54 **Frinton**
☎(0255) 674618 office, 671618 Pro.
1 The Esplanade, Frinton-on-Sea,
Essex CO13 9EP
A133 Colchester to Weeley village,
B1033 to Frinton, right at seafront.
Seaside links course.
18 holes, 6259 yards, S.S.S.70;
18 holes, 2508 yards, Par 66
Designed by Tom Dunn.
Founded 1896
Visitors: welcome weekdays and
weekends by arrangement with Sec;
h/cap cert for main course.
Green Fee: on application.
Societies: Wed and Thurs only.
Catering: meals except Mon.
Snooker.
Hotels: Maplin.

E55 **Fulwell**
☎(081) 977 2733
Wellington Rd, Hampton Hill, Middx
TW12 1JY

2 miles S of Twickenham on A311, opposite Fulwell railway station.
Meadowland course.
18 holes, 6490 yards, S.S.S.71
Designed by D. Morrison.
Founded 1904
Visitors: welcome weekdays, book through Pro shop.
Green Fee: £25/day WD, £35/day WE (£12 with member).
Societies: Wed, Thurs, Fri.
Catering: full service for societies but advisable to phone.
Hotels: Cardinal Wolsey.

E56 Gosfield Lakes
☎(0787) 474747
Hall Drive, Gosfield, Halstead, Essex CO9 1SE
1 mile W of village of Gosfield which is 7 miles N of Braintree on A1017.
Parkland course.
Lakes, 18 holes, 6512 yards, S.S.S.71; Meadows, 9 holes, 4037 yards (for 18)
Designed by Sir Henry Cotton, Howard Swan.
Founded 1988
Visitors: h/cap cert required for Lakes course; with member only from 12am weekends.
Green Fee: Lakes, £20/day (£10 with member), Meadows £8/day (£4 with member).
Societies: welcome by arrangement Mon, Wed, Thurs.
Catering: full bar, snack bar, restaurant facilities from 12am; conference facilities, private functions, company days.

E57 Grimsdyke
☎(081) 428 4539
Oxhey Lane, Hatch End, Pinner, Middx HA5 4AL
Between Harrow and Watford on A4008.
Parkland course.
18 holes, 5598 yards, S.S.S.67
Designed by James Braid.
Founded 1910
Visitors: weekdays with h/cap certs.
Green Fee: on application
Societies: Tues-Fri.
Catering: lunch except Mon; dinner by arrangement.

E58 Hadley Wood
☎(081) 499 4328
Beech Hill, Barnet, Herts EN4 0JJ
From M25 junction 24 take A111 towards Cockfosters, 3rd right into Beech Hill, course 400 yards on left.

Parkland course.
18 holes, 6473 yards, S.S.S.71
Designed by Alister Mackenzie.
Founded 1921
Visitors: weekdays, require h/cap cert or proof of club membership; at weekends playing with member only.
Green Fee: on application.
Societies: by arrangement.
Catering: morning coffee, lunch, dinner for functions and societies.
Hotels: West Park Lodge; Hadley.

E59 Hainault Forest
☎(081) 500 2097, 500 0385 Sec.
Chigwell Row, Hainault, Essex 0JJ
On A217 12 miles from Central London.
Public parkland course.
18 holes, 5754 yards, S.S.S.67; 18 holes, 6445 yards, S.S.S.71
Founded 1912
Visitors: welcome.
Green Fee: on application
Catering: meals served.

E60 Hampstead
☎(081) 455 0203, 455 7089 Pro.
Winnington Rd, Hampstead, London N2 0TU
1 mile down Hampstead Lane from Highgate Village or Hampstead, course adjacent to Spaniards Inn.
Undulating parkland course.
9 holes, 5812 yards, S.S.S.68
Founded 1893
Visitors: welcome weekdays (not Tues) by prior booking with Pro; restricted times weekends.
Green Fee: £23/round (18 holes), £28/day WD; £30/round WE & BH.
Societies: small societies by arrangement.
Catering: lunch by prior booking; snacks available.
Hotels: La Gaffe; Central (Golders Green).

E61 Hanbury Manor Golf & Country Club
☎(0920) 487722, 487692 fax.
Thundridge, Nr Ware, Herts SG12 0SD
22 miles N of London on A10, 8 miles N of M25 junction 25.
Parkland course.
18 holes, 7011 yards, S.S.S.74
Designed by Jack Nicklaus II.
Founded 1990
Visitors: hotel and member's guests only at present; h/cap certs required.
Green Fee: £35 WD, £40 WE.
Catering: bars, 3 restaurants (overseen by Albert Roux).

Practice ground, tennis, squash and full range of leisure club facilities.
Hotels: Hanbury Manor, special golfing packages available.

E62 Hanover
☎(0702) 232377
Hullbridge, Rayleigh, Essex SS6 9QS
Undulating course.
18 hole championship course, Par 73; 18 hole pay-and-play, Par 63
Designed by Reg Plumbridge.
Founded 1991
Visitors: guests of members only.
Societies: PGA associated society enquiries only.

E63 Harefield Place
☎(0895) 31169
The Drive, Harefield Place, Uxbridge, Middx UB10 9PA
2 miles N of Uxbridge.
Public parkland course.
18 holes, 5711 yards, S.S.S.68
Visitors: by arrangement with London Borough of Hillingdon.
Green Fee: on application
Societies: as for visitors.
Catering: full facilities.

E64 Harpenden
☎(0582) 712580
Hammonds End, Redbourn Lane, Harpenden, Herts AL5 2AX
Off A1081 4 miles N of St Albans on B487.
Parkland course.
18 holes, 6363 yards, S.S.S.70
Founded 1931
Visitors: welcome weekdays except Thurs.
Green Fee: on application
Societies: weekdays except Thurs.
Catering: by arrangement.

E65 Harpenden Common
☎(0582) 712856
East Common, Harpenden, Herts AL5 1BL
Adjacent A5183, 4 miles N of St Albans, 1 mile S of Harpenden.
Heathland course.
18 holes, 5613 yards, S.S.S.67
Founded 1931
Visitors: welcome Mon, Wed, Thurs, Fri; h/cap certs required.
Green Fee: £18/round, £25/day.
Societies: Thurs and Fri.
Catering: full bar facilities; lunches, teas and snacks; dinner to order.
Hotels: Gleneagles; Moat House; Aubrey Park (Redbourne).

E66 **Harrow Hill**
☎(081) 864 3754
Kenton Road, Harrow, Middx HA1
Off Harrow main by-pass road at
Northwick Park roundabout.
Public parkland course.
9 holes Par 3, 950 yards
Designed by S. Teahan.
Founded 1982
Visitors: welcome.
Green Fee: £2.50/round.
Catering: soft drinks.

E67 **Harrow School**
Harrow School, 5 High Street,
Harrow-on-the-Hill, Middx HA1 3JE
Parkland course.
9 holes, 3690 yards, S.S.S.57
Designed by Donald Steel.
Visitors: no visitors.

E68 **Hartsbourne G & CC**
☎(081) 950 1133
Hartsbourne Ave, Bushey Heath,
Herts WD2 1JW
Turn S off A411 at Bushey Heath
village 5 miles SE of Watford.
Parkland course.
18 holes, 6305 yards, S.S.S.70;
9 holes, 5432 yards, S.S.S.66
Founded 1946
Visitors: with member only.
Societies: welcome Mon, Wed, Fri.
Catering: daily catering and bar.

E69 **Hartswood**
☎(0277) 218850 Sec
King George's Playing Fields, Ingrave
Rd, Brentwood, Essex
1 mile S of Brentwood on A128.
Municipal parkland course.
18 holes, 6160 yards, S.S.S.69
Founded 1964
Visitors: welcome.
Green Fee: on application
Societies: not weekends.
Catering: lunch, bar snacks, not Sun.

E70 **Harwich & Dovercourt**
☎(0255) 503616
Station Rd, Parkeston, Harwich,
Essex CO12 4NZ
A120 towards Parkeston Quay, after
last roundabout 200 yards on left.
Meadowland course.
9 holes, 5692 yards, S.S.S.68
Founded 1903
Visitors: welcome.
Green Fee: on application.
Societies: welcome by arrangement.
Catering: bar snacks or full catering.
Hotels: Cliff, Towers (Dovercourt).

E71 **Haste Hill**
☎(09274) 26485
The Drive, Northwood, Middx HA6
1HN
On A404.
Public parkland course.
18 holes, 5787 yards, S.S.S.68
Founded 1930
Visitors: welcome.
Green Fee: on application
Societies: by arrangement.
Catering: meals served daily.

E72 **Hatfield London CC**
☎(0707) 42624, 42626
Bedwell Park, Essendon, Hatfield,
Herts AL9 6JA
A1000 from Potters Bar, B158
towards Essendon.
Undulating parkland course.
18 holes, 6854 yards, S.S.S.73
Designed by Fred Hawtree.
Founded 1976
Visitors: welcome; by advance
booking only.
Green Fee: £13 WD, £28 Sat, £29
Sun and Bank Holidays.
Societies: welcome.
Catering: bar snacks at lunchtime.

E73 **Hendon**
☎(081) 346 6023
Off Sanders Lane, Mill Hill, London
NW7 1DG
From Hendon Central take Queens
Rd through Brent St, at roundabout,
take 1st exit on left, club 0.5 mile on
left in Devonshire Rd; from junction 2
M1 southbound, turn left at 1st lights
to roundabout, then as above.
Parkland course.
18 holes, 6266 yards, S.S.S.70
Designed by H.S. Colt.
Founded 1900
Visitors: Sat, Sun, Mon limited;
Tues-Fri all day.
Green Fee: £25/round, £30/day WD;
£35 WE & BH.
Societies: Tues-Fri by prior
arrangement.
Catering: snacks only Mon; other
days lunch, snacks, high tea to 6pm.
Hotels: Hendon Hall.

E74 **High Beech**
☎(081) 508 7323
Wellington Hill, Loughton, Essex IG10
4AH
Red course, 9 holes Par 3; yellow
course, 9 holes Par 3
Visitors: Red course open 7 days;
yellow, members only weekends and
Bank Holidays and after 5pm.

Green Fee: Red course £2.30 for 9
holes, yellow course £2.60.
Catering: club house, café.
5 practice nets.

E75 **Highgate**
☎(081) 340 1906
Denewood Rd, London N6 4AH
Off Hampstead Lane near Kenwood
House, turn into Sheldon Ave then 1st
left into Denewood Rd.
Parkland course.
18 holes, 5982 yards, S.S.S.69
Founded 1904
Visitors: Mon, Tues, Thurs, Fri only;
no visitors weekends.
Green Fee: £27/round, £35/day.
Societies: Tues, Thurs, Fri by
arrangement.
Catering: full, 12am-8pm.

E76 **Hillingdon**
☎(0895) 233956 Sec, 251980 Pro
18 Dorset Way, Hillingdon, Middx
UB10 0JR
Turn off A40 to Uxbridge, past RAF
Station, up Hillingdon Hill to left turn
at Vine public house into Vine Lane,
club gates 0.75 mile on left.
Undulating parkland course.
9 holes, 5459 yards, S.S.S.67
Designed by Harry Woods & Chas E.
Stevens.
Founded 1892
Visitors: welcome Mon, Tues, Wed
and Fri; not Sat, Sun or Bank Holidays
unless with full member after
12.30pm; must be members of golf
club with h/cap cert.
Green Fee: £15/18 holes.
Societies: Mon only.
Catering: bar and catering facilities.
Hotels: Master Brewer; Old Cottage.

E77 **Holiday Inn**
☎(0895) 444232
Stockley Rd, West Drayton, London
In grounds of Holiday Inn Hotel.
Open parkland course.
9 holes, 3236 yards, S.S.S.62
Founded 1975
Visitors: welcome.
Green Fee: on application
Catering: at Holiday Inn Hotel.

E78 **Horsenden Hill**
☎(081) 902 4555
Woodland Rise, Greenford, Middx
UB6 0RD
Signposted off Whitton Ave East.
Public undulating parkland course.
9 holes, 3236 yards, S.S.S.56

Founded 1935
Visitors: welcome.
Green Fee: on application
Catering: snacks; meals on request.

E79 **Hounslow Heath**
☎(081) 570 5271
Staines Rd, Hounslow, Middx TW4 5DS
A315 main road between Hounslow and Bedfont, on left hand side.
Public parkland course.
18 holes, 5820 yards, S.S.S.68
Designed by Fraser.
Founded 1979
Visitors: welcome.
Green Fee: £5.10/round WD, £7.15/round WE.
Societies: welcome by arrangement.
Catering: snacks, soft drinks.
Hotels: Hounslow.

E80 **Ilford**
☎(081) 554 2930
291 Wanstead Park Rd, Ilford, Essex IG1 3TR
0.5 mile from Ilford railway station.
Parkland course.
16 holes, 5414 yards, S.S.S.68
Founded 1906
Visitors: welcome; Sat, Sun and Bank Holidays limited to members and guests.
Green Fee: £13.50/round WD.
Societies: weekdays.
Catering: restaurant most days.

E81 **Kingsway Golf Centre**
☎(0763) 262727
Cambridge Road, Melbourn, Royston, Herts SG8 6EY.
On main A10 N of Royston.
Landscaped farmland course.
9 holes, c. 2500 yards, Par 33; (further 18 holes from end 1992)
Founded Nov 1991
Visitors: welcome any time.
Green Fee: £5/round WD, £6/round WE.
Societies: welcome by arrangement.
Catering: bar and restaurant.
Driving range, 9 hole Par 3.
Hotels: Cambridgeshire Motel.

E82 **Knebworth**
☎(0438) 812752
Deards End Lane, Knebworth, Herts SG3 6NL
1 mile S of Stevenage on B197.
Parkland course.
18 holes, 6492 yards, S.S.S.71
Designed by Willie Park.

Founded 1908
Visitors: weekdays unaccompanied; weekends, Bank Holidays only with member; club h/cap cert required.
Green Fee: £25.50/round/day.
Societies: Mon, Tues, Thurs only.
Catering: facilities daily.
Hotels: Roebuck Inn; Heath Lodge; Clock Motel (Welwyn).

E83 **Laing Sports Club**
☎(081) 959 3636
Page St, Mill Hill, London NW7
9 holes, 4178 yards, S.S.S.60
Visitors: employees of John Laing and members only.

E84 **Langdon Hills**
☎(0268) 548061 club, 548444 Pro.
Lower Dunton Road, Bulphan, Essex RM14 3TY
8 miles from M25 junction 29, A127 towards Southend, right to Bulphan and on towards Horndon on the Hill.
Parkland course.
18 holes, 6485 yards, S.S.S.71;
9 hole course (from June 1992)
Designed by MRM Sandow
Founded June 1991
Visitors: welcome with h/cap cert.
Green Fee: £17.50/round, £25/day WD; £22/round WE.
Societies: welcome weekdays.
Catering: bars and restaurant.
Function suite; driving range, practice ground, 3 practice holes; European School of Golf.
Hotels: Langdon Hills (July 1992).

E85 **Letchworth**
☎(0462) 683203 Sec, 682713 Pro.
Letchworth Lane, Letchworth, Herts SG6 3NQ
2 miles from A1(M) near village of Willian, next to Letchworth Hall Hotel.
Parkland course.
18 holes, 6181 yards, S.S.S.69
Designed by Harry Vardon.
Founded 1905
Visitors: weekdays with h/cap cert, weekends with member only.
Green Fee: £23.50/round, £32.50/day.
Societies: Wed, Thurs, Fri.
Catering: except Mon.
Hotels: Letchworth Hall.

E86 **Little Hay Golf Complex**
☎(0442) 833798
Box Lane, Bovingdon, Hemel Hempstead, Herts HP3 0DQ

Just off A41, left at 1st traffic lights, past Hemel Hempstead station, up hill; course on right, signposted.
Public meadowland course.
18 holes, 6610 yards, S.S.S.72
Designed by Hawtree & Son.
Founded 1977
Visitors: welcome.
Green Fee: £5.90/round WD, £8.75 WE.
Societies: by arrangement.
Catering: full meal facilities.
Driving range.
Hotels: Bobsleigh.

E87 **London Golf Centre**
☎(081) 845 3180
Ruislip Rd, Northolt, Middx UB5 6QZ
500 yards S of Polish War Memorial roundabout on A40.
Public parkland course.
9 holes (18 tees), 5627 yards, S.S.S.71
Founded 1975
Visitors: welcome any time, no restrictions.
Green Fee: £4/round (9 holes) WD, £5.30/round WE; reductions for jnrs and OAPs.
Societies: welcome.
Catering: 2 bars, bistro; functions.
Driving range, golf superstore.

E88 **Loughton**
☎(081) 502 2923
Clay's Lane, Loughton, Essex IG10
From M25 junction 26 take A121 towards Loughton; 3rd exit at roundabout, 1st turning on left.
Public parkland course.
9 holes, 4700 yards, S.S.S.63
Founded 1981
Visitors: welcome, book after Thurs for weekends.
Green Fee: £3.10/9 holes WD, £4.90 WE (reductions for members).
Societies: welcome, limited catering.
Catering: bar.
Hotels: Swallow; Bell (Epping).

E89 **Maldon**
☎(0621) 853212
Beeleigh, Langford, Maldon, Essex CM9 6LL
2 miles NW of Maldon on B1019, turn off at Essex Waterworks in Langford.
Meadowland course.
9 holes, 6197 yards, S.S.S.69
Founded 1891
Visitors: welcome weekdays with h/cap cert.
Green Fee: on application.

Societies: Mon and Thurs by arrangement.
Catering: bar; catering by arrangement.
Hotels: Blue Boar.

E90 Manor of Groves Golf & Country Club

☎(0279) 722333 Club, 600777 Hotel
High Wych, Sawbridgeworth, Herts CM21 0LA
1 mile N of Harlow.
Parkland course.
18 holes, 6200 yards, S.S.S.70
Designed by S. Sharer.
Founded 1991
Visitors: strictly limited; h/cap cert required.
Green Fee: £15 WD, £20 WE.
Societies: any day; numbers restricted weekends; corporate days a speciality.
Catering: restaurant, function room for 200, banqueting.
Snooker, swimming pool.
Hotels: Own hotel on site; weekend golfing breaks available, reduced rates for residents.

E91 Maylands Golf & Country Club

☎(04023) 73080
Colchester Rd, Harold Park, Romford, Essex RM3 0AZ
On A12 between Romford and Brentwood; M25 exit 28 towards London, next U-turn for entrance.
Undulating parkland course.
18 holes, 6172 yards, S.S.S.69
Designed by Colt, Alison & Morrison.
Founded 1936
Visitors: welcome weekdays with member or if member of other club.
Green Fee: £20/round, £30/day WD.
Societies: Mon, Wed, Fri; min 20, max 40; inc meals and 36 holes.
Catering: bar snacks all day, lunch daily; some evenings April-Oct.
Hotels: Post House, Moot House (Brentwood); Hilton National.

E92 Mid-Herts

☎(058 283) 2242
Gustard Wood, Wheathampstead, St Albans, Herts AL4 8RS
On B651 6 miles N of St Albans.
Heathland/parkland course.
18 holes, 6094 yards, S.S.S.69
Founded 1893
Visitors: Tues not before 1pm, Wed not after 1pm; weekends, Bank Holidays only with member.

Green Fee: on application.
Societies: Thurs, Fri only.
Catering: every day except Sun.
Hotels: St Michaels Manor.

E93 Mill Hill

☎(081) 959 2339
100 Barnet Way, Mill Hill, London NW7 3AL
From junction of A1/A41; going N, immediately filter right and cross into Marsh Lane, after 0.5 mile turn left into Hankins Lane, leading to clubhouse; going S, 1 mile from Stirling Corner turn left into clubhouse.
Parkland course.
18 holes, 6286 yards, S.S.S.70
Founded 1925
Visitors: welcome weekdays, weekends reservations only.
Green Fee: on application
Societies: Mon, Wed and Fri.
Catering: daily.

E94 Moor Park

☎(0923) 773146
Moor Park Mansion, Moor Park, Rickmansworth, Herts WD3 1QN
Situated on A404 between Rickmansworth and Northwood, 0.75 mile from Moor Park station.
Parkland course.
High, 18 holes, 6713 yards, S.S.S.72; West, 18 holes, 5815 yards, S.S.S.68; High championship tees, 6903 yards, S.S.S.73.
Designed by H.S. Colt.
Founded 1923
Visitors: welcome with 24 hours notice.
Green Fee: on request.
Societies: accepted on Mon, Tues, Wed, Fri.
Catering: snacks and meals served.
Hotels: Grimsdyke; Bedford Arms.

E95 Muswell Hill

☎(081) 888 1764 Sec, 888 8046 Pro.
Rhodes Ave, Wood Green, London N22 4UT
1 mile from Bounds Green tube station, 1.5 miles from N Circular Rd.
Undulating course.
18 holes, 6474 yards, S.S.S.71
Founded 1893
Visitors: weekdays restricted; weekends and Bank Holidays limited bookings through Pro.
Green Fee: £23/round, £33/day WD; £35/round WE & BH.
Societies: Mon, Wed, Thurs, Fri booked through Sec.
Catering: meals and snacks, bar.

E96 North Middlesex

☎(081) 445 1604 Manager, 445 3060 Pro.
The Manor House, Friern Barnet Lane, Whetstone, London N20 0NL
A1000 5 miles N of Finchley; 5 miles S of M25 junction 23 via A1081.
Undulating parkland course (with 2 large ponds).
18 holes, 5611 yards, S.S.S.67
Designed by Willie Park Jnr.
Founded 1928
Visitors: welcome with h/cap cert.
Green Fee: on application.
Societies: Tues and Thurs.
Catering: full facilities in clubhouse (old manor house with terrace overlooking 18th hole).

E97 Northwood

☎(09274) 25329
Rickmansworth Rd, Northwood, Middx HA6 2QW
On main road between Northwood Hills and Rickmansworth A404.
Parkland course.
18 holes, 6553 yards, S.S.S.71
Designed by James Braid.
Founded 1891
Visitors: welcome weekdays only.
Green Fee: £20/round, £30/day.
Societies: Mon, Thurs and Fri.
Catering: lunchtime catering daily.
Hotels: Tudor Lodge; Long Island.

E98 Old Fold Manor

☎(081) 440 9185, 440 7488 Pro.
Hadley Green, Barnet, Herts EN5 4QN
On Potters Bar road (A1000) 0.25 mile from Barnet; M25 junction 23.
Parkland course.
18 holes, 6449 yards, S.S.S.71
Founded 1910
Visitors: welcome on weekdays, with member only at weekends; Public Days Mon and Wed; h/cap certs required.
Green Fee: £22.50/round, £27.75/day (£9 with member) WD; £11.25 (with member only) WE.
Societies: Thurs, Fri only.
Catering: meals served except Mon and Wed; snooker room.
Hotels: Hadley; West Lodge Park.

E99 Orsett

☎(0375) 891352
Brentwood Rd, Orsett, Essex RM16 3DS
On A128 400 yards from A13 towards Chadwell St Mary.
Heathland course.
18 holes, 6614 yards, S.S.S.72

Designed by James Braid.
Founded 1898
Visitors: weekdays by arrangement.
Green Fee: on application.
Societies: Mon, Tues, Wed.
Catering: restaurant 7 days
8.30am-8.30pm (by arrangement).
Hotels: Plough Motel; Stifford Moat
House.

E100 Panshanger
☎(0707) 333350
Herns Lane, Welwyn Garden City,
Herts
Off B1000 close A1, 1 mile NE of town.
Public undulating parkland course.
18 holes, 6538 yards, S.S.S.70
Founded 1976
Visitors: unrestricted.
Green Fee: on application
Societies: welcome.
Catering: lunch every day.

E101 Perivale Park
☎(081) 575 8655
Ruislip Rd, Greenford, Middx
On Ruislip Rd East between
Greenford and Perivale, entrance
from Argyle Rd.
Public parkland course.
9 holes, 2667 yards, S.S.S.65
Founded 1932
Visitors: welcome, no restrictions.
Green Fee: £5 (9 holes).
Societies: not practical but apply to
Pro.
Catering: none; pavilion burned
down and rebuilding.
Hotels: Kenton (Hanger Hill).

E102 Picketts Lock
☎(081) 803 3611
Picketts Lock Lane, Edmonton,
London N9 0AS
Just off N Circular road.
Public parkland riverside course
9 holes, 2,500 yards, S.S.S.32
Founded 1973
Visitors: welcome; booking system
at weekends and Bank Holidays.
Green Fee: £4.50 WD, £5.50 WE &
BH; reductions for jnrs, OAPs and
members of Picketts Lock Centre.
Catering: bar and bar snacks.
Driving range, full sporting facilities
at leisure centre.

E103 Pinner Hill
☎(081) 866 0963 club, 866 2109
Pro.
Southview Rd, Pinner Hill, Middx
HA5 3YA

From Pinner Green take Pinner Hill
Rd and follow signs into residential
estate.
Hilly parkland course with views over
London and Harrow on the Hill.
18 holes, 6260 yards, S.S.S.70
Designed by J.H. Taylor & Hawtree.
Founded 1928
Visitors: Wed, Thurs unrestricted;
Mon, Tues, Fri with h/cap cert; Sat
h/cap 23 or less by arrangement.
Green Fee: Wed and Thurs
£7.15/round; Mon, Tues and Fri
£25/day; Sat £32/day.
Societies: Mon, Tues, Fri by
arrangement; full catering inc
evening meal.
Catering: full except Wed and Thurs
(stud bar only).

E104 Pipps Hill
☎(0268) 523456
Cranes Farm Rd, Basildon, Essex
Off A127 or A13.
Meadowland course.
9 holes, 2829 yards, S.S.S.67
Visitors: welcome.
Green Fee: on application
Societies: welcome weekdays.
Catering: meals served.

E105 Porters Park
☎(0923) 854127 Manager
Shenley Hill, Radlett, Herts WD7 7AZ
From M25 junction 22 to Radlett via
A5183, turn at rail station, 0.5 mile to
top of Shenley Hill.
Undulating parkland course.
18 holes, 6313 yards, S.S.S.70
Founded 1899
Visitors: welcome weekdays; h/cap
cert required, telephone in advance.
Green Fee: £26/round, £38.50/day.
Societies: Wed, Thurs only, min 20
max 50, £57 inclusive.
Catering: own chef, full catering for
societies; breakfast (ordered in
advance), comprehensive bar menu.
Hotels: Red Lion; Water Splash.

E106 Potters Bar
☎(0707) 52020
Darkes Lane, Potters Bar, Herts EN6
1DE
M25 exit 24, follow signs Potters Bar;
right at 2nd traffic lights into Darkes
Lane; entrance 400 yards on left.
Undulating parkland course.
18 holes, 6273 yards, S.S.S.70
Designed by James Braid.
Founded 1923
Visitors: welcome weekdays.
Green Fee: on application.

Societies: Mon, Tues and Fri by
arrangement.
Catering: lunch served daily.
Hotels: Brookmans Park.

E107 Quietwaters
☎(0621) 860410
Colchester Rd, Tolleshunt Knights,
Maldon, Essex CM9 8HX
B1026 S of Colchester.
Seaside courses.
18 holes, 6194 yards, S.S.S.70;
18 holes, 6767 yards S.S.S.72
Founded 1974 (extended 1990)
Visitors: welcome at most times.
Green Fee: on application.
Societies: weekdays only.
Catering: bars and dining room.
Indoor and outdoor tennis, squash,
bowls, health and fitness, banquets.
Hotels: own 58-bed hotel; bargain
breaks/golf packages on application.

E108 Redbourn
☎(0582) 793493 Pro, 792150 Sec,
793363 bar
Kinsbourne Green Lane, Redbourn,
Herts AL3 7QA
S of MI at junction 9 to A5, turn left
after 1 mile down Luton Lane.
Parkland course.
18 holes, 6407 yards, S.S.S.71;
9 holes, 1361 yards, Par 27 (public).
Designed by H. Stovin.
Founded 1971
Visitors: welcome weekdays.
Green Fee: £12 WD (£10 with
member); WE & BH £15 with member
before 3pm.
Societies: Mon, Tues, Wed, Thurs.
Catering: fully licensed bar, bar
snacks; restaurant meals daily by
arrangement; functions catered for.
Hotels: Aubrey Park.

E109 Rickmansworth
☎(0923) 775278
Moor Lane, Rickmansworth, Herts
WD3 1QL
A4145, 0.5 mile S of town.
Municipal parkland course.
18 holes, 4493 yards, S.S.S.62
Visitors: welcome.
Green Fee: £7.40 WD, £9.70 WE.
Societies: catered for weekdays.
Catering: meals all day, licensed.

E110 Risebridge (Havering)
☎(0708) 741429
Risebridge Chase, Lower Bedfords
Rd, Romford, Essex

Moor Park and Sandy Lodge

In one of the popular television programmes which John Betjeman narrated towards the end of his life, he highlighted the Metropolitan line and the station of Moor Park and Sandy Lodge, shared in its earliest days largely for the convenience of golfers. While the walk to Moor Park involves quite a lengthy climb, Sandy Lodge is no more than a long pitch shot from the station which, until it was elaborately modernised, was a somewhat odd looking basic wooden structure.

Sandy Lodge is a most pleasant course remembered by most golfers for the carry over large, deep bunkers to the 1st green, a prominent sleeper-faced bunker at the 2nd, consecutive short holes at the 7th and 8th and a short hole to finish across a quarry that is much less stark than it used to be.

It also has its 16th green beside the railway and a par 5 17th alongside a wood. Laddie Lucas and Alec Hill were its best known members, and John Jacobs its best known professional. It was at Sandy Lodge that he built up his considerable reputation as a teacher but, in the days when he was a regular figure on the tournament circuit, the opening tournament of what was then a more truncated season was invariably at Moor Park.

The architectural splendour of the clubhouse makes it one of the most photographed in the world but, in addition to the professional tournaments which were always attractions for school boys in the Easter holidays, the Carris Trophy was certainly one of the blue riband events of junior golf.

It involved a round on each of the High and West courses, the High regarded as the sterner of the tests, like Sandy Lodge ending with a short hole, at which Harold Henning once earned £1000 for holing-in-one, a small fortune in the 1960s, during the Esso Round Robin event.

The High and West epitomise the characteristics of parkland golf, but the High is unusually undulating, a factor that adds to the problems it presents. The West dominates the front of the clubhouse, the 1st tee and 18th green on the High being quite a step from its noble pillars. The 1st, crossing the road, has a narrow-looking fairway lined on the right by stately trees, while the 2nd has another demanding drive. If it is not held up sufficiently on the left, it will fall to the right, adding suitable problems to the second shot. But the problem of guardian bunkers to the green is nothing compared to the short 3rd, whose green is virtually encircled.

From the 4th green, one of the lowest points, the next couple of fairways run beside elegant houses into which it is easy to slice. The 8th green lies beside a pond which, before water features became so fashionable, caused quite a stir. The 9th is one of the best holes, with an awkward green to hit and an expensive one to miss, the inward 9 beginning near one of the main entrances to the park with a short hole where I once saw Arthur Havers, the local professional, hole-in-one in a tournament.

The 11th, 12th and 13th confront some of the severer slopes and hollows, while the 14th green is remembered for being very much wider than it is deep. There is an inviting downhill second to the 15th, an up and back element about the 16th and 17th and finally a downhill short hole where out of bounds lurks on the right.

2 miles from Gallows Corner and Romford station.
Public parkland course.
18 holes, 5237 yards, S.S.S.70
Visitors: welcome; bookings for weekends.
Green Fee: on application.
Societies: by arrangement.
Catering: snacks daily.
Pitch & Putt.
Hotels: Brentwood Post Hotel.

E111 Rochford Hundred
☎(0702) 544302
Rochford Hall, Hall Rd, Rochford, Essex SS4 1NW
A127 to Southend, follow signs to airport, then to Rochford; bypass Rochford, turn left under railway bridge, club 400 yards on left.
Parkland course
18 holes, 6255 yards, S.S.S.69
Designed by James Braid.
Founded 1893
Visitors: welcome weekdays, with member only at weekends.
Green Fee: £18/round, £25/day.
Societies: by arrangement on Wed or Thurs.
Catering: lunch only Mon-Fri.
Hotels: Airport.

E112 Romford
☎(0708) 740986
Heath Drive, Gidea Park, Romford, Essex RM2 5QB
1.5 miles from town centre, off A12.
Parkland course
18 holes, 6365 yards, S.S.S.70
Designed by James Braid.
Founded 1894
Visitors: weekdays if member of golf club.
Green Fee: on application
Societies: welcome.
Catering: available.

E113 Royston
☎(0763) 242696
Baldock Rd, Royston, Herts SG8 5BG
On A505 on outskirts of town to E, course on Therfield Heath.
Undulating heathland course.
18 holes, 6032 yards, S.S.S.69
Founded 1892
Visitors: welcome weekdays; weekends with member only.
Green Fee: £20/day WD, £12.50 with member only WE & BH.
Societies: by arrangement with Sec.
Catering: full facilities available.
Snooker table.
Hotels: Old Bull Inn; The Banyers.

E114 Ruislip
☎(0895) 638835, 632004
Ickenham Rd, Ruislip, Middx HA4 7DQ
1 mile N of A40, Hillingdon.
Public parkland course.
18 holes, 5702 yards, S.S.S.68
Designed by Sandy Herd.
Founded 1936
Visitors: welcome, telephoned tee bookings can be made.
Green Fee: on application.
Societies: catered for every day; booking essential.
Catering: breakfast, lunch, snacks, à la carte menu daily until 10pm.
Driving range.

E115 Saffron Walden
☎(0799) 22786
Windmill Hill, Saffron Walden, Essex CB10 1BX
Take B184 from Stumps Cross roundabout on M11 (junction 9), entrance just before entering town.
Parkland course.
18 holes, 6617 yards, S.S.S.72
Founded 1919
Visitors: welcome weekdays, with member weekends and Bank Holidays.
Green Fee: on application.
Societies: Mon, Wed, Thurs.
Catering: lunch available weekdays; evening meals for societies.
Hotels: Saffron.

E116 Sandy Lodge
☎(09274) 25429
Sandy Lodge Lane, Northwood, Middx HA6 2JD
2 miles S of Watford and 2 miles N of Northwood, immediately adjoining Moor Park station, Metropolitan Line.
Links course.
18 holes, 6340 yards, S.S.S.70
Designed by Harry Vardon.
Founded 1910
Visitors: weekdays; weekends and Bank Holidays with member; h/cap cert required.
Green Fee: on application
Societies: Mon, Thurs, Fri.
Catering: full facilities.

E117 Shendish House
☎(0442) 232220
Shendish House, Apsley, Hemel Hempstead, Herts HP3 0AA
M25 junction 20, just before Apsley on A41.
Parkland course.
9 holes, 6076 yards, S.S.S.69
Designed by Henry Cotton.

Founded 1989
Visitors: welcome Mon-Fri with h/cap cert.
Green Fee: £18 for 18 holes, £28/day.
Societies: welcome.
Catering: full facilities.
9 hole Pitch & Putt, tennis, practice ground, snooker.
Hotels: The Post House.

E118 South Herts
☎(081) 445 2035
Links Drive, Totteridge, London N20 8QU
In Totteridge Lane (A5109), 0.5 mile W of junction with High Rd, Whetstone (A1000).
Undulating parkland course.
18 holes, 6432 yards, S.S.S.71; 9 hole short course.
Designed by Harry Vardon.
Founded 1899
Visitors: weekdays with h/cap cert; weekends only with member.
Green Fee: £25/round, £30/day.
Societies: Wed, Thurs and Fri; apply in writing.
Catering: lunch 12.30-1.45pm; bar snacks.

E119 Stanmore
☎(081) 954 2599
Gordon Ave, Stanmore, Middx HA7 2RL
E of Harrow; entrance off Gordon Ave, via Old Church Lane.
Parkland course.
18 holes, 5881 yards, S.S.S.68
Founded 1893
Visitors: public days Mon and Fri; Tues, Wed, Thurs h/cap certs or club membership required; not weekends or Bank Holidays.
Green Fee: £7.40/round, £10.15/day Mon and Fri; £22.50/round, £28/day Tues, Wed, Thurs.
Societies: Wed and Thurs only.
Catering: full facilities daily.
Hotels: Grimsdyke.

E120 Stapleford Abbotts
☎(04023) 81108 Office, 81278 Shop
Horseman's Side, Tysea Hill, Stapleford Abbotts, Essex RM4 1JU
3 miles from M25 Junction 28, off B175 Romford to Ongar, left at Stapleford Abbotts up Tysea Hill.
Parkland course.
Abbots, 18 holes, 6487 yards, S.S.S.71; Priors, 18 holes, 5665 yards, S.S.S.67; Friars, 9 holes, 1140 yards, Par 3

Designed by Howard Swan.
Founded 1972
Visitors: welcome, phone starter;
Abbots tee reservations (04023)
70040; Priors tee (0277) 373344.
Green Fee: Abbotts £25, Priors £15,
Friars £5.
Societies: welcome any day.
Catering: bar and other facilities,
function room.
Sauna and multi-gym.
Hotels: Post House, Brentwood.

E121 **Stevenage**
☎(0438) 880424
Aston Lane, Aston, Stevenage, Herts
SG2 7EL
Leave A1(M) Stevenage South, then
on A602 to Hertford, course
signposted about 1.5 miles.
Public parkland/meadowland
course.
18 holes, 6451 yards, S.S.S.71
Designed by John Jacobs.
Founded 1980
Visitors: welcome every day, but
necessary to book at weekends.
Green Fee: £7.50 WD, £9 WE.
Societies: welcome weekdays.
Catering: full meals and bar snacks.
Hotels: Roebuck; Stevenage Moat
House; Novotel (Knebworth Park).

E122 **Stock Brook Manor Golf & Country Club**
☎(0277) 653616
Queens Park Avenue, Stock,
Billericay, Essex CM12 0SP
M25 exit 28, then A12 to Galleywood/
Stock exit, then B1007 to Stock.
Parkland course.
18 holes, 6728 yards, S.S.S.72;
8 holes, 2997 yards, S.S.S.69.
Designed by Martin Gillett.
Founded 1992
Visitors: apply for details.
Green Fee: on application.
Societies: apply for details.
Catering: from 1993. Country club,
bowls, tennis, croquet from 1993.
Hotels: Heybridge Moat House.

E123 **Stoke-by-Nayland**
☎(0206) 262836
Keepers Lane, Leavenheath,
Colchester, Essex CO6 4PZ
A134 from Colchester for 7 miles,
then B1068 to Stoke-by-Nayland.
Parkland/meadowland course.
18 holes, 6471 yards, S.S.S.71;
18 holes, 6498 yards, S.S.S.71
Founded 1972
Visitors: unrestricted during week;

after 10.30am weekends; must have
h/cap cert and club membership.
Green Fee: on application.
Societies: weekdays only by
arrangement.
Catering: full facilities available.
Hotels: The Mill; The Bull; The Swan.

E124 **Strawberry Hill**
☎(081) 894 0165
Wellesley Rd, Twickenham, Middx
TW2 5SD
Adjacent to Strawberry Hill station.
Parkland course.
9 holes, 2381 yards, S.S.S.62
Designed by J.H. Taylor.
Founded 1900
Visitors: welcome weekdays only.
Green Fee: £18/round (18 holes),
£25/day.
Societies: 24 max number
considered on application.
Catering: bar snacks except Mon
and Tues.

E125 **Sudbury**
☎(081) 902 3713 Sec, 902 7910 Pro.
Bridgewater Rd, Wembley, Middx
HA0 1AL
At junction of Bridgewater Rd A4005
and Whitton Ave East A4090.
Undulating parkland course.
18 holes, 6282 yards, S.S.S.70
Designed by H. Colt.
Founded 1920
Visitors: must produce h/cap cert or
be introduced by member; weekends
with member only.
Green Fee: £22.50/round, £35/2
rounds.
Societies: Tues pm, Wed and Thurs
by appointment.
Catering: full bar and catering.
Hotels: Caernarvon; Cumberland
(Harrow); Kenton (Ealing).

E126 **Theydon Bois**
☎(0992) 813054
Theydon Rd, Epping, Essex CM16 4EH
Off B172 1 mile S of Epping; M25 exit
Waltham Abbey.
Undulating woodland course.
18 holes, 5472 yards, S.S.S.68
Designed by James Braid.
Founded 1897
Visitors: must have proof of
membership of recognised golf club;
not Wed/Thurs am.
Green Fee: £23/round WD; £34 WE.
Societies: Mon, Tues only, £32 per
day, £20 after 2pm.
Catering: full facilities available.
Hotels: The Bell; Trust House Forte.

E127 **Thorndon Park**
☎(0277) 811666
Ingrave, Brentwood, Essex CM13 3RH
2 miles SE of Brentwood on A128.
Parkland course.
18 holes, 6455 yards, S.S.S.71
Founded 1920
Visitors: welcome weekdays and
with member weekends.
Green Fee: £25/round, £35/day.
Societies: catered for Tues and Fri
by arrangement.
Catering: meals served weekdays.
Hotels: Post House.

E128 **Thorpe Hall**
☎(0702) 582205
Thorpe Hall Ave, Thorpe Bay, Essex
SS1 3AT
On seafront, about 2 miles E of
Southend Pier.
Parkland/meadowland course.
18 holes, 6286 yards, S.S.S.71
Founded 1907
Visitors: welcome weekdays with
club h/cap.
Green Fee: on application
Societies: Wed and Fri only by
arrangement.
Catering: lunch served except Mon.
Snooker, squash, sauna.

E129 **Three Rivers CC**
☎(0621) 828631
Stow Rd, Purleigh, Nr Chelmsford,
Essex CM3 6RR
10 miles from Chelmsford on B1012
via A12, A130, A132.
Parkland course.
Kings 18 holes, 6609 yards,
S.S.S.72; Queens 9 holes, 2142
yards, Par 54
Designed by Fred Hawtree.
Founded 1973
Visitors: weekdays, pm weekends
with member only.
Green Fee: on application
Societies: apply to Sec.
Catering: full catering facilities at all
times.
Hotels: Three Rivers Country Club,
phone for details.

E130 **Toothill**
☎(0277) 365747
School Road, Toot Hill, Ongar, Essex
CM5 9PU
Parkland course.
18 holes, 6014 yards, S.S.S.69
Designed by Martin Gillet.
Founded Sept 1991
Visitors: members only.
Societies: by arrangement.

E131 Top Meadow
☎(0708) 852239
Fen Lane, North Ockendon, Essex
RM14 3PR
Off B186 in North Ockendon.
Parkland course.
9 holes Par 3, 2000 yards; from Oct
1992, 18 holes, 5500 yards, Par 69
Founded 1986
Visitors: welcome with member.
Societies: welcome by advance
booking.
Catering: bar and restaurants.
Driving range.

E132 Towerlands
☎(0376) 26802
Panfield Rd, Braintree, Essex CM7
5BJ
On B1053 out of Braintree.
Undulating meadowland course.
9 holes, 2698 yards, S.S.S.66;
18 holes, 5406 yards, S.S.S.66
Designed by G.R. Shiels.
Founded 1985
Visitors: welcome anytime, not
before 12.30pm Sat, Sun.
Green Fee: £8.50 (9 holes), £10.50
(18 holes) WD; £12.50 (18 holes) WE
& BH.
Societies: any time by arrangement.
Catering: full bar and restaurant.
Driving range, squash courts, sports
hall, equestrian centre, indoor bowls.

E133 Trent Park
☎(081) 366 7432
Bramley Rd, Oakwood, London N14
4XS
Near Oakwood tube station
(Piccadilly Line).
Public parkland course.
18 holes, 6008 yards, S.S.S.69
Founded 1973
Visitors: welcome anytime; booking
required.
Green Fee: on application.
Societies: Mon-Thurs only.
Catering: bar, snacks, meals by
arrangement.
Hotels: Royal Chase (Enfield).

E134 Tudor Park
☎(081) 441 2261, 449 0282 ticket
office
Clifford Rd, East Barnet, Herts
Off Potters Rd.
Public parkland course.
9 holes, 1836 yards, S.S.S.57
Visitors: welcome.
Green Fee: £3.20/18 holes (£1.60
jnrs) WD, £4.60 WE.
Catering: clubhouse, members only.

E135 Twickenham Park
☎(081) 783 1698
Staines Rd, Twickenham, Middx TW2
5JD
On A305 near Hope & Anchor
roundabout.
Municipal parkland course.
9 holes, 3050 yards, S.S.S.69
Designed by Charles Lawrie.
Founded 1977
Visitors: welcome.
Green Fee: on application.
Societies: welcome by
arrangement.
Catering: full licensed bar, snacks;
function room.
Driving range to be constructed,
early 1992.
Hotels: Richmond Gate.

E136 Upminster
☎(04022) 22788
114 Hall Lane, Upminster, Essex
A127 towards Southend.
Parkland course.
18 holes, 5926 yards, S.S.S.68
Founded 1927
Visitors: weekdays if member of
recognised club.
Green Fee: on application
Societies: by arrangement.
Catering: meals except Mon.

E137 Verulam
☎(0727) 53327
London Rd, St Albans, Herts AL1 1JG
A1081 to St Albans.
Parkland course.
18 holes, 6432 yards, S.S.S.71
Founded 1905
Visitors: welcome weekdays.
Green Fee: Mon, £12/round,
£16/day; Tues-Fri, £15/round,
£18/day.
Societies: Tues, Thurs, Fri.
Catering: full facilities except Mon
(bar snacks only).
Hotels: Sopwell House; St Michaels
Manor.

E138 Wanstead
☎(081) 989 3938
Overton Drive, Wanstead, London
E11 2LW
Off A12 at Wanstead station, right
into "The Green" into St Mary's Ave,
left at T-junction at St Mary's Church.
Parkland course.
18 holes, 6109 yards, S.S.S.69
Founded 1893
Visitors: welcome on weekdays with
prior arrangement.
Green Fee: £20/day.

Societies: welcome by arrangement
weekdays only.
Catering: bar and restaurant.
Hotels: Sir Alfred Hitchcock; Prince
Regent (Woodford Bridge).

E139 Warley Park
☎(0277) 224891
Magpie Lane, Little Warley,
Brentwood, Essex CM13 3DX
Off M25 junction 29, A127 Southend,
immediately left Gt Warley, left, 1st
right, right into Magpie Lane (6 mins
from M25).
Undulating parkland course.
27 holes (3 x 9), played 1-2,1-3,2-3
Designed by R. Plumbridge.
Founded 1975
Visitors: welcome with h/cap cert.
Green Fee: on application
Societies: by arrangement.
Catering: 1st class restaurant.

E140 Warren
☎(024 541) 3258
Woodham Walter, Maldon, Essex
CM9 6RW
A414 6 miles E of Chelmsford
towards Maldon.
Undulating parkland course.
18 holes, 6211 yards, S.S.S.70
Founded 1934
Visitors: welcome weekdays, after
3pm weekends; booking essential.
Green Fee: on application.
Societies: Mon, Tues, Thurs, Fri.
Catering: full facilities 7 days.
Hotels: Pontlands Park; Blue Boar.

E141 Welwyn Garden City
☎(0707) 325243
Mannicotts, High Oaks Rd, Welwyn
Garden City, Herts AL8 7BP
Leave A1(M) at junction 4, take B197
Stanborough to Valley Road.
Undulating parkland course.
18 holes, 6051 yards, S.S.S.69
Designed by Hawtree and Son.
Founded 1922
Visitors: welcome weekdays.
Green Fee: £21/round, £25/day.
Societies: Wed and Thur only.
Catering: bar snacks, lunch, dinner.
Hotels: Clock; Heath Lodge Motel;
Crest; Comet (Hatfield).

E142 West Essex
☎(081) 529 7558, 529 4367 Pro.
Bury Rd, Sewardstonebury,
Chingford, London E4 7QL
Off A11, 1.5 miles from Chingford
station; M25 junction 26.

Parkland course.
18 holes, 6289 yards, S.S.S.70
Designed by James Braid.
Founded 1900
Visitors: welcome weekdays; with member only Thurs pm, Tues after 11am and weekends.
Green Fee: £28/round, £35/day, (£14 with member).
Societies: Mon, Wed, Fri.
Catering: lunches available by arrangement.
Hotels: Roebuck; Woodford Moat; Forest View; Swallow.

E143 **West Herts**
☎(0923) 36484
Cassiobury Park, Watford, Herts WD1 7SL
2 miles from Watford on A412.
Parkland course.
18 holes, 6488 yards, S.S.S.71
Designed by Tom Morris & Harry Vardon.
Founded 1890
Visitors: welcome weekdays; weekends with member only.
Green Fee: £18.50.
Societies: welcome Wed and Fri by arrangement.
Catering: lunches and teas served except Mon.
Hotels: Dean Park; Southern Cross.

E144 **West Middlesex**
☎(081) 574 3450 Sec, 574 1800 Pro.
Greenford Rd, Southall, Middx UB1 3EE
A40 from Central London to Greenford, take left exit off roundabout, 2 miles straight down road.
Undulating parkland course.
18 holes, 6242 yards, S.S.S.70
Designed by James Braid.
Founded 1890
Visitors: welcome on weekdays, Mon and Wed are Public Days.
Green Fee: on application.
Societies: can be booked only on Tues, Thurs and Fri.

Catering: hot and cold snacks available all week, 3 course meals should be booked in advance.
Hotels: Carnarvan (Ealing Common).

E145 **Whipsnade Park**
☎(044 284) 2330
Studham Lane, Dagnall, Herts HP4 1RH.
Off M1 at junction 9 between villages of Dagnall and Studham.
Parkland course.
18 holes, 6800 yards, S.S.S.72
Founded 1974
Visitors: welcome weekdays.
Green Fee: £20/round, £30/day.
Societies: welcome except Mon and weekends.
Catering: restaurant and bar snacks, except Mon.
Hotels: Post House (Hemel Hempstead).

E146 **Whitehill**
☎(0920) 438495
Dane End, Ware, Herts SG12 0JS
Turn left at Happy Eater on A10 from London.
Undulating course.
18 holes, 6636 yards, S.S.S.72
Designed by Golf Landscapes.
Founded May 1990
Visitors: official club h/cap required or competence certificate from Whitehill Pros.
Green Fee: £14/round, £20/day WD; £18/round WE.
Societies: any time by appointment.
Catering: licensed bar, restaurant. Driving range, practice bunker and grass practice area; beginners classes; snooker.

E147 **Whitewebbs**
☎(081) 363 2951 club, 363 4454 booking office
Beggars Hollow, Clay Hill, Enfield, Middx EN2 9NJ
1 mile N of Enfield town.
Public parkland course.
18 holes, 5863 yards, S.S.S.68

Founded 1932
Visitors: welcome; very busy course, queuing for playing times.
Green Fee: £5.60 WD, £7.20 WE (expected to rise steeply early 1992).
Societies: applications in writing to Hon Sec.
Catering: public café on site.
Nature trails and horse riding.
Hotels: West Lodge; Royal Chase.

E148 **Woodford**
☎(081) 504 0553, 504 3330 Hon Sec.
2 Sunset Ave, Woodford Green, Essex IG8 0ST
A11 to Woodford Green, near Castle public house; M11 to junction 4.
Parkland course.
9 holes, 5806 yards, S.S.S.68
Founded 1890
Visitors: welcome weekdays except Tues and Thurs am, with member only at weekends.
Green Fee: £15/round.
Societies: by arrangement with Hon Sec.
Catering: snacks served and meals by arrangement.
Hotels: Castle; Packfords.

E149 **Wyke Green**
☎(081) 560 8777 Sec, 847 0685 Pro.
Syon Lane, Isleworth, Middx TW7 5PT
From Gillette Corner on A4 Great West Rd, turn NW into Syon Lane; club 0.5 mile on left.
Parkland course.
18 holes, 6242 yards, S.S.S.70
Designed by W.H. Tate.
Founded 1928
Visitors: welcome by arrangement, h/cap cert required.
Green Fee: £25 WD, £37 WE after 3pm.
Societies: Tues and Thurs by appointment; £45 per head inc.
Catering: full facilities.
Hotels: Osterley Motel; Master Robert.

F

BERKSHIRE, BUCKINGHAMSHIRE, OXFORDSHIRE

In men's county golf terms, the amalgamation of Berks, Bucks and Oxon — or BB & O as they are familiarly known — casts a wide net. Twenty years ago, Clubs were thin on the ground but a number of recent developments have boosted the list considerably and, more recently still, Oxfordshire has been inundated with planning applications.

Foremost, perhaps, is The Oxfordshire at Denham, created by Rees Jones for the Nitto Kogyo Company, owners of Turnberry, in the heart of the countryside near Thame, although some may find the introduction of a contrived landscape a trifle harsh in such a natural setting. It is due to open in 1993.

The last few years have seen the Duke's and Duchess courses at Woburn reaching full maturity and taking their place amongst the finest in Britain. Not far away Abbey Hill and Windmill Hill extol the virtues of the more public type of operation, a department in which BB & O are better served than most.

There is Downshire near Bracknell, Farnham Park and Wexham Park near Slough, Hawthorn Hill near Maidenhead and Cherwell Edge near Banbury. More and more such courses are necessary if the demands of the army of new golfers can come close to being met; but many of BB & O's gems remain the longer established Clubs.

There is nothing better than a day's golf over the Red and Blue courses at the Berkshire with a marvellous lunch to rebuild the spirits if the heather has taken its toll. The same goes for Swinley Forest across the road where the Walter Mitty in you imagines it to be your own private course, while the character of heather and birch is echoed by East Berks at Crowthorne, another delightful place to play.

Stoke Poges, Denham and Beaconsfield form a convenient triangle for those staying in the area and seeking a change of scene, the clubhouses at Denham and Beaconsfield lending a cosy, rural air unusual so close to London. Out beyond Harewood Downs and Amersham, the Vale of Aylesbury beckons, where Ellesborough near Chequers offers an ideal stopping place for 18 holes with an unmistakable feeling of having got away from it all.

Over in Berkshire again, Maidenhead, Sonning, Temple and Calcot are always worth a visit while Newbury & Crookham is one of the oldest courses in England, and travellers through Pangbourne along the Thames Valley should look out for Goring & Streatley.

Oxfordshire's best known names are Huntercombe and Frilford Heath, the latter with a pair of courses of great charm and challenge. Frilford has played host to a number of important events including the 1987 English championship for men, its extension from 27 to 36 holes a tribute to the skill of Ken Cotton. The newer part was carved out of the woods that surround the clubhouse, the older version situated looking out on the more open heathland associated with the Club's title.

Since its earliest days, Huntercombe has assumed a more enclosed look, the appearance of the common now liberally laced with trees and bushes. Its distinctive greens bear the hallmark of Willie Park, designer of the Old course at Sunningdale, who use to declare that "a man who can putt is a match for anyone".

BB & O's latest recruit is Mill Ride at North Ascot, 11 holes designed on lovely natural land and the rest from the vastness of polo fields. A number of lakes embellish the look of a course that has the promise of a great future.

F1 Abbey Hill
☎(0908) 562408
Monks Way, Two Mile Ash, Stony
Stratford, Milton Keynes MK8 8AA
2 miles S of Stony Stratford.
Public meadowland course.
18 holes, 6193 yards, S.S.S.69
Founded 1975
Visitors: unrestricted.
Green Fee: £5 WD, £7 WE.
Societies: on application.
Catering: meals and bar snacks.

F2 Aspect Park
☎(0491) 577562
Remenham Hill, Henley on Thames,
Oxon RG9 3EH
On A423 E of Henley, M4 junction 8/9.

Parkland course.
9 holes, 5626 yards, S.S.S.66
Visitors: welcome Mon-Fri.
Green Fee: £8/9 holes, £16/18 holes.
Societies: Mon-Fri by arrangement.
Catering: available; function rooms.
Driving range (green fee payers only).
Hotels: Red Lion (Henley).

F3 Badgemore Park
☎(0491) 572206 Sec, 573667
Clubhouse, 574175 Pro
Henley-on-Thames, Oxon RG9 4NR
Leave M4 at junction 8/9 on Henley
and Oxford spur, over river into
Henley, straight through town, after
0.75 mile on right hand side.
Parkland course.

18 holes, 6112 yards, S.S.S.69
Designed by Bob Sandow.
Founded July 1972
Visitors: welcome weekdays only.
Green Fee: £26/round/day.
Societies: weekdays only, by
arrangement.
Catering: full facilities available.
Hotels: Red Lion; Royal; Little White
Hart.

F4 Beaconsfield
☎(0494) 676545
Seer Green, Beaconsfield, Bucks HP9
2UR
Off M40 onto A355 Amersham road,
right at Jordans sign, adjacent to
Seer Green/Jordans railway halt.

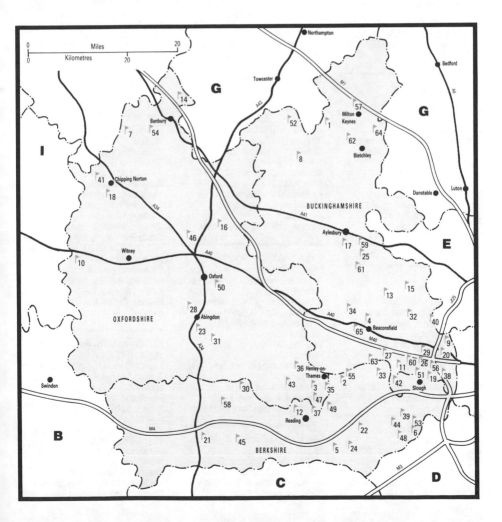

Parkland course.
18 holes, 6469 yards, S.S.S.71
Designed by H.S. Colt.
Founded 1914
Visitors: welcome weekdays.
Green Fee: £30/round, £35/day.
Societies: Tues and Wed.
Catering: full facilities.
Hotels: The Bellhouse.

F5 Bearwood
☎(0734) 760060
Mole Rd, Sindlesham, Berks RG11
5DB
B3030 1.5 miles N of Arborfield Cross.
Parkland course.
9 holes, 2802 yards, S.S.S.68
Founded 1986
Visitors: weekdays only; h/cap cert
required.
Green Fee: £8/9 holes, £15/18 holes.
Catering: meals and bar snacks.
9-hole Pitch & Putt course.
Hotels: The Moat House.

F6 The Berkshire
☎(0344) 21495
Swinley Rd, Ascot, Berks SL5 8AY
On A332 between Ascot and Bagshot.
Heathland course.
Red course, 18 holes, 6356 yards,
S.S.S.70; Blue course, 6258 yards,
S.S.S.70
Designed by Herbert Fowler.
Founded 1928
Visitors: on request to Sec.
Green Fee: £40/round, £55/day.
Societies: book with Sec.
Catering: lunch available.
Hotels: Berystede; Cricketers; Royal
Foresters.

F7 Brailes
☎(0608 85) 336
Sutton Lane, Brailes, Banbury, Oxon
Off B4035, Shipston-on-Stour 4
miles, Banbury 10 miles.
Parkland course.
18 holes, 6270 yards, S.S.S.70
Founded 1992
Visitors: welcome from June 1992.
Green Fee: £22.
Societies: welcome from 1993.
Catering: full facilities.

F8 Buckingham
☎(0280) 815566
Tingewick Rd, Buckingham MK18
4AE
2 miles W of Buckingham on A421, 8
miles from M40 junction 9 via A43,
B4031 to Finmere then A421.

Undulating parkland course.
18 holes, 6082 yards, S.S.S.69
Founded 1914
Visitors: weekdays; members'
guests only at weekend.
Green Fee: £26.
Societies: pre-booking with Sec;
Tues and Thurs only.
Catering: lunch, dinner 7 days.
Hotels: Villiers; Buckingham Lodge.

F9 The Buckinghamshire
Denham Court, Denham, Bucks UB9
5BG
Entrance on N side of Denham
roundabout, 25 mins London West
End via A40.
River-threaded parkland course.
18 holes
Designed by John Jacobs.
Opening July 1992
Visitors: details of visitor
requirements and availability, society
meetings, green fees on application.
Catering: full facilities.
Putting green, practice area, etc.

F10 Burford
☎(099 382) 2583
Burford, Oxon OX8 4JG
19 miles W of Oxford at junction of
A40/A361, at Burford roundabout.
Parkland course.
18 holes, 6405 yards, S.S.S.71
Founded 1936
Visitors: by arrangement.
Green Fee: £24.50/day.
Societies: limited.
Catering: full facilities available.

F11 Burnham Beeches
☎(0628) 661448
Green Lane, Burnham, Bucks SL1 8EG
M40 exit Beaconsfield, follow signs
to Slough, turn right and follow
Burnham signs (not Burnham
Beeches) to Green Lane.
Parkland course.
18 holes, 6415 yards, S.S.S.71
Founded 1891
Visitors: Mon to Fri; weekends guest
of member.
Green Fee: on application
Societies: Wed, Thurs, Fri.
Catering: full facilities except Mon.

F12 Calcot Park
☎(0734) 427124
Bath Rd, Calcot, Reading, RG3 5RN
From junction 12 on M4 take A4 to
Reading for 1 mile, entrance on left.
Undulating parkland course.

18 holes, 6283 yards, S.S.S.70
Designed by H.S. Colt.
Founded 1930
Visitors: welcome weekdays except
Bank Holidays; h/cap cert required.
Green Fee: on application.
Societies: Tues, Wed, Thurs.
Catering: full catering daily.
Hotels: Calcot; Ramada.

F13 Chartridge Park
☎(0494) 791772, 786462 fax
Chartridge, Chesham, Bucks HP5 2TF
3 miles W of town centre.
Parkland course.
9 holes, 3019 yards, S.S.S.69
(England's longest 9-hole course)
Designed by P. Gibbins & Vic Parker.
Founded 1989
Visitors: welcome weekdays.
Green Fee: £12 WD, £15 WE,
Summer Twilight Ticket.
Societies: full service weekdays,
weekends on application.
Catering: full bar up and downstairs;
restaurant; banqueting, functions.
Hotels: accommodation and golf
packages at Chartridge Centre.

F14 Cherwell Edge
☎(0295) 711591
Chacombe, Banbury, Oxon
3 miles E of Banbury via A422; 1.5
miles E of M40 junction 11.
Public parkland course.
18 holes, 5322 metres, S.S.S.68
Designed by Richard Davies.
Founded 1983
Visitors: welcome 7 days.
Green Fee: £5.20/round, £9.20/day
WD; £6.80/round WE; reductions for
jnrs and OAPs Mon-Sat.
Societies: Mon to Sat.
Catering: lunches, bar snacks,
evening meals.
Hotels: Whatley Arms; Thatched
House.

F15 Chesham & Ley Hill
☎(0494) 784541
Ley Hill, Chesham, Bucks HP5 1UZ
Turn off A41 onto B4505 at Boxmoor,
at Bovingdon follow signs for Ley Hill.
Wooded heathland course.
9 holes, 5240 yards, S.S.S.66
Founded 1919
Visitors: welcome Mon, Wed (after
12am), Thurs, Fri (after 1pm); Tues,
weekends and Bank Holidays with
member only.
Green Fee: on application
Societies: Thurs by arrangement.
Catering: snacks except Mon.

F16 Chesterton
☎(0869) 241204, 242023 Pro shop
Chesterton, Bicester, Oxon OX6 8TE
1 mile from M40; from Oxford take
Northampton road, then Chesterton
sign at Weston-on-the-Green, 1 mile.
Meadowland course.
18 holes, 6520 yards, S.S.S.71
Designed by R.R. Stagg.
Founded 1973/74
Visitors: no restrictions.
Green Fee: on application
Societies: weekdays except Tues by
arrangement.
Catering: bar daily, full catering by
arrangement.

F17 Chiltern Forest
☎(0296) 630899 Club, 631267 Sec.
Aston Hill, Halton, Aylesbury, Bucks
HP22 5NQ
Off A4011 between Wendover and
Aston Clinton.
Hilly woodland course.
14 holes; from July 1992, 18 holes,
5755 yards, S.S.S.69
Visitors: welcome weekdays;
weekends and Bank Holidays with
member only.
Green Fee: £18 (£20)/day.
Societies: usually Wed.
Catering: limited food Tues, Thurs.
Hotels: Bell Inn; West Lodge.

F18 Chipping Norton
☎(0608) 642383
Southcombe, Chipping Norton, Oxon
OX7 5QH
0.5 mile E of town towards Oxford;
junction A3400/A44 on left driving N.
Parkland course.
18 holes, 6280 yards, S.S.S.70
Founded 1890
Visitors: welcome weekdays; only
with member weekends and Bank
Holidays.
Green Fee: £20 (£10 with member)
WD.
Societies: weekdays.
Catering: full facilities.
Hotels: Crown & Cushion; White Hart.

F19 Datchet
☎(0753) 543887
Buccleuch Rd, Datchet, Slough,
Berks SL3 9BP
2 miles from Slough and Windsor,
easy access from M4.
Parkland course.
9 holes, 5978 yards, S.S.S.69
Founded 1890
Visitors: welcome weekdays
9am-3pm.

Green Fee: £14/round, £20/day.
Societies: small societies welcome
on Tues only.
Catering: bar snacks and lunches.
Hotels: The Manor.

F20 Denham
☎(0895) 832022
Tilehouse Lane, Denham, Bucks UB9
5DE
Just off A412, 4 miles W of Watford;
from M40 take Uxbridge/Gerrards
cross turn off, take A40 towards
Gerrards Cross, right onto A412
towards Watford, 2nd left to club.
Parkland course.
18 holes, 6439 yards, S.S.S.71
Designed by H.S. Colt.
Founded 1910
Visitors: welcome Mon to Thurs by
prior arrangement.
Green Fee: £42 (36 holes), £28 (18
holes).
Societies: Tues, Wed, Thurs.
Catering: lunches served daily.
Hotels: The Bull (Gerrards Cross).

F21 Donnington Valley Hotel
☎(0635) 32488 Pro shop, 551199
hotel.
Oxford Road, Donnington, Newbury,
Berks RG16 9AG
N of Newbury off old Oxford road.
Parkland course.
18 holes, 4215 yards, S.S.S.63
Founded 1985
Visitors: welcome.
Green Fee: £12/round, £20/day
weedays; £15/round, £25/day WE.
Societies: welcome.
Catering: full facilities.
Hotels: Donnington Valley.

F22 Downshire
☎(0344) 424066
Easthampstead Park, Wokingham,
Berks RG11 3DH
Between Bracknell and Wokingham
off Nine Mile Ride.
Municipal parkland course.
18 holes, 6382 yards, S.S.S.70
Designed by F. Hawtree.
Founded 1973
Visitors: welcome 7 days, bookings
required.
Green Fee: £9.70 WD, £11.30 WE.
Societies: welcome by prior
arrangement.
Catering: bar and cafeteria facilities.
9 hole Pitch & Putt, driving range.
Hotels: Ladbroke Mercury; St Annes
Manor.

F23 Drayton Park
☎(0235) 550607
Steventon Rd, Drayton, Oxon OX14
2RR
Off A34 S of Abingdon.
Public parkland course.
18 holes, 6000 yards, Par 69 (9 holes
only until autumn 1992)
Designed by Hawtree & Co.
Opening spring 1992
Visitors: welcome; phone for details.
Green Fee: on application.
Societies: welcome; phone for
details.
Catering: clubhouse from late 1992.
Driving range, 9 hole Pitch & Putt,
putting green.

F24 East Berkshire
☎(0344) 772041
Ravenswood Ave, Crowthorne, Berks
RG11 6BD
SW of Bracknell on A3095/B3348.
Heathland course.
18 holes, 6315 yards, S.S.S.70
Designed by P. Paxton.
Founded 1903
Visitors: welcome weekdays.
Green Fee: on application
Societies: weekdays.
Catering: lunch and snacks daily.

F25 Ellesborough
☎(0296) 622114
Butlers Cross, Aylesbury, Bucks
HP17 0TZ
1 mile W of Wendover on B4010.
Undulating downland course.
18 holes, 6203 yards, S.S.S.70
Designed by James Braid.
Founded 1906
Visitors: weekdays only, h/cap cert
required.
Green Fee: on application.
Societies: welcome Wed, Thur only,
£50 per day.
Catering: lunches served.
Hotels: Red Lion (Wendover).

F26 Farnham Park
☎(0753) 643332
Park Rd, Stoke Poges, Bucks SL2 4EP
Turn off A4 at Slough, take Farnham
road at Farnham Royal roundabout,
after about 0.5 mile turn right, course
on left.
Municipal parkland course.
18 holes, 4864 yards, S.S.S.68
Designed by Hawtree & Sons.
Founded 1977
Visitors: municipal course.
Green Fee: £7.70/round WD, £10.25
WE; reductions jnrs and OAPs.

Societies: catered for.
Catering: grill etc.
Hotels: Burnham Beeches.

F27 Flackwell Heath
☎(0628) 520929 Sec, 520027 Club
Treadaway Rd, Flackwell Heath,
Bucks HP10 9PE
From London, exit 3 M40 (1.5 miles);
from Oxford, exit 4 M40 (1 mile); turn
off A40 High Wycombe-Beaconsfield
road at Loudwater roundabout, up
Treadaway Hill, on left before apex of
hill into Treadaway Rd.
Undulating heathland course.
18 holes, 6207 yards, S.S.S.70
Founded 1905
Visitors: welcome Mon-Fri; h/cap
cert required.
Green Fee: £22.50 (£27)/day
Societies: Wed, Thurs only.
Catering: Tues-Sun, restricted Mon.
Hotels: Bell House; Crest.

F28 Frilford Heath
☎(0865) 390864/5/6
Frilford Heath, Abingdon, Oxon OX13
5NW
A338 Oxford to Wantage road, 3
miles W of Abingdon.
Wooded heathland course.
18 holes, 6768 yards, S.S.S.73;
18 holes, 6006 yards, S.S.S.69
Designed by J.H. Taylor, C.K. Cotton.
Founded 1908
Visitors: welcome, must have h/cap
cert; advisable to phone in advance.
Green Fee: £35 WD, £45 WE & BH.
Societies: by previous arrangement
Mon, Wed, Fri only.
Catering: cooked meals by prior
arrangement, snacks at any time.
Hotels: Dog House; Crown & Thistle.

F29 Gerrards Cross
☎(0753) 883263 Sec, 885300 Pro.
Chalfont Park, Gerrards Cross, Bucks
SL9 0QA
Leave A40 by A413, continue to 1st
roundabout (approx 1 mile) and leave
by 3rd exit onto private road.
Parkland course.
18 holes, 6295 yards, S.S.S.70
Designed by Len Holland.
Founded 1922
Visitors: welcome weekdays; phone
Pro in advance and bring h/cap cert.
Green Fee: on application
Societies: welcome Wed pm and all
day Thur and Fri.
Catering: bar snacks always
available; lunch to order.
Hotels: Bull; Greyhound; Bellhouse.

F30 Goring & Streatley
☎(0491) 873229
Rectory Rd, Streatley-on-Thames,
Berks RG8 9QA
On A417 Wantage road, 0.25 mile
from Streatley crossroads.
Parkland course.
18 holes, 6255 yards, S.S.S.70
Founded 1893
Visitors: welcome Mon-Fri;
weekend with member only.
Green Fee: on application
Societies: apply for details.
Catering: full, à la carte and table
d'hôte restaurant.

F31 Hadden Hill
☎(0235) 510410
Wallingford Rd, Didcot, Oxon OX11
9BJ
Just E of Didcot on A4130
Wallingford road.
Public parkland course.
18 holes, 6563 yards, S.S.S.71
Designed by Michael V. Morley.
Founded May 1990
Visitors: no restrictions, all starting
times bookable by phone.
Green Fee: 18 holes, £11 WD, £14
WE; 9 holes, £6 WD, £7.50 WE.
Societies: welcome weekdays.
Catering: bar and restaurant all day.
Driving range.
Hotels: George; White Hart
(Dorchester); George, Springs
(Wallingford).

F32 Harewood Downs
☎(0494) 762184
Cokes Lane, Chalfont St Giles, Bucks
HP8 4TA
Off A413 3 miles short of Amersham.
Parkland course.
18 holes, 5448 yards, S.S.S.69
Founded 1907
Visitors: welcome.
Green Fee: £20/round, £27/day WD;
£30 WE.
Societies: weekdays only.
Catering: daily.
Hotels: Crown; Greyhound.

F33 Hawthorn Hill
☎(0628) 75588 bookings, 26035
shop
Drift Rd, Hawthorn Hill, Nr
Maidenhead, Berks SL6 3ST
Leave M4 at exit 8/9; take A330
towards Bracknell for 2.5 miles;
course on right, 1 mile from ICI
Research Centre at Jealotts Hill.
Public undulating parkland course.
18 holes, 6212 yards, S.S.S.70

Designed by Clive D. Smith.
Founded 1984
Visitors: welcome.
Green Fee: £10/18 holes WD, £12
WE.
Societies: by arrangement
Catering: bar snacks, lunch and
dinners; function hall.
Driving range, pool tables.

F34 Hazlemere G & CC
☎(0494) 714722
Penn Rd, Hazlemere, Bucks HP15 7LR
On B474, 0.5 mile from junction with
A404 between High Wycombe and
Amersham.
Undulating parkland course
18 holes, 5855 yards, S.S.S.68
Designed by Terry Murray.
Founded 1982
Visitors: weekdays only; no jeans or
trainers allowed.
Green Fee: £22/round, £27/day.
Societies: welcome by prior
arrangement weekdays only.
Catering: bar and restaurant, bar
snacks and full meals. Snooker.
Hotels: White Hart; Crest; Bellhouse;
Crown.

F35 Henley
☎(0491) 575742
Harpsden, Henley-on-Thames, Oxon
RG9 4HG.
M4 to junction 9 Reading, follow
A4155 to Caversham/Henley, turn
left to Harpsden village 1 mile before
reaching Henley, clubhouse on left.
Parkland course.
18 holes, 6130 yards, S.S.S.69
Designed by James Braid.
Founded 1908
Visitors: welcome weekdays,
weekends with member.
Green Fee: £30/round/day.
Societies: Wed and Thurs.
Catering: bar snacks daily; other by
arrangement.
Hotels: Red Lion; Flohr's; Edwardian.

F36 Huntercombe
☎(0491) 641207
Nuffield, Henley-on-Thames, Oxon
RG9 5SL.
A423, 6 miles from Henley towards
Oxford.
Woodland/heathland course.
18 holes, 6108 yards, S.S.S.70
Designed by Willie Park Jnr.
Founded 1902
Visitors: weekdays after 10am; no 3
balls or 4 balls; jackets and
neckwear required in clubhouse.

Green Fee: on application
Societies: Tues and Thurs only.
Catering: full meals or bar snacks.

F37 Hurst
☎(0734) 3345143
Sandford Lane, Hurst, Berks RG10 0SQ
Between Reading and Twyford, signposted from Hurst village.
Public parkland course
9 holes, 3113 yards, S.S.S.70
Founded 1977
Visitors: welcome, booking advised.
Green Fee: on application
Societies: welcome.
Catering: bar facilities.

F38 Iver
☎(0753) 655615
Hollow Hill Lane, Langley Park Rd, Iver, Bucks SL0 0JJ
Near Langley Station, Slough.
Parkland course.
9 holes, 6214 yards, S.S.S.70
Designed by David Morgan.
Founded 1984
Visitors: always welcome.
Green Fee: £4.50 (9 holes), £7.50 (18 holes) WD; £5.90 (9 holes), £10 (18 holes) WE.
Societies: welcome.
Catering: meals always available.
Hotels: Holiday Inn (Langley).

F39 Lavender Park Golf Centre
☎(0344) 884074.
Swinley Rd, Ascot, Berks SL5 8BD
Public parkland course
9 holes Par 3, 1124 yards
Visitors: no restrictions.
Green Fee: £2.95 (9 holes), £3.95 (18 holes) WD; £3.75 (9 holes), £6 (18 holes) WE.
Catering: lunchtime weekdays.
Driving range.

F40 Little Chalfont
☎(0494) 764877
Lodge Lane, Little Chalfont, Bucks
200 yards from A404 at Little Chalfont.
Undulating parkland course.
9 holes, 6800 yards, S.S.S.68
Re-designed by James Dunne.
Founded 1980
Visitors: welcome.
Green Fee: £7 WD, £9 WE.
Societies: welcome weekdays.
Catering: full facilities.
Hotels: Sportsman (Chorley Wood).

F41 Lyneham
☎(0993) 831841, 642909 Sec.
Lyneham, Chipping Norton, Oxon OX7 6QQ
4 miles W of Chipping Norton off A361 Chipping Norton-Burford road.
Parkland course.
18 holes, 6808 yards, S.S.S.73
Designed by D. Carpenter, A. Smith.
Founded July 1991
Visitors: no restrictions.
Green Fee: on application.
Societies: welcome from April 1992.
Catering: available from April 1992.
Hotels: Mill; White Hart; Shaven Crown; Hillsborough.

F42 Maidenhead
☎(0628) 24693 Sec, 20545 Club, 24067 Pro.
Shoppenhangers Rd, Maidenhead, Berks SL6 2PZ
Off A308, adjacent to Maidenhead railway station.
Parkland course.
18 holes, 6360 yards, S.S.S.70
Founded 1896
Visitors: Mon-Thurs, Fri am only; h/cap cert required.
Green Fee: £27/round/day.
Societies: welcome by arrangement.
Catering: snack lunch, tea available; full lunch, dinner by arrangement.
Hotels: Frederick's; Holiday Inn.

F43 Mapledurham
☎(071) 499 4944 head office
Mapledurham, Reading, Berks
Off A4047 NW of Reading in village of Mapledurham.
Gently undulating parkland course.
18 holes, 5624 yards, Par 69
Designed by MRM Sandow
Opening Sept 1992
Visitors: welcome; details on application.
Societies: apply for details.
Catering: bar and restaurant.
Practice ground, Pitch & Putt, practice bunkers, putting green

F44 Mill Ride
☎(0344) 886777
Mill Ride Estate, Mill Ride, North Ascot, Berkshire SL5 8LT
Turn right into Fernbank Rd at 1st traffic lights on A329 between Ascot and Bracknell; 0.5 mile on left.
Parkland/inland links" course.
18 holes, 6639 yards, S.S.S.72
Designed by Donald Steel
Founded 1990
Visitors: welcome, but must book.

Green Fee: £15/round WD; £30/round WE
Societies: weekdays only.
Catering: morning coffee, lunch, tea, dinner, bar snacks; private dining room.
Practice ground, saunas, steam bath (men only).
Hotels: Royal Berkshire; Berystede; 4 guest bedrooms on site.

F45 Newbury & Crookham
☎(0635) 40035
Bury's Bank Rd, Greenham, Newbury, Berks RG15 8BZ
2 miles SE of Newbury off A34.
Parkland course.
18 holes, 5880 yards, S.S.S.68
Designed by J.H. Turner.
Founded 1873
Visitors: weekdays members of other clubs; weekends with members only.
Green Fee: £25 (£10 with member).
Societies: Wed, Thurs and Fri.
Catering: lunch, snacks and evening meals.
Hotels: Bacon Arms; Chequers; Enborne Grange; Hilton.

F46 North Oxford
☎(0865) 54924
Banbury Rd, Oxford OX2 8EZ
Between Kidlington and N Oxford, 2.5 miles N of city centre.
Parkland course.
18 holes, 5805 yards, S.S.S.67
Founded 1921
Visitors: welcome weekdays.
Green Fee: £25.
Societies: book with Sec.
Catering: facilities available.
Hotels: Moat House; Linton Lodge; Randolf.

F47 Reading
☎(0734) 472909
Kidmore End Rd, Emmer Green, Reading, Berks RG4 8SG
2 miles N of Reading off Peppard Rd (B481).
Parkland course.
18 holes, 6207 yards, S.S.S.70
Founded 1910
Visitors: Mon to Thurs (unless with member)
Green Fee: £26/day/round
Societies: Tues, Thurs unlimited; Wed 25 max.
Catering: full catering facilities except Mon.
Hotels: Ramada; Rainbow Corner (Caversham).

F48 Royal Ascot
☎(0344) 25175
Winkfield Rd, Ascot, Berks SL5 7LJ
In centre of Royal Ascot racecourse.
Heathland/moorland course.
18 holes, 5653 yards, S.S.S.68
Designed by J.H. Taylor.
Founded 1887
Visitors: not allowed.
Societies: Wed and Thurs by arrangement.
Catering: all week by arrangement.
Hotels: Forresters; Berystede.

F49 Sonning
☎(0734) 693332
Duffield Rd, Sonning-on-Thames, Berks RG4 0GJ
A4 Maidenhead/Reading road, behind Readingensians Rugby Ground.
Parkland course.
18 holes, 6360 yards, S.S.S.70
Founded 1914
Visitors: welcome weekdays with h/cap cert.
Green Fee: on application
Societies: by prior arrangement.
Catering: full service available.

F50 Southfield
☎(0865) 242158
Hill Top Rd, Oxford OX4 1PF
Cowley Rd, Southfield Rd, then right into Hill Top Rd; between Headington and Cowley.
Undulating parkland course.
18 holes, 6230 yards, S.S.S.70
Designed by James Braid.
Founded 1920
Visitors: welcome weekdays.
Green Fee: on application
Societies: welcome weekdays.
Catering: daily except Mon.

F51 Stoke Poges
☎(0753) 526385, 523609 Pro shop
North Drive, Park Rd, Stoke Poges, Slough, Bucks SL2 4PG
Off M4 or A4 at Slough into Stoke Poges Lane, then 1.5 miles on left.
Parkland course.
18 holes, 6654 yards, S.S.S.72
Designed by H.S. Colt.
Founded 1908
Visitors: weekdays by arrangement with Pro, weekends and Bank Holidays with member only; letter of intro. or h/cap cert required.
Green Fee: £22/round, £33/day.
Societies: Mon, Wed, Thurs, Fri.
Catering: full service available.
Hotels: Holiday Inn; Bull.

F52 Stowe
☎(0280) 813650 Sec.
Stowe, Buckingham, Bucks MK18 5EH
Parkland course.
9 holes, 4573 yards, S.S.S.63
Founded 1974
Visitors: with member only.
Green Fee: £10/18 holes.
Catering: clubhouse.

F53 Swinley Forest
☎(0344) 20197
Coronation Rd, South Ascot, Berks SL5 9LE
1.5 miles from Ascot station, through S Ascot village, right into Coronation Rd and 4th right to club.
Undulating heathland course
18 holes, 6011 yards, S.S.S.69
Designed by H.S. Colt.
Founded 1909
Visitors: only by invitation of member.
Green Fee: on application.
Societies: apply to Sec.
Catering: lunch served.
Hotels: Berystede; Royal Foresters; Brockenhurst.

F54 Tadmarton Heath
☎(0608) 737278
Wigginton, Banbury, Oxon OX15 5HL
5 miles W of Banbury off B4035
Shipston-on-Stour road at Tadmarton village.
Heathland course.
18 holes, 5917 yards, S.S.S.69
Designed by Major C.K. Hutchinson.
Founded 1922
Visitors: weekdays only; must be members of other clubs with h/cap certs.
Green Fee: on application.
Societies: Tues, Wed, Fri.
Catering: full facilities.
Hotels: Banbury Moat House; Old School House (Bloxham).

F55 Temple
☎(0628) 824795 Sec, 4248 Steward, 4254 Pro.
Henley Rd, Hurley, Maidenhead, Berks SL6 5LH
A423 Maidenhead to Henley from M4 or A404 from M40.
Undulating parkland course.
18 holes, 6206 yards, S.S.S.70
Designed by Willie Park.
Founded 1909
Visitors: welcome on weekdays; must have proof of h/cap.
Green Fee: £35.

Societies: catered for Mon, Tues, Wed, Fri; max 40.
Catering: full bar and restaurant facilities.
Hotels: Eurocrest (Maidenhead); Compleat Angler (Marlow).

F56 Thorney Park
☎(0895) 422095
Thorney Mill Lane, Iver, Bucks SL0 9AL
From M4 junction 5 follow signs to Iver.
Public parkland course.
9 holes, 3000 yards, S.S.S.34
Designed by Grundon Leisure.
Opening Sept 1992
Visitors: welcome; phone for details.
Green Fee: to be decided.
Societies: catered for all year round.
Catering: well provided; banqueting and night club.
Practice ground, tennis, snooker.
Hotels: in Heathrow area (5 mins).

F57 Wavenden Golf Centre
☎(0908) 281811
Lower End Road, Wavendon, Milton Keynes MK17 8DA
From M1 junction 13 take A421 to Milton Keynes, 1st left at roundabout, 1st left into Lower End Rd.
Public parkland course.
18 holes, 5361 yards, S.S.S.66; 9 holes Par-3, 1424 yards, S.S.S.25
Designed by John Drake/Nick Elmer.
Founded Nov 1989
Visitors: welcome 7 days.
Green Fee: £9 WD, £12 WE.
Societies: welcome weekdays.
Catering: carvery, downstairs bar, bar meals.
Driving range.
Hotels: The Bell (Woburn); Broughton.

F58 West Berks
☎(048 82) 574
Chaddleworth, Newbury, Berks RG16 0HS
Off M4 at junction 14, follow signs to RAF Welford.
Downland course.
18 holes, 7053 yards, S.S.S.74
Founded 1978
Visitors: welcome weekdays with prior reservation.
Green Fee: £22.
Societies: welcome by prior arrangement.
Catering: full catering service available.

The Duchess takes her Bow

When the idea of golf at Woburn was first conceived, the Dukes and Duchess courses were planned and cleared together. As events finally turned out the Duchess was delayed while the Dukes earned immediate praise, but now the Duchess forms a twin attraction that has very few equals.

In terms of character, the two courses have much in common, arising from the same dense forest in which it was virtually impossible seven or eight years ago to see more than ten yards ahead. The massive tree felling operation was the biggest ever undertaken on a new golf course in Britain but from the moment in the summer of 1979 when 18 holes on the Duchess were open for play, a remarkable story was complete.

Work only began on its construction in the summer of 1978, and in May 1979, after the severest winter for many years, half of it was not yet sown. Yet by October of that year all 18 holes were being played. Adjustments to the shape and levels of greens were made to mould with the natural contours, thus avoiding regular and artificial patterns. This was all achieved by the club's own green-keeping staff who wrought wonders. They were not alone in believing that it would have been impossible to have found a finer piece of land for an inland course in Britain; nor in thinking that you could hardly improve upon the arrangement whereby a course is built by those who subsequently have to look after it.

Now the course has seen a number of professional tournaments and filmed matches as well as hosting the English Amateur strokeplay championship for the Brabazon Trophy.

The Duchess is not as long, nor does it have the spectacular rises and falls that mark the beginning of the Dukes, but it is a supreme test of control, manoeuvrability and varied shotmaking.

The enjoyment of the Duchess lies in an ideal balance of its holes. There is contrast in the par 5s; the short holes vary nicely in length and there is a good mixture of par 4s from a drive and pitch to two full shots. The 1st gives a good first impression, the distant green on an elusive plateau being reached only with a well struck second from a tumbling fairway.

In four holes, in fact, there is all the variation you can have. The 2nd, a par 3 needs a shot through the eye of a needle; the 3rd calls for a straight drive and well judged pitch over a belt of heather and the 4th, a left hand dogleg, is a par 5 where there are many ways of taking six.

The 5th green in its alcove of giant beech is the first on the other side of the lane leading down to Bow Brickhill Church while the 6th, changing direction yet again, rewards positional play more than most par 5s.

It is a rare feature that no two consecutive holes follow the same direction and the short 7th twists back over the ancient earth-works that make an excellent golfing landmark. Next comes the 8th, a classic dogleg to a three level green, and then the turn is reached by way of the 9th green which, like the 10th tee, needed enormous build-up.

Over the brow at the 10th, the chief hazard is the angled green, but the 11th, 12th and 13th all have distinctive markings, the 13th occupying a natural little punchbowl. From there it is over the road again with two spanking two shot holes for the experts and two three shot holes for the rest.

There is no doubt that the finish is demanding but the 16th and 17th offer scenic relief, if nothing else; and by then the 18th is the only obstacle, though a tough one, between you and the other delights which Woburn has to offer. Swimming, tennis and squash await those with the energy to tackle them but a relaxing drink will be the comfort that most seek. In which case you can survey a sylvan setting and ponder whether golf has anything better to offer.

F59 Weston Turville
☎(0296) 24084
New Rd, Weston Turville, Aylesbury,
Bucks HP22 5QT
A41 or A312, situated 2 miles from
Aylesbury town centre between
Aston Clinton and Wendover.
Parkland course.
18 holes, 6002 yards, S.S.S.69
Founded 1975
Visitors: welcome except Sun am.
Green Fee: on application
Societies: weekdays, occasional
weekends.
Catering: lunches, evening snacks.

F60 Wexham Park
☎(0753) 663271
Wexham St, Wexham, Slough, Berks
SL3 6ND
2 miles from Slough towards
Gerrards Cross, follow signs to
Wexham Park Hospital and club is
0.5 mile further on.
Parkland course.
18 holes, 5890 yards, S.S.S.66;
9 holes, 2851 yards, S.S.S.34;
9 holes, 2283, S.S.S.32
Designed by Emil Lawrence and
David Morgan.
Founded 1976
Visitors: welcome.
Green Fee: on application.
Societies: welcome.
Catering: full service available.
Hotels: Wexham Park Hall, weekend
golfing breaks and midweek
packages inc hotel, golf & tuition.

F61 Whiteleaf
☎(0844) 274058 Sec.
The Clubhouse, Whiteleaf, Aylesbury,
Bucks
1.5 miles from Princes Risborough
on Aylesbury road, turn right for
Whiteleaf.
Undulating course.
9 holes, 5391 yards, S.S.S.66
Founded 1904
Visitors: not weekends.
Green Fee: £18 (18 holes), £25/day.
Societies: catered for on Thurs only.
Catering: lunch served except Mon.
Hotels: Bernard Arms; Thatchers.

F62 Windmill Hill
☎(0908) 378623
The New Clubhouse, Tattenhoe
Lane, Bletchley, Milton Keynes,
Bucks MK3 7RB
M1 exit 13, A421 through Bletchley
towards Buckingham, turn left at
roundabout, Standing Way.
Public meadowland course.
18 holes, 6773 yards, S.S.S.72
Designed by Henry Cotton.
Founded 1972
Visitors: welcome at all times.
Green Fee: £3.50 WD, £5 WE
(subject to increases).
Societies: Mon to Fri.
Catering: by prior arrangement.
Hotels: Post House (Milton Keynes).

F63 Winter Hill
☎(0628) 527613
Grange Lane, Cookham,
Maidenhead, Berks SL6 9RP
4 miles from Maidenhead via M4; 6
miles from M40 via Marlow.
Parkland course.
18 holes, 6408 yards, S.S.S.71
Designed by Charles Lawrie.
Founded 1976
Visitors: welcome weekdays only.
Green Fee: £22 WD.

Societies: welcome, main day Wed.
Catering: full service available.
Hotels: Eurocrest.

F64 Woburn CC
☎(0908) 370756/7/8
Bow Brickhill, Milton Keynes MK17
9LJ
Junction 13 off M1, into Woburn
Sands, turn left for Woburn, after 0.5
mile turn right at sign.
Dukes, 18 holes, 6940 yards,
S.S.S.74; Duchess, 18 holes, 6641
yards, S.S.S.72
Designed by Charles Lawrie.
Founded 1976
Visitors: weekdays only by
arrangement.
Green Fee: on application.
Societies: welcome by prior
arrangement.
Catering: meals served.
Hotels: Bedford Arms.

F65 Wycombe Heights Golf Centre
☎(0494) 816686
Rayners Ave, Loudwater, High
Wycombe, Bucks HP10 9SW
M40 Junction 3, off A40
Pay-as-you-play parkland course.
18 holes, 6253 yards, S.S.S.72; 18
hole Par 3, 1955 yards
Designed by John Jacobs
Founded 1991
Visitors: welcome, pay-as-you-play.
Green Fee: £10 WD, £13 WE.
Societies: Tues-Fri, min 18.
Catering: bar, restaurant, family
room.
Driving range.
Hotels: Post House Forte; Cressex;
Alexandria.

G

BEDFORDSHIRE, NORTHAMPTONSHIRE, CAMBRIDGESHIRE, LEICESTERSHIRE

Since the last edition of the Golf Course Guide, Northampton has gained two new courses on opposite sides of the city. Collingtree is an example of the American style of design and construction while the relocation of the Northampton Golf Club on Lord Spencer's Estate at Althorp epitomises the method of blending the courses harmoniously into a lovely, natural landscape.

Johnny Miller planned Collingtree on the lines of excavating a great lake and using the material to create a series of hills and mounds to balance an area that hitherto was a trifle barren. The lake itself has given rise to a par 5 18th hole with an island green. An impressive part of the development is the extensive teaching and practice facilities.

Harlestone Lake is very much a feature of the new home of the Northampton Golf Club, the 16th and 18th holes played across it in full view of a delightful clubhouse that enjoys a magnificent position. Close by lies the Northamptonshire County Club at Church Brampton, which upholds a justifiably high reputation as amongst the best inland courses in England. It has the capacity to test all departments of a golfer's game as well as appealing to the aesthetic senses of those who care more about where they play than how they play.

Cold Ashby and Staverton Park are among Northamptonshire's other new courses in the last 20 years but the mantle of seniority belongs to Kettering GC which last year celebrated its Centenary in spite of the new by-pass running beside one corner of the course.

Gog Magog, east of Cambridge, is the pick of Cambridgeshire's Clubs with its 27 holes but Ramsey, St Ives and St Neots boast a countryside whose largely agricultural character has not been little eroded by the spread of the game. Large, open fen-like fields are not ideal for golf but a word for Ely City and Cambridgeshire Moat House Hotel which meet local needs adequately enough.

Bedfordshire was the birthplace of Henry Longhurst who played most of his early golf at the Bedfordshire GC then known a little less grandly as the Bedford GC. Bedford and County followed in 1912 and nowadays Bedford has a public course called Mowsbury. Memories of Dunstable Downs, South Bedfordshire at Luton and the excellent John O'Gaunt (36 holes) at Biggleswade involve county matches with BB & O in the south-eastern group, but Northamptonshire falls in the Midlands Group along with Leicestershire, where golf revolves much around the county town of Leicester itself.

Rothley Park, Glen Gorse, Leicestershire and Kirby Muxloe are all based on pleasant parkland but, though only 9 holes, one of the most charming courses is Charnwood Forest near the M1 at Loughborough. Hinckley and Market Harborough are established courses, Hinckley starting life as Burbage Common. Humberstone Heights and Kibworth are more recent while Rushcliffe and Willersley Park deserve a visit.

The stock of Leicestershire golf was enhanced considerably by the crowning as Amateur champion of Gary Wolstenholme who learned and played all his early golf in the county.

G1 Abbotsley

☎(0480) 215153, 74000
Eynesbury Hardwicke, St Neots,
Cambs PE19 4XN
3 miles E of A1(M) through St Neots,
12 miles W of Cambridge on A45;
easy access along A45 from M11
junction 13
Daleland/meadowland course.
18 holes, 6150 yards, S.S.S.70;
further 18 opening spring 1992.
Designed by Derek Young, Vivien
Saunders, Jenny Wisson.
Founded 1986
Visitors: welcome every day.
Green Fee: £15 WD, £18 WE.
Societies: weekdays and off-peak
weekends.
Catering: snacks, meals served 7
days; restaurant and bar facilities.
Driving range, squash (6 courts),
snooker, practice facilities, Vivien
Saunders residential golf school.
Hotels: accommodation available in
12th century farmhouse on course.

G2 Aspley Guise & Woburn Sands

☎(0908) 583596
West Hill, Aspley Guise, Milton
Keynes MK17 8DX
2 miles W of M1 junction 13, between
Aspley Guise and Woburn Sands.
Parkland course.
18 holes, 6248 yards, S.S.S.70
Designed by Sandy Herd.
Founded 1914
Visitors: welcome weekdays with
h/cap cert; with member weekends.
Green Fee: £16/round, £21/day.
Societies: Wed and Fri.
Catering: full facilities except Mon.
Hotels: Bedford Arms; Moore Place;
Broughton.

G3 Beadlow Manor Hotel

☎(0525) 60800
Beadlow, Shefford, Beds
On A507 between Silsoe and
Shefford, 1.5 miles W of Shefford.
Parkland course.
18 holes, 6238 yards, S.S.S.71;
9 holes, 6042 yards, S.S.S.70
Founded 1973
Visitors: welcome weekdays,
weekends with h/cap cert.
Green Fee: on application
Societies: welcome anytime.
Catering: bar and restaurant.
Hotels: on site.

G4 Bedford & County

☎(0234) 52617
Green Lane, Clapham, Beds MK41
6ET
Off A6 N of Bedford before Clapham.
Parkland course.
18 holes, 6347 yards, S.S.S.70
Founded 1912
Visitors: welcome weekdays, phone
first; with member weekends.
Green Fee: on application
Societies: Tues, Thurs and Fri.
Catering: available.

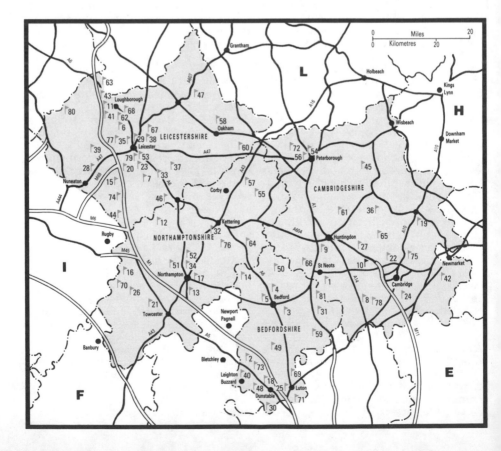

G5 Bedfordshire

☎(0234) 261669 Sec, 53241
Members
Bromham Rd, Biddenham, Bedford
MK40 4AF
1.5 miles from town centre on A428,
NW of town boundary.
Parkland course.
18 holes, 6172 yards, S.S.S.69
Founded 1891
Visitors: welcome weekdays only.
Green Fee: on application
Societies: catered for on weekdays.
Catering: lunch daily.

G6 Birstall

☎(0533) 674322
Station Rd, Birstall, Leicester LE4 3BB
3 miles N of town just off A6.
Parkland course.
18 holes, 5988 yards, S.S.S.69
Founded 1900
Visitors: not weekends.
Green Fee: £25.
Societies: Wed and Fri.
Catering: not Mon.

G7 Blaby

☎(0533) 784804
Lutterworth Rd, Blaby, Leics LE8 3DP
From Leicester, through Blaby
village, course on left hand side.
9 holes, 2600 yards, Par 34
Founded 1991
Visitors: welcome, pay-as-you-play.
Green Fee: £4 (9 holes), £6 (18 holes)
WD; £6 (9 holes), £8 (18 holes) WE.
Societies: welcome; also specialists
in company days.
Catering: bar, bar meals.

G8 Bourn

☎(0954) 718057
Toft Rd, Bourn, Cambridge CB3 7TT
From Cambridge take road to Sandy,
branch off on B1046; from M11
junction 12, take A603 to Sandy then
B1046.
Parkland course.
18 holes, 6273 yards.
Designed by J. Hull and S. Bonham.
Founded Sept 1991
Visitors: requirements and fees to
be arranged, phone for details.
Societies: welcome weekdays.
Catering: clubhouse under
construction.

G9 Brampton Park

☎(0480) 434700 Sec, 434705 Pro.
Buckden Rd, Brampton, Huntingdon,
Cambs PE18 8NF
0.5 mile E of A1; Northbound take 1st
Huntingdon turning, Southbound
take turning signposted RAF
Brampton.
Picturesque meadowland course by
river with wooded lakes section.
18 holes, 6364 yards, S.S.S.73
Designed by Simon Gidman of
Hawtree & Sons.
Founded 1990
Visitors: Welcome.
Green Fee: £24/day WD, £36/day
WE.
Societies: Welcome by arrangement
with Sec except Sat and Sun.
Catering: Members bar; bar snacks
and à la carte restaurant for lunch
and dinner.
Hotels: limited overnight
accommodation on site; bargain
break weekend and single night
packages at Lion (Buckden).

G10 Cambridgeshire Moat House Hotel

☎(0954) 780555
Bar Hill, Cambs CB3 8EU
Adjacent to A604, 4 miles NW of
Cambridge.
Undulating parkland course.
18 holes, 6734 yards, S.S.S.72
Founded 1974
Visitors: must be members of a golf
club with letter of intro. or
membership card (unless hotel
residents); phone to check course
availability.
Green Fee: £19 WD, £25 WE & BH.
Societies: welcome; only resident
societies at weekends.
Catering: full facilities.
Leisure facilites for Hotel residents.
Hotels: Cambridgeshire Moat House,
bargain breaks/inclusive packages
available.

G11 Charnwood Forest

☎(0509) 890259
Breakback Rd, Woodhouse Eaves,
Loughborough, Leics LE12 8TA
B591 off A6 at Quorndon, follow
signs to Woodhouse Eaves; or M1
junction 23.
Undulating heathland course.
9 holes, 5960 yards, S.S.S.69
Founded 1890
Visitors: appointments required.
Green Fee: £17.50 WD, £20.50 WE
and BH.
Societies: weekdays.
Catering: full facilities; light catering
Mon and Thur.
Hotels: Kings Head; Quorn Country
Club; Johnscliffe.

G12 Cold Ashby

☎(0604) 740548, 740099 Pro.
Cold Ashby, Northampton NN6 7EP
5 miles E of M1 junction 18, just off
A50 Northampton-Leicester road.
Undulating meadowland course.
18 holes, 6010 yards, S.S.S.69
Designed by John Day.
Founded 1973
Visitors: welcome weekdays; after
2pm weekends; no h/cap
restrictions.
Green Fee: £12/round, £18/day WD;
£15/round WE.
Societies: welcome weekdays.
Catering: full bar and restaurant
facilities daily.
Hotels: Post House (Crick); Broomhill
(Spratton).

G13 Collingtree Park

☎(0604) 700000, (0604) 702600
Windingbrook Lane, Northampton
NN4 0XN
From M1 Junction 15, follow A508 to
Nottingham.
Parkland course, 18th hole is an
Island Green.
18 holes, 6692 yards, S.S.S.72
Designed by Johnny Miller.
Founded 1987
Visitors: welcome, bookings taken 1
week in advance.
Green Fee: £35/round, £60/day WD;
£50/round, £90/day WE.
Societies: welcome Mon-Fri by
arrangement; specialists in
Corporate Golf Day entertainment.
Catering: bar snacks at all times;
Conservatory Restaurant, à la carte
and table d'hôte, banqueting.
Golf Academy – driving range,
practice grounds etc.

G14 Colworth

☎(0234) 222221
Unilever Research, Colworth House,
Sharnbrook, Bedford MK44 1LQ
10 miles N of Bedford off A6 through
village of Sharnbrook.
Parkland course.
9 holes, 2500 yards, S.S.S.32
Founded 1985
Visitors: with member only.
Green Fee: £3 with member only.

G15 Cosby

☎(0533) 864759
Chapel Lane, off Broughton Rd,
Cosby, Leics LE9 5RG
A46 or A426 out of Leicester, in
Cosby village take Broughton Rd.
Undulating parkland course.

18 holes, 6277 yards, S.S.S.70
Founded 1895
Visitors: welcome weekdays before 4pm; with member only weekends and Bank Holidays.
Green Fee: on application.
Societies: book with Sec in advance.
Catering: bar and meals except Mon; book with Steward.
Snooker.
Hotels: Time Out (Blaby).

G16 **Daventry & District**
☎(0327) 702829
Norton Rd, Daventry, Northants NN11 4AA
1 mile N of town, next to BBC Station.
Undulating meadowland course.
9 holes, 5582 yards, S.S.S.67
Founded early 1920
Visitors: welcome, not before 11am Sun.
Green Fee: on application
Societies: contact Pro.
Catering: societies only.

G17 **Delapre Park**
☎(0604) 764036
Eagle Drive, Nene Valley Way, Northampton NN4 0DU
3 miles from M1 junction 15 on A508.
Public parkland course.
18 holes, 6293 yards, S.S.S.70; further 9 holes from end 1991
Designed by J. Jacobs and J. Corby.
Founded 1976
Visitors: welcome.
Green Fee: on application.
Societies: welcome most days, applications in writing.
Catering: daily 9am to 9.30pm.
Driving range.
Hotels: Swallow; Moat House (preferential rates for societies, golf schools).

G18 **Dunstable Downs**
☎(0582) 604472
Whipsnade Rd, Dunstable, Beds LU6 2NB
2 miles from Dunstable on B4541 Whipsnade road; from London via M1 junction 9, A5 to town centre, left onto A505, left onto B4541; from N via M1 junction 11, A505 and B4541.
Downland course.
18 holes, 6184 yards, S.S.S.70
Designed by James Braid.
Founded 1907
Visitors: welcome weekdays if member of recognised club; h/cap cert required.
Green Fee: £25/round/day.

Societies: Tues and Thurs.
Catering: full facilites except Mon.
Hotels: Old Palace Lodge; Kitts Inn.

G19 **Ely City**
☎(0353) 662751
Cambridge Rd, Ely, Cambs CB7 4HX
On A10, on S outskirts of Ely going towards Cambridge.
Parkland course.
18 holes, 6602 yards, S.S.S.72
Designed by Henry Cotton.
Founded 1962
Visitors: h/cap cert required at all times unless playing with member.
Green Fee: £22/day WD, £30 WE & BH.
Societies: welcome Tues-Fri.
Catering: full facilities; restaurant, bar and bar snacks.
Hotels: Fenland Lodge; Nyton House; Lamb; Highways Motel.

G20 **Enderby**
☎(0533) 849388
Mill Lane, Enderby, Leics
From M1 junction 21 to Enderby, then signposted to Leisure Centre.
Public heathland course.
9 holes, 4232 yards, S.S.S.61
Founded 1986
Visitors: no restrictions.
Green Fee: on application
Societies: welcome by arrangement.
Catering: bar and bar snacks.
Leisure Centre.

G21 **Farthingstone Hotel Golf & Leisure Centre**
☎(032 736) 291, 560, 566
Farthingstone, Towcester, Northants NN12 8HA
Junction 16 off M1, W off A5 between Weedon and Towcester, 3 miles from Weedon.
Undulating parkland course.
18 holes, 6330 yards, S.S.S.71
Designed by M. Gallagher.
Founded 1974
Visitors: welcome at all times.
Green Fee: on application
Societies: welcome at all times.
Catering: full facilities.
Snooker, squash, aerobics, etc.
Hotels: Farthingstone.

G22 **Girton**
☎(0223) 276169
Dodford Lane, Girton, Cambs CB3 0QE
3 miles N of Cambridge on A604.
Flat open course.

18 holes, 6085 yards, S.S.S.69
Founded 1936
Visitors: welcome weekdays.
Green Fee: £8/day with h/cap cert, £23/day without.
Societies: weekdays.
Catering: lunches, dinners served except Mon.
Hotels: Post House (Impington).

G23 **Glen Gorse**
☎(0533) 714159
Glen Rd, Oadby, Leicester LE2 4RF
Follow A6 out of Leicester towards Market Harborough, club on right just past Oadby.
Parkland course.
18 holes, 6641 yards, S.S.S.72
Founded 1933
Visitors: welcome weekdays.
Green Fee: £20/day (£7 with member).
Societies: weekdays; snacks or full meals available.
Catering: snack meals, sandwiches, full meals served except Mon.
Hotels: Leicester Moat House.

G24 **Gog Magog**
☎(0223) 247626
Shelford Bottom, Cambridge CB2 4AB
2 miles S of Cambridge on A1307 Colchester road
Undulating course.
18 holes, 6386 yards, S.S.S.70; 9 holes, 5532 yards, S.S.S.68
Founded 1901
Visitors: welcome weekdays with introduction by member or h/cap cert.
Green Fee: on application to Pro.
Societies: welcome on Tues and Thurs only.
Catering: lunches served daily.
Hotels: University Arms; Garden House; Gonville.

G25 **Griffen**
☎(0582) 415573
Caddington, Luton, Beds
Signposted from Caddington village, 2 miles S of Luton.
Meadowland course.
9 holes, 5516 yards, S.S.S.68
Founded 1982
Visitors: half set per person, golf shoes, no jeans.
Green Fee: £10/day (£5 with member) WD, full price WE after 2pm.
Societies: by arrangement.
Catering: bar and snacks, meals to order.

G26 Hellidon Lakes Hotel and Country Club

☎(0327) 62550
Hellidon, Nr Daventry, Northants
NN11 6LN
15 miles from M1 junction 16 by A45
and A361 Banbury road, turn right in
village of Charwelton; 15 miles from
M40 junction 11 by A361.
Undulating parkland course.
18 holes, 6700 yards, S.S.S.72
Designed by David Snell.
Founded Jan 1991
Visitors: welcome but must book
through Pro shop; bona fide h/cap
certs required at weekends.
Green Fee: £19 WD, £26 WE.
Societies: welcome by arrangement.
Catering: full facilities, restaurant,
bar meals, conference and
banqueting rooms.
5 hole practice ground, driving
range, fly fishing, riding, tennis,
snooker, health studio.
Hotels: own 4-star hotel, inclusive
golfing packages.

G27 Hemingford Abbots

☎(0480) 495000
Cambridge Rd, Hemingford Abbots,
Cambs PE18 9HQ
Alongside A604 between Huntingdon
and St Ives.
Public parkland course.
9 holes, 5468 yards, S.S.S.68
Designed by Advanced Golf Services
Ltd.
Founded 1991
Visitors: welcome.
Green Fee: on application.
Societies: small meetings welcome.
Catering: bar, snacks etc.
Affiliated driving range.
Hotels: St Ives; The Bridge.

G28 Hinckley

☎(0455) 615124
Leicester Rd, Hinckley, Leics LE10
3DR
NE boundary of Hinckley on A47.
Lakeside parkland course.
18 holes, 6592 yards, S.S.S.71
Founded 1894 (as Burbage
Common; name changed 1981).
Visitors: Mon, Wed, Thurs and Fri;
limited at weekends.
Green Fee: £20/round, £25/day after
9am.
Societies: Mon and Wed only by
arrangement.
Catering: daily except Sun evenings.
2 snooker rooms
Hotels: Sketchley Grange; Hinckley
Island; Three Pots Inn.

G29 Humberstone Heights

☎(0533) 761905 Office, 764674 Pro.
Gipsy Lane, Leicester LE5 0TB
Off the Uppingham road opposite
Towers Hospital.
Municipal parkland course
18 holes, 6444 yards, S.S.S.71
Designed by Hawtree & Son.
Founded 1978
Visitors: no restrictions.
Green Fee: on application
Societies: weekdays only.
Catering: bar snacks; meals by
arrangement.
Pitch & Putt course.

G30 Ivinghoe

☎(0296) 668696
Wellcroft, Ivinghoe, Leighton
Buzzard, Beds LU7 9EF
Behind The Kings Head in Ivinghoe
village, 4 miles from Tring and 6
miles from Dunstable.
Meadowland course.
9 holes, 4508 yards, S.S.S.62
Designed by R. Garrad & Sons.
Founded 1967
Visitors: after 9am weekdays, after
8am weekends.
Green Fee: £6 (18 holes) WD, £8 (18
holes) WE.
Societies: weekdays.
Catering: lunches except Mon.
Hotels: Rose & Crown (Tring); Stocks
(Aldbury).

G31 John O'Gaunt

☎(0767) 260360
Sutton Park, Sandy, Beds SG19 2LY
On B1040 between Potton and
Biggleswade.
Undulating parkland courses.
John O'Gaunt, 18 holes, 6513 yards,
S.S.S.71; Carthagena, 18 holes,
5869 yards, S.S.S.68
Visitors: welcome, advisable to
contact club.
Green Fee: £35/day WD, £50/day
WE.
Societies: weekdays only.
Catering: full catering available.
Hotels: Rose & Crown (Potton);
Stratton House (Biggleswade).

G32 Kettering

☎(0536) 512074
Headlands, Kettering, Northants
NN15 6XA
Headlands joins Bowling Green Rd,
on which are the Council Offices;
continue along Headlands for c. 0.5
mile, past Fire Station on left, club is
over railway bridge on right.

Meadowland course.
18 holes, 6036 yards, S.S.S.69
Designed by Tom Morris.
Founded 1891
Visitors: welcome weekdays; with
member weekends, Bank Holidays.
Green Fee: on application.
Societies: Wed and Fri.
Catering: lunch and evening meal
except Mon.
Hotels: George; Royal.

G33 Kibworth

☎(0533) 792301
Weir Rd, Kibworth, Beauchamp,
Leics LE8 0LP
8 miles SE of Leicester on A6.
Meadowland course.
18 holes, 6282 yards, S.S.S.70
Founded 1962
Visitors: welcome weekdays.
Green Fee: £18/day (£5 with
member).
Societies: Mon, Wed, Thurs.
Catering: full facilities; special all-in
package for societies including
morning coffee, lunch and dinner.
Hotels: Angel; The Yews.

G34 Kingsthorpe

☎(0604) 710610 Sec, 711173 Club
Kingsley Rd, Northampton NN2 7BU
2 miles from town centre, off A508.
Undulating parkland course.
18 holes, 6006 yards, S.S.S.69
Founded 1908
Visitors: welcome weekdays by
arrangement, not weekends.
Green Fee: £16/round/day (£8 with
member).
Societies: welcome by arrangement,
green fees £16 per day/round.
Catering: lunches, dinners served.
Hotels: Moat House; Swallow,
Stakis; Holiday Inn.

G35 Kirby Muxloe

☎(0533) 393457 Sec.
Station Rd, Kirby Muxloe, Leicester
LE9 9EP
On A47 3 miles W of Leicester.
Parkland course.
18 holes, 6303 yards, S.S.S.70
Founded 1893
Visitors: must have valid h/cap cert;
Captain's permission required
weekends.
Green Fee: on application.
Societies: weekdays except Tues on
application.
Catering: full facilities.
Snooker room, banqueting.
Hotels: Post House; Moat House.

G36 **Lakeside Lodge**
☎(0487) 740540 Sec, 741541 Pro.
Fen Road, Pidley, Huntingdon,
Cambs PE17 3DD
On B1040 Ramsey-St Ives road.
Modern, challenging public course;
suits all standards of golfer.
18 holes, 6556 yards; 9 holes Par-3
Designed by Alistair Headley.
Founded 1991
Visitors: welcome at any time.
Green Fee: 18 holes, £7 WD, £14
WE; 9 holes, £4 WD, £7 WE; Par-3
course £2 any time.
Societies: welcome weekdays.
Catering: full facilities available.
Driving range.
Hotels: Slepe Hall; George.

G37 **Langton International**
☎(085) 884374
Langton Hall, Leicester LE16 7TY
11 miles S of Leicester on A6, turn
left after Kibworth, 1.5 miles on left.
Parkland course.
18 holes, 6965 yards, Par 72
Designed by Hawtree & Co.
Opening summer 1992
Visitors: subject to h/cap.
Green Fee: £25/round WD,
£35/round WE.
Societies: welcome.
Catering: bar and restaurant.
Practice area and driving range.

G38 **Leicestershire**
☎(0533) 738825
Evington Lane, Leicester LE5 6DJ
Evington village in SE district of
Leicester, 2 miles from city centre.
Parkland course.
18 holes, 6312 yards, S.S.S.70
Founded 1891
Visitors: welcome.
Green Fee: on application.
Societies: welcome weekdays by
prior arrangement.
Catering: lunches and teas daily.
Hotels: Daval; Rowans; Thornwood;
Stanfre House; Gordon Lodge.

G39 **Leicestershire Forest Golf Centre**
☎(0455) 824800
Markfield Lane, Botcheston, Leics
LE9 9FJ
2 miles from Botcheston, 3 miles SW
of A50; 10 mins from M1 junction 21.
Well-wooded parkland course.
18 holes, 6111 yards, S.S.S.69
Founded March 1991
Visitors: welcome any time, pay-as-
you-play; advisable to book tee times.

Green Fee: £10/round WD,
£14/round WE.
Societies: any time by arrangement.
Catering: bar, restaurant (temporary
clubhouse).
Driving range.

G40 **Leighton Buzzard**
☎(0525) 373811/2
Plantation Rd, Leighton Buzzard,
Beds LU7 7JF
1 mile N of Leighton Buzzard off
A418, take left fork at Stag Inn.
Parkland course.
18 holes, 6101 yards, S.S.S.70
Founded 1925
Visitors: welcome weekdays except
Tues with h/cap cert.
Green Fee: £18/round, £25/day,
(£10 with member).
Societies: welcome except Tues and
weekends.
Catering: available 7 days.
Hotels: Swan; Hunt.

G41 **Lingdale**
☎(0509) 890035 Club, 890703 Sec,
890684 Pro.
Joe Moore's Lane, Woodhouse Eaves,
Loughborough, Leics LE12 8TF
5 miles S of Loughborough on B5330.
Undulating parkland course.
18 holes (from May 1992), 6114
metres, S.S.S.72
Designed by D.W. Tucker & G. Austin.
Founded 1967
Visitors: welcome.
Green Fee: on application.
Societies: Mon to Fri by prior
arrangement with Sec.
Catering: full catering facilities.
Hotels: Kings Head; De Montford.

G42 **Links**
☎(0638) 662708
Cambridge Rd, Newmarket, Suffolk
1 mile S of Newmarket High St.
Undulating parkland course.
18 holes, 6162 yards, S.S.S.71
Founded 1902
Visitors: not before 11.30am Sun
unless with member; h/cap certs
required.
Green Fee: £17.50 WD, £24 WE.
Societies: by arrangement.
Catering: full service except Mon.
Hotels: White Hart.

G43 **Longcliffe**
☎(0509) 239129
Snell's Nook Lane, Nanpantan,
Loughborough, Leics LE11 3YA

1 miles from M1 junction 23 off A512
towards Loughborough.
Heathland course.
18 holes, 6551 yards, S.S.S.71
Founded 1904
Visitors: weekdays 8.30am-4.30pm
with h/cap cert; weekends with
member only.
Green Fee: £22/round, £27/day.
Societies: Mon-Fri excluding Tues.
Catering: bar snacks, restaurant.
Hotels: Kings Head.

G44 **Lutterworth**
☎(0455) 552532 Sec, 557199 Pro.
Rugby Rd, Lutterworth, Leics LE17
5HN
0.5 mile from M1 exit 20 on A4114.
Undulating course.
18 holes, 5570 yards, S.S.S.67
Designed by D. Snell.
Founded 1904
Visitors: welcome weekdays;
weekends with member only.
Green Fee: on application
Societies: Mon to Fri.
Catering: full facilities 7 days.

G45 **March**
☎(0353) 52364
Frogs Abbey, Grange Rd, March,
Cambs
A141 W of March bypass, signposted.
Parkland course.
9 holes, 6200 yards, S.S.S.70
Founded 1920
Visitors: weekdays only.
Green Fee: on application

G46 **Market Harborough**
☎(0858) 463684
Oxendon Rd, Market Harborough,
Leics
1 mile S of town on A508
Northampton road.
Parkland course.
9 holes (18 from end 1992), 6168
yards, S.S.S.69
Founded 1898
Visitors: welcome weekdays; with
member only weekends.
Green Fee: £12.
Societies: welcome by arrangement.
Catering: facilities available.
Hotels: Three Swans.

G47 **Melton Mowbray**
☎(0664) 62118
Thorpe Arnold, Melton Mowbray,
Leics LE14 4SD
2 mile NE of Melton Mowbray on
A609 Grantham road.

Northampton

Histories of Golf Clubs show that a great many of them began life on sites different to those which they now enjoy. Some early beginnings are recorded on photographs and plans that adorn clubhouse walls but, though moves have become rarer, one recent exception has been Northampton GC, which forsook their old home in the centre of the city in favour of an exciting future at Harlestone on the edge of Lord Spencer's estate near Althorp.

It came about as a result of intricate negotiations involving the Estate, the Club and a company wishing to develop the city site. Similar deals elsewhere have been discussed, but Northampton is one of the few that have brought hope to life. Having faced the increasing problem of existing within four rigid boundaries, the sense of spaciousness and rural splendour is profound.

However, an equally attractive part of the deal is a fine new clubhouse looking out over Harlestone Lake and three finishing holes which are unusual to say the least. The short 16th and 18th demand shots to carry the water while the 17th is a teasing hole where courage with the drive reaps a telling reward.

As the approach to the clubhouse dips down and up past the church, it is immediately clear that the modern Northampton has a special character that combines challenge with enjoyment — the principle requirements of any good course. There is a pleasant start with a second shot at the 1st to a green below, a short hole over water to a clearing in the wood and a par 5 from a high tee which needs a controlled drive in order to obtain the correct line for a second shot which is compellingly tree lined. This formed part of a clearance operation and the piping of a small stream that supplies the lake on the 2nd.

There are three or four changes of character in the layout which next introduces a dogleg round the perimeter of the wood and then, after another short hole, ventures forth into more open territory where the main features are a few large established trees and the boundary walls of mellow Northamptonshire stone.

Before the turn is reached back near the clubhouse, the 8th has another dropping second shot down a shallow valley while the 9th threads its way between ancient trees that are more trunk than foliage — a haven for owls and insects. The 10th scales a slight crest, leading back to the open ground where several holes run parallel, the par 5 12th carrying the added threat of out of bounds to sliced shots.

Bunkers guard the short 13th but gradually Harlestone Lake looms, the 15th carrying players down a long slope to a green in front of the old boat house reconstructed as a condition of planning approval. The 15th green lies close to the 18th but before the round is complete, there is a searching test of skill, nerve and decision, a climax that will be the centre of much debate, much gnashing of teeth and much jubilation.

Water holes are becoming more common in British golf, although few are more teasing than the par 3 16th with its green that is far wider than it is deep. Clearing the lake is one thing, but there are penalties for being big. Trees and sharp banks surround a sloping putting surface.

Position from the tee is important on the 17th but, in spite of a formidable carry from the 18th and an undulating fairway the other side, the pitch to the green can be quite demanding.

Together with the Collingtree course on the other side of town, the new Northampton has added a powerful dimension to the county's golf.

Undulating course.
18 holes, 6253 yards, S.S.S.71
Founded 1925
Visitors: welcome with h/cap cert.
Green Fee: £10 WD, £15 WE.
Societies: weekdays by
arrangement.
Catering: bar and restaurant.
Hotels: George; Harborough;
Stapleford Park.

G48 **Mentmore**
☎(0296) 662020, (071) 499 4944
membership enquiries
Mentmore, Leighton Buzzard, Beds
LU7 0QN
On B489 4 miles SW of Leighton
Buzzard.
Rolling parkland course with lakes
and trees.
Roseberry, 18 holes, 6864 yards, Par
72; Rothschild, 18 holes, 6896 yards,
Par 72
Designed by Bob Sandow
Opening Sept 1992
Visitors: welcome; apply for details.
Societies: apply for details.
Catering: bar, restaurant.
Practice ground, tennis courts (3),
indoor swimming pool, sauna etc.

G49 **Millbrook**
☎(0525) 840252
Ampthill, Beds MK45 2JB
Between Ampthill and Ridgmont on
Woburn road, A418.
Parkland course.
18 holes, 7100 yards, S.S.S.73
Designed by Will Sutherland.
Founded 1980
Visitors: Mon, Tues, Wed, Fri before
12am, weekends and Bank Holidays
with member only.
Green Fee: on application
Societies: Mon, Tues, Wed only.
Catering: bar and restaurant.

G50 **Mowsbury**
☎(0234) 771041 Sec, 216374
Pro/bookings
Cleat Hill, Kimbolton Rd, Bedford
MK41 8DQ
On Kimbolton Rd, from Bedford 2
miles N of city centre.
Municipal parkland course.
18 holes, 6514 yards, S.S.S.71
Designed by Hawtree.
Founded 1975
Visitors: welcome.
Green Fee: £5/round WD, £8/round
WE.
Societies: on application to Facilities
Manager (0234) 771493.

Catering: snacks, meals, drinks
available; functions.
Driving range, squash.

G51 **Northampton**
☎(0604) 845155, 845102
Harlestone, Northampton NN7 4EF
On A428 Rugby road, c. 4 miles out of
Northampton.
Parkland course.
18 holes, 6534 yards, S.S.S.71
Designed by Donald Steel.
Founded 1893
Visitors: currently only with member.
Green Fee: £25/day.
Societies: weekdays, not Wed.
Catering: full facilities available.
Snooker, banqueting.
Hotels: Northampton Moat House;
Heyford Manor.

G52 **Northamptonshire County**
☎(0604) 843025 Sec, 842170 Club,
842226 Pro.
Golf Lane, Church Brampton,
Northampton NN6 8AZ
Off A50 Northampton-Leicester road,
4.5 miles from Northampton.
Heathland/parkland course.
18 holes, 6503 yards, S.S.S.71
Designed by H.S. Colt.
Founded 1909
Visitors: with h/cap by arrangement;
ladies Sat after 3.30pm; Sun after
11.15am.
Green Fee: £30/round/day; £10 with
member.
Societies: Wed, some Thurs.
Catering: snack menu 11am-6pm,
otherwise by arrangement.
Hotels: Broomhill; Pytchley; Red
Lion.

G53 **Oadby**
☎(0533) 709052, 700215 Steward
Leicester Rd, Oadby, Leics LE2 4AB
On A6 from Leicester, just outside
city limits, inside Race Course.
Public meadowland course.
18 holes, 6228 yards, S.S.S.69
Founded 1975
Visitors: welcome.
Green Fee: on application
Societies: on application to Oadby
and Wigston Borough Council.
Catering: apply to Steward.

G54 **Orton Meadows**
☎(0733) 237478
Ham Lane, Orton Waterville,
Peterborough, Cambs PE2 0UU

On A625 Peterborough-Oundle road,
2 miles W of Peterborough at entrance
to Ferry Meadows Country Park.
Municipal parkland course.
18 holes, 5800 yards, S.S.S.68
Designed by Dennis & Roger Fitton.
Founded 1987
Visitors: advance bookings
welcome.
Green Fee: £6.20 WD, £8.70 WE &
BH; reductions jnrs, OAPs,
unemployed.
Societies: welcome except before
11am Sun.
Catering: adjoining steakhouse "The
Granary".
Hotels: Moat House (Peterborough).

G55 **Oundle**
☎(0832) 273267
Benefield Rd, Oundle, Northants PE8
4EZ
On A427 Oundle-Corby road, 1.5
miles from Oundle.
Undulating parkland course.
18 holes, 5600 yards, S.S.S.67
Founded 1893
Visitors: after 10.30am weekends
and Bank Holidays, otherwise no
restriction.
Green Fee: £18/day WD, £25/day
WE.
Societies: welcome except Mon and
weekends.
Catering: full service available.
Hotels: Talbot; Bridge (Thrapston).

G56 **Peterborough Milton**
☎(0733) 380489
Milton Ferry, Peterborough, PE6 7AG
On A47 4 miles W of Peterborough.
Parkland course.
18 holes, 6431 yards, S.S.S.71
Designed by James Braid.
Founded June 1938
Visitors: weekdays only by prior
arrangement with Sec.
Green Fee: on application.
Societies: weekdays only by prior
arrangement with Sec.
Catering: full facilities except Mon.
Hotels: Haycock Inn; Moat House.

G57 **Priors Hall**
☎(0536) 60756
Stamford Rd, Weldon, Northants
A43 Corby to Stamford road, 2 miles
E of Weldon.
Public parkland course.
18 holes, 6677 yards, S.S.S.72
Founded 1965
Visitors: unlimited.
Green Fee: on application.

Societies: welcome weekdays.
Catering: snacks and meals.
Hotels: Charlon Manor.

G58 RAF Cottesmore

☎(0572) 812241 ext 7760
Oakham, Leicester LE15 7BL
7 miles N of Oakham off B668.
Parkland course.
9 holes, 5622 yards, S.S.S.67
Founded 1980
Visitors: with member only.
Green Fee: £4

G59 RAF Henlow

☎(0462) 851515 ext 7083
Clubhouse, 7556 Sec
Henlow Camp, Beds SG16 6DN
3 miles SE of Shefford on A505,
follow signs to RAF Henlow.
Meadowland course.
9 holes, 5204 yards, S.S.S.66
Founded 1985
Visitors: only with member.
Green Fee: £3/day/round.
Societies: arranged through Sec.
Catering: light refreshment.
Hotels: Bird in Hand.

G60 RAF North Luffenham

☎(0780) 720041 ext 431
North Luffenham, Oakham, Leics
LE15 8RL
Follow signposts for RAF North
Luffenham from A606.
Meadowland course.
9 holes, 6010 yards, S.S.S.70
Founded 1975
Visitors: only in company of member.
Green Fee: £7.
Societies: arranged through Sec.
Catering: bar and restaurant.
Hotels: George; Crown.

G61 Ramsey

☎(0487) 812600
4 Abbey Terrace, Ramsey,
Huntingdon, Cambs PE17 1DD
12 miles SE of Peterborough, off
B1040.
Parkland course.
18 holes, 6133 yards, S.S.S.70
Designed by J. Hamilton Stutt.
Founded 1965
Visitors: weekdays only, on
production of h/cap cert.
Green Fee: £20 (£10 with member).
Societies: Mon, Tues, Wed.
Catering: full facilities.
6-rink outdoor bowling green.
Hotels: George (Ramsey).

G62 Rothley Park

☎(0533) 302019 Clubhouse,
302809 Sec, 303023 Pro.
Westfield Lane, Rothley, Leicester
LE7 7LH
6 miles N of Leicester, W of A46.
Parkland course.
18 holes, 6487 yards, S.S.S.71
Founded 1912
Visitors: welcome if member of
recognised club with h/cap;
members' guests only Tues,
weekends and Bank Holidays.
Green Fee: £25 WD.
Societies: Wed and Thurs.
Catering: full catering except Mon.
Hotels: Rothley Court.

G63 Rushcliffe

☎(0509) 852959
Stocking Lane, East Leake,
Loughborough, Leics LE12 5RL
Between Gotham and East Leake 6
miles N of Loughborough; easy reach
of M1 junction 24.
Well-wooded heathland course.
18 holes, 6100 yards, S.S.S.69
Founded 1910
Visitors: welcome, properly dressed
and preferably club golfers.
Green Fee: £18.50.
Societies: Mon, Wed, Thurs, Fri,
April 1 to Oct 31.
Catering: bar and restaurant.

G64 Rushden

☎(0933) 312581
Kimbolton Rd, Chelveston,
Wellingborough, Northants NN9 6AN
On A45 2 miles E of Higham Ferrers.
Undulating meadowland course.
10 holes, 6335 yards, S.S.S.70
Founded 1919
Visitors: welcome weekdays except
Wed pm; weekends with member
only.
Green Fee: £12 (£8 with member).
Societies: bookable in advance.
Catering: any time.
Hotels: Westwood; Tudor Gate
(Finedon).

G65 St Ives

☎(0480) 68392
Westwood Rd, St Ives, Cambs PE17
4RS
B1040 off A45.
Parkland course.
9 holes, 6100 yards, S.S.S.69
Founded 1923
Visitors: welcome weekdays; with
member only weekends.
Green Fee: £20.

Societies: not weekends.
Catering: not Mon.
Hotels: Slepe Hall.

G66 St Neots

☎(0480) 72363 Sec, 74311 Club
Crosshall Rd, St Neots, Huntingdon,
Cambs PE19 4AE
On A45 1.5 miles W of St Neots.
Parkland course with water hazards.
18 holes, 6027 yards, S.S.S.69
Designed by Harry Vardon (original 9).
Founded 1890
Visitors: welcome; with member
weekends; h/cap cert required.
Green Fee: on application.
Societies: welcome except Sat, Sun,
Fri and Mon.
Catering: full service in clubhouse.
Snooker.
Hotels: Stephensons Rocket; Kings
Head.

G67 Scraptoft

☎(0533) 418863
Beeby Rd, Scraptoft, Leics LE7 9SJ
Turn off A47 main Leicester-
Peterborough road to Scraptoft at
Thurnby.
Meadowland course.
18 holes, 6146 yards, S.S.S.69
Founded 1928
Visitors: welcome; jacket, collar and
tie.
Green Fee: on application.
Societies: Mon-Fri.
Catering: meals served except Mon.
Hotels: White House.

G68 Shelthorpe

☎(0509) 267766
Poplar Road, Loughborough, Leics
From Leicester on A6 turn right at 1st
traffic lights, over island, then 2nd
left, signposted.
Municipal parkland course.
18 holes Par 3, c. 3000 yards
Visitors: welcome.
Green Fee: £2.30 (£1.15 jnrs/OAPs);
£1.70 (85p) for 9 holes.

G69 South Bedfordshire

☎(0582) 591500 Sec, 591209 Pro.
Warden Hill Rd, Luton, LU2 7AA
3 miles N of Luton on A6, signposted
(right) into Warden Hill Rd; left at end,
slip road to right of School.
Undulating course; some trees,
hawthorn hedges; dries well.
Galley course, 18 holes, 6342 yards,
S.S.S.71; Warden course, 9 holes,
2490 yards, S.S.S.64

Founded 1892
Visitors: welcome; Galley weekdays only with h/cap cert unless by prior arrangement; Warden any time.
Green Fee: Galley, £17/round, £27/day; Warden, £11 (18 holes).
Societies: not Tues.
Catering: snacks 10.30am-9.30pm; set lunch, dinner by arrangement. Snooker.
Hotels: Culverdene; Chiltern; Strathmore.

G70 **Staverton Park**
☎(0327) 705911
Staverton, Daventry, Northants NN11 6JT
On A425 Daventry-Leamington road, 1 mile S of Daventry; near M1 junctions 16/18 and M40 junctions 11/12.
Undulating meadowland course.
18 holes, 6204 yards, S.S.S.70
Designed by Comm. John Harris.
Founded 1978
Visitors: welcome.
Green Fee: £19 WD, £21 WE.
Societies: welcome Mon-Fri.
Catering: full facilities at all times.
Snooker, solarium, sauna, trimnasium, banqueting suites.
Hotels: special golf inclusive Badger Breaks, phone for details.

G71 **Stockwood Park**
☎(0582) 413704 Pro.
Stockwood Park, London Rd, Luton, Beds LU1 4LX
Junction 10 off M1, turn left towards town centre, then left at 1st set of traffic lights into Stockwood Park.
Meadowland course.
18 holes, 5973 yards, S.S.S.69
Founded 1973
Visitors: welcome at all times.
Green Fee: £4.55 WD, £6.65 WE.
Societies: welcome Mon-Thurs, contact Pro.
Catering: breakfast and lunch.
Driving range, 9-hole Pitch & Putt.
Hotels: Strathmore.

G72 **Thorpe Wood**
☎(0733) 267701
Nene Parkway, Peterborough PE3 6SE
On A47 to Leicester 2 miles W of Peterborough, next to Moat House Hotel.
Parkland course.
18 holes, 7086 yards, S.S.S.74
Designed by Peter Alliss & Dave Thomas.
Founded 1975
Visitors: unrestricted.
Green Fee: £6.20 WD, £8.70 WE & BH.

Societies: by arrangement up to a year in advance.
Catering: at Greenkeeper.
Hotels: The Moat House.

G73 **Tilsworth**
☎(0525) 210721
Dunstable Rd, Tilsworth, Leighton Buzzard, Beds
On A5, 1 mile N of Dunstable.
Parkland course.
9 holes, 5443 yards, S.S.S.67; extending to 18 holes spring 1992
Founded 1972
Visitors: welcome all times except Sun 7.30-11.30am.
Green Fee: £4 (18 holes) WD, £5 (18 holes) WE.
Societies: welcome all times except Sun am.
Catering: hot and cold food available lunchtimes Mon-Sat, also Thurs, Fri, Sat evenings.
Hotels: Swan; Crest (Luton).

G74 **Ullesthorpe**
☎(0455) 209023
Frolesworth Rd, Ullesthorpe, Lutterworth, Leics
B577 off A5 to Claybrooke and Ullesthorpe, follow signs to course.
Meadowland course.

18 holes, 6650 yards, S.S.S.72
Visitors: weekdays.
Green Fee: on application
Societies: weekdays.
Catering: bar snacks and restaurant.

G75 Waterbeach Barracks
☎(0223) 861048 Sec.
39th Engineering Regiment,
Waterbeach, Cambs CB5 9PA
Fenland course.
9 holes, 6237 yards, S.S.S.70
Founded 1972
Visitors: HM Forces welcome,
civilians must be introduced by and
play with member.
Green Fee: £8/day (jnrs, military
students £2.50).
Catering: limited bar.

G76 Wellingborough
☎(0933) 677234
Harrowden Hall, Great Harrowden,
Wellingborough, Northants NN9 5AD
1 mile NE of Wellingborough to right
of A509.
Parkland course.
18 holes, 6604 yards, S.S.S.72
Designed by Hawtree & Sons.
Founded 1893
Visitors: welcome weekdays except
Tues, with h/cap cert.
Green Fee: £22/round, £27/day.
Societies: Wed, Thurs, Fri by prior
arrangement; with h/cap certs.
Catering: bar, snacks, restaurant.
Snooker, swimming pool.
Hotels: Hind; Oak House; Tudor Gate.

G77 Western Park
☎(0533) 872339
Scudamore Rd, Braunstone Frith,
Leicester LE3 1UQ
Off A47, 2 miles W of city centre; M1
junction 21.

Public parkland course.
18 holes, 6532 yards, S.S.S.71
Designed by F.W. Hawtree.
Founded c. 1900
Visitors: welcome; book at
weekends.
Green Fee: on application
Societies: welcome.
Catering: 7 days a week.

G78 Whaddon Golf Centre
☎(0223) 207325
Church St, Whaddon, Nr Royston,
Cambs SG8 5RX
4 miles N of Royston, 9 miles S of
Cambridge.
Public parkland course.
9 holes Par 3, 795 yards
Designed by Richard Green
Founded 1987
Visitors: welcome.
Green Fee: £2.50 (9 holes) WD, £3
WE.
Catering: clubhouse opening
summer 1992.
Driving range, putting green.

G79 Whetstone
☎(0533) 861424
Cambridge Rd, Cosby, Leicester LE9
5SH
4 miles from M1 junction 21, SE of
Leicester; take A46 to Narborough,
then signposts to Whetstone.
Wooded parkland course with water
features.
18 holes, 5795 yards, S.S.S.68
Designed by Nick Leatherland.
Founded 1963
Visitors: welcome; restricted
weekends, book in advance.
Green Fee: £10/round WD;
£12.50/round WE.
Societies: welcome by prior
arrangement.

Catering: bar and cold snacks
available.
Driving range.
Hotels: Time Out (Blaby).

G80 Willesley Park
☎(0530) 414596
Tamworth Rd, Ashby-de-la-Zouch,
Leics LE6 5PF
On B5006 approx 1.5 miles from
centre of Ashby-de-la-Zouch S
towards Tamworth; from M42
junction 11, 2 miles N towards
Ashby-de-la-Zouch on B5006.
Undulating parkland/heathland
course.
18 holes, 6304 yards, S.S.S.70
Designed by C.K. Cotton.
Founded 1921
Visitors: welcome with reservation,
must be bona fide members of
another club.
Green Fee: £25 WD, £30 WE & BH.
Societies: welcome Wed, Thurs and
Fri during April-Sept by prior
arrangement.
Catering: full catering facilities
available.
Snooker.
Hotels: Royal; Fallen Knight.

G81 Wyboston Lakes
☎(0480) 219200
Wyboston Lakes, Wyboston, Beds
MK44 3AL
Off A1 S of St Neots.
Public parkland course set round
lakes.
18 holes, 5310 yards, S.S.S.69
Designed by Neil Oackden.
Founded 1981
Visitors: welcome.
Green Fee: £14 WD, £16 WE.
Societies: welcome.
Catering: bar, snacks.
Hotels: motel on site.

H

SUFFOLK, NORFOLK

Suffolk and Norfolk provide all the ingredients for a perfect golfing holiday, any number of excellent courses — seaside and inland — in settings that give golfers a special sense of escape.

Journeys from London have been considerably assisted by new roads plus a bridge over the River Orwell at Ipswich which is spectacular, but East Anglia remains something of a quiet backwater which contributes greatly to its popularity. Felixstowe Ferry, the place where Bernard Darwin learned to play, is the oldest, retaining a measure of its quaintness in spite of many changes since the clubhouse was based around its famous Martello Tower.

The best holes are those nearest the sea, those on the other side of the road filling the flatter land, although perhaps the most unusual hole, the short 12th, straddles the road with the tee shot having to clear a safety net to protect the passers-by — motorised and pedestrian.

Further up the coast lie Aldeburgh and Thorpeness, contrasting Clubs and courses that can, nevertheless, be conveniently taken together. For all the nearness of the sea, neither can be classed as seaside, Thorpeness with a profusion of heather and Aldeburgh weaving its crafty way between the gorse across the common.

Woodbridge is another Suffolk delight in an area around Ipswich which includes Purdis Heath and Rushmere.

Crossing the county boundary into Norfolk, the coastal path heads for Great Yarmouth & Caister, founded in 1882, Sheringham, Brancaster and Hunstanton. Lovers of racing will have identified Great Yarmouth & Caister from the stands, the first and last holes hurdling the rails and several others enclosed by the track.

The best is very good after a slightly mundane start but the focus for the connoisseur is fixed on Hunstanton and the Royal West Norfolk links at Brancaster which occupy as remote a tract as any on which the game is played. Hunstanton, 100 years old in 1991, is a full-blown championship test divided by a central ridge of dunes that gives it a bit of a Jekyll and Hyde character. Brancaster, on the other hand, derives its character more from deep sleepered bunkers, sandy turf, a unique stretch of marshland and a rich variety in the size, angling, shaping and defence of its greens. A year junior to Hunstanton, it rubs shoulders with nature in all its aspects, adverse weather adding a wild, bleak dimension that, for all its ferocity, can add appeal.

On more modern lines are the two courses and varied leisure facilities at Barnham Broom on the outskirts of Norwich, which gain in popularity.

Cambridge University golfers have an understandably soft spot for East Anglia, fixtures, in addition to Hunstanton, including Royal Norwich and, in the old days, a final trial at Thetford which has had a fine new clubhouse and a changed course since then. The changes, dictated by the Thetford-by-pass, necessitated intrusion into the forest — or at least what was forest until the terrible storm of October 1987. Only a few scraggy pines survived the blast but Thetford, ancient and modern, is full of charm that deserves to be sampled.

From Thetford, it is relatively plain sailing to Cambridge either through or round Newmarket but, on the way, there is a port of call at Royal Worlington & Newmarket which you overlook at your peril.

Given the accolade by Bernard Darwin of "the sacred nine", it is a masterpiece of simple design, a triumph in fitting a quart into a pint pot. In winter, it is a veritable haven that offers the ideal of a day of foursomes with the lure of characteristic refreshment to re-fuel the system. Throughout the world, I have enjoyed nothing better.

H1 Aldeburgh
☎(0728) 452890
Saxmundham Rd, Aldeburgh, Suffolk
IP15 5PE
6 miles E of A12 midway between
Ipswich and Lowestoft.
Heathland course.
18 holes, 6330 yards, S.S.S.71;
9 holes, 4228 yards, S.S.S.64
Founded 1884
Visitors: welcome weekdays;
weekends by arrangement with Sec.
Green Fee: on application.
Societies: welcome by arrangement
with Sec.
Catering: lunches served.
Hotels: Wentworth; White Lion;
Brudenell; Uplands.

H2 Alnesbourne Priory
☎(0473) 727393
Priory Park, Ipswich, Suffolk IP10 0JT
Leave A45 Ipswich southern by-pass
at exit marked Ransomes Europark,
Nacton; follow signs to Industrial
Estate; take 1st left after 200 yards,
follow single lane road for 1 mile.
Pretty parkland course fronting
Orwell estuary.
9 holes, 1760 yards, S.S.S.58
Founded 1987
Visitors: always closed Tues,
experienced golfers in correct attire
welcome any other time.
Green Fee: between £9 and £12 for
afternoon or day ticket.
Societies: restricted to Tues only by
arrangement.
Catering: bar and restaurant.
Function room; tennis, heated
outdoor swimming pool in summer,
Adventure Playground, nature trails.
Hotels: log cabin accommodation on
site; also 50 executive touring sites.

H3 Barnham Broom Hotel Golf & Country Club
☎(060 545) 393
Honingham Rd, Barnham Broom,
Norwich, Norfolk NR9 4DD
10 miles SW of Norwich between
A11 and A47.
River valley and parkland courses.
Hill, 18 holes, 6628 yards, S.S.S.72;
Valley, 18 holes, 6470 yards, S.S.S.71
Designed by Frank Pennink (Valley),
Donald Steel (Hill).
Founded 1977
Visitors: welcome weekdays;
residents 7 days; proof of club
membership required.
Green Fee: £25/round, £30/day.
Societies: welcome, details on
application.

Catering: full restaurant, snack bar.
Leisure centre, squash, tennis,
snooker etc.
Hotels: Barnham Broom, golf
"getaway breaks", details on request.

H4 Bawburgh
☎(0603) 746390
Long Lane, Bawburgh, Norwich,
Norfolk NR9 3LX
Turn left off A47 leaving Norwich at
Round Well public house; adjacent to
Norfolk Show ground.
Parkland course.
9 holes, 5278 yards, S.S.S.66
Founded 1978
Visitors: welcome except Bank
Holidays, weekends before 12am.
Green Fee: on application.
Societies: only by notice previous
year; restricted.
Catering: bar and snack meals.
Driving range (1993)

H5 Bungay & Waveney Valley
☎(0986) 892337
Outney Common, Bungay, Suffolk
NR35 1DS
A143 Bury St Edmunds to Great
Yarmouth road, about 0.5 mile from
town centre.

Heathland course.
18 holes, 5950 yards, S.S.S.68
Designed by James Braid.
Founded 1889
Visitors: welcome weekdays only;
with member at weekends.
Green Fee: £18/day/round.
Societies: arranged by writing to
club; weekdays only.
Catering: full facilities except Mon
(snacks only).
Hotels: The Swan; King's Head.

H6 Bury St Edmunds
☎(0284) 755979
Tuthill, Bury St Edmunds, Suffolk
IP28 6LG
1st exit eastbound off A45 for Bury,
0.25 mile down B1106, on right.
Parkland course.
18 holes, 6615 yards, S.S.S.72;
9 holes, 4664 yards, S.S.S.62
Designed by Hawtree (9 hole).
Founded 1924
Visitors: welcome weekdays inc
Bank Holidays; only with member
weekends.
Green Fee: £22/day; jnrs half price.
Societies: welcome weekdays by
arrangement; not weekends or Bank
Holidays.
Catering: full service available.
Snooker.

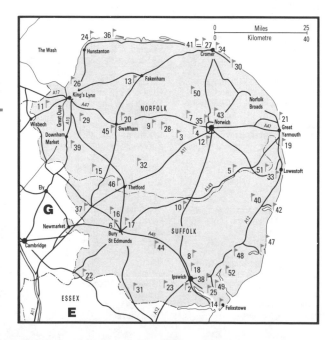

H7 Costessy Park
☎(0603) 746333
Old Costessy, Norwich, Norfolk NR8 5AL
3 miles W of Norwich, turn off A47 at Round Well public house.
Parkland/river valley course.
18 holes, 5964 yards, S.S.S.69
Designed by Frank Macdonald.
Founded 1983
Visitors: welcome, not before 11.30am weekends.
Green Fee: £14/day WD, £17/day WE.
Societies: by arrangement.
Catering: full bar and catering.
Practice area; golf cart hire for physically handicapped.

H8 Cretingham
☎(0728) 685275
Cretingham, Woodbridge, Suffolk IP13 7BA
2 miles from A1120 at Earl Soham.
Public parkland course.
9 holes, 1955 yards, S.S.S.30
Founded 1984
Visitors: welcome every day from 8am until dusk.
Green Fee: £6 WD, £9 WE & BH.
Societies: by arrangement.
Catering: coffee, soft drinks, snacks.

H9 Dereham
☎(0362) 695900
Quebec Rd, Dereham, Norfolk NR19 2DS
Take B1105 from Dereham.
Parkland course.
9 holes, 6225 yards, S.S.S.70
Founded 1934
Visitors: welcome with h/cap cert; only with member weekends.
Green Fee: £16 WD, £10 WE (with member).
Societies: by arrangement.
Catering: by arrangement.
Hotels: Phoenix; George; Kings Head.

H10 Diss
☎(0379) 642847
Diss, Norfolk
Between Norwich and Ispwich, 2 miles W of A140 (turn at Scole).
Commonland course.
9 holes, 5900 yards, S.S.S.68
Founded 1903
Visitors: welcome weekdays before 4pm and weekends after 4pm in summer; no restrictions Oct-March.
Green Fee: on application
Societies: welcome weekdays.
Catering: full facilities.

H11 Eagles
☎(0553) 827147
39 School Road, Tilney All Saints, King's Lynn, Norfolk PE34 4RS
On A47 between King's Lynn and Wisbech.
Moorland course.
9 holes, 4284 yards, S.S.S.64;
9 holes Par 3
Designed by David W. Horn.
Founded Nov 1990
Visitors: welcome; restricted Sat and Sun am.
Green Fee: £5 (9 holes) WD, £6 WE.
Societies: ring for details.
Catering: bar facilities from summer 1992. Driving range.

H12 Eaton
☎(0603) 51686
Newmarket Rd, Norwich NR4 6SF
Off A11 into Sunningdale, signposted; approx 2 miles from centre of Norwich.
Undulating course.
18 holes, 6125 yards, S.S.S.69
Founded 1908
Visitors: welcome all week.
Green Fee: £25 WD, £30 WE.
Societies: by arrangement.
Catering: lunches served weekdays; teas all week.
Hotels: Post House; Hotel Norwich.

H13 Fakenham
☎(0328) 862867 reception, 863534 Pro.
Sports Centre, The Race Course, Fakenham, Norfolk
B1146 from Dereham or A1067 from Norwich.
Parkland course.
9 holes, 5992 yards, S.S.S.69
Designed by Charles Lawrie.
Founded 1981
Visitors: welcome.
Green Fee: on application.
Societies: by arrangement.
Catering: in Sports Centre.
Hotels: Crown; Limes; The Mill.

H14 Felixstowe Ferry
☎(0394) 286834
Ferry Rd, Felixstowe, Suffolk IP11 9RY
A45 to Felixstowe, avoid turning right off A45; follow signs to Yatching Centre.
Links course.
18 holes, 6042 yards, S.S.S.70
Designed by Henry Cotton & Sir Guy Campbell.
Founded 1880
Visitors: welcome weekdays and after 10.30am weekends and Bank Holidays.
Green Fee: £18/day WD, £21 WE & BH.
Societies: Tues, Wed and Fri.
Catering: lunch available 7 days; evening meals by arrangement.
Hotels: Orwell Moat House.

H15 Feltwell
☎(0842) 827644, 827762
Thor Ave, Feltwell, Thetford, Norfolk
0.5 mile S of Feltwell on B112; right towards 2 large "golf balls" (satellite tracking station).
Open heathland course.
9 holes (18 tees), 6260 yards, S.S.S.70
Founded 1972
Visitors: welcome, sometimes restricted at weekends.
Green Fee: £12 WD, £20 WE & BH.
Societies: any weekday.
Catering: bar; catering by arrangement.
Hotels: Brandon House (Brandon).

H16 Flempton
☎(0284) 728291
Flempton, Bury St Edmunds, Suffolk
4 miles NW of Bury St Edmunds on A1101 to Mildenhall.
Breckland course.
9 holes, 6074 yards, S.S.S.69
Designed by J. H. Taylor.
Founded 1895
Visitors: with members only at weekends and Bank Holidays; h/cap certs required except when playing with member.
Green Fee: £17.50 (18 holes), £22.50/day.
Societies: very limited.
Catering: excellent by arrangement.
Hotels: Angel Hotel (Bury St Edmunds); Bell Hotel (Mildenhall).

H17 Fornham Park
☎(0284) 706777
St John's Hill Plantation, The Street, Fornham All Saints, Bury St Edmunds, Suffolk IP28 6JQ
Off A45 to Bury St Edmunds (2 miles), B1101 to Brandon; or A134 Bury-Thetford road at Fornham St Martin.
Parkland course.
18 holes, 6079 yards, S.S.S.69
Founded 1976
Visitors: welcome, phone Pro; not Tues pm, not before 1pm weekends.
Green Fee: £20/round, £25/day WD; £25/round WE after 1pm.

VICTORIA ROAD, ALDEBURGH, SUFFOLK, IP15 5DX

Uplands is a country house hotel with a long, golfing, tradition. Relax and enjoy fine food served in attractive and comfortable surroundings.

Restaurant open to non-residents for evening meals.

Extensive range of malt whiskies available.
Golfing tee-off times arranged.

Tel: ALDEBURGH 0728 - 452420

Societies: welcome weekdays only.
Catering: 2 bars, bar meals daily; also Lark River Restaurant (0284) 760329.
Hotels: Butterfly; Suffolk; Angel; Swan (Lavenham).

H18 **Fynn Valley**
☎(0473) 785463, 785632 fax.
Witnesham, Ipswich, Suffolk IP6 9JA
On B1077, 2 miles due N of Ipswich.
Parkland course.
9 holes, 2800 yards, S.S.S.33 (18 holes, 5700 yards, S.S.S.67 from autumn 1992); 9 holes Par 3, 1000 yards.
Designed by Tony Tyrrell.
Founded April 1991
Visitors: not Sun or Thurs am (Ladies'); proper golf equipment and clothing on main course.
Green Fee: £7.50 (9 holes), £12 (18 holes), £15/day; Par 3 course, £3.50/round, £5/day; reductions for jnrs.
Societies: any weekday except Thurs.
Catering: bar and light refreshments. Driving range, multi-level practice bunkers, chipping and putting greens.

H19 **Gorleston**
☎(0493) 661911
Warren Rd, Gorleston, Great Yarmouth, Norfolk NR31 6JT
Off A12 Yarmouth to Lowestoft road, Yarmouth end of dual carriageway, follow signs down Links Rd to Squash Club; 200 yards on left.
Seaside course.
18 holes, 6404 yards, S.S.S.71
Founded 1906
Visitors: welcome all times, but phone call advisable; h/cap cert required.
Green Fee: on application.
Societies: welcome weekdays, by prior arrangement.
Catering: available.
Hotels: Cliff; St Edmunds.

H20 **Granary Hotel Golf & Country Club**
☎(0328) 701310
Little Dunham, Nr Swaffham, King's Lynn, Norfolk PE32 2DF
Off A47 at Necton.
Parkland course with lakes.
9 holes, 4422 yards, Par 64
Founded 1987
Visitors: welcome.
Green Fee: £8 WD, £10 WE.

Societies: welcome.
Catering: full; first class restaurant. Putting green, tennis, swimming.
Hotels: Granary Hotel.

H21 **Great Yarmouth & Caister**
☎(0493) 728699
Beach House, Caister-on-Sea, Great Yarmouth, Norfolk NR31 5TD
About 1 mile N of Great Yarmouth on A149 take right turn at roundabout, then right into signposted lane.
Seaside links course.
18 holes, 6235 yards, S.S.S.70
Founded 1882
Visitors: welcome, advisable to telephone in advance.
Green Fee: on application.
Societies: welcome by arrangement.
Catering: coffee, lunch and evening meals always available.
Hotels: Carlton; Cavendish; Hamilton; Ocean Edge; Sandringham; Windyshore.

H22 **Haverhill**
☎(0440) 61951
Coupals Rd, Haverhill, Suffolk CB9 7UW

Leave Haverhill on A604 towards Colchester, pass under railway viaduct, 2nd left into Chalkstone Way, then 1st right into Coupals Rd.
Parkland course.
9 holes, 5707 yards, S.S.S.68
Designed by Charles Lawrie.
Founded 1973
Visitors: welcome
Green Fee: £15 (£7.50 with member) WD, £21 (£10.50 with member) WE & BH.
Societies: welcome by prior arrangement.
Catering: bar facilities available; no catering.
Hotels: Woodlands Hotel.

H23 **Hintlesham Hall**

☎(0473) 87761
Hintlesham, Ipswich, Suffolk IP3 8NS
4 miles W of Ipswich, 10 mins from A12, A45.
Parkland course.
18 holes, 6630 yards, S.S.S.72.
Designed by Hawtree & Sons.
Founded 2nd Sept, 1991
Visitors: welcome; h/cap certs required.
Green Fee: £39.50 WD, £45 WE.
Societies: Mon-Fri by prior booking with Sec.
Catering: Stud bar, lounge bar, restaurant; snacks available.
Hotels: Hintlesham Hall.

H24 **Hunstanton**

☎(0485) 532811
Golf Course Rd, Old Hunstanton, Norfolk PE36 6JQ
Off A149 in Old Hunstanton (signposted to club), 1 mile NE of Hunstanton.
Links course.
18 holes, 6670 yards, S.S.S.72
Founded 1891
Visitors: welcome, h/cap cert required; prior booking advisable; no 3/4 ball play.
Green Fee: £28/day (£12 with member) WD, £34/day (£25 with member) WE & BH.
Societies: welcome by prior arrangement with Sec.
Catering: full facilities available except Mon.
Hotels: Le Strange Arms; Lodge; Linksway.

H25 **Ipswich**

☎(0473) 728941
Purdis Heath, Bucklesham Rd, Ipswich, Suffolk IP3 8UQ

3 miles E of Ipswich off A45, at roundabout by St Augustine's Church turn into Bucklesham Rd.
Heathland course.
18 holes, 6405 yards, S.S.S.71; 9 holes, 3860 yards, S.S.S.59
Designed by James Braid, Hawtree & Taylor.
Founded 1895
Visitors: only by advance agreement.
Green Fee: £25.50/day/round WD, £31/day/round WE; 9 hole £7.50 WD, £10 WE.
Societies: Mon, Thurs, Fri by advance booking.
Catering: full catering facilities available.

H26 **King's Lynn**

☎(0553) 631654 Sec, 631655 Pro, 631656 Steward
Castle Rising, King's Lynn, Norfolk PE31 6BD
On A149 King's Lynn to Hunstanton, at Castle Rising sign turn left, about 0.75 mile on left hand side.
Parkland course.
18 holes, 6646 yards, S.S.S.72
Designed by Peter Alliss & Dave Thomas.
Founded 1923
Visitors: weekdays except Tues.
Green Fee: £26 WD, £33 WE & BH.
Societies: catered for on Thurs and Fri only.
Catering: lunches daily weekdays; evening meals by arrangement. Snooker.
Hotels: Red Cat; Dukes Head; Knights Hill.

H27 **Links Country Park**

☎(026 375) 691
West Runton, Norfolk NR27 9QH
In West Runton village 2 miles from Sheringham, turn for railway station, over the bridge 100 yards on left.
Undulating downland course.
9 holes, 2407 yards, S.S.S.32
Founded 1978
Visitors: welcome.
Green Fee: on application
Societies: by arrangement.
Catering: full facilities. Tennis, saunas etc.
Hotels: Links Country Park (free golf for residents).

H28 **Mattishall**

☎(0362) 850111
South Green, Mattishall, Dereham, Norfolk

B1063 to Mattishall, right at church, 1 mile on left.
Parkland course.
9 holes, 2953 yards, S.S.S.68; 9 hole Pitch & Putt
Founded June 1990
Visitors: all welcome.
Green Fee: £8 WD, £10 WE. Pitch & Putt £2
Catering: none at present.
Hotels: Phoenix (East Dereham).

H29 **Middleton Hall**

☎(0553) 841800
Hall Orchards, Middleton, Nr Kings Lynn, Norfolk PE32 1RH
Off A47 4 miles from King's Lynn, between church and station in Middleton then 1st left.
Parkland course.
9 holes, 5570 yards, S.S.S.67
Founded 1989
Visitors: welcome, must have valid h/cap cert.
Green Fee: on application.
Societies: welcome by prior booking.
Catering: bar, bar snacks. Driving range, putting green.

H30 **Mundesley**

☎(0263) 720095 Sec, 720279 Clubhouse
Links Rd, Mundesley, Norwich, Norfolk NR11 8ES
Turn off the Mundesley-Cromer road by Mundesley Church, signposted as you enter the village.
Undulating course.
9 holes, 5410 yards, S.S.S.66
Designed by Harry Vardon (in part).
Founded 1903
Visitors: welcome except 12.30-3.30pm Wed (Ladies) or until 12am Sun (Men).
Green Fee: on application
Societies: welcome by prior arrangement.
Catering: full facilities available except Tues.

H31 **Newton Green**

☎(0787) 77501
Newton Green, Sudbury, Suffolk
On A134, 3 miles E of Sudbury towards Colchester.
Moorland course.
9 holes, 5488 yards, S.S.S.67
Founded 1907
Visitors: weekdays; no visitors weekends, Bank Holidays.
Green Fee: on application
Catering: snacks served.

H32 Richmond Park
☎(0953) 881803
Saham Road, Watton, Thetford, Norfolk IP25 6EA
A11 to Thetford, then A1075 to Watton, turn left at top of High St, Saham Rd at bottom.
Parkland/meadowland course.
18 holes, c. 6300 yards, S.S.S.71
Founded July 1990
Visitors: welcome weekdays, with h/cap cert weekends.
Green Fee: £14 WD, £18 WE.
Societies: welcome, advance bookings only
Catering: bar meals 7 days, à la carte retaurant Tues-Sat.
Putting green, practice ground/nets, mini gym.

H33 Rookery Park
☎(0502) 560380
Carlton Colville, Lowestoft, Suffolk NR33 8HJ
2 miles W of Lowestoft on A146.
Parkland course.
18 holes, 6650 yards, S.S.S.72
Designed by Charles Lawrie.
Founded 1975
Visitors: welcome all year.
Green Fee: £20/day WD, £25 WE & BH.

Societies: any weekday except Tues am.
Catering: full facilities 7 days.
9-hole Par 3 course, snooker.
Hotels: Hedley House; Broadlands.

H34 Royal Cromer
☎(0263) 512884
145 Overstrand Rd, Cromer, Norfolk NR27 0JH
1 mile E of Cromer on B1159 coast road, adjoins Cromer lighthouse.
Undulating seaside course.
18 holes, 6508 yards, S.S.S.71
Designed by James Braid.
Founded 1888
Visitors: accepted weekdays and after 11am most weekends; booking essential 1st April-31st Oct.
Green Fee: £25 WD, £30 WE & BH.
Societies: accepted weekdays.
Catering: daily.
Hotels: Cliftonville; Cliff House; Anglia Court; Red Lion.

H35 Royal Norwich
☎(0603) 49928
Drayton High Rd, Hellesdon, Norwich NR6 5AH
500 yards down A1067 Fakenham road from ring road.

Parkland/heathland course.
18 holes, 6603 yards, S.S.S.72
Founded 1893
Visitors: must have h/cap.
Green Fee: on application
Societies: book in advance.
Catering: restaurant facilities.

H36 Royal West Norfolk
☎(0485) 210223, 210087 Sec.
Brancaster, King's Lynn, Norfolk PE31 8AX
7 miles E of Hunstanton on A149, take Beach Rd from Brancaster village to club.
Seaside links course.
18 holes, 6428 yards, S.S.S.71
Designed by Holcombe Ingleby.
Founded 1892
Visitors: must be members of recognised golf club, hold official h/cap cert and prior arrangements with Sec; no visitors, unless with member, from beginning of last week in July to end 1st week Sept.
Green Fee: £25 WD, £30 WE.
Societies: small societies by arrangement; no new visiting societies at weekends.
Catering: snacks; lunch on request.
Hotels: The Manor; The Lodge; Le Strange Arms; Caley Hall.

H37 Royal Worlington & Newmarket
☎(0638) 712216
Golf Links Rd, Worlington, Bury St
Edmunds, Suffolk IP28 8SD
6 miles NE of Newmarket, A45 then
A11 towards Thetford; follow signs to
Worlington.
Inland links course.
9 holes, 3105 yards, S.S.S.70
Designed by H.S. Colt.
Founded 1893
Visitors: weekdays only, phone first;
h/cap cert required.
Green Fee: £25 WD.
Societies: Tues, Thurs by
appointment; limited 24 players.
Catering: lunch and tea only.
Hotels: Bull; Bell; Worlington Hall.

H38 Rushmere
☎(0473) 725648
Rushmere Heath, Ipswich, Suffolk
IP4 5QQ
Northern outskirts of Ipswich,
signposted from A12.
Heathland course (some common
land).
18 holes, 6287 yards, S.S.S.70
Founded 1927
Visitors: weekdays only; h/cap cert
or bona fide member of golf club.
Green Fee: £18/round/day.
Societies: when dates available.
Catering: full facilities.

H39 Ryston Park
☎(0366) 383834 Sec, 382133
Steward
Denver, Downham Market, Norfolk
PE38 0HH
On A10 just before turning to Denver,
1 mile S of Downham Market.
Parkland course.
9 holes, 6292 yards, S.S.S.70
Founded 1933
Visitors: weekdays.
Green Fee: on application
Societies: weekdays.
Catering: full facilities except Mon.

H40 St Helena
☎(0986) 875567, 874565 Fax.
Bramfield Rd, Halesworth, Suffolk
IP19 9XA
1 mile from Halesworth off A144
Bramfield road.
Parkland course.
18 holes, 6580 yards, S.S.S.72;
9 holes, 3059 yards, S.S.S.36
Designed by J.W. Johnson.
Founded 1990
Visitors: welcome, no restrictions.

Green Fee: 18 holes, £12.30/round,
£15.40/day (£9.20 with member)
WD; £18.40 (£13.30 with member)
WE: 9 holes, £6.20/round.
Societies: welcome.
Catering: full facilities.
Driving range.

H41 Sheringham
☎(0263) 823488
Weybourne Rd, Sheringham, Norfolk
NR26 8HG
0.5 mile from Sheringham on A149.
Seaside course.
18 holes, 6464 yards, S.S.S.71
Founded 1891
Visitors: welcome with h/cap; phone
first.
Green Fee: £25 WD, £30 WE & BH.
Societies: by arrangement with Sec
weekdays.
Catering: available all week.
Hotels: Beaumaris; Burlington;
Southlands; The Links.

H42 Southwold
☎(0502) 723234
The Common, Southwold, Suffolk
IP18 6TB
From A12 follow A1095 signposted
Southwold, turn right at Kings Head
Hotel, proceed across Common, golf
club about 0.5 mile on right.
Commonland course.
9 holes, 6001 yards, S.S.S.69
Founded 1884
Visitors: welcome except on
competition days; phone in advance.
Green Fee: £13 WD, £16 WE.
Societies: by arrangement.
Catering: bar and catering facilities.

H43 Sprowston Park
☎(0603) 410657 Sec.
Wroxham Rd, Sprowston, Norwich,
Norfolk NR7 8RP
1.5 miles from ring road on A1151
Wroxham road; follow Sprowston
Park signs.
Parkland course
18 holes, 5985 yards, S.S.S.69
Founded Oct 1980
Visitors: welcome.
Green Fee: £10/round WD, £12 WE
& BH.
Societies: welcome 7 days.
Catering: snacks, meals, dinners,
Sun lunch; spacious dining room.
East Anglian Academy of Golf; driving
range, 18-hole putting green.
Hotels: Sprowston Manor; bargain
breaks and golf breaks on application
(0603) 410871.

H44 Stowmarket
☎(0449) 736473
Lower Rd, Onehouse, Stowmarket,
Suffolk IP14 3DA
2.5 miles SW of Stowmarket, off
B1115 Stowmarket-Bidlestone road;
look for Shepherd & Dog public
house at junction with Lower Rd.
Parkland course.
18 holes, 6101 yards, S.S.S.69
Founded reformed in 1962
Visitors: welcome weekdays;
weekends must have h/cap cert.
Green Fee: £18.50 (£7.50 with
member) WD, £29 (£12.50 with
member) WE.
Societies: Thurs and Fri.
Catering: meals usually available at
all times.
Hotels: Cedars (Stowmarket).

H45 Swaffham
☎(0760) 721611
Cley Rd, Swaffham, Norfolk PE37 8AE
1 mile out of town on Cockley Cley
road, signposted in market place.
Heathland course.
9 holes, 6252 yards, S.S.S.70
Founded 1922
Visitors: welcome weekdays,
weekends only with member.
Green Fee: £15/round.
Societies: welcome by arrangement.
Catering: snacks 7 days, full
catering except Mon and Tues.
Hotels: George.

H46 Thetford
☎(0842) 752169 Sec, 752258 club,
752662 Pro.
Brandon Rd, Thetford, Norfolk IP24
3NE
Take B1107 signposted Brandon
from roundabout on A11 Thetford
by-pass, course few yards on left.
Heathland course.
18 holes, 6879 yards, S.S.S.73
Designed by C.H. Mayo, D.M.A. Steel.
Founded 1912
Visitors: welcome weekdays with
current h/cap cert; weekends and
Bank Holidays with member only.
Green Fee: £26 WD.
Societies: Wed, Thurs, Fri only.
Catering: available daily.
Hotels: Bell; Thomas Paine;
Wereham House.

H47 Thorpeness
☎(0728) 452176
Thorpeness, Suffolk IP16 4NH
Leave A12 at Saxmundham, on to
B119, then B1353.

Royal Worlington & Newmarket

Royal Worlington, like the Old Course at St Andrews, has always struck me as a freak of nature. No one seems to know who designed it but since 1892, when the golf course and Club came into being, it has grown up on its own and today has the reputation of being the greatest 9-hole course in the world. I have never heard anyone beg to differ since no one playing over what Bernard Darwin described as "The Sacred Nine" has ever claimed to have played a better.

It has other similarities with the Old Course at St Andrews, having been laid out for the gutty ball and yet, with scarcely any modifications, it remains a great test with the rubber core ball and the steel shaft. Like St Andrews, too, it may not quite measure up at first sight to all the tributes paid to it but the more familiar it becomes the more the special quality of the golf becomes evident. Not for a moment is one deterred by the prospect of playing the same holes eight times in a weekend. Rather the opposite.

For generations, Cambridge golfers have been blessed by being allowed to adopt it as their golfing home and, for this reason, they are one up on Oxford every March before they start. In early days the undergraduates' journey ended with the guard producing a special pair of steps for their descent from the train at Worlington Halt close to the 4th green but even before the line was declared unplayable by Dr Beeching, the fashionable means of transport was a varied assortment of cars which, depending on their vintage, took between 17 and 35 minutes for the 23 odd miles.

The course has been well described as seaside links inland, a characteristic that has been religiously preserved by wise committees along with greens, managed with the minimum of artificial aids, which are unbelievably fast and true.

The short game, is vital, to low scoring at Worlington but there is one other similarity with the Old Course at St Andrews. Nobody would describe Worlington as a narrow course and yet it is essentially a great driver's course since, owing to the pace of the greens, it is

necessary to place the tee shot at every hole in order to get a shot at the flag; and, again owing to the pace of the greens, good iron play is rewarded almost more than anywhere else.

For a course laid out on an unbelievably small acreage, it is a wonderfully complete test but each hole offers something different rather, it is said, like Beethoven's Symphonies. The 9 begins with a splendid par 5 with the threat of the road on the right adding menace to the drive and is followed by a long, short hole whose green is about as hard to stay on as a policeman's helmet. It is guarded by a deep bunker, and slopes to the left towards some grassy pimples.

Then comes the glorious hole that in the days of the gutty ball must have held even more challenge than it does today; then, with two more short holes in between, come the 4th, 6th and 8th sometimes in range of 2 shots and sometimes not.

The 6th offers a superb second to a green set into the gap at the end of the majestic line of pine trees that dominates the course; and the 8th, another over a row of good, old-fashioned cross bunkers, offers a testing second shot before the 9th turns for home with one of the best short par 4's in the country. There is the temptation to bite off more than is wise with the drive although the drive must be bold if there is any hope of pitching close to the flag.

The scratch man is expected to be out in about 35 but it is doubtful whether he will be and, though one of the beauties of a 9-hole course is that scores should not vary much in view of knowing what to expect the second time round, this seldom applies at Worlington. Each round is joyously different.

The celebrated short 5th with its long glassy hog's back green, where tee shots can be in sight of a 2 one minute and doomed for a 5 the next is no respecter for the law of averages; indeed one of the favourite local stories is of the golfer who was once on the green in one and off in 10; and the 5th has no bunkers to bolster its defences.

Moorland course.
18 holes, 6241 yards, S.S.S.71
Designed by James Braid.
Founded 1923
Visitors: welcome weekdays.
Green Fee: £20.50/round WD,
£25.50/round WE.
Societies: weekdays only.
Catering: full catering service.
Hotels: Thorpeness Golf Club.

H48 Ufford Park Hotel
☎(0394) 383555
Yarmouth Road, Ufford, Woodbridge,
Suffolk IP12 1QW
Approx 2 miles N of Woodbridge on
B1438.
Parkland course in Deben valley.
18 holes
Founded Oct 1991
Visitors: welcome at any time.
Green Fee: £15/day WD, £18/day
WE & BH.
Societies: welcome at any time.
Catering: bar, bar snacks,
restaurant; banqueting, conferences.
Indoor swimming pool, sauna,
health, fitness and beauty facilities.
Hotels: own hotel and Leisure Centre
from April 1992, weekend breaks
and golfing packages available.

H49 Waldringfield Heath
☎(0473) 36768
Newbourne Road, Waldringfield,
Woodbridge, Suffolk IP12 4PT

3 miles NE of Ipswich.
Heathland course
18 holes, 5837 yards, S.S.S.68
Designed by P. Pilgrem.
Founded 1 April 1983
Visitors: welcome weekdays, after
10am weekends.
Green Fee: on application.
Societies: weekdays.
Catering: full facilities.
Hotels: Marlborough (Ipswich).

H50 Wensum Valley
☎(0603) 261012
Beech Avenue, Taverham, Norwich,
Norfolk NR8 6HP
Parkland course.
9 holes, 2953 yards, S.S.S.68;
further 18 holes, April 1992
Founded July 1989
Visitors: welcome.
Green Fee: £12 WD, £15 WE.
Societies: welcome at all times.
Catering: full bar and catering
facilities.
Driving range, snooker, bowls.
Hotels: accommodation at club; golf
breaks arranged; phone for details.

H51 Wood Valley (Beccles)
☎(0502) 712244
The Common, Beccles, Suffolk NR34
9BX
1 mile off A146, 18 miles Norwich,
10 miles Lowestoft.

Heathland course.
9 holes, 2781 yards, S.S.S.67
Founded 1899
Visitors: welcome, weekdays
unrestricted, weekends with
member or phone.
Green Fee: £9 (18 holes) WD, £10
WE & BH.
Societies: welcome by
arrangement, not Sun.
Catering: bar and bar snacks; meals
to order.
Hotels: Kings Head; Waveney House;
Broadland.

H52 Woodbridge
☎(0394) 382038
Bromeswell Heath, Woodbridge,
Suffolk IP12 2PF
Leave A12 N of Woodbridge on road
signposted to Melton; after traffic
lights follow road to Orford.
Heathland course.
18 holes, 6314 yards, S.S.S.70;
9 holes, S.S.S.31
Designed by F. Hawtrey.
Founded 1893
Visitors: weekdays only; h/cap certs
required; advance phone call
advisable.
Green Fee: £22/round/day.
Societies: by advance booking only,
Mon-Fri.
Catering: bar and dining room
facilities.
Hotels: Melton Grange; Seckford
Hall.

I

GLOUCESTERSHIRE, WARWICKSHIRE, HEREFORD & WORCESTER

The Three Choirs Festival, the province of the cathedrals of Hereford, Worcester and Gloucester, would have been close to the heart of Sir Edward Elgar, the most English of all composers. Less well known was his love of golf and, in particular, his connections with the Worcestershire Golf Club at Malvern Wells, although how much inspiration his musical scores owed to the latter is not clear.

Judging by the excellent centenary history of the Club, it can be assumed that his game was based more on hope than glory — perhaps even enigmatic and variable — but the beauty of the Malvern Hills has been solace to many and it is appropriate therefore to head an introduction to this section with mention of the most senior Club in the area. Almost 20 years later came the Alister Mackenzie designed Worcester Golf and County Club on more parkland surroundings, but one of Worcestershire's most attractive courses is undoubtedly Blackwell near Bromsgrove.

Far more modern is Abbey Park at Redditch which is a valuable addition to the county's facilities but, as an example of true dedication and private enterprise, there is nothing in the entire country, to match the tale of Ross-on-Wye. Having existed for almost 60 years as a nine-hole course, they built themselves a new 18-hole home in pleasant woodland in the 1960s. What is more, the cost of course and clubhouse did not exceed £50,000 although the sacrifices and contributions of the original course committee, a gallant and cheerful band, never featured in the calculations.

In those days, golf in Herefordshire was confined to Kington, the highest golf course in the land, one at Raven's Causeway and the 9 holes at Ross but Ross emerged from a wilderness of roots, scrub, thickets, marsh and typical red earth that, at first, Ken Cotton believed to be unsuitable; but his skill, allied to the faith, patience and determination of the small committee, worked a minor miracle in a corner of England still blessed with meadows, orchards and green hills.

Ross is a short drive from Gloucester, a county not as well populated with courses as its size — or the playing strength of their men's county team in recent years — might suggest. From Tewkesbury Park in the north to Cotswold Edge and Westonbirt in the south, the setting for the game is generally one of pasture and park with the exception of the higher reaches of Gloucester itself and the more ancient elevated common at Minchinhampton.

Two Ryder Cup matches at the Belfry have done a lot to publicise golf in the Birmingham area in recent years, but Warwickshire, particularly in the area around Birmingham, is full of variety. Some of the older clubs include Handsworth, Edgbaston, Harborne, Moseley, Robin Hood and Sandwell Park, a mere stone's throw from the home of West Bromwich Albion Football Club.

Olton and Copt Heath are the pride of Solihull, both ideal as enjoyable, if stiff, tests but, besides the Belfry, there is a fine new hotel complex at Forest of Arden. The Arden course was bought by Country Club Hotels who added both hotel and a second course named after Lord Aylsford, on whose ancestral estate the development stands.

With the Belfry, it is the only 36-hole complex in the area, although Kings Norton has an honourable 27.

I1 Abbey Park G & CC
☎(0527) 63918
Dagnell End Rd, Redditch, Worcs B98 7BD
A441 Redditch-Birmingham Road.
Parkland course.
18 holes, 6411 yards, S.S.S.71
Designed by Donald Steel.
Founded 1985
Visitors: welcome subject to available tee times.
Green Fee: £10/round WD, £12.50/round WE.
Societies: by arrangement.
Catering: 3 bars, restaurant; meals all day.
Snooker, swimming pool, gym etc.
Hotels: Abbey Park (32 beds), bargain breaks available.

I2 Atherstone
☎(0827) 713110
The Outwoods, Atherstone, Warwicks CV9 2RL
Coleshill Rd out of Atherstone, 0.5 mile on left down private road.
Undulating parkland course.
11 holes (18 tees), 6239 yards, S.S.S.70
Founded 1894
Visitors: welcome weekdays.
Green Fee: £15 (£7 with member), BH £25 (£7 with member).
Societies: weekdays by prior arrangement.
Catering: full facilities.
Hotels: Old Red Lion; Three Tuns.

I3 The Belfry
☎(0675) 470301
Lichfield Rd, Wishaw, N Warwicks B76 9PR
M6 junction 4, follow signs to Lichfield along A446, sited at the apex of A4091 to Tamworth and A446 to Lichfield; or exit 9 from M42.
Parkland course, Championship courses.
Brabazon, 18 holes, 6975 yards, S.S.S.72; Derby, 18 holes, 6077 yards, S.S.S.70
Designed by Peter Alliss & Dave Thomas.
Founded 1977
Visitors: welcome at all times.
Green Fee: on application
Societies: welcome at all times.
Catering: full facilities within hotel.

I4 Belmont Lodge Hotel
☎(0432) 352666
Belmont House, Belmont, Hereford HR2 9SA
2 miles S of Hereford on Abergavenny road, A465.
Undulating meadowland course.
18 holes, 6448 yards, S.S.S.71
Designed by R. Sandow.
Founded 1983
Visitors: welcome.
Green Fee: on application
Societies: welcome.
Catering: restaurant and bar snacks.
Hotels: hotel on course.

I5 Blackwell
☎(021) 445 1994 Sec, 445 1781 Steward, 445 3113 Pro.
Blackwell, Bromsgrove, Worcs B60 1PY
3 miles E of Bromsgrove; from Blackwell village centre, along Station Rd and under railway bridge, club entrance on left after 40 yards.
Parkland course.
18 holes, 6202 yards, S.S.S.71
Founded 1983
Visitors: unrestricted weekdays; with member only weekends and Bank Holidays.
Green Fee: £36/day; parties over 16 £29.
Societies: Wed, Thurs, Fri by arrangement with Sec.
Catering: full by prior arrangement.

I6 Boldmere
☎(021) 354 3379
Monmouth Drive, Sutton Coldfield, W Midlands
A452 Chester road, 6 miles NE of Birmingham City centre.
Municipal parkland course.
18 holes, 4463 yards, S.S.S.62
Founded 1936
Visitors: welcome any time.
Green Fee: £5.10 WD, £5.60/round.
Catering: light snacks only.
Hotels: Parson & Clerk.

I7 Broadway
☎(0386) 853683
Willersey Hill, Broadway, Worcs WR12 7LG
1.25 miles E of Broadway off A44.
Undulating parkland course.
18 holes, 6216 yards, S.S.S.70
Designed by James Braid.
Founded 1896
Visitors: must book, h/cap cert required; not before 4pm Sat; some restrictions Sun & BH for club competitions.
Green Fee: £20.50 (up to 27 holes), £25.50 (36 holes) WD; £25.50 (up to 27 holes) WE & BH.
Societies: Wed, Thur, Fri; max number 40.
Catering: bar, restaurant, not Mon.
Hotels: Dormy House; Noel Arms.

I8 Bromsgrove Golf Centre
☎(0527) 575886
Stratford Road, Bromsgrove, Worcestershire B60 1LD
At junction of A38 Bromsgrove eastern by-pass and A448 Redditch road; take A38 from M5 junction 4 or 5, or M42 junction 1.
Public, pay-as-you-play, course; grade 2 undulating farmland.
9 holes, 3250 yards, S.S.S.36
Designed by Hawtree & Sons
Visitors: course opening spring 1992; phone for details.
Green Fee: approx £5/9 holes.
Driving range.

I9 Burghill Valley
☎(0432) 760456
Tillington Road, Burghill, Hereford HR4 7RW
A4110 from Hereford, at Three Elms Inn take Tillington road for 2 miles, club on left.
Parkland course.
9 holes (further 9 from 1993), 3073 yards, S.S.S. (applied for).
Founded July 1991
Visitors: welcome any time.
Green Fee: £6 (9 holes), £10 (18 holes).
Societies: by arrangement.
Catering: bar and light meals available all day.
Hotels: Priory (Stretton Sugwas, 0432 760264), golfing packages available.

I10 Chipping Sodbury
☎(0454) 319042
Chipping Sodbury, Bristol BS17 6PU
Leave M4 at exit 18 and M5 at exit 14; from Chipping Sodbury take Wickwar road, first turn on right.
Parkland course.
18 holes, 6912 yards, S.S.S.73; 9 holes, 3076 yards
Designed by Fred Hawtree.
Visitors: welcome, but after 12am at weekends.
Green Fee: on application.
Societies: welcome by arrangement on weekdays.
Catering: meals served.
Practice ground.
Hotels: Moda; Cross Hands; The Poplars.

I11 **Churchill & Blackdown**

☎(0562) 700200
Churchill Lane, Blakedown,
Kidderminster, Worcs DY10 3NB
Off A456 3 miles NE of
Kidderminster, turn under railway
viaduct in village of Blakedown.
Hilly, meadowland course.
9 holes, 5399 yards, S.S.S.67
Founded 1926
Visitors: welcome Mon-Fri; Sat/Sun,
Bank Holidays with member only.
Green Fee: on application
Societies: apply to Sec.
Catering: lunch, evening meals
except Mon.

I12 **Cirencester**

☎(0285) 653939
Cheltenham Rd, Bagendon,
Cirencester, Glos GL7 7BH

Adjoins A435
Cirencester-Cheltenham road, 1.5
miles from Cirencester.
Undulating course.
18 holes, 6002 yards, S.S.S.69
Designed by James Braid.
Founded 1893
Visitors: welcome at all times, h/cap
certs required.
Green Fee: £20 (£10 with member)
WD, £25 (£13 with member) WE & BH.
Societies: Tues, Wed, Fri.
Catering: lunch and evening meals.
Hotels: Kings Head; Stratton House;
Fleece.

I13 **City of Coventry (Brandon Wood)**

☎(0203) 543141
Brandon Lane, Brandon, Coventry
On A45 6 miles S of Coventry, 120
yards S of London Rd roundabout.
Public parkland course.
18 holes, 6530 yards, S.S.S.71
Designed by Frank Pennink.
Visitors: welcome.
Green Fee: on application.
Societies: welcome but must book.
Catering: meals served every day.
Driving range.
Hotels: Brandon Hall.

I14 **Cleeve Hill**

☎(0242) 672025 club, 672592 Pro
shop
Cheltenham, Glos GL52 3PW
Approx 6 miles N from M5, 4 miles N
of Cheltenham off A46.
Municipal heathland course.
18 holes, 6217 yards, S.S.S.70
Founded 1891
Visitors: welcome.

Green Fee: £6/round WD, £7 WE.
Societies: any day by arrangement.
Catering: bar and restaurant daily.
Skittles, pool table.
Hotels: Malvern View; De La Bere;
Cleeve Hill.

I15 Cocks Moor Woods

☎(021) 444 3584
Alcester Rd South, Kings Heath,
Birmingham B14 6ER
On A435, near city boundary.
Public parkland course.
18 holes, 5888 yards, S.S.S.68
Founded 1924
Visitors: welcome.
Green Fee: on application
Societies: by arrangement.
Catering: snacks served.

I16 Copt Heath

☎(0564) 772650
1220 Warwick Rd, Knowle, Solihull,
W Midlands B93 9LN
On A4141 0.25 mile S of M42
junction 5.
Parkland course.
18 holes, 6500 yards, S.S.S.71
Designed by H. Vardon.
Founded 1910
Visitors: members of recognised
club with official club h/cap welcome.
Green Fee: £30/round/day.
Societies: Mon, Wed and Thurs by
arrangement with Sec.
Catering: full facilities except Mon.
Hotels: Greswolde.

I17 Cotswold Edge

☎(0453) 844167 Sec, 844398 Pro.
Upper Rushmire, Wotton-under-
Edge, Gloucestershire GL12 7PT
On B4058 Wotton-Tetbury road, 8
miles from M5 junction 14.
Meadowland course.
18 holes, 5816 yards, S.S.S.68
Founded 1980
Visitors: welcome weekdays, phone
in advance; with member only
weekends.
Green Fee: £15/day.
Societies: by arrangement with Sec.
Catering: full facilities available.
Hotels: Hare & Hounds; Amberley
Inn; Calcot Manor; Thornbury Castle.

I18 Cotswold Hills

☎(0242) 515264 Sec, 515263 Pro.
Ullenwood, Cheltenham, Glos GL53
9QT
3 miles S of Cheltenham, between
A436 and B4070.

Undulating course.
18 holes, 6716 yards, S.S.S.72
Designed by M.D. Little.
Founded 1902
Visitors: members of recognised
clubs welcome.
Green Fee: £21/round, £26/day.
Societies: Wed and Thurs.
Catering: bar snacks, lunch, dinner
except Mon (sandwiches available).
Hotels: Royal George (Birdlip).

I19 Coventry

☎(0203) 414152
St Martin's Rd, Finham Park,
Coventry, Warwicks CV3 6PJ
2 miles S of Coventry off A45 on
A444 Stoneleigh-Leamington road.
Parkland course.
18 holes, 6613 yards, S.S.S.72
Founded 1887
Visitors: welcome weekdays only.
Green Fee: £30.
Societies: Wed and Thurs, May-Sept
only.
Catering: full facilities.
Hotels: Leofric; Trust House Forte;
Windmill Farm.

I20 Coventry Hearsall

☎(0203) 713470 Sec, 713156 Pro.
Beechwood Ave, Earlsdon, Coventry
CV5 6DF
Just off A45 on Kenilworth-Coventry
road.
Parkland course.
18 holes, 5983 yards, S.S.S.69
Founded 1894
Visitors: welcome Mon-Fri, Sat, Sun
with member only.
Green Fee: on application.
Societies: Mon or Thurs by prior
arrangement.
Catering: lunches, sandwiches,
evening meals by prior arrangement.
Hotels: Leofric; De Vere; Hylands.

I21 Droitwich G & CC

☎(0905) 774344
Westford House, Ford Lane,
Droitwich WR9 0BQ
M5 exit 5, off A38 1 mile N of town.
Undulating meadowland course.
18 holes, 6040 yards, S.S.S.69
Founded 1897
Visitors: welcome Mon-Fri with
h/cap cert; Sat/Sun with member
only.
Green Fee: £22/day.
Societies: Wed and Fri.
Catering: bar, bar meals, restaurant.
Snooker.
Hotels: Raven; St Andrews.

I22 Dudley

☎(0384) 254020
Turners Hill, Rowley Regis, Warley, W
Midlands B65 9DP
1 mile S of town centre.
Undulating parkland course.
18 holes, 5704 yards, S.S.S.68
Founded 1893
Visitors: weekdays only.
Green Fee: £18/day.
Societies: by arrangement.
Catering: lunch and evening meals
available.
Hotels: Station; Ward Arms.

I23 Edgbaston

☎(021) 454 1736
Church Rd, Edgbaston, Birmingham
B15 3TB
A38 1 mile from Five Ways in
Birmingham city centre, entrance to
clubhouse next door to Edgbaston
Old Church.
Parkland course.
18 holes, 6118 yards, S.S.S.69
Designed by H.S. Colt.
Founded 1896
Visitors: h/cap cert required;
members only before 9.30am and
12.30-1.30pm daily.
Green Fee: £27.50/day WD, £35 WE.
Societies: weekdays only by prior
arrangement.
Catering: bar and bar lunches, other
meals by arrangement.
Snooker.

I24 Evesham

☎(0386) 860395 Club, 861144 Pro.
Craycombe Links, Old Worcester Rd,
Fladbury, Pershore, Worcs WR10 2QS
3 miles from Evesham on B4084, 4
miles from Pershore on B4984.
Parkland course.
9 holes (18 tees), 6415 yards,
S.S.S.71
Founded 1894
Visitors: welcome weekdays;
weekends only with member.
Green Fee: £15/round, £25/day (£7
with member).
Societies: by arrangement, max 30.
Catering: bar snacks daily; special
meals by arrangement.
Hotels: Waterside, Northwick; Star.

I25 Filton

☎(0272) 694169
Golf Course Lane, Filton, Bristol BS12
7QS
From M4/M5 interchange take A38
towards Bristol; after 2 miles turn
right at roundabout and right at lights.

Parkland course.
18 holes, 6042 yards, S.S.S.69
Designed by F. Hawtree & Son.
Founded 1909
Visitors: welcome on weekdays;
weekends with member only.
Green Fee: £16/round, £22/day WD
(£10 with member).
Societies: catered for on weekdays.
Catering: by arrangement.
Hotels: Crest Hotel; Hambrook.

I26 Forest Hills
☎(0594) 562899
Mile End Rd, Coleford, Glos
On road from Coleford centre to Mile
End on left hand side.
Parkland course.
18 holes, 5900 yards, S.S.S.68
Designed by Adrian Stiff.
Opening July 1992
Visitors: welcome.
Green Fee: £12/round, £20/day WD);
£15/round, £25/day WE.
Societies: by arrangement.
Catering: full facilities.
Hotels: Wyndham Arms; Angel;
Speech House; Lambsquay.

I27 Forest of Arden Hotel G & CC
☎(0676) 22335, 23721
Maxstoke Lane, Meriden, Coventry,
Warwicks CV7 7HR
Off A45 10 miles NW of Coventry, 2.5
miles E of Birmingham International
Airport; take Maxstoke turn off from
A45 and follow lane for 2 miles.
Parkland course.
Aylesford, 18 holes, 6525 yards,
S.S.S.69; Arden, 6915 yards,
S.S.S.71
Designed by Donald Steel.
Founded 1970 (Hotel open 1989)
Visitors: welcome with h/cap cert
except Sat, Sun am.
Green Fee: on application.
Societies: welcome weekdays by
arrangement with golf co-ordinator
(weekends residential only).
Catering: restaurant 10am-10pm,
bar and lounge; private facilities.
Tennis (floodlit), snooker, swimming,
squash, health and beauty facilities.
Hotels: Forest of Arden (153 beds),
golf breaks, details on request.

I28 Fulford Heath
☎(0564) 822806, 824758
Tanners Green Lane, Wythall,
Birmingham B47 6BH
1 mile from main Alcester Rd,
signposted to Tanners Green.

Parkland course.
18 holes, 6216 yards, S.S.S.70
Founded 1934
Visitors: welcome weekdays.
Green Fee: £25.
Societies: Tues or Thurs.
Catering: lunches and evening
meals served except Mon.
Hotels: George; Regency.

I29 Gay Hill
☎(021) 430 6523/8544/7077, 474
6001
Alcester Rd, Hollywood, Birmingham
B47 5PP
On A435, 7 miles from city centre, 3
miles from M42 junction 3.
Meadowland course.
18 holes, 6532 yards, S.S.S.71
Founded 1913 (1921 on present site).
Visitors: unaccompanied weekdays;
with member only weekend.
Green Fee: on application.
Societies: Thurs only.
Catering: meals available.

I30 Gloucester
☎(0452) 411331
Robinswood Hill, Matson Lane,
Gloucester GL4 9EA
2 miles S of Gloucester city centre on
B4073 to Painswick.
Parkland course.
18 holes, 6100 yards, S.S.S.69;
9 holes Par 3, 990 yards
Designed by Donald Steel.
Founded 1976
Visitors: welcome any time; phone
for tee times.
Green Fee: £19 WD, £24 WE; Par 3
course, £2.50 WD, £3 WE.
Societies: weekdays only, £37.25 for
36 holes, coffee, lunch and dinner.
Catering: full facilities available.
Driving range, snooker.
Hotels: Gloucester Hotel at course,
weekend and weekday golf breaks.

I31 Grange
☎(0203) 451465
Copsewood, Coventry, W Midlands
CV3 1HS
2.5 miles from Coventry centre on
Binley Rd, A428
Meadowland course.
9 holes, 6002 yards, S.S.S.69
Re-designed by T.J. McAuley.
Founded 1924
Visitors: welcome weekdays before
2pm; Sun after 11am; not Sat.
Green Fee: on application.
Societies: by arrangement with Sec.
Catering: may arrange for societies.

I32 Habberley
☎(0562) 745756
Habberley, Kidderminster, Worcs
DY11 5RG
3 miles N of Kidderminster on
Trimpley road.
Hilly parkland course.
9 holes, 5104 yards, S.S.S.69
Founded 1924
Visitors: welcome weekdays if
member of recognised club.
Green Fee: on application.
Societies: by arrangement.
Catering: by prior notice.
Hotels: Gainsborough; Swan.

I33 Hagley
☎(0562) 883701 Clubhouse,
883852 Pro shop
Wassell Grove, Hagley, W Midlands
DY9 9JW
4 miles S of Birmingham on A456,
right into Wassell Grove, 0.5 mile.
Undulating parkland course.
18 holes, 6353 yards, S.S.S.72
Founded 1979
Visitors: welcome weekdays; with
member only weekends, after 10am.
Green Fee: £20/round, £25/day.
Societies: welcome weekdays; prior
arrangement essential through Club
Manager.
Catering: bar and full restaurant
facilities. Squash.

I34 Halesowen
☎(021) 501 3606
The Leasowes, Halesowen,
W Midlands B62 8QF
Junction 3 off M5, to Kidderminster,
then to Halesowen.
Parkland course.
18 holes, 5486 yards, S.S.C.67
Founded 1902
Visitors: not weekends; Bank
Holidays by arrangement.
Green Fee: £15/round, £20/day.
Societies: by arrangement.
Catering: not Mon.

I35 Handsworth
☎(021) 554 0599 Clubhouse, 554
3387 Office, 523 3594 Pro.
11 Sunningdale Close, Handsworth
Wood, Handsworth B20 1NP
M5 junction 1 towards Birmingham,
left at lights into Island Rd, Oxhill Rd,
left at lights into Friary Rd, 2nd left
Greystone Ave, then 2nd left: M6
junction 7, take A34 through lights,
1st right Old Walsall Rd, up
Hamstead Hill, right into Vernon Ave,
right into Craythorne Ave, 1st left.

Parkland course
18 holes, 6312 yards, S.S.S.70
Founded 1895
Visitors: welcome weekdays; h/cap
certs required.
Green Fee: £20/day (£6.50 with
member).
Societies: weekdays by
arrangement; packages available.
Catering: lunch, dinner except Mon.
Squash.
Hotels: Villa Nova; Post House; Moat
House.

I36 Harborne
☎(021) 427 3058
40 Tennal Rd, Birmingham B32 2JE
Via Harborne village and War Lane,
SW of Birmingham.
Undulating parkland/moorland
course.
18 holes, 6235 yards, S.S.S.70
Designed by H.S. Colt.
Founded 1893
Visitors: weekdays; Bank Holidays
and weekends with member only.
Green Fee: £25 (£7 with member).
Societies: Wed, Thurs, Fri.
Catering: available except Mon.
Hotels: Claremont; Apollo.

I37 Harborne Church Farm
☎(021) 427 1204
Vicarage Rd, Harborne, Birmingham
B17 0SN
From Birmingham, via Broad St,
Harborne Rd and War Lane.
Municipal parkland course.
9 holes, 4514 yards, S.S.S.63
Founded 1926
Visitors: welcome.
Green Fee: on application.
Catering: snacks and meals in café.

I38 Hatchford Brook
☎(021) 743 9821
Coventry Rd, Sheldon, Birmingham
B26 3PY
Almost on city boundary adjacent to
Airport, on main A45 Coventry road.
Public parkland course.
18 holes, 6164 yards, S.S.S.69
Founded 1969
Visitors: all welcome.
Green Fee: £5.20/round.
Catering: canteen facilities while
course open.

I39 Henbury
☎(0272) 500044
Henbury Hill, Westbury-on-Trym,
Bristol BS10 7BQ

M5 junction 17, 2nd exit from round-
about, right at 2nd roundabout, left at
T-junction, course at top of hill.
Parkland course.
18 holes, 6039 yards, S.S.S.70
Founded 1891
Visitors: welcome weekdays with
h/cap cert.
Green Fee: on application.
Societies: catered for on Tues and
Fri by arrangement.
Catering: full range available.
Hotels: Henbury Lodge; Ship.

I40 Hereford Municipal
☎(0432) 271639
Holmer Road, Hereford HR4 9UD
A49 through Hereford towards
Leominster.
Public course in middle of race
course.
9 holes, 2898 yards, S.S.S.68
Founded 1983
Visitors: welcome, after 11am Sat;
closed on race days.
Green Fee: £2.80 (9 holes), £4.50
(18 holes) WD; £3.70 (9 holes), £6.15
(18 holes) WE.
Societies: welcome with advance
booking.
Catering: bar and restaurant.
Practice ground, adjacent leisure
centre.

I41 Herefordshire
☎(0432) 71219
Ravens Causeway, Wormsley,
Hereford HR4 8LY
6 miles NW of Hereford on Weobley
road, B4110; left at Three Elms Inn.
Undulating parkland course.
18 holes, 6200 yards, S.S.S.69
Designed by Major Hutchison.
Founded 1898
Visitors: welcome weekdays;
limited at weekends.
Green Fee: £12 WD, £16 WE;
reduced by £4 playing with member.
Societies: by arrangement.
Catering: daily except Mon.
Hotels: Red Lion; Pilgrim; The Priory.

I42 Hill Top
☎(021) 554 4463
Park Lane, Handsworth Wood,
Birmingham B21 8JP
Public parkland course.
18 holes, 6200 yards, S.S.S.69
Founded 1980
Visitors: welcome.
Green Fee: on application
Societies: welcome.
Catering: available.

I43 Kenilworth
☎(0926) 58517, 512732 Pro, 54038
catering
Crew Lane, Kenilworth, Warwicks
CV8 2EA
A429 Kenilworth road, then via
Common Lane, Knowle Hill and Crew
Lane to clubhouse.
Undulating course.
18 holes, 6408 yards, S.S.S.71
Founded 1889
Visitors: welcome daily; advisable to
ring Pro beforehand.
Green Fee: on application.
Societies: apply in writing; society
days Weds.
Catering: full bar and restaurant
facilities daily, advisable to contact
Caterer.
Hotels: De Montfort; Avonside;
Chesford Grange.

I44 Kidderminster
☎(0562) 822303
Russell Rd, Kidderminster, Worcs
Course signposed off A449, within 1
mile of town centre.
Parkland course.
18 holes, 6223 yards, S.S.S.70
Founded 1909
Visitors: welcome weekdays only;
proof of membership of recognised
golf club must be provided.
Green Fee: £22.
Societies: welcome by prior
arrangement usually Thurs.
Catering: full catering facilities daily
except Mon.

I45 Kings Norton
☎(0564) 826789
Brockhill Lane, Weatheroak,
Alvechurch, Birmingham B48 7ED
8 miles from centre of Birmingham
between A435 and A441; from M42
junction 3 turn towards Birmingham,
follow signs to club on left after 200
yards.
Parkland course
27 holes (3 loops of 9); Blue 9 holes,
3567 yards; Red 9 holes, 3294
yards; Yellow 9 holes, 3283 yards;
S.S.S.72: also 12 hole Par 3 course.
Designed by F. Hawtree & Son.
Founded 1892
Visitors: weekdays only, with
member only at weekends;
accredited h/cap required.
Green Fee: £24 (18 holes), £27/day.
Societies: weekdays only.
Catering: full bar and restaurant
facilities; conferences and
banqueting.
Hotels: St Johns (Solihull).

I46 Kington

☎(0544) 230340
Bradnor, Kington, Herefordshire HR5
3RE
Take B4355 from Kington centre;
signposted to left 1 mile out.
Moorland course; highest 18 hole
course in England and Wales.
18 holes, 5820 yards, S.S.S.68
Designed by C.K. Hutchinson.
Founded 1925
Visitors: welcome.
Green Fee: £11/round, £14/day WD;
£16/round, £20/day WE & BH.
Societies: welcome especially
weekdays.
Catering: lunches and dinners;
snacks only Mon.
Hotels: Burton; Oxford Arms.

I47 Ladbrook Park

☎(05644) 2264
Poolhead Lane, Tanworth-in-Arden,
Warwicks B94 5ED
A4023 4 miles from Hockley Heath.
Undulating parkland course.
18 holes, 6407 yards, S.S.S.71
Designed by H.S. Colt.
Founded 1908
Visitors: welcome by prior
arrangement.
Green Fee: on application.
Societies: by prior arrangement.
Catering: daily except Mon by prior
arrangement.
Hotels: George; St Johns Swallow;
Aylesbury House.

I48 Lansdown

☎(0225) 422138 Sec, 425007
Clubhouse/Steward, 420242 Pro.
Lansdown, Bath, Avon BA1 9BT
From M4 junction 18, take A46
towards Bath; at roundabout take
A420 towards Bristol, take 1st left
and club is approx 2 miles on right by
Bath Racecourse.
Elevated parkland course.
18 holes; 6299 yards, S.S.S.70
Designed by Harry Colt.
Founded 1894/5
Visitors: welcome weekdays, with
h/cap weekends; not competition
days.
Green Fee: £16/round, £22/day WD;
£30/round/day WE & BH; season
tickets (WD only) £50/week,
£100/month.
Societies: welcome by prior
arrangement.
Catering: full range of snacks and
meals available.
Hotels: Lansdowne Grove; Francis;
Hilton.

I49 Lea Marston Hotel & Leisure Complex

☎(0675) 470468
Haunch Lane, Lea Marston,
Warwickshire B76 0BY
1 mile from M42 Junction 9 on
A4097 Kingsbury road; 2 miles from
Belfry golf course.
Public parkland course.
9 holes Par 3
Founded 1983
Visitors: smart casual dress.
Green Fee: £3.50 9 holes, £4.25 18
holes.
Societies: any time.
Catering: 6 bars, restaurant (100).
Driving range, 3 tennis courts, crown
green bowls, putting green, pool,
skittles, darts.
Hotels: Lea Marston on site; special
golfing breaks.

I50 Leamington & County

☎(0926) 425961
Golf Lane, Whitnash, Leamington
Spa, Warwicks CV31 2QA
2 miles S of town centre, off A452.
Undulating parkland course.
18 holes, 6425 yards, S.S.S.71
Designed by H.S. Colt.
Founded 1909
Visitors: welcome.
Green Fee: on application.
Societies: welcome Wed, Thurs.
Catering: lunch and evening meal
served except Mon. Snooker.
Hotels: Regent; Ladbroke Mercury.

I51 Leominster

☎(0568) 612863
Ford Bridge, Leominster, Hereford
HR6 0LE
On A49 Leominster bypass 3 miles S
of Leominster, clearly signposted.
Undulating meadowland course.
18 holes, 5891 yards, S.S.S.68
Designed by Bob Sandow.
Founded 1967
Visitors: welcome weekdays;
weekends by prior arrangement.
Green Fee: £14.50 WD, £17.50 WE
& BH.
Societies: weekdays except Mon.
Catering: full facilities except Mon.
Coarse fishing on River Lugg.
Hotels: Talbot; Royal Oak; Green
Dragon (Hereford).

I52 Lickey Hills (Rose Hill)

☎(021) 453 3159
Lickey Hills, Rednal, Birmingham
M5 exit 4, on city boundary.
Public parkland course.

18 holes, 6010 yards, S.S.S.69
Designed by Carl Bretherton.
Founded 1927
Visitors: welcome.
Green Fee: on application
Societies: by arrangement.
Catering: snacks served.

I53 Lilley Brook

☎(0242) 526785
Cirencester Rd, Charlton Kings,
Cheltenham, Glos GL53 8EG
3 miles from centre of Cheltenham
on Cirencester road, A435.
Parkland course.
18 holes, 6226 yards, S.S.S.70
Founded 1922
Visitors: bona fide members of golf
club with official h/cap.
Green Fee: £20 WD.
Societies: Wed and Thurs.
Catering: lunch and dinner served
except Mon.
Hotels: Queens; Carlton.

I54 Little Lakes

☎(0299) 266385
Lye Head, Rock, Bewdley, Worcs
DY12 2UU
A456 2 miles W of Bewdley, turn left
at Greenhouse and Garden Centre,
proceed for 0.5 mile.
Undulating parkland course.
9 holes, 6247 yards, S.S.S.72
Designed by Michael Cooksey.
Founded 1975
Visitors: welcome weekdays; not
weekends or Bank Holidays.
Green Fee: £12/round, £15/day WD.
Societies: weekdays by
arrangement.
Catering: lunches served.
Hotels: Heath; George; Black Boy.

I55 Lydney

☎(0594) 842614, 843940 Sec.
Off Lakeside Ave, Lydney, Glos GL15
5QA
Entering Lydney on A48 from
Gloucester, turn left at bottom of
Highfield Hill and look for Lakeside
Ave, 7th turning on left.
Parkland course.
9 holes, 5382 yards, S.S.S.66
Founded 1909
Visitors: welcome; weekends and
Bank Holidays with member only.
Green Fee: £12/day.
Societies: small societies welcome,
full facilities available, lunch, dinner
but not morning coffee.
Catering: light snacks only.
Hotels: Wyndham Arms (Clearwell).

I56 Mangotsfield

☎(0272) 565501
Carson's Rd, Mangotsfield, Bristol
M32, leave at junction Filton/
Downend, follow sign for Downend
and Mangotsfield.
Hilly meadowland course.
18 holes, 5300 yards, S.S.S.66
Founded 1975
Visitors: welcome.
Green Fee: on application
Societies: apply to Manager.
Catering: meals served.

I57 Maxstoke Park

☎(0675) 464915
Castle Lane, Coleshill, Warwicks B46
2RD
3 miles NE of Coleshill, M6 junction 4.
Parkland course.
18 holes, 6478 yards, S.S.S.71
Founded 1898
Visitors: welcome weekdays; with
member only weekends and Bank
Holidays.
Green Fee: £20/round, £30 more
than 18 holes.
Societies: Tues and Thurs.
Catering: full bar and restaurant.
Hotels: Swan; Coleshill.

I58 Memorial Park

☎(0203) 675415
Memorial Park Golf Office,
Leamington Rd, Coventry, W
Midlands
About 5 miles from city centre;
access from Leamington Rd car park
at Memorial Park.
18 hole Par 3 municipal course.
Visitors: 8.30am-2pm (last round)
winter; 9am-9pm summer.
Green Fee: £1.35 WD, £1.75 WE;
reductions OAPs & jnrs (under 16).
Catering: café in park in summer.
Bowling greens, 10 tennis courts,
playground, aviary.

I59 Minchinhampton

☎(0453) 833866 New, 832642 Old.
New Course, Minchinhampton,
Stroud, Glos GL6 9BE; Old (Amberley
Section), Minchinhampton, Stroud,
Glos GL6 9AQ
Leave M5 at junction 13; New Course,
3 miles E of M'hampton on Avening
road; Old Course, 1 mile W of
M'hampton on M'hampton Common.
Parkland course (New), common
land course (Old).
New, 18 holes, 6675 yards,
S.S.S.72; Old, 18 holes, 6295 yards,
S.S.S.71

Designed by F.W. Hawtree (New),
Robert Wilson (Old)
Founded 1889
Visitors: welcome at all times with
prior notice; h/cap certs required for
New Course.
Green Fee: New, £22.50 WD, £28
WE & BH; Old, £12 WD, £15 WE & BH.
Societies: welcome by prior
arrangement.
Catering: available most times;
limited hours in winter.
Hotels: Bear at Rodborough;
Burleigh Court; Amberley Inn; Hare
and Hounds (Tetbury).

I60 Moor Hall

☎(021) 308 6130
Moor Hall Park, Sutton Coldfield, W
Midlands B75 6LN
From M42 take A446 to Bassets Pole
roundabout, follow Sutton Coldfield
road to 1st traffic lights, entrance
200 yards on left.
Parkland course.
18 holes, 6249 yards, S.S.S.70
Founded 1932
Visitors: welcome weekdays only.
Green Fee: £23/round, £30/day.
Societies: Tues and Wed only.
Catering: full service except Mon.
Hotels: Moor Hall; Penns Hall.

I61 Moseley

☎(021) 444 4957 Sec (10am-1pm),
444 2115 Club
Springfield Rd, Kings Heath,
Birmingham B14 7DX
On Birmingham ring road, 0.5 mile E
of Alcester Rd.
Parkland course.
18 holes, 6227 yards, S.S.S.70
Founded 1892
Visitors: welcome weekdays by
letter of intro.
Green Fee: on application
Societies: Thurs.
Catering: by arrangement with
Stewardess.

I62 Newbold Comyn

☎(0926) 421157
Newbold Terrace East, Leamington
Spa, Warwicks
Off B4099 Willes Rd, centrally
located.
Parkland course.
18 holes, 6259 yards, S.S.S.70
Founded 1972
Visitors: welcome.
Green Fee: on application
Societies: apply to Pro.
Catering: bar and restaurant.

I63 North Warwickshire

☎(0676) 22259
Hampton Lane, Meriden, W Midlands
CV7 7LL
6 miles N of Coventry on A45.
Parkland course.
9 holes, 3181 yards, S.S.S.70
Founded 1894
Visitors: weekdays except Thur
(Ladies Day); weekends with
member only.
Green Fee: £20 WD, £15 WE (with
member only).
Societies: welcome by prior
arrangement.
Catering: bar snacks.
Hotels: Manor Hotel (Meriden); Post
House (Coventry).

I64 North Worcestershire

☎(021) 475 1047
Frankley Beeches Rd, Northfield,
Birmingham B31 5LP
Main A38 road to Northfield, turn up
Frankley Beeches Rd, then 3rd road
on left brings you straight to club.
Meadowland course.
18 holes, 5919 yards, S.S.S.69
Designed by James Braid.
Founded 1907
Visitors: welcome weekdays; with
member weekends and Bank
Holidays.
Green Fee: on application
Societies: Tues and Thurs.
Catering: full facilities.

I65 Nuneaton

☎(0203) 347810
Golf Drive, Whitestone, Nuneaton,
Warwicks CV11 6QF
Leave M6 at junction 3 on A444, 2
miles S of Nuneaton.
Wooded undulating meadowland
course.
18 holes, 6429 yards, S.S.S.71
Founded 1906
Visitors: welcome weekdays, with
member only weekends.
Green Fee: on application.
Societies: Wed, Fri only.
Catering: full facilities except Mon.
Hotels: Long Shoot; Chase.

I66 Olton

☎(021) 705 1083
Mirfield Rd, Solihull, W Midlands B91
1JH
2 miles off junction 5 M42 – A41 to
Birmingham.
Parkland course.
18 holes, 6229 yards, S.S.S.71
Founded 1893

Visitors: welcome weekdays except Wed; not weekends unless with member.
Green Fee: £30 (£8 with member) WD.
Societies: weekdays by arrangement, not Wed.
Catering: available.
Snooker.
Hotels: St Johns; George.

I67 Ombersley
☎(0905) 620747
Bishops Wood Road, Lineholt, Ombersley, Droitwich, Worcs WR9 0LE
Off A449 between Worcester and Kidderminster, left at Mitre Oak public house.
Parkland course with views over Malvern Hills.
18 holes, 6139 yards, Par 72
Designed by On Course Design (David Morgan).
Founded Sept 1991
Visitors: no restrictions.
Green Fee: £9/round WD, £12 WE; reductions for jnrs and OAPs.
Societies: welcome, not weekends.
Catering: full facilities.
Hotels: Stourport Moat House; Mitre Oak.

I68 Painswick
☎(0452) 812180
Painswick Beacon, Painswick, Stroud, Glos GL6 6TL
1 mile N of Painswick village on A46.
Commonland course.
18 holes, 4780 yards, S.S.S.64
Founded 1891
Visitors: welcome weekdays; Sat, Sun with member only.
Green Fee: £8 (£5 with member) WD, £12 (£7 with member) WE.
Societies: by prior arrangement with Sec.
Catering: by arrangement with Steward; snacks normally available.
Hotels: Hatton Court; Painswick.

I69 Pitcheroak
☎(0527) 541054
Plymouth Rd, Redditch, Worcs B97 4PB
In centre of Redditch, signposted.
Municipal parkland course
9 holes (18 tees), 4500-5000 yards, S.S.S.62
Founded 1973
Visitors: welcome any time.
Green Fee: on application
Catering: bar and restaurant.

I70 Purley Chase G & CC
☎(0203) 393118 office, 397468 club, 395348 Pro shop
Ridge Lane, Nr Nuneaton, N Warwicks CV10 0RB
4 miles W of Nuneaton, 2 miles SW of Atherstone, signposted.
Parkland course.
18 holes, 6734 yards, S.S.S.71
Designed by B. Tomlinson.
Founded 1976
Visitors: welcome weekdays, at weekends subject to availability.
Green Fee: on application.
Societies: welcome weekdays.
Catering: full facilities.
Driving range.
Hotels: Mancetter Manor; Lea Marston.

I71 Pype Hayes
☎(021) 351 1014
Eachelhurst Rd, Walmley, Sutton Coldfield, W Midlands B76 8EP
Off M6 at Spaghetti Junction, onto Tyburn Rd, 1 mile to Eachelhurst Rd.
Public parkland course.
18 holes, 5811 yards, S.S.S.68
Founded 1932
Visitors: welcome.
Green Fee: on application
Societies: welcome.
Catering: full facilities; no bar.

I72 Redditch
☎(0527) 543309
Lower Grinsty Lane, Callow Hill, Redditch, Worcs B97 5JP
3 miles W of town centre; take Heathfield road off A448 Redditch-Bromsgrove road.
Parkland course (1st 9), woodland (2nd 9).
18 holes, 6671 yards, S.S.S.72
Designed by F. Pennink.
Founded 1913
Visitors: members of recognised golf club welcome weekdays; with member weekends.
Green Fee: £23/day (£7.50 with member).
Societies: weekdays by arrangement.
Catering: full service except Mon.
Snooker.
Hotels: Southcrest; Hotel Montville.

I73 Robin Hood
☎(021) 706 0061 Sec, 706 0806 Pro.
St Bernards Rd, Solihull, W Midlands B92 7DJ
From Olton station (6 miles S of

Birmingham on A41) travel NE up St Bernards Rd for 1 mile, drive to clubhouse on right.
Parkland course.
18 holes, 6609 yards, S.S.S.72
Designed by H.S. Colt.
Founded 1893
Visitors: welcome weekdays except official holidays, Tues am and Wed pm.
Green Fee: £26/round, £31/day.
Societies: Tues pm, Thurs and Fri.
Catering: bar snacks Tues to Fri; evening meals by arrangement.
Hotels: St Johns Swallow; George; Flemings.

I74 Ross-on-Wye
☎(0989 82) 267, 439 Pro, 660 Steward
Two Park, Gorsley, Ross-on-Wye, Hereford HR9 7UT
Adjacent M50 junction 3, 5 miles N of Ross.
Parkland course.
18 holes, 6500 yards, S.S.S.73
Designed by Frank Pennink, Cotton & Partners.
Founded 1903
Visitors: must be members of recognised club.
Green Fee: on application.
Societies: Wed, Thurs, Fri, 20 min.
Catering: full bar and restaurant facilities; bar snacks only Mon.
2 snooker tables.
Hotels: Chase; Royal.

I75 Royal Forest of Dean
☎(0594) 32583, 33689 Pro.
Lords Hill, Coleford, Glos GL16 8BD
Between M4, M5 and M50; from M5, M50 4 miles Monmouth, 8 miles Ross; from M4, 8 miles Chepstow.
Parkland/meadowland course.
18 holes, 5535 yards, S.S.S.69
Designed by John Day of Alphagreen Ltd.
Founded 1973
Visitors: welcome; car hire £13/round.
Green Fee: £14 WD, £16 WE.
Societies: Mon-Thurs; lunch, 3-course evening meal, 36 holes, £23 per person.
Catering: bar open all day; restaurant serving table d'hôte, à la carte meals and snacks all year round; banqueting for up to 170. Outdoor swimming pool, tennis, bowls.
Hotels: own 32 bedroom hotel in centre of course, sporting weekends including free golf available.

I76 **Rugby**

☎(0788) 2306
Clifton Rd, Rugby, CV21 3RD
On Rugby-Market Harborough road,
on right just past railway bridge as
leaving town.
Parkland course.
18 holes, 5457 yards, S.S.S.67
Founded 1891
Visitors: welcome weekdays;
weekends and Bank Holidays with
member.
Green Fee: on application
Societies: weekdays by
arrangement.
Catering: meals except Tues.

I77 **Sapey Golf**

☎(08867) 288/567, 485 fax.
Upper Sapey, Nr Worcester, Worcs
WR6 6XT
Midway between Bromyard and
Stourport on B4203.
Open parkland course.
18 holes, 5,900 yards, S.S.S.69
Founded July 1990
Visitors: welcome with 24 hours
notice.
Green Fee: £12/round, £19/day WD;
£19/round, £25/day WE & BH.
Societies: all times with 14 days
notice.
Catering: bar 7 days, restaurant
Wed-Sun inclusive.
Driving rnage.
Hotels: The Granary (Collington).

I78 **Shirehampton Park**

☎(0272) 822083 Sec, 823059 Club,
822488 Pro.
Park Hill, Shirehampton, Bristol BS11
0UL
1.5 miles from M5 junction 18,
B4018 through village of
Shirehampton; course at top of hill
overlooking River Avon.
Undulating parkland course.
18 holes, 5493 yards, S.S.S.67
Founded 1908
Visitors: weekdays welcome,
weekends only with member.
Green Fee: £16.50/round, £26/day
WD.
Societies: Mon only by arrangement
with Sec.
Catering: snacks, lunch always
available; evening meals by
arrangement.

I79 **Shirley**

☎(021) 744 6001
Stratford Rd, Monkspath, Shirley,
Solihull, W Midlands B90 4EW

From M42 junction 4, 500 yards on
left towards Birmingham.
Parkland course.
18 holes, 6510 yards, S.S.S.71
Founded 1953
Visitors: welcome weekdays, h/cap
cert required.
Green Fee: £25/round, £30/day.
Societies: Mon-Fri by arrangement.
Catering: meals and snacks daily.
Snooker.
Hotels: St John's; Regency.

I80 **Sphinx**

☎(0203) 458890, 451361 after 7pm
Siddeley Ave, Coventry, W Midlands
CV3 1FZ
Approx 4 miles S of centre of
Coventry, close to main Binley Rd.
Parkland course
9 holes, 2101 yards, Par 60.
Founded 1940s (as Rolls Royce
Sports Club).
Visitors: welcome; not Sun am; not
Fri after 4.30pm in summer.
Green Fee: on application
Catering: bar and bar meals.

I81 **Stinchcombe Hill**

☎(0453) 542015
Stinchcombe Hill, Dursley, Glos GL11
6AQ
1 mile along narrow lane
(signposted) off A4135 Tetbury-
Dursley road; or approach direct
from Dursley town centre, 0.5 mile
up hill past bus station.
Meadowland/downland course.
18 holes, 5723 yards, S.S.S.68
Founded 1889
Visitors: welcome any day;
restricted weekends and Bank
Holidays except with member.
Green Fee: £18 WD (£9 with
member), £20 WE (£10 with
member).
Societies: weekdays by
arrangement, preferred Wed.
Catering: full facilities available.
Hotels: Hare and Hounds; Prince of
Wales.

I82 **Stourbridge**

☎(0384) 395566
Worcester Lane, Stourbridge DY8
2RB
2 miles from Stourbridge town centre
on Worcester road.
Parkland course.
18 holes, 6178 yards, S.S.S.69
Founded 1892
Visitors: welcome weekdays; with
member only weekends.

Green Fee: £22.
Societies: restricted to Tues and Fri.
Catering: available except Mon.
Hotels: Pedmore House.

I83 **Stratford Oaks**

☎(0789) 731571
Bearley Road, Snitterfield,
Stratford-upon-Avon, Warwicks
CV37 0EZ
Close M40 junction 15, or A34 to
Stratford and follow signs for
Snitterfield.
Parkland course.
18 holes, 6400 yards, S.S.S.71
Designed by Howard Swan.
Founded May 1989
Visitors: welcome any time.
Green Fee: £15 WD, £20 WE.
Societies: Mon-Fri.
Catering: bar, restaurant.
Driving range, putting greens,
practice areas.
Hotels: Swan, Windmill Park, Hilton
National (Stratford).

I84 **Stratford-upon-Avon**

☎(0789) 205749
Tiddington Rd, Stratford-upon-Avon,
Warwicks CV37 7BA
0.5 mile from river bridge on B4089.
Parkland course.
18 holes, 6309 yards, S.S.S.70
Founded 1894 (1928 on present site)
Visitors: weekdays by arrangement.
Green Fee: on application
Societies: Tues and Thurs by
arrangement.
Catering: snacks and meals.

I85 **Streamleaze**

☎(0453) 843128
Canons Court Farm, Bradley,
Wotton-under-Edge, Glos GL12 7PN
Turn left off B4058 3 miles from M5
junction 14.
Farmland course.
9 holes, 2291 yards
Founded 1982
Visitors: welcome.
Green Fee: £5/day WD, £6-£7 WE.
Catering: bar and bar snacks.
Hotels: caravan site adjacent.

I86 **Sutton Coldfield**

☎(021) 353 9633, (Sutton Coldfield
Ladies GC (021) 353 1682)
110 Thornhill Rd, Streetly, Sutton
Coldfield B74 3ER
In Sutton Park, 9 miles NE of
Birmingham on B4138; nearest
motorway access is M6 junction 6.

Ross-on-Wye

In the summer of 1961, Ken Cotton was busy building two new courses, one in the stately old deer park of St Pierre beside the Newport Road out of Chester and the other in rather damp woodland on the outskirts of Ross-on-Wye. Both were adventurous, new ventures at a time when golf course building had only just begun to revive after the War.

It was a happy day therefore when Cotton phoned to extend an invitation to see the construction work, but not the least remarkable part of a remarkable tale is that it very nearly did not happen at all.

At the behest of a small group of men who had formed a special committee of the existing 9-hole Ross-on-Wye Club, he inspected the land in question only to report that he felt it unsuitable. It was only when the committee drove to Cotton's house near Pangbourne to plead with him to give it a try that he relented. The committee had previously searched high and low for a suitable site and saw this as their last chance. The decision to start was an act of faith by all concerned because the first steps involved a comprehensive clearance operation unsurpassed even with the making of Woburn a dozen or so years later.

My first memory was the sight of the head woodsman, then in his eighties, fuelling a woodland fire with fresh scrub and branches and cooking a lunch of bacon and eggs on the back of a carefully cleaned shovel. Even after working on many, many new courses, it is still something of a marvel that it all took shape as, indeed, was the speed with which Cotton conceived his layout.

After walking round the perimeter in pouring rain, and cogitating later in his bath, he presented the committee with a plan that needed virtually no change, although the patience needed to implement it requires almost as much praise as the initial inspiration.

Without the enormous personal contribution and sacrifice of the committee it would undoubtedly have failed and neither before nor since has there been such a shining example of unselfish enterprise. They had only the aim in mind of assuring the future of Ross-on-Wye Golf Club, an aspiration they achieved with flying colours. The new course was more than just a notable addition in an area virtually devoid of golf, it now ranks as one of the best inland courses in Britain. It has a handful of blind shots and there is a high demand on control from the tee, but from an enclosed, dark woodland, has emerged a beautiful setting for the game, one in which the distant beauty enhances the aesthetic pleasures of trees and pretty flowers.

It is hard nowadays to believe the problems faced at the outset but it needs a realisation of them to judge the success achieved and to pay tribute to the vision and skill which brought it about.

It made the official opening on May 7th 1967 an auspicious occasion. For one thing, new courses were rare in those days and, for another, the opening ceremony was performed by one of Cotton's partners, Frank Pennink, in his capacity as President of the English Golf Union.

It was a happy gathering that followed the exhibition game, marvelling how the course had been so patiently moulded from the forest and how the whole operation, including purchase of the land and the building of the clubhouse, had been performed for only £41,000. Twenty-five years later, that would have provided no more than a couple of holes.

Heathland course.
18 holes, 6248 yards, S.S.S.71
Re-designed by Dr Mackenzie.
Founded 1889
Visitors: welcome weekdays except Tues am.
Green Fee: £30/day (£6 with member).
Societies: not accepted on Tues, weekends or Bank Holidays; written applications required.
Catering: lunches, snacks daily.
Snooker.
Hotels: Parson & Clerk; Fairlawns; Sutton Court.

I87 Tewkesbury Park Hotel

☎(0684) 295405
Lincoln Green Lane, Tewkesbury, GL20 7DN
0.5 mile S of town on A38, 3 miles from M5 junction 9.
Parkland course.
18 holes, 6533/6197 yards, S.S.S.71/69
Designed by Frank Pennink.
Founded 1976
Visitors: welcome, h/cap cert required.
Green Fee: on application
Societies: welcome; weekends residential only.
Catering: snacks and meals available.
Hotels: Tewkesbury Park.

I88 Thornbury Golf Centre

Bristol Rd, Thornbury, Avon
On S side of Thornbury from A38.
Newly landscaped parkland course.
18 holes, c. 6500 yards, Par 72;
18 holes Par 3, c.2800 yards.
Designed by Hawtree & Co.
Opening early summer 1992
Visitors: welcome; apply for details of course availability, membership, green fees and society meetings.
Catering: full facilities.
Driving range.

I89 Tolladine

☎(0905) 21074, 726180 Pro shop
Tolladine Rd, Worcester WR4 9BA
Leave M5 at junction 6 Warndon, about 1 mile from city centre opposite Virgin Tavern.
Meadowland course.
9 holes, 5134 yards, S.S.S.67
Founded 1898
Visitors: welcome weekdays, weekends with member only.

Green Fee: male, £12 (£5 with member) WD, £6 WE & BH; female, £6 (£4 with member) WD, £5 WE & BH.
Societies: by appointment weekdays.
Catering: at Virgin Tavern.
Hotels: Fownes; The Star; Gifford.

I90 Tracy Park CC

☎(027 582) 2251
Bath Rd, Wick, Bristol BS15 5RN
Junction 18 off M4, S on A46 for 4 miles, right on A420 for 2 miles.
Parkland course.
3 x 9 holes; Avon, 6834 yards, S.S.S.73; Bristol, 6861 yards, S.S.S.73; Cotswold, 6203 yards, S.S.S.70
Designed by Grant Aitken.
Founded 1975
Visitors: welcome, telephone ahead.
Green Fee: on application.
Societies: welcome 7 days by arrangement.
Catering: lunch, dinner, bar snacks.
Squash, tennis, swimming, croquet, snooker.
Hotels: Lansdown Grove; Linden; Manor House.

I91 The Vale G & CC

☎(038 682) 781, 520 Pro shop, 660 fax.
Hill Furze Rd, Bishampton, Pershore, Worcs WR10 2LZ
Off B4084 near Bishampton village, 7 miles M5 junction 6, 6 miles Evesham, 5 miles Pershore.
Parkland/downland course.
International, 18 holes, 6519-7779 yards, S.S.S.73-76; Lenches, 9 holes, 5836 yards, S.S.S.68
Founded June 1991
Visitors: welcome, phone Pro to book.
Green Fee: International, £18/day; Lenches £5/round (9 holes).
Societies: society/company days welcome any day, 2 courses available.
Catering: Vale bar, Spikes bar, snacks and brunch, full à la carte restaurant and carvery; function room (140), conference room.
Driving range.
Hotels: Chequers (Fladbury), golf packages available.

I92 Walmley

☎(021) 373 0029
Brooks Rd, Wylde Green, Sutton Coldfield, W Midlands B72 1HR

6 miles N of Birmingham, turn off Birmingham to Sutton Coldfield road 0.25 mile N of Chester Rd (Yenton Pub), right into Greenhill Rd, Brooks Rd continues from this.
Parkland course.
18 holes, 6537 yards, S.S.S.72
Founded 1902
Visitors: welcome weekdays.
Green Fee: £20/round, £25/day, (£5 with member).
Societies: weekdays.
Catering: not Mon.
Hotels: Penns Hall (Wylde Green).

I93 Warley

☎(021) 429 2440
Lightwood Hill, Smethwick, Warley, W Midlands
Off A456 4.5 miles W of centre of Birmingham, behind Dog public house.
Municipal parkland course.
9 holes, 2606 yards, S.S.S.64
Founded 1921
Visitors: welcome at all times.
Green Fee: £4.60 peak times, £4 off-peak.
Catering: available.

I94 Warwick

☎(0926) 494316
The Racecourse, Warwick, CV34 6HW
Centre of Warwick Racecourse.
Public meadowland course.
9 holes, 2682 yards, S.S.S.66
Designed by D.G. Dunkley.
Founded 1886
Visitors: welcome except race days.
Green Fee: £3.50 (9 holes) WD, £5 (9 holes) WE.
Catering: bar only.
Driving range.
Hotels: Tudor House; Fourpenny Shop; Hilton Inernational.

I95 Welcombe Hotel

☎(0789) 295252
Warwick Rd, Stratford-upon-Avon, Warwicks CV37 0NR
5 miles from M40 junction 15 on A439 towards Stratford.
Parkland course.
18 holes, 6202 yards, S.S.S.70
Designed by T.J. McCauley.
Founded 1980
Visitors: phone booking essential.
Green Fee: £30.
Societies: weekdays only on request.
Catering: Pub style food and bar.
Floodlit tennis.
Hotels: Welcombe, golf breaks available.

I96 Westonbirt

☎(0666) 880242
Tetbury, Glos GL8 8QG
Turn off A433 3 miles SW of Tetbury,
through Westonbirt village, take
turning opposite Westonbirt
Arboretum entrance.
Parkland course.
9 holes, 4504 yards, S.S.S.62
Designed by Monty Hearn.
Visitors: welcome.
Green Fee: £6/day WD, £6/round WE
& BH.
Societies: by arrangement.
Catering: available at Holford Arms.
Hotels: Hare & Hounds.

97 Wharton Park

☎(0299) 405222
Long Bank, Bewdley, Worcs
On A456 at W end of Bewdley
by-pass.
Undulating parkland course in Wyre
Forest.
18 holes, c. 6500 yards, Par 72
Visitors: opening for limited play
(members only) autumn 1992;
casual visitors from 1993, phone for
details.
Societies: bookings for 1993.
Catering: full facilities, conferences,
function room.

I98 Windmill Village Hotel

☎(0203) 407241
Birmingham Road, Allesley,
Coventry, W Midlands CV5 9AL
Off A45 westbound Coventry-
Birmingham road.
Part flat, part hilly course.
18 holes, 4778 yards, S.S.S.64
Designed by Robert Hunter & Johm
Harrhy.
Founded 1990
Visitors: welcome except Sun am.
Green Fee: £9.40/round WD,
£10.50/round WE.
Societies: welcome weekdays only.
Catering: 2 bars, 2 restaurants.
Swimming pool, 8 snooker tables,
fitness gym, sauna, conference
facilities.
Hotels: Windmill Village (90 beds).

I99 Woodlands

☎(0454) 773361
Woodlands Lane, Almondsbury,
Bristol BS12 4JZ
M5 exit 16 to large roundabout, left
exit signed Woodlands Lane.
Public parkland course.
18 holes, 6068 yards, Par 70
Founded 1989
Visitors: welcome, pay-as-you-play.
Green Fee: £10 WD, £12 WE.
Societies: welcome by prior
arrangement.
Catering: full facilities.
Hotels: The Grange, Starkeys, Aztec
West (Bradley Stoke).

I100 Worcester G & CC

☎(0905) 422555 Sec, 422044 Pro,
421132 Catering
Boughton Park, Worcs WR2 4EZ
1.5 miles from town centre on
Bransford Rd (A4103); from M5
junction 7 follow signs for Hereford.
Parkland course.
18 holes, 5946 yards, S.S.S.68
Designed by Dr. A. Mackenzie.
Founded 1898
Visitors: welcome with h/cap cert;
with member only at weekends;
phone Pro.
Green Fee: £21.
Societies: welcome weekdays by
arrangement.
Catering: every day.
Tennis, squash, snooker.

I101 Worcestershire

☎(0684) 575992 or 573905
Wood Farm, Malvern Wells, Worcs
WR14 4PP
2 miles S of Great Malvern, turn off
A449 on to B4209, follow signs.
Meadowland/parkland course.
18 holes, 6449 yards, S.S.S.71
Designed by Colt, Mackenzie, Braid
and later Jiggins and Hawtree.
Founded 1879/1880
Visitors: members of recognised
club with h/cap certs, no play before
10am weekends.
Green Fee: £20 WD, £25 WE.
Societies: welcome Thurs and Fri by
arrangement.
Catering: max 70 seating; full
facilities except Mon.
2 snooker tables.
Hotels: Abbey; Foley Arms; Cottage
in the Wood; Mount Pleasant; Royal
Malvern.

J
WALES

Golf in Wales can be divided very clearly into North and South with one or two notable exceptions in the central region like Borth & Ynyslas, which is well worth a break in any journey.

Road access to the Principality is usually by way of the Severn Bridge, the coast road from Chester to Bangor or into the mountain heart by way of Shrewsbury, Llangollen or Dolgellau. Bernard Darwin, who always favoured the train, made the latter a much publicised route, and was able to recite at will the stations that came between Shrewsbury and his beloved Aberdovey where he spent an annual holiday.

The station at Aberdovey itself is right beside the clubhouse and little time need be lost in launching a round across an historic piece of land, which Darwin described with sentimental love and warmth. It is among a host of Clubs celebrating their centenary in 1992. Although two years' Aberdovey's junior, Royal St David's enjoys an even more resplendent setting, under the historic shadow of Harlech Castle, with more distant views of Snowdonia. It is a well trodden favourite for the staging of Welsh championships.

The north coast is well served by Conwy (Caernarvonshire) and by Prestatyn which, after a somewhat flat beginning, blossoms into ideal duneland territory. Llandudno GC at Maesdu and North Wales GC next door are familiar names.

For an instant introduction to Welsh golf in the south, nothing beats the convenience of St Pierre, which was one of the first new courses to be built in the wake of World War II and undoubtedly one of the best. It weaves a most pleasant path through stately trees of ancient origin, providing a sheltered home for the game that contrasts sharply with the exposed reaches of Royal Porthcawl, Southerndown, Pyle & Kenfig, Ashburnham and Tenby.

Temptation to reach Porthcawl may make travellers overlook the charms of Newport at Rogerstone, but Porthcawl is rightly hailed the most noble of the Welsh championship links, every hole commanding sight of the ocean and the first three rubbing shoulders with it. There is greater change of level at Porthcawl than on any other seaside course in England and Wales. For a lofty perch, however, Southerndown is a distinguished example — enjoying a bird's eye view of Porthcawl into the bargain.

The drive to the Club scales the side of a mountain while the first hole climbs what is left. Pyle & Kenfig, on the other side of Porthcawl, returns to sea level, the course split in two by a road which also acts as a division of character.

Pennard beyond Swansea is a lovely, remote links that never attracts the praise it warrants but this is more the province of West Wales, with the attractions of Ashburnham and Tenby which combine a stern challenge with scenic blessings.

Ashburnham is as well known for golf as the neighbouring town of Llanelli is for rugby, but Tenby beckons for those who look upon themselves as connoisseurs of glorious places to play. Host to countless championships, it is a seaside links of unrivalled joy and beauty and, for the historically minded, it has an important additional qualification — it is the oldest constituted Club in the Principality.

It is golf on the grand scale, frequently influenced by the wind and calling for an ability to flight the ball low and indulge in the art of the chip and run which many in other parts of the world regard as a relic of a lost age.

This section has been dominated by north and south but Cradoc at Brecon, Knighton and Llandrindod Wells are some contrasting courses in contrasting settings for those desirous of exploring more central parts.

J1 Aberdare

☎(0685) 871188 club, 872797 Sec, 878735 Pro.
Abernant, Aberdare, Mid-Glam CF44 0RY
0.5 mile from town centre (A4059), past General Hospital.
Mountain course with parkland features.
18 holes, 5845 yards, S.S.S.69
Founded 1921
Visitors: welcome weekdays; Sat with member only; Sun and Bank Holidays by advance notice to Sec.
Green Fee: £13 WD, £16 WE & BH.
Societies: welcome on application to Sec.
Catering: full range of bar snacks and meals; not Mon.
Snooker.
Hotels: Baverstock; Ty Newydd.

J2 Aberdovey

☎(0654) 767210
Aberdovey, Gwynedd LL35 0RT
On main A493 immediately W of Aberdovey.
Seaside links course.
18 holes, 6445 yards, S.S.S.71
Founded 1892
Visitors: welcome; h/cap certs required.
Green Fee: from £18/round to £30/day.
Societies: weekdays only.
Catering: daily 10.30am-8.30pm; bar 11am-11pm.
Snooker.
Hotels: list available from Sec.

J3 Abergele & Pensarn

☎(0745) 824034
Tan-y-Gopa Rd, Abergele, Clwyd LL28 8DS
Through Abergele from A55, turn left in direction of Llanddulas; course below Gwrych Castle.
Parkland course.
18 holes, 6450 yards, S.S.S.71
Designed by Hawtree & Sons.
Founded 1910
Visitors: welcome.
Green Fee: on application
Societies: by prior arrangement.
Catering: restaurant except Mon.
Snooker.

J4 Abersoch

☎(0758) 812622
Golf Rd, Abersoch, Gwynedd LL53 7EY
6 miles from Pwllheli; 1st left through village.

Seaside links course.
18 holes, 5792 yards, S.S.S.68
Designed by Harry Vardon.
Founded 1910
Visitors: welcome with h/cap cert; booking required.
Green Fee: £12 WD, £15 WE.
Societies: by arrangement.
Catering: meals served.
Hotels: Egryn; Wylfa; Riverside; Neigwl; Devgoch.

J5 Aberystwyth

☎(0970) 615104
Bryn y-Mor, Aberystwyth, Dyfed SY23 3QD
N end of promenade immediately behind sea front hotels, access road adjacent to Cliff Railway, 1 mile from town centre.
Undulating meadowland course.
18 holes, 5735 yards, S.S.S.68
Designed by Harry Vardon.
Founded 1911
Visitors: limited at weekends.
Green Fee: £15.
Societies: by appointment.
Catering: bar and restaurant.
Hotels: Belle Vue Royal (25% reduction on green fees).

J6 Alice Springs

☎(0873) 880772
Bettws Newydd, Usk, Gwent NP5 1JY
A449 into Usk, N on B4598, after 1.5 miles take right to Bettws Newydd, course (Queens) 1.5 miles on left; for Kings course (from July 1992) take same B4598, do not turn off, course 3 miles N on right.
Parkland course.
Queens, 18 holes, 6041 yards, S.S.S.69; Kings (from July 1992), 6868 yards, S.S.S.71
Designed by Keith R. Morgan.
Founded Aug 1989
Visitors: phone for tee time weekends and Bank Holidays.
Green Fee: £12.50/round.
Societies: Mon-Fri; weekends by arrangement.
Catering: bar and snacks all day, restaurant with phone booking.

J7 Anglesey

☎(0407) 811202 Manager, 810219 Steward
Station Rd, Rhosneigr, Gwynedd LL64 5QT
S off A5 about 8 miles from Holyhead onto A4080, in 3 miles turn right at Llanfaelog church, about 1 mile from course.

Seaside links course.
18 holes, 5713 yards, S.S.S.68
Founded 1914
Visitors: welcome.
Green Fee: on application.
Societies: by arrangement.
Catering: meals served.
Hotels: Maelog Lake (Rhoslan).

J8 Ashburnham

☎(055 46) 2269 Sec.
Cliffe Terrace, Burry Port, Dyfed SA16 0HN
9 miles from Llanelli exit on M4, 4 miles from Llanelli on A484.
Championship links course.
18 holes, 6916 yards, S.S.S.73; 18 holes, 6627 yards, S.S.S.72
Founded 1894
Visitors: weekdays; some weekends.
Green Fee: on application
Societies: welcome weekdays.
Catering: full facilities.

J9 Bala

☎(0678) 520359
Penlan, Bala, Gwynedd LL23 7SR
Take A494 out of Bala to Dolgellau, turn 1st right on leaving Bala.
Upland course.
10 holes, 4962 yards, S.S.S.64
Founded 1973
Visitors: welcome, some restrictions Sat and Sun pm.
Green Fee: £10 (£5 with member); £30/week.
Societies: by prior arrangement.
Catering: bar; catering by prior arrangement. Snooker, pool.
Hotels: Plas Goch; White Lion; Pale Hall.

J10 Bala Lake Hotel

☎(0678) 520344
Bala, Gwynned, LL23 7YF
Off B4403 1.5 miles from Bala.
Public parkland course.
9 holes, 4281 yards, S.S.S.61
Founded 1960
Visitors: welcome.
Green Fee: £8/day WD, £9/day WE.
Societies: welcome.
Catering: full facilities.
Open air swimming pool.
Hotels: Bala Lake Hotel.

J11 Bargoed

☎(0443) 830143
Heolddu, Bargoes, Mid-Glam
20 miles from Cardiff on A469 to town centre; moorland road.

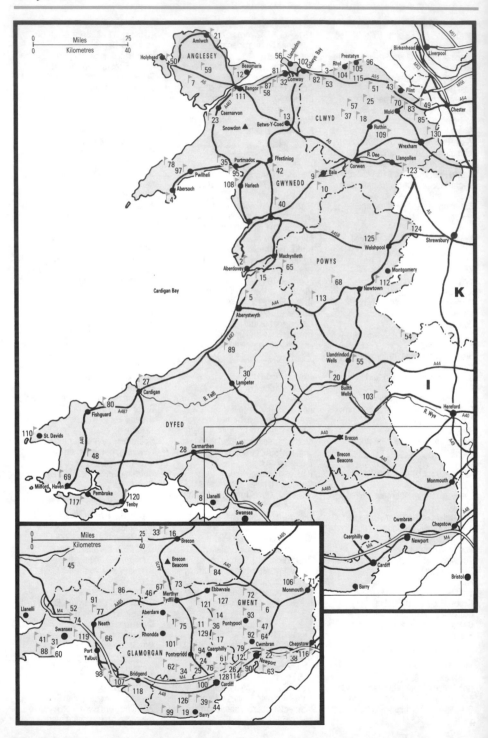

Moorland course.
18 holes, 6213 yards, S.S.S.70
Founded c. 1921
Visitors: welcome weekdays;
weekends with member only.
Green Fee: £13 WD (£8 with
member).
Societies: by arrangement.
Catering: bar snacks and evening
meals served.
Hotels: Park Hotel; Maes Manor.

J12 Baron Hill
☎(0248) 810231
Beaumaris, Gwynedd LL58 8YN
Signposted from Beaumaris, 0.75
mile from town centre.
Undulating seaside course.
9 holes, 5564 yards, S.S.S.67
Founded 1895
Visitors: welcome.
Green Fee: on application
Societies: apply to Hon Sec.
Catering: light snacks.

J13 Betws-y-Coed
☎(0690) 710556
Betws-y-Coed, Gwynedd
Just off main A5 road in the middle of
village of Betws-y-Coed.
Parkland course.
9 holes, 4996 yards, S.S.S.64
Founded 1977
Visitors: welcome.
Green Fee: £10 WD, £15 WE.
Societies: arrangements to be made
in writing to Sec.
Catering: every day except Mon.
Hotels: Royal Oak; Plas Hall.

J14 Blackwood
☎(0495) 223152
Cwmgelli, Blackwood, Gwent
0.75 mile N of Blackwood on A4048,
Tredegar road.
Meadowland course.
9 holes, 5304 yards, S.S.S.66
Founded 1914
Visitors: welcome weekdays,
weekends by arrangement.
Green Fee: £10.50 WD, £12.50 WE
& BH.
Societies: weekdays by
arrangement.
Catering: golf societies only by
arrangement.
Hotels: Maes Manor; Plas Inn.

J15 Borth & Ynyslas
☎(0970) 871325 Sec, 871202
Clubhouse, 871154 fax.
Borth, Dyfed SY24 5JS

8 miles N of Aberystwyth towards
Machynlleth, turn left N side of
village of Bow Street.
Traditional links course (oldest in
Wales).
18 holes, 6110 yards, S.S.S.70
Founded 1895
Visitors: members of a golf club with
club h/cap.
Green Fee: £12/day WD, £15/day
WE.
Societies: and properly constituted
parties catered for after consultation
with Sec; 7 days, but weekends may
be difficult.
Catering: full facilities, prior booking.
Hotels: Cliff Haven; Golf Hotel;
Railway; Glanmor; Ynyshir Country
House; Black Lion.

J16 Brecon
☎(0874) 622004
Newton Park, Llanfaer, Brecon,
Powys LD3 8PA
300 yards from roundabout on
by-pass S of town.
Meadowland course.
9 holes, 5218 yards, S.S.S.66
Founded 1902
Visitors: welcome.
Green Fee: £8/day.
Societies: by arrangement.
Hotels: Castle of Brecon; Bishops
Meadow; several guest houses.

J17 Bryn Meadows G & CC
☎(0495) 225590 or 227276
The Bryn, Hengoed, Mid-Glam CF8
7SM
A469 15 miles from Cardiff, turn up
lane opposite filling station near
Crown Hotel.
Parkland course.
18 holes, 6132 yards, S.S.S.69
Designed by E. Jefferies & B. Mayo.
Founded 1973
Visitors: welcome weekdays.
Green Fee: £17.50 (£12.50 with
member) WD, £22.50 (£17.50 with
member) WE.
Societies: welcome weekdays.
Catering: full facilties except Sun.
Banqueting; indoor heated pool,
jacuzzi, full leisure facilities.
Hotels: Bryn Meadows, special
2-day packages.

J18 Bryn Morfydd Hotel
☎(074) 578280
The Duchess Course, Llanrhaeadr,
Nr Denbigh LL16 4NP
2.5 miles E of Denbigh on A525.
Parkland course.

Dukes, 9 holes, 5266 yards,
S.S.S.67; Duchess, 9 holes, 1200
yards, S.S.S.27
Founded 1982
Visitors: welcome.
Green Fee: £7/day.
Societies: welcome.
Catering: full facilities.
British School of Golf, practice
ground, tennis, swimming pool.
Hotels: Bryn Morfydd.

J19 Brynhill
☎(0446) 720277 Sec, 735061
Clubhouse
Port Rd, Barry, S Glam CF6 7PH
A48 to Culverhouse Cross from
Cardiff, then road to Barry, golf club
on Port Rd near Colcot Arms Hotel.
Undulating meadowland course.
18 holes, 5511 metres, S.S.S.69
Designed by G.K. Cotton.
Founded 1921
Visitors: welcome Mon-Sat; no
visitors Sun.
Green Fee: £15 (£8 with member)
WD, inc Sat.
Societies: catered for weekdays.
Catering: lunch, dinner, except Mon.
Hotels: Mount Sorrel; International.

J20 Builth Wells
☎(0982) 553296
Golf Club Rd, Builth Wells, Powys
LD2 3NF
A483 immediately W of Builth Wells.
Parkland course.
18 holes, 5760 yards, S.S.S.67
Founded 1923
Visitors: welcome any time.
Green Fee: £14 WD, £18 WE & BH.
Societies: any time.
Catering: available on request.
Hotels: send for brochure.

J21 Bull Bay
☎(0407) 830960, 831188 Pro.
Bull Bay Rd, Amlwch, Anglesey LL68
9RY
A5025 15 miles from Menai Bridge.
Undulating seaside course.
18 holes, 6160 yards, S.S.S.70
Designed by Herbert Fowler and
Walton Heath.
Founded 1913
Visitors: welcome, h/cap cert
required.
Green Fee: £12 WD, £18 WE.
Societies: by arrangement with Sec;
discount for parties over 12.
Catering: full facilities available.
Hotels: Trecastell; Gadlys; Bull Bay;
Erw Felin.

J22 Caerleon
☎(0633) 420342
Broadway, Caerleon, Newport,
Gwent NP6 1AY
3 miles from M4 junction 25.
Public parkland course.
9 holes, 3092 yards, S.S.S.34
Founded 1974
Visitors: welcome.
Green Fee: £2.80 (9 holes) WD,
£3.50 WE.
Catering: snack bar.
Driving range, pool.

J23 Caernarfon
☎(0286) 2783
Aberforeshore, Llanfaglan,
Caernarfon LL54 5RP
2 miles S of town off
Caernarfon-Pwllheli road.
Parkland course.
18 holes, 5870 yards, S.S.S.69
Founded 1902
Visitors: welcome.
Green Fee: £12/round, £15/day.
Societies: by arrangement.
Catering: full facilities. Pool.
Hotels: Bryn Eisteddfod; Erw Fair;
Caeau Capel; Black Boy; Devgoch;
Seiont Manor.

J24 Caerphilly
☎(0222) 883481 club, 863441 Sec.
Pencapel, Mountain Rd, Caerphilly,
Mid-Glam CF8 2SY
7 miles from Cardiff centre on A469;
12 miles from Newport; 6 miles from
M4 on A470 N; 250 yards from
bus/rail station.
Mountain/parkland course; 2 holes
on steep gradient.
14 holes, 6253 yards, S.S.S.71
Designed by Fernie (original 9).
Founded 1905
Visitors: welcome weekdays with
proof of club membership and h/cap
cert; not Sun or Bank Holidays unless
with member.
Green Fee: £16/day (£10 with
member); jnrs £4.50.
Societies: Mon-Fri only.
Catering: bar; restaurant meals by
arrangement. Snooker.
Hotels: Mount; Greenhill; Moat
House; Cedar Tree.

J25 Caerwys Nine Of Clubs
☎(0352) 720692
Caerwys, Mold, Clwyd CH7 5AQ
1.5 miles S of A55 expressway midway between Holywell and St Asaph.
Undulating parkland course.

9 holes, 3088 yards, Par 60
Founded 1988
Visitors: welcome.
Green Fee: £3.50 (18 holes) WD, £5
WE; reductions for jnrs.
Societies: by booking only.
Catering: light refreshments.
Putting green, snooker, table tennis.
Hotels: Holywell; Afonwen.

J26 Cardiff
☎(0222) 753320 Sec, 753067
Clubhouse, 754772 Pro.
Sherborne Ave, Cyncoed, Cardiff,
S Glam CF2 6SJ
Take A48M off the M4, 3 miles to
Pentwyn exit, take industrial road for
2 miles to village, turn left at
roundabout and again left at Spar
shop, club 150 yards.
Undulating parkland course.
18 holes, 6016 yards, S.S.S.70
Founded 1921
Visitors: welcome weekdays
arranged in advance, restricted Tues
am (Ladies Day); with member only
at weekends.
Green Fee: on application.
Societies: Thurs by advance
booking.
Catering: full facilities available.
Hotels: Post House; Stakis Inn.

J27 Cardigan
☎(0293) 612035
Gwbert-on-Sea, Cardigan, Dyfed
SA43 1PR
3 miles NW of Cardigan, take left fork
at Cenotaph at N end of town.
Seaside meadowland course.
18 holes, 6641 yards, S.S.S.72
Founded 1928
Visitors: unrestricted.
Green Fee: £15/day WD, £18/day
WE & BH.
Societies: welcome any day with
previous arrangement.
Catering: full facilities.
Squash, pool.
Hotels: Cliff; Castell Malgwyn
(Llechryd); Gwbert.

J28 Carmarthen
☎(0267) 214
Blaenycoed Rd, Carmarthen, Dyfed
SA33 6EH
4 miles NW of Carmarthen.
Undulating course.
18 holes, 6212 yards, S.S.S.71
Visitors: welcome.
Green Fee: on application
Societies: by arrangement.
Catering: available except Wed.

J29 Castell Heights
☎(0222) 886666 bookings, 886686
club.
Blaengwynlais, Caerphilly,
Mid-Glamorgan CF8 1NG
4 miles from M4 junction 32 on
Tongwynlais-Caerphilly road, by
Mountain Lakes Golf Club.
Public, mountainside course.
9 holes, 2688 yards, S.S.S.66
Founded 1982
Visitors: welcome, pay-as-you-play.
Green Fee: £4.50 WD, £5 WE.
Societies: by arrangement.
Catering: bar and bar snacks.
Mountain Lakes Driving Range.

J30 Cilgwyn
☎(057 045) 286
Llangybi, Lampeter, Dyfed SA48 8NN
5 miles NE of Lampeter on A485 in
village of Llangybi.
Parkland course.
9 holes, 5327 yards, S.S.S.67
Founded 1905
Visitors: welcome.
Green Fee: on application.
Societies: catered for all year.
Catering: restaurant and bar meals
available Tues to Sun.
Hotels: Black Lion; Falcondale.

J31 Clyne
☎(0792) 401989
120 Owls Lodge Lane, Mayals, Black
Pill, Swansea SA3 3DR
Coast road from Swansea to Blackpyl
(3 miles); turn right into Mayals Rd.
Moorland course.
18 holes, 6312 yards, S.S.S.71
Designed by H.S. Colt.
Founded 1921
Visitors: welcome.
Green Fee: £17/day WD, £22/day
WE.
Societies: not weekends; £17 per
head 1-20, £15 per head 21+.
Catering: full facilities except Mon.
Hotels: Dragon; Osborne.

J32 Conwy (Caernarvonshire)
☎(0492) 593400
Morfa, Conwy, Gwynedd LL32 8ER
From Conwy, A55 to Bangor, down
Morfa Drive over cattle grid,
clubhouse 300 yards on left.
Championship links course.
18 holes, 6901 yards, S.S.S.73
Founded 1890
Visitors: welcome weekdays;
restricted weekends and Bank
Holidays.

Green Fee: £18/day WD, £23/day WE & BH; 5 day ticket Mon-Fri £72.
Societies: catered for on application to Sec.
Catering: available except Mon evening and Tues.
Hotels: Castle Bank; Bryn Cregin; Caerlyr.

J33 Cradoc
☎(0874) 623658
Penoyre Park, Cradoc, Brecon, Powys LD3 9LP
2 miles N of Brecon on B4520.
Parkland course.
18 holes, 6318 yards, S.S.S.71
Designed by C.K. Cotton.
Founded 1974
Visitors: welcome; not Sun.
Green Fee: £15 WD, £18 Sat and Bank Holidays.
Societies: welcome with prior arrangement; not Sun.
Catering: full facilities daily except Mon by special arrangement.
Hotels: Wellington; Castle of Brecon; George; Bishops Meadow; Lake (Llangammarch Wells).

J34 Creigiau
☎(0222) 890263
Creigiau, Cardiff, S Glam CF4 8NN
4 miles NW of Cardiff towards Llantrisant.
Parkland course.
18 holes, 5955 yards, S.S.S.69
Founded 1926
Visitors: welcome weekdays; Tues Ladies Day.
Green Fee: £20.
Societies: welcome weekdays by arrangement.
Catering: lunch and dinner served except Mon.
Hotels: Miskin Manor; Park; Royal; Angel.

J35 Criccieth
☎(0766) 522154
Ednyfed Hill, Criccieth, Gwynedd
A497, 4 miles from Portmadoc, turn right past Memorial Hall, 0.5 mile up hill.
Undulating hilltop course.
18 holes, 5787 yards, S.S.S.68
Founded around 1904
Visitors: welcome.
Green Fee: on application.
Societies: welcome.
Catering: meals and snacks served by arrangement with Steward.
Hotels: George IV; Bron Eifion; Marine; Lion.

J36 Cyncoed (Oakdale)
☎(0495) 220044
Llwynon Lane, Oakdale, Gwent NP2 0NF
Public parkland course.
9 holes, 1235 yards, S.S.S.28
Designed by Ian Goodenough.
Founded 1990
Visitors: welcome
Green Fee: £3 (9 holes) WD, £3.50 WE; jnrs £2.50 any day.
Societies: welcome, bookings only.
Catering: snacks in clubhouse (no license).
Driving range.
Hotels: The Old Forge.

J37 Denbigh
☎(0745) 816669 Sec, 814159 Pro, 816664 Caterer
Henllan Rd, Denbigh, Clwyd
B5382 Denbigh to Henllan road, 1 mile out of Denbigh.
Undulating parkland course.
18 holes, 5650 yards, S.S.S.67
Founded 1922
Visitors: welcome; phone Pro shop for reservation.
Green Fee: £15/day WD, £20/day WE & BH.
Societies: daily except Thurs.
Catering: full facilities 7 days. Snooker.
Hotels: Bryn Morfydd (British School of Golf, Llanrhaeadr); Tan y Gyrt Hall (Nantglyn)

J38 Dewstow
☎(0291) 430444
Caerwent, Newport, Gwent NP6 4AH
1 mile S of A48 at Caerwent, 4 miles W of Chepstow.
Parkland course.
18 holes, 6100 yards, S.S.S.70
Founded 1988
Visitors: welcome, good golf dress required.
Green Fee: £10 WD, £12 WE.
Societies: Mon-Fri.
Catering: lounge bar, dining room.
Driving range.

J39 Dinas Powis
☎(0222) 512727 Sec, 512157 Club
Golf House, Old Highwalls, Dinas Powis, S Glam CF6 4AJ
M4 junction 33, on A4055 to Dinas Powis via Barry (Cardiff Airport).
Parkland course.
18 holes, 5377 yards, S.S.S.66
Founded 1914
Visitors: welcome with h/cap cert and proof of club membership.

Green Fee: £16 WD, £21 WE.
Societies: limited to 40; fee £13.
Catering: bar and restaurant.
Hotels: Star.

J40 Dolgellau
☎(0341) 422603
Pencefn, Golf Rd, Dolgellau, Gwynedd LL40 1SL
Turn off town by-pass onto old A494 road, turn right just after main bridge, signposted from there on; 0.5 mile from town centre.
Parkland course.
9 holes (18 tees), 4671 yards, S.S.S.63
Founded 1911
Visitors: welcome weekdays; ring Sat.
Green Fee: £10/day, £12 WE & BH.
Societies: by arrangement.
Catering: available throughout the year.
Hotels: Royal Ship; Bontoon Hall; Dolserau Hall.

J41 Fairwood Park
☎(0792) 297849 Sec, 203648 Steward, 299194 Pro.
Blackhills Lane, Upper Killay, Swansea SA2 7JN
From central Swansea follow signs for Sketty and Killay then Swansea Airport; take left turn opposite Airport entrance; course 0.5 mile up Blackhills Lane on left.
Parkland championship course.
18 holes, 6606 yards, S.S.S.72
Founded 1969
Visitors: welcome with h/cap cert; advisable to phone in advance.
Green Fee: £18 WD, £23 WE & BH.
Societies: welcome weekdays and weekends by prior arrangement.
Catering: breakfast, lunch, dinner, tea, coffee, snacks; licensed bar. Pool, darts.

J42 Ffestiniog
☎(0766 76) 2637
Clwb Golffi Ffestiniog, Y Cefn, Ffestiniog, Gwynned
1 mile from Ffestiniog on Bala road.
Scenic mountain course.
9 holes, 5032 metres, S.S.S.66
Founded 1893
Visitors: welcome, hardly any restrictions.
Green Fee: £6 daily.
Societies: by prior arrangement only.
Catering: bar only.
Hotels: Pengwern; Abbey Arms.

The Mill at Glynhir

J43 Flint

☎(0352) 732327, 733461, 732186 Sec (home).
Cornist Park, Flint, Clwyd CH6 5HJ
A548 coast road, or M56/A55; course is 1 mile from town centre; from Town Hall, follow signs to Cornist Park.
Parkland course.
9 holes, 5953 yards, S.S.S.69
Founded 1966
Visitors: welcome weekdays.
Green Fee: £8/day.
Societies: Mon-Fri.
Catering: prior arrangement for catering and bar. Snooker.
Hotels: Chequers; Northop Hall; Springfield; Pentre.

J44 Glamorganshire

☎(0222) 701185 Sec, 707048 members
Lavernock Rd, Penarth, S Glam CF6 2UP
Take junction 33 off M4, join A4232 and then A4267 which passes club.
Parkland course.
18 holes, 6150 yards, S.S.S.70
Founded 1890
Visitors: welcome except on competition days, Bank Holidays and when Societies on course; must have bona fide h/cap cert from own club.
Green Fee: £22 WD, £28 WE & BH.
Societies: on application to Sec.
Catering: first class facilities, à la carte, bar snacks, lunches every day.
Hotels: Walton House.

J45 Glynhir

☎(0269) 850472
Glynhir Rd, Llandybie, Ammanford, Dyfed SA18 2TF
1.25 miles from Ammanford on A483 Llandybie road, turn right up Glynhir Rd, continue almost 2 miles to club.
Undulating parkland/meadowland course.
18 holes, 5952 yards, S.S.S.69
Designed by F.W. Hawtree.
Founded 1964 – moved from previous course at Llandeilo.
Visitors: bona fide members of recognised golf clubs with current h/cap certs welcome weekdays and by permission weekends and holidays in summer.
Green Fee: £12 WD, £16 WE & BH summer; £6 WD, £10 WE & BH winter.
Societies: weekdays welcome, Sat only on occasions, not Sun or holidays; all by prior appointment.
Catering: restaurant, bar meals daily.
Hotels: The Mill at Glynhir; Glynhir Golf Clubhouse; Cawdor, White Hart (Llandeilo); Red Lion (Llandybie).

J46 Glynneath

☎(0639) 720452
Pen-y-craig, Pontneathvaughan, Nr Glynneath, W Glam SA11 5UH
11 miles N of Neath, 2 miles NE of Glynneath on B4242.
Hillside course.
18 holes, 5456 yards, S.S.S.67
Designed by Cotton, Pennink, Lawrie & Partners.
Founded 1931
Visitors: no restrictions.
Green Fee: on application
Societies: weekdays by arrangement.
Catering: by arrangement; bar from 12am.

J47 Greenmeadow

☎(06333) 69321, 62626 Pro.
Treherbert Road, Croesyceiliog, Cwmbran, Gwent NP44 2BZ
Off A4042.
Parkland course.

14 holes, 5597 yards, S.S.S.67
Founded 1978
Visitors: welcome.
Green Fee: £12/day WD, £20/day
WE.
Societies: welcome.
Catering: full facilities.
Hotels: Parkway; Commodore.

J48 Haverfordwest
☎(0437) 764523
Arnolds Down, Haverfordwest, Dyfed
SA61 2XQ
1 mile E of town on A40.
Parkland course.
18 holes, 6005 yards, S.S.S.69
Founded 1904
Visitors: bona fide golfers welcome.
Green Fee: £14/day WD, £22/day
WE.
Societies: by arrangement.
Catering: small restaurant; hot and
cold bar snacks; licensed bar.
Hotels: Hotel Mariners; St Brides(
Saundersfoot).

J49 Hawarden
☎(0244) 531447
Groomsdale Lane, Hawarden,
Deeside, Clwyd CH5 3EH
A55 9 miles W of Chester, 1st left
after Hawarden station.
Parkland course.
9 holes, 5620 yards, S.S.S.67
Founded 1911
Visitors: with member only.
Green Fee: £10.
Societies: by arrangement with Sec.
Catering: full facilities.
Hotels: St Davids (Ewloe).

J50 Holyhead
☎(0407) 763279 Sec, 762119 bar,
762022 Pro.
Trearddur Bay, Holyhead, Gwynedd
LL65 2YG
Follow A5 from Bangor, left at Valley
traffic lights, course approx 4 miles
on left.
Undulating course.
18 holes, 6058 yards, S.S.S.70
Designed by James Braid.
Founded 1912
Visitors: welcome, h/cap cert
required.
Green Fee: £14.50 WD, £16.50 WE
& BH.
Societies: recognised societies
welcome subject to prior
arrangement with Sec.
Catering: lunchtime bar snacks;
evening meals by arrangement.
Hotels: Beach; Trearddur Bay.

J51 Holywell
☎(0352) 710040
Brynford, Nr Holywell, Clwyd CH8 8LQ
Turn left at traffic lights on A5026 off
A55, 1 mile to crossroads, turn right.
Undulating moorland course.
18 holes, 6005 yards, S.S.S.70
Founded 1906
Visitors: welcome except on
competition days; h/cap certs.
Green Fee: £8 WD, £12 WE.
Societies: by prior arrangement with
Sec.
Catering: lunch and evening meals.
Snooker.
Hotels: Fielding Arms; Victoria;
Stamford Gate; Kinsale Hall.

J52 Inco
☎(0792) 844216, 843336 Sec.
Clydach, Swansea, W Glamorgan
2 miles N of M4 junction 45.
Flat parkland course with river and
trees.
12 holes, 6273 yards, S.S.S.70
Founded 1965
Visitors: welcome.
Green Fee: £11/round WD,
£13/round WE.
Societies: welcome by arrangement.
Catering: bar and snacks (evenings
only).

J53 Kinmel Park Golf Complex
☎(0745) 833548
Bodelwyddan, Clwyd, N Wales LL18
5SR
Just off main A55 expressway at
Bodelwyddan between Abergele and
St Asaph.
9 hole Par 3 course, transformed at
dusk into Britain's first night-time
course – "lightsticks" and luminous
balls.
Visitors: welcome; booking
essential for night-time through
Peter Stebbings Golf.
Green Fee: from £2/round.
Societies: by arrangement.
Catering: bar and restaurant.

J54 Knighton
☎(0547) 528646
The Ffrydd, Knighton, Powys LD7 1EF
0.5 mile S of Knighton.
Undulating course.
9 holes, 5320 yards, S.S.S.66
Designed by Harry Vardon.
Founded 1913
Visitors: welcome.
Green Fee: £7 WD and WE.
Societies: by arrangement with Sec.

Catering: snacks at weekends, other
by prior arrangement.
Hotels: Red Lion; Knighton.

J55 Llandrindod Wells
☎(0597) 823873 Sec/manager,
2010 Club
Llandrindod Wells, Powys LD1 5NY
Signposted from A483, 0.5 mile E of
town, above lake.
Mountain course.
18 holes, 5759 yards, S.S.S.68
Designed by Harry Vardon.
Founded 1907
Visitors: welcome at all times.
Green Fee: £10 WD, £15 WE.
Societies: by prior arrangement.
Catering: bar, restaurant; not Tues.
Hotels: Metropole; Commodore;
Glen Usk; Llanerch,; Bell Inn;
Pencerrig; Guidfa House.

J56 Llandudno
☎(0492) 76450
Hospital Rd, Llandudno, Gwynedd
LL30 1HU
Alongside main Llandudno Hospital,
approx 1 mile from town centre.
Seaside parkland course.
18 holes, 6513 yards, S.S.S.72
Designed by Tom Jones.
Founded 1915
Visitors: members of recognised
clubs.
Green Fee: on application
Societies: any day; max 30 Sat/Sun.
Catering: prior booking.

J57 Llanerch Park
☎(0745) 730805
North Wales Golf Range & Course,
Llanerch Park, St Asaph, Clwyd LL17
0BD
On A525 Denbigh-St Asaph road,
Tourist Board signposted.
Parkland course.
9 holes, 1652 yards, Par 30
Founded 1988
Visitors: welcome 10am until dusk;
pay-as-you-play.
Green Fee: £2/9 holes (£1.50 jnrs).
Societies: by prior arrangement,
start before 10am.
Catering: light refreshments.
Driving range.

J58 Llanfairfechan
☎(0248) 680144
Llannerch Road, Llanfairfechan,
Gwynned LL33 0EB
In Llanfairfechan between Conwy
and Bangor.

Parkland course.
9 holes, 3119 yards, S.S.S.57
Founded 1972
Visitors: welcome any time except during competitions (mostly Sun).
Green Fee: £6 WD, £10 WE & BH.
Societies: write to Sec.
Catering: bar open all evenings, and 11.30am-2pm weekends.
Hotels: Split Willow.

J59 **Llangefni (Public)**
☎(0248) 722193
Llangefni, Anglesey, N Wales
A5 to Llangefni.
Parkland course.
9 holes, 1467 yards, S.S.S.28
Designed by Hawtree & Sons.
Founded 1983
Visitors: welcome.
Green Fee: on application

J60 **Llangland Bay**
☎(0792) 366023
Llangland Bay, Swansea, SA3 4QR
M4 to Swansea, 6 miles W.
Seaside parkland course.
18 holes, 5827 yards, S.S.S.69
Founded 1904
Visitors: welcome if member of recognised club.
Green Fee: winter £16 (£9 with member), summer £20 (£10 with member).
Societies: welcome if booked in advance, max 36.
Catering: bar meals; cooked meals to order before playing.
Hotels: Osborne.

J61 **Llanishen**
☎(0222) 755078
Cwm, Lisvane, Cardiff CF4 5UD
5 miles N of Cardiff centre, 1.5 miles N of Llanishen church via Heol Hir.
Parkland course.
18 holes, 5296 yards, S.S.S.66
Founded 1905
Visitors: weekdays unlimited; weekends and Bank Holidays with member only; h/cap cert required.
Green Fee: £20.
Societies: Thurs only by previous arrangement.
Catering: full facilities except Mon.
Hotels: Phoenix (Cardiff).

J62 **Llantrisant & Pontyclun**
☎(0443) 222148, 224601
Lanlay Rd, Talbot Green, Mid-Glam CF7 8HZ

M4 junction 34, then A4119 to Talbot Green.
Parkland course.
12 holes, 5712 yards, S.S.S.68
Founded 1927
Visitors: welcome weekdays.
Green Fee: £20 (£8 with member).
Societies: weekdays, max 25.
Catering: by prior arrangement with Steward.
Hotels: Heronstone; New Inn; City Inn.

J63 **Llanwern**
☎(0633) 412029
Tennyson Ave, Llanwern, Newport, Gwent NP6 2DY
1 mile from M4 junction 24.
Parkland course.
18 holes, 6115 yards, S.S.S.69;
9 holes, 5237 yards, S.S.S.67
Founded 1928
Visitors: with proof of h/cap and membership of recognised club.
Green Fee: 25/day.
Societies: Wed and Thurs by arrangement.
Catering: full bar and restaurant facilities. Snooker table.
Hotels: Stakis County Court.

J64 **Llanyravon Golf Course**
☎(0633) 874636
Llanfrechfa Way, Cwmbran, Gwent
M4 junction 26, head N to Pontypool, turn left into Llanfrechfa Way.
Public parkland course.
9 holes Par 3
Founded 1981
Visitors: no restrictions.
Green Fee: £1.80/round WD, £2.70/round WE; reductions jnrs and OAPs.
Hotels: Commodore, Park Way, Central.

J65 **Machynlleth**
☎(0654) 702000
Ffordd, Drenewydd, Machynlleth, Powys SY20 8UH
Approaching Machynlleth on A489 turn left before speed restriction signs.
Undulating course.
9 holes, 5726 yards, S.S.S.67
Designed by James Braid.
Founded 1907
Visitors: welcome apart from competition days; welcome Sun.
Green Fee: £10 WD and WE.
Societies: by arrangement.
Catering: by arrangement.
Hotels: Wynnstay; White Lion.

J66 **Maesteg**
☎(0656) 734106 Sec.
Mount Pleasant, Neath Rd, Maesteg, Mid-Glam CF34 9PR
Adjacent to main Maestag to Port Talbot road; 0.5 mile from Maesteg town centre on B4282.
Moorland course.
18 holes, 5900 yards, S.S.S.69
Founded 1912
Visitors: no restrictions; over 8 visitors in group by arrangement.
Green Fee: £12 WD, £15 WE & BH.
Societies: by arrangement.
Catering: meals except Thurs.

J67 **Merthyr Tydfil**
☎(0685) 723308
Cloth Hall Lane, Cefn Coed, Merthyr Tydfil, Mid-Glam CF48 2NU
Take turning to Pontsticill off A470 at Cefn Coed, then 1st left.
Mountain course in Brecon Beacons National Park.
11 holes, 5820 yards, S.S.S.68
Founded 1908
Visitors: welcome at all times except Sun.
Green Fee: £12 WD, £14 WE.
Societies: apply in writing.
Catering: evenings only.

J68 **Mid-Wales Golf Centre**
☎(0686) 688303
Measmawr, Caersws, Nr Newtown, Powys
30 miles W of Shrewsbury, 3 miles W of Newtown.
Public farmland course.
9 holes Par 3, 1268 yards.
Opening July 1992
Visitors: welcome; ring for details.
Catering: light refreshments.
Driving range, children's driving range.

J69 **Milford Haven**
☎(0646) 692368
Woodbine House, Hubberston, Milford Haven
On road to Dale, 0.75 mile W of town.
Meadowland course.
18 holes, 6071 yards, S.S.S.71
Designed by David Snell.
Founded 1913
Visitors: welcome at all times.
Green Fee: £12 WD, £15 WE.
Societies: welcome at most times; fees negotiable on numbers.
Catering: full facilities available.
Hotels: Lord Nelson; Sir Benfro; Little Haven.

J70 Mold

☎(0352) 740318
Cilcain Rd, Pantymwyn, Mold, Clwyd
3 miles from Mold; leave on Denbigh
road, left at Clegg Arms, right at
T-junction, club is 2.5 miles on left.
Undulating parkland course.
18 holes, 5521 yards, S.S.S.69
Founded 1909
Visitors: welcome.
Green Fee: on application.
Societies: welcome.
Catering: bar snacks, full facilities.
Hotels: Bryn Awel; Chequers.

J71 Monmouth

☎(0600) 712212, (0594) 833394
Sec.
Leasebrook Lane, Monmouth, Gwent
1 mile along A40 Monmouth to Ross
road.
Parkland course.
9 holes, 5454 yards, S.S.S.66
Founded 1921
Visitors: welcome weekdays, with
member weekends.
Green Fee: £10 WD, £15 WE & BH.
Societies: by arrangement with Sec.
Catering: every day except Mon.
Hotels: King's Head; Pilgrim.

J72 Monmouthshire

☎(0873) 852606 Sec, 852532 Pro.
Llanfoist, Abergavenny, Gwent NP7
9HE
M4 to Newport then A4042, take
road to Llanfoist, between Llanfoist
and Llanellen.
Meadowland course.
18 holes, 6054 yards, S.S.S.69.
Designed by James Braid.
Founded 1892
Visitors: must have h/cap cert and
membership of recognised club.
Green Fee: on application.
Societies: Mon and Fri only, apply
before Dec preceding year.
Catering: full facilities except Tues.
Hotels: Angel; Llanwenarth Arms.

J73 Morlais Castle

☎(0685) 722822
Pant, Dowlais, Merthyr Tydfil,
Mid-Glam CF48 2UY
Follow signs for Brecon Mountain
Railway.
Moorland course.
18 holes, 6320 yards, S.S.S.71
Founded 1900
Visitors: welcome except Sat pm
and Sun am.
Green Fee: £14/day (£8 with
member).

Societies: apply to Sec.
Catering: bar and bar snacks;
lunches and evening meals served to
order.
Hotels: Castle; Tregenna;
Baverstocks.

J74 Morriston

☎(0792) 771079
160 Clasemont Rd, Morriston,
Swansea, W Glam SA6 6AJ
3 miles N of Swansea city centre on
A4067, then 0.5 mile W along A48;
from M4 junction 45, E on A48.
Parkland course.
18 holes, 5734 yards, S.S.S.68
Founded 1919
Visitors: welcome at all times.
Green Fee: £15 WD, £21 WE & BH;
50% reduction with member.
Societies: on application.
Catering: lunch served except Mon.
Hotels: Dragon; Dolphin; Forest
Motel; Hilton; Holiday Inn.

J75 Mountain Ash

☎(0443) 472265
Cefnpennar, Mountain Ash,
Mid-Glam CF45 4DT
A470 Cardiff to Abercynon, then
A4059 to Mountain Ash.
Mountain course.
18 holes, 5458 yards, S.S.S.68
Founded 1908
Visitors: welcome; with member
only weekends.
Green Fee: £14 WD (£7 with
member), £14 with member WE.
Societies: welcome.
Catering: full catering facilities
except Mon.
Hotels: Baverstock.

J76 Mountain Lakes

☎(0222) 861128
Blaengwynlais, Caerphilly,
Mid-Glamorgan CF8 1NG
4 miles from M4 junction 32 on
Tongwynlais-Caerphilly road, by
Castell Heights Golf course.
Tree-lined mountain championship
course.
18 holes, 6800 yards, S.S.S.73
Designed by Bob Sandow.
Founded 1988
Visitors: h/cap certs required; not
Sun am.
Green Fee: £15/round.
Societies: by arrangement.
Catering: full bar and restaurant
facilities; banqueting, conference
and function rooms.
Hotels: International (Cardiff).

J77 Neath

☎(0639) 643615
Cadoxton, Neath, W Glam SA10 7AH
2 miles from Neath, opposite
Cadoxton Church.
Mountain course.
18 holes, 6465 yards, S.S.S.72
Designed by James Braid.
Founded 1934
Visitors: welcome.
Green Fee: on application
Societies: apply to Sec.
Catering: full except Mon.
Snooker.

J78 Nefyn & District

☎(0758) 720996 Sec, 720218 Pro &
Steward
Morfa Nefyn, Pwllheli, Gwynedd
LL53 6DA
1 mile W of Nefyn, 20 miles W of
Caernarfon on B4417.
Seaside clifftop course.
18 holes, 6335 yards, S.S.S.71
Founded 1907
Visitors: h/cap certs required
April-Oct incl.
Green Fee: £16/round, £20/day WD;
£22.50/round £30/day WE.
Societies: by prior arrangement with
Sec, limited weekends.
Catering: full services available.
Snooker.
Hotels: Caeau Capel; Linksway;
Woodlands Hall; Nanhoran Arms.

J79 Newport

☎(0633) 892643, 896794
Great Oak, Rogerstone, Newport,
Gwent NP1 9FX
From M4 junction 27 take B4691 for
1 mile, across roundabout then right
at Saab Garage.
Parkland course.
18 holes, 6370 yards, S.S.S.71
Founded 1903
Visitors: welcome weekdays,
members of recognised club only.
Green Fee: £25 (18 holes), £40 (27
or 36 holes).
Societies: Wed, Thurs, Fri.
Catering: bar (men's), mixed lounge,
dining room.
Hotels: Country Court; Lodge; Harris.

J80 Newport (Pembs)

☎(0239) 820244
Newport, Dyfed SA42 0NR
Follow signs to Newport Sands from
Newport.
Seaside course.
9 holes, 5815 yards, S.S.S.68
Founded 1925

Visitors: welcome.
Green Fee: on application.
Societies: by arrangement.
Catering: full bar and restaurant.
Hotels: self-catering holiday flats adjacent to clubhouse; Golden Lion.

J81 North Wales
☎(0492) 875325
72 Bryniau Rd, West Shore,
Llandudno, Gwynedd LL30 2DZ
1.5 miles from town centre.
Seaside links course.
18 holes, 6132 yards, S.S.S.69
Founded 1894
Visitors: by prior reservation.
Green Fee: £17 WD, £22 WE & BH.
Societies: welcome by prior reservation.
Catering: full facilities available.
Snooker.

J82 Old Colwyn
☎(0492) 515581.
Woodland Ave, Old Colwyn, Clwyd LL29 9NL
200 yards off A55 in Old Colwyn, turn into Boddelwyddan Ave between chapel and M & K Garage.
Undulating meadowland course.
9 holes, 5800 yards, S.S.S.66
Founded 1907
Visitors: welcome except Sat pm and Tues and Wed evenings.
Green Fee: on application
Societies: by arrangement except Sat.
Catering: by arrangement.

J83 Old Padeswood
☎(0244) 547401
Station Rd, Padeswood, Mold, Clwyd CH7 4JL
2.5 miles S of Mold, 8 miles W of Chester on A5118.
Meadowland course.
18 holes, 6728 yards, S.S.S.72
Designed by Arthur Joseph.
Founded 1933
Visitors: welcome except Competition Days.
Green Fee: £12 WD, £20 WE & BH.
Societies: weekdays only by appointment.
Catering: bar and restaurant facilities at all times.
Hotels: Bryn Awel; St David's Park.

J84 Old Rectory Hotel
☎(0873) 810373
Llangattock, Crickhowell, Powys NP8 1PH

Off A40 to Crickhowell between Abergavenny and Brecon.
Parkland course.
9 holes, 2360 yards, S.S.S.54
Founded 1979
Visitors: welcome.
Green Fee: £10/day.
Societies: welcome.
Catering: bar, restaurant, function suites. Outdoor swimming pool.
Hotels: Old Rectory.

J85 Padeswood & Buckley
☎(0244) 550537 Office, 543636 Pro and Members
The Caia, Station Lane, Padeswood, Mold, Clwyd CH7 4JD
Off A5118, 3 miles E of Mold, 2 miles S of Buckley, 2nd club on right.
Parkland/meadowland course.
18 holes, 5823 yards, S.S.S.68
Founded 1933
Visitors: welcome weekdays 9.30am-4.30pm; permission of Sec or Captain required on Sun.
Green Fee: £16/round WD (£6 with member), £18 WE & BH (£8 with member); reductions for jnrs.
Societies: weekdays.
Catering: snacks, lunches and evening meals.
Hotels: The Druid; Chequers; Beaufort Palace.

J86 Palleg
☎(0639) 842524
Palleg Rd, Lower Cwmtwrch, Swansea, W Glam
15 miles N of Swansea on Brecon road A4067, left at Aubrey Arms roundabout, 1 mile.
Meadowland/moorland course.
9 holes, 3260 yards, S.S.S.72
Designed by C.K. Cotton.
Founded 1930
Visitors: welcome.
Green Fee: on application
Societies: not Bank Holidays.
Catering: by arrangement, not Mon.

J87 Penmaenmawr
☎(0492) 623330
Conway Rd, Penmaenmawr, Gwynedd LL34 6RD
Main A55 from Conway to Penmaenmawr, left at Mountain View Hotel along Conway Old Rd for 1 mile.
Undulating parkland course.
9 holes, 5031 yards, S.S.S.65
Founded 1910
Visitors: welcome.
Green Fee: £10/day WD, £14/day WE.

Societies: welcome; fees by arrangement.
Catering: by prior arrangement.
Hotels: Caerlyr; Sychnant Pass; Split Willow (Llanfairfechan).

J88 Pennard
☎(044 128) 3131
2 Southgate Rd, Southgate, Swansea, W Glam SA3 2BT
8 miles W of Swansea, on A4067 and B4436 to Pennard Church, then unclassified to club.
Undulating seaside course.
18 holes, 6289 yards, S.S.S.71
Founded 1908
Visitors: welcome at all times.
Green Fee: £14 (£10 with member) WD, £18 (£13 with member) WE & BH; £56 weekly.
Societies: by arrangement, not weekends or Bank Holiday weeks.
Catering: bar snacks; lunches and evening meals by prior arrangement.
Snooker.
Hotels: Osborne.

J89 Penrhos G & CC
☎(0974) 202999
Llanrhystud, Nr Aberystwyth, Dyfed, SY23 5AY
Between Aberystwyth and Aberaeron, just off A487 on B4337.
Parkland course.
18 holes, 6578 yards, S.S.S.71
Designed by Jim Walters
Founded July 1991
Visitors: welcome; booking advised.
Green Fee: £11 WD, £16 WE.
Societies: welcome by arrangement.
Catering: full facilities.
Leisure complex, tennis, bowls, driving range.
Hotels: Conrah County; Marine.

J90 Peterstone G & CC
☎(0633) 680009
Peterstone, Wentlooge, Cardiff CF3 8TM
Off A48, turning to Marshfield.
Seaside parkland course.
18 holes, 6497 yards, S.S.S.71
Designed by Sandow.
Founded May 1990
Visitors: welcome.
Green Fee: £12.50/round WD, £16.50/round WE.
Societies: welcome.
Catering: bar, à la carte restaurant, conference room.
Driving range.
Hotels: accommodation (7 rooms) in Country Club.

J91 **Pontardawe**
☎(0792) 863118, 830041
Cefn Llan, Pontardawe, Swansea, W
Glam SA8 4SH
4 miles N of M4 on A4067.
Meadowland course.
18 holes, 6061 yards, S.S.S.70
Founded 1924
Visitors: welcome weekdays;
weekends by prior arrangement only.
Green Fee: £12.50 WD.
Societies: on application.
Catering: full except Mon (bookable).
Snooker.
Hotels: Pen-yr-Allt.

J92 **Pontnewydd**
☎(06333) 2170
West Pontnewydd, Cwmbran, Gwent
NP4 4AR
Follow signs for West Pontnewydd or
Upper Cwmbran, W slopes of
Cwmbran.
Meadowland course.
10 holes, 5353 yards, S.S.S.67
Founded 1875
Visitors: welcome weekdays,
weekends only with member.
Green Fee: £10 WD.
Catering: available.
Hotels: Parkway; Commodore.

J93 **Pontypool**
☎(0495) 763655
Lasgarn Lane, Trevethin, Pontypool,
Gwent NP4 8TR
1 mile N of Pontypool.
Heathland/parkland course.
18 holes, 6046 yards, S.S.S.69
Founded 1903
Visitors: welcome; h/cap certs
required.
Green Fee: £13.50 WD, £18 WE &
BH.
Societies: welcome; h/cap certs
required.
Catering: available daily.
Hotels: Commodore; Parkway.

J94 **Pontypridd**
☎(0443) 402359
Ty-Gwyn, The Common, Pontypridd,
Mid-Glam CF37 4DJ
9 miles from Cardiff, take A470 N to
Pontypridd and Merthyr.
Wooded undulating mountain course.
18 holes, 5650 yards, S.S.S.68
Designed by Bradbeer.
Founded 1905
Visitors: welcome weekdays if
member of bona fide club; only with
member weekends and Bank
Holidays.

Green Fee: £15 (£10 with member)
WD, £15 with member only WE & BH.
Societies: by arrangement.
Catering: snacks served, meals by
arrangement. Snooker.

J95 **Porthmadog**
☎(0766) 512037
Morfa Bychan, Porthmadog,
Gwynedd LL49 9UU
2 miles W of Porthmadog, take road
to Morfa Bychan and Black Rock
Sands; turn at Woolworths in High St.
Seaside heathland course.
18 holes, 6320 yards, S.S.S.70
Founded 1900
Visitors: welcome.
Green Fee: on application to Match
Sec.
Societies: by arrangement with
Match Sec.
Catering: meals and snacks served.
Newly extended clubhouse, snooker
room.
Hotels: Royal Sportsman; Tyddyn
Lywyn; Plas Gwyn.

J96 **Prestatyn**
☎(0745) 854320
Marine Rd East, Prestatyn, Clwyd
LL19 7HS
Follow A548 coast road to Prestatyn,
cross railway bridge and turn right at
Pontins, Prestatyn Sands.
Links championship course.
18 holes, 6764 yards, S.S.S.73
Designed by S. Collins.
Founded 1905
Visitors: welcome, except Sat and
Tues mornings.
Green Fee: £16 WD, £20 WE & BH.
Societies: by arrangement with Sec
only; no Sats or Tues.
Catering: full facilities.
Hotels: Bryn Gwalia; Nant Hall;
Kinmel Manor (Abergele).

J97 **Pwllheli**
☎(0758) 612520
Golf Rd, Pwllheli, Gwynedd LL53 5PS
Turn into Cardiff Rd in town centre,
bear right at 1st fork.
Parkland/links course.
18 holes, 6091 yards, S.S.S.69
Founded 1900
Visitors: welcome.
Green Fee: on application.
Societies: any day.
Catering: full facilities.
Snooker table.
Hotels: Caeau Capel (Nefyn);
Woodlands Hall (Edern); Bryn
Eisteddfod (Clynnogfawr).

J98 **Pyle & Kenfig**
☎(0656) 783093
Waun-y-Mer, Kenfig, Mid-Glam
CF33 4PU
Leave M4 at junction 37, follow
Porthcawl signs; 1st right after 3rd
roundabout.
Seaside links and downland course.
18 holes, 6650 yards, S.S.S.73
Designed by H. Colt.
Founded 1922
Visitors: welcome weekdays,
advisable to phone in advance; with
member only weekends and Bank
Holidays.
Green Fee: £20/round, £25/day
(£12.50 with member).
Societies: by arrangement with Sec.
Catering: full facilities available.
Hotels: Seabank; Rose and Crown;
Fairways; Atlantic.

J99 **RAF St Athan**
☎(0446) 751043
St Athan, Barry, S Glam
1st right after St Athan village.
Public parkland course.
9 holes, 6100 yards, S.S.S.71
Founded 1982
Visitors: any time except Sun am.
Green Fee: £10 WD, £15 WE.
Societies: apply to Sec.
Catering: available.

J100 **Radyr**
☎(0222) 842408 Manager, 842442
Members
Drysgol Rd, Radyr, Cardiff CF4 8BS
M4 junction 32, off A470 at Taffs Well.
Parkland course.
18 holes, 6015 yards, S.S.S.70
Founded 1902
Visitors: weekdays with h/cap cert;
weekends with member only.
Green Fee: £22/day.
Societies: Wed and Fri.
Catering: full facilities 7 days.
Snooker.

J101 **Rhondda**
☎(0443) 433208
Golf House, Penrhys, Rhondda CF43
3PW
On Cardiff to Rhondda road 3 miles
from Porth.
Mountain-top course.
18 holes, 6246 yards, S.S.S.70
Founded 1904/1910
Visitors: welcome weekdays,
weekends with member.
Green Fee: £12 WD, £15 WE.
Societies: weekdays by
arrangement.

Catering: meals, bar snacks except Mon. Snooker.
Hotels: Dunraven; Heritage.

J102 Rhos-on-Sea
☎(0492) 549641, 549100
Penrhyn Bay, Llandudno, Gwynedd LL30 3PU
A55 to Old Colwyn, follow coast road to Penrhyn Bay, course by sea.
Parkland course without trees.
18 holes, 6064 yards, S.S.S.69
Founded 1899
Visitors: welcome anytime, pre-booking required for large parties and weekends.
Green Fee: c. £14 WD, £20 WE.
Societies: welcome any day by booking.
Catering: lounge bar daily, breakfasts, bar snacks, restaurant meals. Snooker tables.
Hotels: Dormy House Hotel on site.

J103 Rhosgoch
☎(0497) 851251
Rhosgoch, Builth Wells, Powys LD2 3JY
5 miles N of Hay-on-Wye.
Parkland course.
9 holes, 4842 yards, S.S.S.64
Designed by Herbie Poore.
Founded 1984
Visitors: welcome.
Green Fee: £7/day WD, £10/day WE.
Societies: welcome.
Catering: bar, snacks; dinner by arrangement.
Hotels: 2 holiday appartments available.

J104 Rhuddlan
☎(0745) 590217
Meliden Rd, Rhuddlan, Clwyd LL18 6LB
Off A55 3 miles N of St Asaph.
Parkland course.
18 holes, 6487 yards, S.S.S.71
Designed by Hawtree & Co.
Founded 1930
Visitors: welcome; guests of members only on Sun.
Green Fee: £18 WD, £25 Sat and BH.
Societies: welcome Mon-Fri.
Catering: lunch and dinner daily.
Snooker.

J105 Rhyl
☎(0745) 353171
Coast Rd, Rhyl, Clwyd LL18 3RE
1 mile from station on A548.
Seaside links course.

9 holes, 6153 yards. S.S.S.70
Founded 1890
Visitors: welcome except competition days.
Green Fee: £10 WD, £12 WE & BH.
Societies: by arrangement with Sec.
Catering: bar snacks, meals all day. Snooker.
Hotels: Grange.

J106 The Rolls of Monmouth
☎(0600) 715353
The Hendre, Monmouth, Gwent NP5 4HG
3.25 miles W of Monmouth on B4233 (Abergavenny road).
Undulating parkland course.
18 holes, 6723 yards, S.S.S.72
Designed by Urbis Planning.
Founded 1982
Visitors: welcome at all times.
Green Fee: £25 WD, £30 WE & BH.
Societies: welcome weekdays and weekends.
Catering: full facilities 7 days.
Hotels: Kings Head; Priory Motel; Pilgrim.

J107 Royal Porthcawl
☎(0656) 782251
Rest Bay, Porthcawl, Mid-Glam CF36 3UW
Leave M4 at junction 37 to Porthcawl seafront, turn right, follow to Locks Common and bear left.
Links course.
Championship course 18 holes, 6691 yards, S.S.S.74
Designed by Charles Gibson.
Founded 1891
Visitors: welcome with introduction by member or Club Sec; h/cap cert required.
Green Fee: on application.
Societies: by arrangement (no weekends).
Catering: lunches, teas and dinner by arrangement.
Hotels: Atlantic; Seabank; Fairways.

J108 Royal St David's
☎(0766) 780857 Pro and tee bookings, 780361 Sec/Manager
Harlech, Gwynedd LL46 2UB
Between Barmouth and Porthmadog on A496.
Links championship seaside course.
18 holes, 6427 yards, S.S.S.71
Founded 1894
Visitors: welcome weekdays and weekends, prior arrangement advisable; must have regular h/cap.

Green Fee: £20/day WD, £25/day WE & BH.
Societies: catered for.
Catering: full catering facilities.
Hotels: St David's; Maes y Newydd; Talsarnau; Noddfa; Rum Hole; Castle; Castle Cottage; Byrdir GH.

J109 Ruthin Pwllglas
☎(08242) 4658
Ruthin Pwllglas, Ruthin, Clwyd
2.5 miles S of Ruthin in A494, right fork before Pwllglas village.
Parkland/moorland course.
9 holes, 5418 yards, S.S.S.66
Designed by David Lloyd Rees.
Founded 1906
Visitors: welcome.
Green Fee: £10 WD, £15 WE & BH.
Societies: by arrangement.
Catering: parties by arrangement.
Hotels: Ruthin Castle.

J110 St Davids City
☎(0348) 831607
Whitesands Bay, St Davids, Pembrokeshire
2 miles W of St David's, follow signs for Whitesands Bay (Hotel).
Links course.
9 holes, 5911 yards, S.S.S.70
Founded 1902
Visitors: no restrictions but no bag sharing please.
Green Fee: £10/day.
Societies: welcome at all times, prior arrangement with Sec advisable.
Catering: at Whitesands Bay Hotel, 150 yards from Course.
Hotels: Whitesands Bay; St Nons; Warpool Court: all have arrangements for free golf on course.

J111 St Deiniol
☎(0248) 353098
Bangor, Gwynedd LL57 1PX
Off A5/A55 junction on to A5122 for 1 mile into Bangor; on E outskirts of town, golf club signposted.
Undulating parkland course.
18 holes, 5500 yards, S.S.S.67
Designed by James Braid.
Founded 1906
Visitors: welcome at any time; parties by arrangement.
Green Fee: £10/day WD, £15/day WE & BH.
Societies: welcome by prior arrangement.
Catering: full catering service. Snooker.
Hotels: British Hotel; Eryl Mor.

St Pierre

In the summer of 1987, St Pierre celebrated its 25th anniversary. In a game which goes back centuries, that might not seem much of a landmark but St Pierre earned itself pride of place by being the first post-war championship course to be built in Britain — the herald of a new era.

When it comes to personal sentiment, it was the first new course I saw under construction. In the winter of 1961-2, Ken Cotton was invited to design two courses in the border country of England and Wales, one in the old deer park alongside the main road to Newport and Cardiff and the other in unpromising woodland at Ross-on-Wye. He thought a visit to see how it was done would be a good experience for a young writer — and how right he was.

The two courses could not possibly have been more of a contrast. St Pierre was largely ready-made in terms of fairways whereas Ross-on-Wye, a miracle of enterprise by a devoted band, had to be stripped root by root before the holes took shape.

That Cotton succeeded in both instances showed that he was a master of his craft. You can only judge the results if you knew the original terrain, the difficulties encountered and the budgets available. Both St Pierre and Ross-on-Wye were built on the thinnest of shoestrings. Bill Graham, who had dreamed of a course in the lovely park in St Pierre, drove past one day, and discovering that it was on the market, proved himself a man of action by buying it.

The land, the ancient manor house where the Crown Jewels were stored during the Battle of Agincourt, and the cost of construction of the course came to something under £30,000. However absurdly modest that seems nowadays, one or two sacrifices had to be made but Graham's reasons for purchasing had to be commercially based and here he showed how valid his instincts were. Floodlit golf proved to be one of his few ideas to misfire. When St Pierre was built the motorway systems were already well launched, and the opening of the Severn Bridge only a few years away. St Pierre was, and is, wonderfully accessible from London, Birmingham and Bristol, as well as South Wales.

It wasn't given long to settle down before it was much in demand. Dunlop made it a frequent home for their much lamented Masters and in 1980 the Ladies Golf Union paid it the ultimate compliment by holding the Curtis Cup there. Regular calls have been made upon it by organisers of small tournaments and company days, all of whom flock to take advantage of its residential amenities and a host of other sporting facilities.

The addition of the second course brought alteration to Cotton's orgiinal design, and more land was purchased on higher ground. However, nothing destroyed Cotton's first impression that, for Club golfers at large, it is a delightful place to play.

Stately ancient trees feature strongly. After a mild introduction to them at the 1st, the 2nd is dominated by them, although there follows a break on the loftier reaches of the 3rd to the 6th. At the 6th, the eye is caught by the distant sights but with the 7th the trees return and from then on there is no let-up.

Several recent changes and a few new back tees have made the professionals flex their muscles a little more. However, one hole where no change is contemplated, and certainly none required, is the 18th across the lake. One of golf's oldest clichés is that nothing is certain until the last putt is holed: nowhere is it more apt than at St Pierre.

J112 **St Giles**
☎(0686) 625844
Pool Rd, Newtown, Powys SY16 3AJ
0.5 mile E of Newtown on main
Welshpool to Newtown road, A483.
Undulating parkland course.
9 holes, 5864 yards, S.S.S.68
Founded 1910
Visitors: welcome weekdays, some weekends.
Green Fee: on application
Societies: welcome by arrangement, contact Sec.
Catering: meals except Mon.

J113 **St Idloes**
☎(05512) 2559
Pen Rhallt, Llanidloes, Powys SY18 6LG
Off A470 at Llanidloes, 1 mile B4569.
Slightly undulating course on hill plateau with superb views.
9 holes, 5320 yards, S.S.S.66
Founded 1920
Visitors: welcome with club h/cap cert.
Green Fee: £12/round/day, £50/week.
Societies: very welcome by appointment with Sec.
Catering: available on request; banqueting, functions.
Hotels: Lloyds; Trewythen Arms; Lion; Mount Inn.

J114 **St Mellons**
☎(0633) 680408 Sec, 680101 Pro, 680401 Club
St Mellons, Cardiff, S Glam CF3 8XS
On A48 between Newport and Cardiff on left, follow yellow sign for St Mellons Country Club.
Parkland course.
18 holes, 6275 yards, S.S.S.70
Founded 1964
Visitors: welcome.
Green Fee: £23.
Societies: weekdays only by arrangement.
Catering: available.
Hotels: St Mellons Country Club.

J115 **St Melyd**
☎(0745) 854405
The Paddock, Prestatyn Clwyd LL19 9NB
Situated between Prestatyn and Meliden village on main road A547.
Undulating meadowland course.
9 holes, 5805 yards, S.S.S.68
Founded 1922
Visitors: welcome.
Green Fee: £6 WD, £8 WE & BH.

Societies: catered for on weekdays and limited weekends.
Catering: lunch and restaurant except Tuesdays.
Hotels: Pontins Holiday Village; Nant Hall; Bryn Gwalia.

J116 **St Pierre Hotel G & CC**
☎(0291) 625261
St Pierre Park, Chepstow, Gwent NP6 6YA
On A48 Chepstow-Newport road, 1 mile from Chepstow.
Old course parkland, New course meadowland.
Old, 18 holes, 6700 yards, S.S.S.73; New, 18 holes, 5762 yards, S.S.S.68
Designed by C.K. Cotton (Old), Bill Cox (New).
Founded 1962
Visitors: h/cap cert required; booking advised.
Green Fee: on application
Societies: Mon to Fri; weekends residential only.
Catering: full facilities.
Hotels: St Pierre.

J117 **South Pembrokeshire**
☎(0646) 683817
Defensible Barracks, Pembroke Dock, Dyfed
1.5 miles S of Hobbs Point, W end of A477, 0.5 mile from Pembroke Dock.
Seaside parkland course.
9 holes, 5804 yards, S.S.S.69
Founded 1970
Visitors: welcome.
Green Fee: on application
Societies: apply to Sec.
Catering: bar except Mon, meals by arrangement.

J118 **Southerndown**
☎(0656) 880476
Ewenny, Bridgend, Mid-Glam CF35 5BT
4 miles from Bridgend on the coast road to Ogmore-by-Sea; turn off at Pelican Inn opposite Ogmore Castle.
Links/downland course.
18 holes, 6613 yards, S.S.S.73
Designed by W. Herbert Fowler, Willie Park, H.S. Colt.
Founded Feb 1906
Visitors: weekdays; weekends with member; h/cap certs required.
Green Fee: £24 WD, £30 WE.
Societies: weekdays only by arrangement with Sec.
Catering: facilities daily. Snooker.
Hotels: Sea Lawns; Sea Bank; Court Colman.

J119 **Swansea Bay**
☎(0792) 814153, 812198
Jersey Marine, Neath, W Glam SA10 6JP
Just off main A48 road between Neath and Swansea.
Links course.
18 holes, 6302 yards, S.S.S.70
Founded 1892
Visitors: welcome.
Green Fee: £15 WD, £20 WE & BH.
Societies: catered for.
Catering: meals served.
Hotels: Castle.

J120 **Tenby**
☎(0834) 2787
The Burrows, Tenby, Dyfed SA70 7NP
A40 from Carmarthen to St Clears, then A477 on W of Tenby centre.
Seaside links course.
18 holes, 6232 yards, S.S.S.71
Founded 1888
Visitors: welcome if member of recognised club with h/cap cert.
Green Fee: £18 WD, £22.50 WE & BH.
Societies: welcome with prior booking.
Catering: full facilities, bar snacks; restaurant meals to be pre-booked.
Hotels: Kinloch Court; Imperial.

J121 **Tredegar & Rhymney**
☎(0685) 840743
Cwmtysswg, Rhymney, Mid-Glam B4256 1.5 miles from Rhymney.
Undulating mountain course.
9 holes, 2788 yards, S.S.S.67
Founded 1921
Visitors: welcome.
Green Fee: £7.50 (£5 with member) WD, £10 (7.50 with member) WE.
Societies: weekdays only.
Catering: no catering daytime; evenings by arrangement.
Hotels: Red Lion Inn (Tredegar).

J122 **Tredegar Park**
☎(0633) 894433 Sec, 895219 Club, 894517 Pro.
Bassaleg Rd, Newport, Gwent NP9 3PX
Leave M4 at junction 27, to Newport, 1st right in Western Ave and right at end of Western Ave.
Parkland course.
18 holes, 6097 yards, S.S.S.70
Designed by James Braid.
Founded 1923
Visitors: must be member of affiliated club and produce evidence thereof.
Green Fee: £16 WD, £22 WE & BH.

Societies: welcome by prior arrangement.
Catering: for members and visitors only.
Hotels: The Kings; Celtic Manor.

J123 Vale of Llangollen
☎(0978) 860040
Llangollen, Clwyd LL20 7PR
On A5, 1 mile S of Llangollen.
Parkland course.
18 holes, 6661 yards, S.S.S.72
Founded 1908
Visitors: welcome weekdays and some weekends.
Green Fee: £18 WD, £23 WE.
Societies: weekdays by prior arrangement with Sec.
Catering: full catering facilities available.
Hotels: Royal; The Hand; Tyn y Wern; Bryn Howel.

J124 Welsh Border Golf Complex
☎(0743) 884247
Bulthy Farm, Bulthy, Middletown, Nr Welshpool, Powys SY21 8ER
Via A458 Shrewsbury/Welshpool road, turn off to club signposted in Middletown.
Parkland course.
9 holes, 3250 yards, Par 70; 9 holes Par 3, 1600 yards
Designed by Andrew Griffiths.
Founded 1991
Visitors: proper dress and h/cap certs required; no restrictions for Par 3 course.
Green Fee: £8 (9 holes), £12 (18 holes), £18/day; Par 3 course, £4 (9 holes), £6 (18 holes).
Societies: welcome weekdays.
Catering: bar and restarant.
Driving range.
Hotels: Rowlon Castle; Bulthy Farm Guest House.

J125 Welshpool
☎(0938) 83249
Golfa Hill, Welshpool, Powys
4 miles from Welshpool on A458.
Mountain course.
18 holes, 5708 yards, S.S.S.69
Designed by James Braid.
Founded 1929
Visitors: welcome.
Green Fee: £10 WD, £15 WE & BH.
Societies: welcome by prior arrangement.
Catering: catering facilities available.
Hotels: Golfa Hall; Royal Oak.

J126 Wenvoe Castle
☎(0222) 594371 Sec, 593649 Pro.
Wenvoe, Cardiff CF5 6BE
A48 W from Cardiff, left after 3 miles onto A4050, course 2 miles on right.
Parkland course.
18 holes, 6411 yards, S.S.S.71
Founded 1936
Visitors: welcome with member or with recognised club card.
Green Fee: on application.
Societies: catered for Mon, Thurs and Fri.
Catering: lunch and dinners available except Tues.

J127 West Monmouthshire
☎(0495) 310233
Pond Rd, Nantyglo, Gwent NP3 6XS
Heads of Valley road A465, western valley A467 to Semtex roundabout, follow Winchestown signs.
Heathland course.
18 holes, 6118 yards, S.S.S.69
Founded 1906
Visitors: welcome.
Green Fee: £8 WD, £10 Sat, £15 Sun.
Societies: welcome by advance appointment.
Catering: bar and restaurant.

J128 Whitchurch (Cardiff)
☎(0222) 620985 Sec, 620125 Club
Pantmawr Rd, Whitchurch, Cardiff, S Glam CF4 6XD
Off M4 at exit 32, 0.5 mile on A470 to Cardiff.
Parkland course.
18 holes, 6319 yards S.S.S.70
Re-designed by James Braid.
Founded 1915
Visitors: welcome weekdays with h/cap cert; Sat before 10.30am, Sun after 11.30am; only with member weekends and Bank Holidays.
Green Fee: £21 WD, £26 WE & BH.
Societies: Thurs only.
Catering: facilities every day.
Hotels: Travelodge; Masons Arms.

J129 Whitehall
☎(0443) 740245
Nelson, Treharris, Mid-Glam
Take Treharris and Nelson exit at roundabout on A470, turn right and head S for 0.25 mile, take 1st left turning up Mountain Rd.
Mountain course.
9 holes, 5750 yards, S.S.S.68
Founded 1922
Visitors: welcome weekdays; with member at weekends.
Green Fee: on application
Catering: by arrangement.

J130 Wrexham
☎(0978) 364268, 261033, 351476
Holt Rd, Wrexham, Clwyd LL13 9SB
On A534 2 miles E of Wrexham.
Undulating sandy course.
18 holes, 6139 yards, S.S.S.69
Designed by James Braid.
Founded 1906 (1923 on present site).
Visitors: welcome.
Green Fee: on application.
Societies: Mon, Thurs, Fri.
Catering: full facilities. Snooker.
Hotels: Holt Lodge.

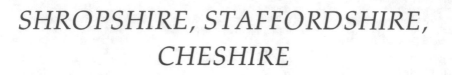

K

SHROPSHIRE, STAFFORDSHIRE, CHESHIRE

In the last few years, Staffordshire and Shropshire have made the headlines on account of their golfing sons and daughters. Diane Bailey and Geoffrey Marks became the first to captain victorious Curtis and Walker Cup teams on American soil. David Gilford, a member of Trentham Park, won a place in the Ryder Cup team last year along with Ian Woosnam, whose county golf as an amateur was played for Shropshire in company with Sandy Lyle who was raised at Hawkstone Park. Hawkstone is part of a hotel complex that provides popular golfing facilities about 14 miles north of Shrewsbury in an area that is full of largely rural delights.

In Shropshire, Church Stretton, Hill Valley, Ludlow, Lilleshall Hall, Shifnal, Oswestry, Wrekin and Shrewsbury itself are the pick with Telford Hotel now a firm part of one of England's well known new towns but, while Shropshire's courses are relatively few and far between, Staffordshire enjoys quantity as well as quality. It includes Little Aston, Penn, home of the late and great Charlie Stowe, and South Staffordshire at Wolverhampton, as well as the delights of Beau Desert, Drayton Park, Leek, Trentham, Trentham Park, Enville, Uttoxeter (which the locals pronounce Uttcheter) and Patshull Park.

Enville was the home course as a girl of Diane Bailey (neé Robb) while Geoffrey Marks has remained loyal all his playing days to Trentham — to the south of Stoke-on-Trent. Trentham is a parkland course with nice changes of level, very much like its neighbour Trentham Park.

Newcastle Municipal is a relatively recent public course that is now much used, but probably the best courses in this section are Whittington Barracks, a slightly forbidding name for a moorland retreat that has championship status, and Little Ashton which epitomises the very best of parkland golf, the main hazards taking the form of characteristically large bunkers a couple of lakes, some majestic trees and a degree of undulation which tests one's judgment of distance

South of the Mersey the first ports of call after emerging from the tunnel are the celebrated links of Wallasey and Royal Liverpool. Wallasey is less well known in spite of its association in bygone days with Dr Frank Stableford, mastermind of the excellent scoring system that bears his name — a system less cruel than the rigours of undiluted medal play.

Maybe he devised the idea from his battles with Wallasey's glorious seaside links and the winds that plague golfers even more. The latest version of the course incorporates rather more of the flat, plain land than it used to, but flatness is also a feature of Royal Liverpool at Hoylake, which few have seen fit to criticise in an area that has changed hardly at all in character since the Club was founded in 1869.

As the second oldest seaside course in England, Royal Liverpool wears the local crown but Caldy and Heswall are other Wirral landmarks not far off the road back to Chester, where most of the best golfing country lies to the east and the south-east.

Sandiway, Delamere Forest and Mere are all redoubtable courses in beautiful settings but nothing could match the splendour of the setting of Portal at Tarporley, which opened its doors for the first time last summer. Its permanent clubhouse position will be as fine as any in the world, a fitting focal point for a natural course around which is situated a landscape that is quite superb.

K1 **Alderley Edge**
☎(0625) 585583
Brook Lane, Alderley Edge, Cheshire
SK9 7RU
From Alderley Edge, turn left off A34
opposite Tower Garage towards
Mobberley/Knutsford, B5085.
Undulating parkland course.
9 holes, 5839 yards, S.S.S.68
Designed by T. G. Renouf.
Founded 1907
Visitors: proof of h/cap required;
restricted Tues, Wed, weekends.
Green Fee: £16 WD, £20 WE & BH.
Societies: catered for Thurs.
Catering: full facilities except Mon.
Hotels: De Trafford Arms.

K2 **Alsager G & CC**
☎(0270) 875700
Audley Rd, Alsager, Stoke-on-Trent
ST7 2UR
Leave M6 at junction 16, follow
Alsager signs.
Parkland course.
18 holes, 6206 yards, S.S.S.70
Founded 1976
Visitors: correct dress required, no
jeans, ties and jackets after 7pm.
Green Fee: on application
Societies: Mon, Wed, Thurs.
Catering: available.
Banqueting, snooker, bowls.

K3 **Altrincham**
☎(061) 928 0761
Stockport Rd, Timperley, Altrincham,
Cheshire WA15
On A560 1 mile W of Altrincham.
Public undulating parkland course.
18 holes, 6162 yards, S.S.S.69
Founded 1935
Visitors: welcome; advance
bookings at all times.
Green Fee: £4.25 WD, £5.85 WE.
Catering: no facilities at club;
Beefeater restaurant next door.
Hotels: Cresta Court; Woodlands
Park.

K4 **Arrowe Park**
☎(051) 677 1527
Arrowe Park, Woodchurch,
Birkenhead, Merseyside
3 miles from town centre, take
Borough Rd, Woodchurch Rd and
then opposite Landicon Cemetery.
Public parkland course.
18 holes, 6377 yards, S.S.S.70
Founded 1932
Visitors: welcome, phone first.
Green Fee: on application
Societies: arrange with Pro.

K5 **Ashton on Mersey**
☎(061) 973 3220
Church Lane, Sale, Cheshire M33
5QQ
2 miles from Sale station.
Parkland course.
9 holes, 6202 yards, S.S.S.69
Founded 1897
Visitors: welcome, except Tues after
3pm (Ladies Day).
Green Fee: on application.
Societies: by arrangement.
Catering: snacks, lunches, evening
meals.
Hotels: Cresta Court.

K6 **Astbury**
☎(0260) 272772
Peel Lane, Astbury, Nr Congleton,
Cheshire CW12 4RE
On outskirts of Congleton; leave A34
Newcastle road at Astbury village.
Meadowland course.
18 holes, 6269 yards, S.S.S.70
Founded 1922
Visitors: members of recognised
golf clubs welcome; must be
accompanied by member weekends.
Green Fee: £25/day (£6 with
member).
Societies: Thurs only, by
arrangement; £20/person/day.
Catering: by prior arrangement only.
Hotels: Bulls Head; Lion and Swan.

K7 **Barlaston**
☎(078 139) 2867 Sec, 2795 Pro shop
Meaford Rd, Stone, Staffs ST15 8UX
From M6 junction 14 take A34
towards Stoke-on-Trent; over Warton
roundabout at Stone, past Wayfarers
public house on left and turn right
0.25 mile after traffic lights; club is
300 yards beyond power station.
Moorland course.
18 holes, 5800 yards, S.S.S.68
Designed by Peter Alliss.
Founded 1977
Visitors: welcome weekdays, not
before 10am weekends.
Green Fee: £13.50 WD, £18 WE.
Societies: weekdays only.
Catering: bar daily, meals by
arrangement.
Hotels: Stonehouse.

K8 **Beau Desert**
☎(0543) 422626
Hazel Slade, Cannock, Staffs WS12
5PJ
Take A460 from Cannock through
Hednesford, right as signposted
Hazel Slade, and next left.
Moorland course.
18 holes, 6300 yards, S.S.S.71
Designed by H. Fowler.
Founded 1921
Visitors: welcome weekdays; Sat
and Sun phone Pro.
Green Fee: £30/day.
Societies: welcome.
Catering: available.
Hotels: Cedar Tree; Roman Way.

K9 **Bidston**
☎(051) 638 3412
Scoresby Rd, Leasowe, Wirral,
Merseyside L46 1QQ
A551 from Wallasey, 0.75 mile.
Parkland course.
18 holes, 6207 yards, S.S.S.70
Founded 1913
Visitors: welcome weekdays.
Green Fee: on application
Societies: weekdays only.
Catering: full facilities.

K10 **Birchwood**
☎(0925) 818819
Kelvin Close, Risley, Warrington,
Cheshire WA3 7PB
M62 junction 11; follow A574 for
Risley/Birchwood; (opposite Digital).
Parkland course.
18 holes, 6850 yards, S.S.S.73
Designed by T. J. McAuley.
Founded 1979
Visitors: welcome weekdays.
Green Fee: £20-£28.
Societies: Mon, Wed, Thurs.
Catering: à la carte, bar snacks,
carvery, 7 days. Banqueting, snooker.
Hotels: Lord Daresbury; Garden
Court.

K11 **Bloxwich**
☎(0922) 476593 Sec, 476889 Pro,
405724 club
136 Stafford Rd, Bloxwich, Walsall,
W Midlands WS3 3PQ
Off main Walsall-Cannock road
(A34), 4 miles N of Walsall centre.
Parkland course.
18 holes, 6258 yards, S.S.S.70
Designed by J. Sixsmith.
Founded 1924
Visitors: weekdays only, not Bank
Holidays.
Green Fee: £20/round, £25/day (£5
with member).
Societies: Wed, Thurs; reduced
rates over 20.
Catering: bar lunches, teas, evening
meals by arrangement except Mon.
Hotels: Barons Court; Crest; County;
Royal.

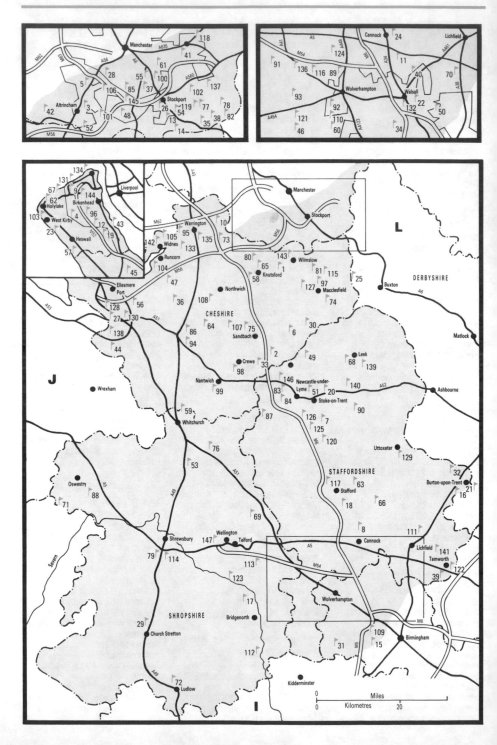

K12 Brackenwood

☎(051) 608 5394
Bracken Lane, Bebington, Wirral,
Merseyside L63 2LY
M53 junction 7, to Clatterbridge and
Bebington.
Public parkland course.
18 holes, 6285 yards, S.S.S.70
Founded 1933
Visitors: on application to Pro.
Green Fee: on application.
Societies: by arrangement.
Catering: at Pro's shop.
Hotels: Thornton Hall; Village,
Dibinsdale (Bromborough).

K13 Bramhall

☎(061) 439 4057, 439 6092 Sec.
Ladythorn Rd, Bramhall, Stockport,
Cheshire SK7 2EY
Near Bramhall station, 8 miles S of
Manchester on A5102.
Meadowland course.
18 holes, 6293 yards, S.S.S.70
Founded 1905
Visitors: welcome, subject to
members competitions.
Green Fee: on application.
Societies: catered for Wed.
Catering: à la carte, bar snacks.
Hotels: Moat House.

K14 Bramhall Park

☎(061) 485 3119
20 Manor Rd, Bramhall, Stockport
SK7 3LY
8 miles S of Manchester, A6 to
Bramhall Lane, then A5102 to
Carrwood Rd.
Parkland course.
18 holes, 6214 yards, S.S.S.70
Founded 1894
Visitors: not Fri (no catering).
Green Fee: on application.
Societies: Tues up to 60 players;
Thurs small parties up to 25.
Catering: full except Fri.
Hotels: Alma Lodge; Raven (Cheadle
Hulme).

K15 Brand Hall

☎(021) 552 2195
Heron Road, Oldbury, Warley,
W Midlands B68 8AQ
6 miles NW of Birmingham, 1.5 miles
from M5 junction 2.
Public parkland course.
18 holes, 5734 yards, S.S.S.68
Visitors: welcome.
Green Fee: £4.75 WD, £6 WE.
Societies: welcome.
Catering: café, clubhouse, bar.
Putting green.

K16 Branston

☎(0283) 43207
Burton Rd, Branston, Burton-on-
Trent DE14 3DP
Take A5121 off the A38 towards
Burton-on-Trent, past church on
right, over railway bridge, past petrol
station on right, entrance to club 200
yards on right.
Parkland course.
18 holes, 6408 yards, S.S.S.71
Founded 1976
Visitors: welcome on weekdays.
Green Fee: £12 WD, £18 WE, (£9
with member).
Societies: weekdays.
Catering: full catering, except Mon.
Hotels: Riverside; Dog & Partridge.

K17 Bridgnorth

☎(0746) 763315
Stanley Lane, Bridgnorth, Shropshire
WV16 4SF
Through High St, along Broseley Rd
for 400 yards, right into Stanley
Lane.
Parkland course.
18 holes, 6668 yards, S.S.S.72
Founded 1889
Visitors: daily.
Green Fee: £16.50/day WD, £25 WE
& BH, (half price with member).
Societies: catered for weekdays by
arrangement with Sec.
Catering: full catering except Mon.
Hotels: Falcon; Kings Head; Croft;
Whitburn Grange.

K18 Brockton Hall

☎(0785) 6622627, 661901 Manager
Brocton, Stafford ST17 0TH
4 miles S of Stafford on A34, turn left
at crossroads signposted Brocton,
club entrance 300 yards on left.
Parkland course.
18 holes, 6095 yards, S.S.S.69
Designed by Harry Vardon.
Founded 1894
Visitors: accepted.
Green Fee: £25 WD, £30 WE & BH.
Societies: bookings accepted on
Tues and Thurs.
Catering: by arrangement with the
caterer.
Hotels: Tillington Hall.

K19 Bromborough

☎(051) 334 2155, 334 4499 Pro.
Raby Hall Rd, Bromborough, Wirral,
Merseyside L63 0NW
0.5 mile from Bromborough station,
0.75 mile from A41 Birkenhead-
Chester road; M53 junction 7.
Parkland course.
18 holes, 6650 yards, S.S.S.73
Founded 1904
Visitors: welcome weekdays; book
with Pro at weekends.
Green Fee: £18 (£7 with member)
WD, £25 (£7 with member) WE & BH.
Societies: Wed; early booking
essential.
Catering: snacks daily, lunches
except Sun, meals by arrangement.
Hotels: Dibbinsdale; Thornton Hall.

K20 Burslem

☎(0782) 837006
Wood Farm, High Lane, Tunstall,
Stoke-on-Trent ST6 7JT
2 miles N of Hanley, situated on High
Lane.
Moorland course.
11 holes, 5527 yards, S.S.S.67
Founded 1907
Visitors: welcome weekdays; not
weekends.
Green Fee: on application
Societies: weekdays.
Catering: apply to Steward.

K21 Burton-on-Trent

☎(0283) 44551
43 Ashby Rd East, Burton-on-Trent
DE15 0PS
3 miles E of Burton-on-Trent on A50.
Undulating wooded parkland course.
18 holes, 6555 yards, S.S.S.71
Founded 1894
Visitors: welcome, letter of intro.,
h/cap cert required; phone
reservation advisable.
Green Fee: £20/round WD,
£25/round WE & BH.
Societies: weekdays except Mon.
Catering: full facilities except Mon.
Snooker.
Hotels: Stanhope Arms (Bretby);
Newton Park (Newton Solney).

K22 Calderfields

☎(0922) 640540 club manageress,
32243 Pro shop
Aldridge Rd, Walsall, W Midlands
WS4 2JS
From M6 junction 7, take A454
Aldridge-Walsall road; entrance by
Dilke Arms public house.
Parkland course.
18 holes, 6700 yards, S.S.S.72
Designed by Roy Winter.
Founded 1983
Visitors: welcome any time, no
restriction except weekends am.
Green Fee: £12/round, £16/day WD;
£16/round WE.

Societies: welcome any day; phone manageress.
Catering: full bar and restaurant. Pool tables, darts.
Hotels: Crest; Post House; Barons Court.

K23 **Caldy**

☎(051) 625 5660
Links Hey Rd, Caldy, Wirral, Merseyside, L48 1NB
A540 from Chester turn left at Caldy crossroads.
Seaside/parkland course.
18 holes, 6665 yards, S.S.S.73
Designed by James Braid, John Salvesen.
Founded 1907
Visitors: welcome weekdays; Tues Ladies Day; weekends with member.
Green Fee: on application
Societies: Thurs main day; not Wed.
Catering: lunch; dinner by arrangement.

K24 **Cannock Park**

☎(0543) 578850
Stafford Rd, Cannock, Staffs WS11 2AL
On A46 Stafford road, 0.5 mile from Cannock centre.
Municipal parkland course.
18 holes, 4783 yards, S.S.S.65
Founded 1988
Visitors: welcome; busy course, advisable to book by phone weekdays, 1 week in advance at weekends.
Green Fee: £4.10/round WD, £6.15/round WE; jnrs half price.
Societies: welcome.
Catering: full facilities.
Putting green, swimming, badminton, gym etc.

K25 **Chapel-en-le-Frith**

☎(0298) 812118 Club, 813943 Sec.
The Cockyard, Manchester Rd, Chapel-en-le-Frith, Stockport, Cheshire SK12 6UH
1 mile N of Chapel-en-le-Frith on B5470 almost opposite Hanging Gate public house.
Meadowland course.
18 holes, 6089 yards, S.S.S.69
Founded 1906
Visitors: welcome, small numbers without reservation.
Green Fee: £15 WD, £25 WE & BH.
Societies: by arrangement.
Catering: all meals daily except Mon.
Hotels: Kings Arms.

K26 **Cheadle**

☎(061) 491 4452 Sec, 428 2160 Club, 491 3878 Steward, 428 9878 Pro.
Shiers Drive, Cheadle, Cheshire SK8 1HW
1.5 miles from junction 11 M63, follow signs for Cheadle; 1 mile S of Cheadle village, 1.5 miles from Cheadle Hulme railway station.
Undulating parkland course.
9 holes, 5006 yards, S.S.S.65
Designed by R. Renouf.
Founded 1885
Visitors: members of golf club with official h/cap; not Tues or Sat.
Green Fee: on application.
Societies: by written application to Sec; no parties Sat, Sun or Tues.
Catering: bar and lunches daily except Thur, at other times by arrangement with Steward. Snooker.
Hotels: The Village; Alma Lodge.

K27 **Chester**

☎(0244) 677760
Curzon Park North, Chester CH4 8AR
1 mile from centre of Chester, off A55, behind Chester Racecourse.
Parkland course.
18 holes, 6487 yards, S.S.S.71
Founded 1901
Visitors: welcome by arrangement.
Green Fee: £20 WD, £25 WE.
Societies: by arrangement.
Catering: full facilities.

K28 **Chorlton cum Hardy**

☎(061) 881 3139, 881 5830 Sec, 881 9911 Pro.
Barlow Hall Rd, Chorlton, Manchester M21 2JJ
3 miles from city centre, off A5103, near Southern Cemetery.
Meadowland course.
18 holes, 6004 yards, S.S.S.69
Founded 1903
Visitors: telephone Pro.
Green Fee: £18 WD, £20 WE.
Societies: Thurs.
Catering: bar snacks, evening meals to order except Mon (sandwiches only).
Hotels: Longford Park; Trust House; Post House; Northenden.

K29 **Church Stretton**

☎(0694) 722281
Hunters Moon, Trevor Hill, Church Stretton, Shropshire SY6 6JH
0.25 mile W of town centre, off Cardingmill Valley Rd, up the winding Trevor Hill.

Hillside course on Longmynd.
18 holes, 5020 yards, S.S.S.65
Designed by James Braid.
Founded 1898
Visitors: welcome weekdays; not 9-10.30am or 1.30-2.30pm Sat; not before 10.30am or 12.30-3.30pm Sun.
Green Fee: £10 WD, £15 WE & BH.
Societies: by arrangement only, EGU registered preferred.
Catering: bar and catering.
Hotels: Denehurst; Longmynd.

K30 **Congleton**

☎(0260) 273540
Biddulph Rd, Congleton, Cheshire SW12 3LZ
1 mile SE of Congleton station on main Congleton-Biddulph road A527.
Parkland course.
9 holes, 5080 yards, S.S.S.65
Founded 1898
Visitors: welcome daily.
Green Fee: on application
Societies: Monday.
Catering: snacks; phone for full meals; not Mon.

K31 **Corngreaves**

☎(0384) 67880
Corngreaves Rd, Cradley Heath, W Midlands
2 miles E of Dudley.
Public parkland course.
18 holes Par 3
Founded 1985
Visitors: welcome.
Green Fee: municipal rates.

K32 **Craythorne Golf Centre**

☎(0283) 64329, 33745 Pro shop.
Craythorne Rd, Stretton, Burton-on-Trent, Staffs DE13 0AZ
Take N exit for Burton-on-Trent from A38, into Stretton, right at church.
Parkland course.
18 holes, 5230 yards, S.S.S.66; 9 holes, Par 3
Designed by Cyril Johnson.
Founded 1972
Visitors: welcome any time; booking at weekends.
Green Fee: £12/round, £18/day WD; £15/round, £20/day Sat; £18/round, £25/day Sun.
Societies: weekdays only by arrangement.
Catering: full bar and restaurant. Driving range.
Hotels: Craythorne Farm (special golfing breaks available).

K33 Crewe

☎(0270) 584099 Sec, 585032 Pro, 584227 Steward
Fields Rd, Haslington, Crewe, Cheshire CW1 1TB
1 mile SW of A534 at Haslington, between Crewe and Sandbach.
Parkland course.
18 holes, 6030 yards, S.S.S.70
Founded 1911
Visitors: weekdays only unless with member.
Green Fee: £21 (£16 after 1pm), (£8 with member).
Societies: Tues only by prior arrangement.
Catering: bar snacks, lunches and dinners served.
Snooker.
Hotels: Crewe Arms; Saxon Cross Motel; Lamb (Nantwich).

K34 Dartmouth

☎(021) 588 2131
Vale St, West Bromwich, W Midlands B71 4DW
West Bromwich to Walsall road, right at Churchfield, behind Churchfield High School.
Undulating meadowland course.
9 holes, 6060 yards, S.S.S.69
Founded 1910
Visitors: welcome except Medal Days.
Green Fee: on application
Societies: welcome by prior arrangement.
Catering: full facilities with prior notice.

K35 Davenport

☎(0625) 877321 Clubhouse, 877319 Pro, 876951 Sec.
Worth Hall, Middlewood Rd, Poynton, Stockport, Cheshire SK12 1TS
From Stockport take A6 to Rising Sun at Hazel Grove, then A523 Macclesfield road, at Poynton traffic lights turn left into Park Lane, club is approx 1.5 miles.
Undulating parkland course.
18 holes, 6066 yards, S.S.S.69
Designed by Fraser Middleton.
Founded 1913
Visitors: welcome most days, phone Pro to check.
Green Fee: £15 WD, £18 WE; one-third price with member.
Societies: welcome Tues and Thurs by arrangement.
Catering: available by prior arrangement with Steward; fixed hours for snacks.
Hotels: Belfry; Belgrade.

K36 Delamere Forest

☎(0606) 882807
Station Rd, Delamere, Northwich, Cheshire CW8 2JE
From A556 Manchester-Chester road take B5152 towards Frodsum; lane to club on right, c. 1 mile from A556, beside Delamere station.
Undulating heathland course.
18 holes, 6305 yards, S.S.S.70
Designed by Herbert Fowler.
Founded 1910
Visitors: welcome; 2 balls only weekends and Bank Holidays.
Green Fee: £20/round, £30/day WD (£5 with member); £25/round WE & BH (£5 with member).
Societies: Tues and Thurs.
Catering: bar snacks; restaurant if booked in advance.
Hotels: Hartford Hall; Swan; Willington Hall.

K37 Didsbury

☎(061) 998 9278 Sec, 998 2811 Pro.
Ford Lane, Northenden, Manchester M22 4NQ
Off M63 junction 9, near Northenden Church, club sign on wall.
Parkland course.
18 holes, 6273 yards, S.S.S.70
Founded 1891
Visitors: Ladies day Tues; not weekends unless by arrangement.
Green Fee: £18 (£7-£12 with member) WD, £22 (£8-£15 with member) WE.
Societies: Thurs and Fri.
Catering: restaurant and snacks.
Hotels: Post House; Britannia.

K38 Disley

☎(0663) 762071
Stanley Hall Lane, Jackson's Edge, Disley, Cheshire SK12 2JX
A6, 6 miles S of Stockport.
Moorland/meadowland course.
18 holes, 6015 yards, S.S.S.69
Designed by James Braid.
Founded 1889
Visitors: Mon, Tues and Wed.
Green Fee: £20 WD.
Societies: Tues and Wed.
Catering: bar; catering all days except Mon.
Hotels: Moorside (Stockport).

K39 Drayton Park

☎(0827) 251139
Drayton Park, Tamworth, Staffs B78 3TN
2 miles S of Tamworth on A4091.
Parkland course.

18 holes, 6214 yards, S.S.S.71
Designed by James Braid.
Founded 1897
Visitors: by arrangement weekdays.
Green Fee: £22/day/round.
Societies: Tues and Thurs.
Catering: full facilities from 10.30am. Snooker.
Hotels: Gungate; Castle.

K40 Druids Heath

☎(0922) 55595
Stonnall Rd, Aldridge, W Midlands WS9 8JZ
Off A452 6 miles NW of Sutton Coldfield.
Undulating course.
18 holes, 6914 yards, S.S.S.73
Founded 1973
Visitors: welcome weekdays.
Green Fee: on application.
Societies: weekdays.
Catering: by prior arrangement.
Hotels: Barons Court; Fairlawns.

K41 Dukinfield

☎(061) 338 2340
Yew Tree Lane, Dukinfield, Cheshire SK16 5DF
From Ashton Rd 1 mile then right into Yew Tree Lane, club 1 mile on right, on hill behind Senior Service factory.
Hillside course.
18 holes, 5544 yards, S.S.S.67
Founded 1913
Visitors: weekdays except Wed pm.
Green Fee: on application.
Societies: by arrangement with Sec.
Catering: meals by arrangement.
Hotels: York House.

K42 Dunham Forest G & CC

☎(061) 928 2605
Oldfield Lane, Altrincham, Cheshire WA14 4TY
2 miles N of M56 junction 7, proceed towards Manchester, course on left.
Parkland course.
18 holes, 6800 yards, S.S.S.72
Founded 1961
Visitors: welcome.
Green Fee: on application.
Societies: weekdays except Wed.
Catering: bar and restaurant.
Hotels: Bowdon; Cresta Court.

K43 Eastham Lodge

☎(051) 327 3008 Pro, 327 3003 Sec, 327 1483 Club
117 Ferry Rd, Eastham, Wirral L62 0AP

Off A41 Birkenhead-Chester road, follow signs for Eastham Country Park, club on left of Ferry Rd approaching Country Park. Parkland course.
15 holes, 5805 yards, S.S.S.68
Designed by Hawtree & Sons.
Founded 1975
Visitors: welcome on weekdays, at weekends only with member.
Green Fee: £18/day/round (£7.50 with member).
Societies: Tues only.
Catering: bar snacks or full meal pre-ordered. Snooker.
Hotels: Village Hotel & Leisure Centre (Bromborough).

K44 **Eaton**
☎(0244) 680474 Sec/Steward, 680170 Pro.
Eaton Park, Eccleston, Chester CH4 9JF
About 3 miles S of Chester off A483 Wrexham road through Ecclestone.
Parkland course.
18 holes, 6446 yards, S.S.S.71
Designed by M.G. Hawtree.
Founded 1965
Visitors: by arrangement only.
Green Fee: on application
Societies: by arrangement only.
Catering: full facilities.

K45 **Ellesmere Port**
☎(051) 339 7689
Chester Rd, Hooton, S Wirral L66 1QH
W on M53, take A41 turning S towards Chester for 2 miles, club at rear of St Paul's Church, Hooton.
Public parkland/meadowland course.
18 holes, 6432 yards, S.S.S.71
Designed by Cotton, Pennink, Lawrie & Partners.
Founded 1971
Visitors: welcome weekdays.
Green Fee: on application
Societies: weekdays.
Catering: available.

K46 **Enville**
☎(0384) 872074 Sec and Manager, 872551 Club, 872585 Pro.
Highgate Common, Enville, Stourbridge, W Midlands DY7 5BN
5 miles W of Stourbridge; from A449 follow A458 Bridgenorth road for 1.8 miles; club signposted.
Heathland/woodland course.
Highgate, 18 holes, 6541 yards, S.S.S.72; Ledge, 18 holes, 6207 yards, S.S.S.70
Founded 1935

Visitors: welcome weekdays and with member at weekends.
Green Fee: £20/round, £30/day.
Societies: by arrangement a year in advance if possible; weekdays only.
Catering: full except Mon evening.
Hotels: Anchor (Kinver).

K47 **Frodsham**
☎(0928) 32159 Office, 39442 shop
Simons Lane, Frodsham, Cheshire WA6 6HE
10 minutes from M56 junction 12; turn left at lights in Frodsham centre onto B5152, 0.75 mile turn right after pedestrian crossing, 0.5 mile up hill turn right, club is first on left.
Parkland course.
18 holes, 6289 yards, Par 70
Designed by John Day.
Founded July 1990
Visitors: welcome all days except competition days; tee times booked through shop.
Green Fee: £15/day WD, £19/day WE & BH.
Societies: welcome weekdays only, contact office for details.
Catering: full bar and wide selection of food served throughout the day.
Hotels: Self catering accommodation close to clubhouse; favourable rates for inclusive packages; contact office.

K48 **Gatley**
☎(061) 437 2091 or 436 2830 Pro.
Waterfall Farm, off Styal Rd, Heald Green, Cheadle, Cheshire SK8 3TW
Off Yew Tree Grove and Styal Rd 2 miles from Cheadle, 1 mile from Manchester Airport.
Parkland course.
9 holes, 5934 yards, S.S.S.68
Founded 1912
Visitors: welcome weekdays except Tues.
Green Fee: on application
Societies: apply to Sec.
Catering: full facilities.

K49 **Goldenhill**
☎(0782) 784715
Mobberley Rd, Goldenhill, Stoke-on-Trent, Staffs ST6 55S
On A50 between Tunstall and Kidsgrove.
Public parkland/meadowland course (in old open-cast mine basin).
18 holes, 5957 yards, S.S.S.68
Founded 1983
Visitors: welcome; booking system at weekends.

Green Fee: £4.10/round WD, £4.70/round WE; reductions for jnrs and OAPs.
Societies: welcome by arrangement.
Catering: bar and restaurant.
Practice ground, putting green.

K50 **Great Barr**
☎(021) 358 4376
Chapel Lane, Great Barr, Birmingham B43 7BA
Adjacent to exit 7, off M6, 6 miles NW of Birmingham.
Meadowland course.
18 holes, 6545 yards, S.S.S.72
Designed by J. Hamilton Stutt.
Founded 1961
Visitors: weekdays.
Green Fee: £15 WD.
Societies: small societies Tues, Thurs.
Catering: by arrangement.
Hotels: Post House.

K51 **Greenway Hall**
☎(0782) 503158
Stockton Brook, Stoke-on-Trent ST9 9LI
Off A53 Stoke to Leek road, approx 5 miles from Stoke.
Meadowland course.
18 holes, 5676 yards, S.S.S.67
Founded 1908
Visitors: with member only.
Green Fee: on application
Societies: by appointment only.
Catering: by prior arrangement.

K52 **Hale**
☎(061) 980 4225
Rappax Rd, Hale, Altrincham, Cheshire WA15 0NU
2 miles SE of Altrincham.
Undulating parkland course.
9 holes, 5780 yards, S.S.S.68
Founded 1903
Visitors: weekdays except Thurs; weekends and Bank Holidays only with member.
Green Fee: £15 WD.
Societies: by arrangement with Sec.
Catering: lunch except Tues and Thurs by arrangement with Steward.
Hotels: Bowdon; Ashley.

K53 **Hawkstone Park Hotel**
☎(093 924) 611 Hotel, 209 Pro shop, (093 924) 311 Fax
Weston-under-Redcastle, Shrewsbury, Shropshire SY4 5UY
14 miles N of Shrewsbury on A49.
Parkland courses.

Hawkstone, 18 holes, 6174 yards, S.S.S.70; Weston, 18 holes, 5070 yards, S.S.S.65
Designed by Alex Lyle.
Founded 1935
Visitors: welcome; h/cap required for Hawkstone course; must book.
Green Fee: on application
Societies: book through hotel.
Catering: bar and restaurant.
Hotels: own hotel.

K54 Hazel Grove
☎(061) 483 3978
Buxton Rd, Hazel Grove, Stockport, Cheshire SK7 6LU
Buxton Rd is on A6.
Parkland course.
18 holes, 6300 yards, S.S.S.70
Founded 1913
Visitors: welcome weekdays.
Green Fee: on application
Societies: Thurs and Fri.
Catering: daily except Mon.

K55 Heaton Moor
☎(061) 432 2134, 432 0846 Pro.
Heaton Mersey, Stockport, Cheshire SK4 3NX
2 miles from Stockport.
Parkland course.
18 holes, 5876 yards, S.S.S.68
Founded 1892
Visitors: welcome except Tues, Wed.
Green Fee: on application to Pro.
Societies: by arrangement.
Catering: meals served.

K56 Helsby
☎(0928) 722021
Towers Lane, Helsby, Warrington, Cheshire WA6 0JB
M56 junction 14 to Helsby; through traffic lights, 1st right, signposted Alvanley and Manley, into Primrose Lane; 1st right into Towers Lane.
Parkland course.
18 holes, 6262 yards, S.S.S.70
Designed by James Braid.
Founded 1902
Visitors: welcome weekdays.
Green Fee: £18/round, £24/day.
Societies: Tues and Thurs only.
Catering: full service except Mon.
Hotels: Chester Grosvenor; Queens.

K57 Heswall
☎(051) 342 1237 or 342 7431
Cottage Lane, Gayton, Heswall, The Wirral, Cheshire L60 8PB
M53 exit 4; at roundabout turn into Well Lane, leads into Cottage Lane.

Parkland course.
18 holes, 6472 yards, S.S.S.72
Founded 1901
Visitors: not Tues and Thurs; phone call advisable.
Green Fee: £24/day WD, £30/day WE & BH.
Societies: Wed and Fri only; full catering min 24.
Catering: bar snacks every day; full facilities except Mon.
Large practice area, 2 snooker tables.
Hotels: Craxton Wood; Crabwell Manor; Mollington Banastre; Thornton Hall; Woodhey.

K58 Heyrose
☎(0565) 893664 Sec, 894267 Pro, 893623 Steward
Budworth Rd, Tabley, Knutsford, Cheshire WA16 0HY
0.75 mile from M6 junction 19, 3 miles W of Knutsford.
Wooded converted farmland with water features.
18 holes, 6473 yards, S.S.S.72
Founded June 1990
Visitors: welcome by appointment.
Green Fee: £15/day WD, £20 WE.
Societies: by arrangement.
Catering: bar and restaurant.
Practice ground, putting green, snooker.
Hotels: Cottons; Swan.

K59 Hill Valley G & CC
☎(0948) 3584
Terrick Rd, Whitchurch, Shropshire SY13 4JZ
Off A49/A41, 1 mile from centre of Whitchurch.
Undulating parkland course.
18 holes, 6050 yards, S.S.S.69;
9 holes, 2553 yards, S.S.S.66
Designed by P. Alliss & D. Thomas.
Founded 1975
Visitors: welcome at all times.
Green Fee: 18-hole course, £18 WD, £24 WE; 9-hole course, £9 WD, £14 WE.
Societies: at all times.
Catering: breakfast, lunch, dinner 8am-11pm daily; conferences, wedding receptions up to 200.
Hotels: Terrick Hall; motel accommodation within clubhouse.

K60 Himley Hall Golf Centre
☎(0902) 895207
Log Cabin, Himley Hall Park, Dudley, W Midlands DY3 4DF

From A449 Wolverhampton-Kidderminster road turn at traffic lights signposted Dudley onto B4176, then turn into Himley Hall Park on left.
Public parkland course.
9 holes, 6180 yards, S.S.S.71
Designed by D.A. Baker.
Founded 1980
Visitors: welcome.
Green Fee: £3 (9 holes), £4.50 (18 holes) WD; £3.50 (9 holes), £5 (18 holes) WE.
Societies: by prior arrangement.
Catering: café, snacks only.
Hotels: Himley House; Park Hall.

K61 Houldsworth
☎(061) 224 5055
Wingate House, Higher Levenshulme, Manchester M19 3JW
M63 to Stockport, left onto A6 Stockport-Manchester road, right at lights at Barlow Rd.
Parkland course.
18 holes, 6078 yards, S.S.S.69
Designed by T.G. Renouf.
Founded 1911
Visitors: welcome weekdays (Ladies Day Tues 1.30-3.30pm).
Green Fee: on application
Societies: advance booking only.
Catering: full facilities.

K62 Hoylake Municipal
☎(051) 632 2956 or 632 4883
Carr Lane, Hoylake, Merseyside L47 4BG
Off M53 10 miles SW of Liverpool, follow signs for Hoylake, 100 yards from Hoylake station.
Municipal parkland course.
18 holes, 6330 yards, S.S.S.70
Designed by James Braid.
Founded 1933
Visitors: unrestricted; phone for weekends one week in advance.
Green Fee: on application
Societies: unrestricted, phone Pro.
Catering: snacks, meals, bar meals.

K63 Ingestre Park
☎(0889) 270845
Ingestre, Weston, Stafford ST18 0RE
6 miles E of Stafford off A51 via Great Haywood and Tixall Rd.
Undulating parkland course.
18 holes, 6334 yards, S.S.S.70
Designed by Hawtrees.
Founded 1977
Visitors: welcome with h/cap cert weekdays; only with member weekends and Bank Holidays.

Green Fee: £20/round, £25/day WD (£8 with member); £10 with member WE.
Societies: Mon, Tues, Thurs, Fri by arrangement with Manager.
Catering: snacks and meals daily.
Snooker.

K64 Knights Grange
☎(0606) 552780
Grange Lane, Winsford, Cheshire
In centre of Winsford.
Public meadowland course
9 holes, 2995 metres, S.S.S.71
Founded 1983
Visitors: no restrictions.
Green Fee: on application
Societies: welcome by arrangement.
Catering: bar and bar snacks.
Tennis, squash, bowls etc.

K65 Knutsford
☎(0565) 633355
Mereheath Lane, Knutsford, Cheshire
2 miles from junction 19 on M6, make for Knutsford entrance to Tatton Park, club a few yards on right down Mereheath Lane.
Parkland course.
10 holes, 6288 yards, S.S.S.70
Founded 1891
Visitors: welcome weekdays by arrangement with Sec.
Green Fee: on application.
Societies: catered for on certain weekdays, mainly Thurs.
Catering: by arrangement with Steward.
Hotels: George; Angel; Cottons; Rose & Crown; Swan.

K66 Lakeside (Rugeley)
☎(0889) 583181
Rugeley Power Station, Armitage Rd, Rugeley, Staffs WS15 1PR
Between Lichfield and Stafford.
Parkland course.
18 holes, 5534 yards, S.S.S.67
Founded 1969
Visitors: only with member.
Green Fee: £6.
Societies: by arrangement.
Catering: evening only.

K67 Leasowe
☎(051) 677 5852
Leasowe Rd, Moreton, Wirral L46 3RD
Take Wallasey turn off M53 1 mile after Queensway tunnel, 1 mile W of Wallasey village.
Seaside course.
18 holes, 6204 yards, S.S.S.71

Founded 1891
Visitors: welcome weekdays, weekends by arrangement.
Green Fee: £16 WD, £20 WE.
Societies: welcome by arrangement.
Catering: restaurant, bar, snacks.
Hotels: Leasowe Castle.

K68 Leek
☎(0538) 384779 Sec, 385899 Club
Cheddleton Rd, Leek, Staffs ST13 5RE
0.75 mile S of Leek on A520.
Semi-moorland course.
18 holes, 6240 yards, S.S.S.70
Founded 1892
Visitors: welcome weekdays before 3pm.
Green Fee: £22 WD, £27.50 WE.
Societies: Wed only.
Catering: lunches served except Sun; evening meals except Sun and Mon.
Snooker.
Hotels: Abbey Inn; Three Horseshoes; Jester.

K69 Lilleshall Hall
☎(0952) 604776, 603840
Lilleshall, Newport, Shropshire TF10 9AS
5 miles from Newport turn off A41 into Sheriffhales Rd, after 2 miles right into Abbey Rd, course is to N.
Parkland course.
18 holes, 5906 yards, S.S.S.68
Designed by H.S. Colt.
Founded 1937
Visitors: weekdays unaccompanied; weekends with members only.
Green Fee: £18/day (£9 with member) WD, £30 Bank Holidays and following day, Christmas week.
Societies: by prior arrangement.
Catering: 9am-6.30pm daily.
Hotels: Royal Victoria; White House (Donnington).

K70 Little Aston
☎(021) 353 2066
Streetly, Sutton Coldfield B74 3AN
3 miles N of Sutton Coldfield in Little Aston Park.
Parkland course.
18 holes, 6724 yards, S.S.S.73
Designed by Harry Vardon.
Founded 1908
Visitors: welcome weekdays.
Green Fee: on application.
Societies: weekdays only.
Catering: lunches served to order except Mon.
Hotels: Fairlawns.

K71 Llanymynech
☎(0691) 830542
Pant, Oswestry, Shropshire SY10 8LB
1 mile W of A483 Welshpool-Oswestry road and 6 miles S of Oswestry, turn by Cross Guns Inn, signposted to club in village of Pant.
Upland course.
18 holes, 6114 yards, S.S.S.69
Founded 1933
Visitors: welcome.
Green Fee: on application
Societies: apply to Sec.
Catering: lunch and dinner except Mon.

K72 Ludlow
☎(0584 77) 285, 366 Pro.
Bromfield, Ludlow, Shropshire SY8 2BT
Take A49 Shrewsbury road, turn right 2 miles N of Ludlow, signposted.
Parkland course.
18 holes, 6239 yards, S.S.S.70
Founded 1889
Visitors: welcome, ring Pro in advance.
Green Fee: on application.
Societies: weekdays April-Oct by arrangement.
Catering: bar and restaurant

K73 Lymm
☎(092 575) 5020
Whitbarrow Rd, Lymm, Cheshire WA13 9AN
5 miles SE of Warrington.
Parkland course.
18 holes, 6319 yards, S.S.S.70
Founded 1907
Visitors: welcome weekdays, only with member weekends and Bank Holidays.
Green Fee: £20.
Societies: usually on Wed.
Catering: meals available.
Hotels: Lymm; Statham Lodge; Dingle.

K74 Macclesfield
☎(0625) 615845 Sec, 423227 Club
Hollins Rd, Macclesfield, Cheshire SK11 7EA
Turn into Windmill St at traffic island in Leek Rd (A527).
Hilly course.
9 holes (18 from early 1993), 5974 yards, S.S.S.69
Designed by Hawtree.
Founded 1889
Visitors: welcome most days.
Green Fee: £15 WD, £17 WE.
Societies: by arrangement.

Catering: bar and restaurant, not Tues.
Hotels: Sutton Hall.

K75 Malkins Bank
☎(0270) 765931
Betchton Rd, Sandbach, Cheshire
1.5 miles from junction 17 off M6.
Municipal parkland course.
18 holes, 6071 yards, S.S.S.69
Designed by Hawtree & Son.
Founded 1980
Visitors: welcome 7 days.
Green Fee: on application.
Societies: catered for daily.
Catering: bar and catering daily.
Hotels: Old Hall, Sandbach.

K76 Market Drayton
☎(0630) 652266
Sutton, Market Drayton, Shropshire
1.5 miles S of town.
Undulating meadowland course.
18 holes, 6230 yards, S.S.S.70
Founded 1911
Visitors: welcome except Sun and Bank Holidays.
Green Fee: £16
Societies: welcome on application to Sec.
Catering: available all day.
Hotels: Corbet Arms; Bear Inn.

K77 Marple
☎(061) 427 2311
Hawk Green, Marple, Stockport,
Cheshire SK6 7EL
Off A6 at High Lane for 2 miles, left at Hawk Green.
Parkland/meadowland course.
18 holes, 5700 yards, S.S.S.67
Founded 1892
Visitors: welcome excluding competition days.
Green Fee: on application.
Societies: Tues and Wed only; special inclusive package for societies of 12 or more.
Catering: full facilities.
Hotels: West Towers.

K78 Mellor & Townscliffe
☎(061) 427 2208
Tarden, Gibb Lane, Mellor, Stockport,
Cheshire SK6 5NA
Off A626 opposite Devonshire Arms on Longhurst Lane, Mellor.
Parkland/moorland course.
18 holes, 5925 yards, S.S.S.69
Founded 1894
Visitors: welcome, except Sat when must be with member.

Green Fee: £16/day (£6 with member) WD, £25 (£8 with member) WE & BH.
Societies: welcome except Tues and Sat by arrangement.
Catering: full catering facilities, except Tues.
Hotels: West Towers (Marple).

K79 Meole Brace
☎(0743) 364050
Meole Brace, Shrewsbury,
Shropshire SY2 6QQ
S of Shrewsbury at junction of A5/A49.
Municipal parkland course with water features.
9 holes, 2915 yards, S.S.S.68
Founded 1976
Visitors: welcome.
Green Fee: £2.50 (9 holes), £3.50 (18 holes) WD; £3.10, £4.40 WE.
Societies: welcome, booking weekends.

K80 Mere G & CC
☎(0565) 830155, 830518 fax.
Chester Rd, Mere, Knutsford,
Cheshire WA16 6LJ
From junction 19 off M6 take A556 for 1 mile; from junction 7 off M56 take A556 past Swan at Bucklow Hill.
Parkland course.
18 holes, 6817 yards, S.S.S.73
Designed by George Duncan and James Braid.
Founded 1934
Visitors: by prior arrangement Mon, Tues and Thurs.
Green Fee: £40.
Societies: Mon, Tues, Thurs.
Catering: very extensive; breakfast, lunch and dinner 7 days.
Hotels: Swan (Bucklow Hill), discounted rates.

K81 Mottram Hall Hotel
☎(0625) 820064, 828135 bookings
Wilmslow Road, Mottram St Andrew,
Prestbury, Cheshire SK10 4QT
From M56 junction 6 follow A538 through Wilmslow into Prestbury.
Parkland/woodland course.
18 holes, 6905 yards, S.S.S.72
Designed by David Thomas.
Founded May 1991
Visitors: welcome with h/cap cert.
Green Fee: £25/round WD, £35/round WE.
Societies: welcome.
Catering: bar and restaurant.
Putting green, practice facilities.
Hotels: Mottram Hall (133 beds).

K82 New Mills
☎(0663) 43485
Shaw Marsh, New Mills, Stockport,
Cheshire
Take St Mary Rd from centre of New Mills, about 0.75 miles.
Moorland course.
9 holes, 5707 yards, S.S.S.68
Founded 1907
Visitors: welcome weekdays and Sat am except competition days.
Green Fee: on application.
Societies: welcome weekdays by arrangement with Sec.
Catering: snacks and meals served.
Hotels: Pack Horse and Sportsman; Moorside.

K83 Newcastle Municipal
☎(0782) 627596
Newcastle Rd, Keele, Staffs ST5 2QB.
Off M6 at junction 15 onto A525 for 2 miles.
Public parkland course.
18 holes, 6256 yards, S.S.S.70
Founded 1975
Visitors: rounds bookable any time.
Green Fee: £3.85 WD, £4.50 WE.
Societies: on application to Newcastle B.C. (0782) 717717.
Catering: bar/bar meals.
Driving range.
Hotels: Keele University Hospitality (opposite course), golf packages.

K84 Newcastle-under-Lyme
☎(0782) 618526 Pro, 616583 Steward
Whitmore Rd, Newcastle-under-Lyme, Staffs ST5 2QB
1.5 miles SW of Newcastle on A53.
Parkland course.
18 holes, 6229 yards, S.S.S.70
Founded 1908
Visitors: welcome weekdays; h/cap cert required.
Green Fee: £25/day.
Societies: catered for Mon all day and Thurs pm.
Catering: bar and restaurant.
Snooker.
Hotels: Post House; Borough Arms.

K85 Northenden
☎(061) 998 4738 Sec, 998 2934 Steward/Members, 998 4079 Pro.
Palatine Rd, Northenden,
Manchester M22 4FR
M63 exit 9, 1 mile into Northenden.
Parkland course.
18 holes, 6469 yards, S.S.S.71
Founded 1913

Visitors: no restrictions, phone beforehand.
Green Fee: £17.50 (£7 with member) WD, £20.50 (£8 with member) WE.
Societies: Tues and Fri.
Catering: bar and restaurant. Snooker.
Hotels: Britannia; Post House.

K86 Oaklands G & CC
☎(0829) 733884
Forest Road, Tarporley, Cheshire CW6 0JA
Approx 15 miles S of Warrington on A49, 0.5 mile N of Tarporley village.
Undulating parkland course.
18 holes, 6473 yards, S.S.S.71.
Designed by Tim Rouse of Golf Corporation (UK) Ltd.
Founded May 1990
Visitors: welcome Mon-Fri.
Green Fee: £21/round, £24/day (includes use of pool, gymnasium, jacuzzi etc).
Societies: Mon-Fri by arrangement.
Catering: full restaurant and bar. Leisure club, swimming, jacuzzi, sauna, gym, snooker; function room, banqueting for up to 200.
Hotels: Swan; Wild Boar (Beeston).

K87 Onneley
☎(0782) 750577
Onneley, Crewe, Cheshire CW3 5QF
1 mile from Woore on A51 to Newcastle.
Undulating meadowland course.
9 holes, 5584 yards, S.S.S.67
Founded 1968
Visitors: welcome Mon, Wed, Thur, Fri; Sat only with member.
Green Fee: £12.50/round (£6 with member).
Societies: welcome by prior booking with Sec; £12.50 per day.
Catering: by arrangement with Stewardess (0782) 750835.
Hotels: Wheatsheaf Inn.

K88 Oswestry
☎(069 188) 221 or 535
Aston Park, Oswestry, Shropshire SY11 4JJ
NW of Shrewsbury, just off A5, 2 miles from Oswestry.
Parkland course.
18 holes, 6038 yards, S.S.S.69
Designed by James Braid.
Founded 1930
Visitors: welcome, must be member of club and hold h/cap cert or play with member.

Green Fee: £15 WD, £20 WE; reduction if playing with member.
Societies: Wed and Fri only.
Catering: every day.
Hotels: Wynstay; Sweeney Hall; Ashfield Country.

K89 Oxley Park
☎(0902) 25892 Sec.
Bushbury, Wolverhampton WV10 6DE
Off A449, 1 mile N of Wolverhampton.
Parkland course.
18 holes, 6168 yards, S.S.S.69
Founded 1913
Visitors: welcome, booking advisable at weekends.
Green Fee: £16.50/round WD, £18.50/round WE.
Societies: catered for on Wed by arrangement.
Catering: breakfast, lunch, dinner. Snooker.
Hotels: Mount; Goldthorn; Park Hall.

K90 Parkhall
☎(0782) 599584 Course Manager, (0831) 456409
Hulme Road, Weston Coyney, Stoke-on-Trent, Staffs ST3 5BH
1 mile outside Longton on main A50.
Public moorland course.
18 holes, 2335 yards, Par 54
Founded Nov 1989
Visitors: welcome.
Green Fee: £3 (£1.70 Junior) WD, £3.30 (£2.90 Junior) WE.
Societies: booking times: weekends and Bank Holidays only.

K91 Patshull Park Hotel
☎(0902) 700100, 700342 resident Pro.
Pattingham, Shropshire, WV6 7HR
M54 junction 3, back on A41 towards Wolverhampton, then through Albrighton: also off A41 Wolverhampton-Whitchurch road via Perton and Pattingham.
Parkland course.
18 holes, 6460 yards, S.S.S.71
Designed by John Jacobs.
Founded 1979
Visitors: welcome, telephone for tee reservation.
Green Fee: from £20 WD, £25 WE.
Societies: full range of packages available.
Catering: full facilities; conferences, banqueting.
Swimming pool, snooker, coarse and trout fishing, leisure club.
Hotels: own hotel group.

K92 Penn
☎(0902) 341142
Penn Common, Penn, Wolverhampton, WV4 5JN
2 miles SW of W'hampton off A449.
Heathland course.
18 holes, 6449 yards, S.S.S.71
Founded 1908
Visitors: welcome weekdays.
Green Fee: £20.
Societies: weekdays.
Catering: lunch weekdays except Mon; dinner except Mon and Wed.
Hotels: Goldthorn; Park Hall.

K93 Perton Park Golf Centre
☎(0902) 380103
Wrottesley Park Road, Perton, Wolverhampton, WV6 7HL
6 miles from Wolverhampton, just off A454 Bridgnorth-W'hampton road: or A41 W'hampton-Newport road 4 miles from W'hampton.
Flat meadowland course in open countryside.
18 holes, 7036 yards, S.S.S.72
Founded 1990
Visitors: pay-as-you-play.
Green Fee: £5/round WD, £6/round Sat, £7/round Sun and Bank Holidays.
Societies: welcome by arrangement.
Catering: new club house with fully licensed bar and restaurant.
Driving range, snooker tables; buggies for hire.

K94 Portal
☎(0829) 733933
Cobblers Cross, Tarporley, Cheshire CW6 0H22
0.5 mile N of Tarporley village on A49, 10 miles N of Chester.
Public parkland course.
18 holes, 7145 yards, S.S.S.73.
Designed by Donald Steel
Founded May 1991
Visitors: welcome, no restrictions.
Green Fee: on application.
Societies: corporate business days, catered for 7 days a week.
Catering: full facilities 7 days a week; 3 banqueting suites.
Hotels: Nunsmere Hall (Tarporley).

K95 Poulton Park
☎(0925) 812034, 825220
Dig Lane, Cinnamon Brow, Warrington
Off A574, turn into Crab Lane, 3 miles from Warrington.
Meadowland course.

Portal

On the basis of Alister Mackenzie's contention that "a golf course is only as good as the land you have to build it on", Portal had a head start. From the site of the proposed permanent clubhouse, the whole of Cheshire, it seems, unfurls in front of you but the eye is caught equally by the beauty of the foreground and views of the holes embraced by it. There is at once an air of vastness and spaciousness that has become increasingly rare among new courses. The problem in the design of Portal was almost an embarrassment of riches. All too often, it is a case of fitting a quart into a pint pot but the responsibility that quickly became apparent was to blend the course into the surroundings and not to indulge in huge volumes of earth moving that would have been costly, artificial and second best.

Portal is a monument to what might be termed the British way of doing things, preserving the great, natural blessings and also representing a prime example of value for money. The actual construction cost for the entire 18 holes was just over half a million pounds, although the cost of embellishing the lakes was a separate item. Even so, the stone used to face them came from a quarry behind the 11th tee.

Construction and design were also achieved with the removal of only three trees, which is perhaps less surprising when you consider the strategic element they lend to play. It is more usual for golf course architects to have to fill prairie-like spaces with huge planting schemes and to wait years for full maturity. At Portal, the established look was instant.

There are three sides to Portal's character; the lovely, rolling countryside that stretches away in front of the clubhouse; the area of the 2nd, 3rd and 4th holes on the other side of the little lane and the landscaped parkland that circles around the lake, so apparent on the 13th, 14th and 15th. In May and June, there is the added attraction of as fine a display of rhododendrons as I have ever seen, one of the Augustan touches with which the late John Lilley, owner of Portal, hoped to create something quite outstanding.

It was both a delight and privilege to be able to try and sustain that aim and, while overall judgments must be left to others, personal assessment of some of the holes is, I hope, permissible. After, a somewhat enclosed start, the next three holes are among my favourites, a downhill, short 2nd and two par 4s that cut pleasant avenues between giant trees and which virtually made themselves.

Returning across the bridge, the 5th plays from a high tee to a fairway that used to be the outfield of the old cricket ground, the longest hole on the course ending with a shot to skirt another of the lakes. Another par 5 follows, completing a gradual rise to an elevated green beside the 15th, one of the places where the two nines come together.

The short 7th and par 4 8th, are lined by trees on the left, the tee at the 7th opening up glimpses of glorious distant views that undoubtedly give a lift to the spirits. The outward half ends beside the 1st tee with a relatively straightforward 4 but the inward half begins with one of the hardest of the 4s. The first real threat of out of bounds looms on the left and, if avoided, there is a long second to a green set against the skyline.

A steady descent gives the par 5 11th a deceptive look of innocence, the 12th leading on beside the road to the picturesque short 13th, already much photographed. Set in an alcove of trees and shrubs and guarded on three sides by water, the green is a short iron from the tee, but nerve and control are essential.

The 14th and 15th, where the lakes are again apparent, go down and back through the ancient parkland before the final crossing of the avenue is made to the 16th, for which I have a soft spot because it turned out so much better than I expected. It plays round the slope of the great hill that could make such a marvellous, natural grandstand. On the 17th, the drive has to scale the peak of this hill and then it is back up the slope with the fourth par 5, sights firmly set on the flags at the site of the new clubhouse which will complete a superb complex.

9 holes, 4937 metres, S.S.S.66
Founded 1978
Visitors: welcome weekdays,
restricted weekends.
Green Fee: £13 WD (£7 with
member), £15 WE (£8 with member).
Societies: weekdays.
Catering: meals served except Mon.
Hotels: Paddington House; Garden
Court.

K96 **Prenton**
☎(051) 608 1053 or 608 1461
Golf Links Rd, Prenton, Birkenhead,
Wirral L42 8LW
2 miles W of Birkenhead off A552;
M53 junction 3.
Flat parkland course.
18 holes, 6411 yards, S.S.S.71
Designed by Colt Mackenzie & Co.
Founded 1905
Visitors: welcome any day except
competition days (Sat in summer).
Green Fee: £23 (£7 with member)
WD, £25 WE & BH; £75 weekly
(Mon-Fri).
Societies: Wed; small societies Mon
and Fri.
Catering: full catering service
available.
Hotels: Leasowe Castle; Riverhill;
Bowler Hat.

K97 **Prestbury**
☎(0625) 828241
Macclesfield Rd, Prestbury, Cheshire
SK10 4BJ
2 miles NW of Macclesfield on
Macclesfield Rd leaving Prestbury
village.
Undulating parkland course.
18 holes, 6359 yards, S.S.S.71
Designed by Colt & Morrison.
Founded 1920
Visitors: welcome weekdays, with
member at weekends; advisable to
phone in advance.
Green Fee: £22/day.
Societies: Thurs only.
Catering: lunches, dinners and bar
snacks served except Mon.
Snooker.
Hotels: Edge; Mottram Hall.

K98 **Queen's Park**
☎(0270) 666724
Queen's Park Gardens, Crewe,
Cheshire
Just off Victoria Ave to S of Crewe
centre.
Public meadowland course
9 holes, 2460 yards, S.S.S.64
Founded 1985

Visitors: welcome except Sun before
10.30am.
Green Fee: on application
Societies: welcome by prior
arrangement.
Catering: bar and bar meals.
Bowls, tennis.

K99 **Reaseheath**
☎(0270) 625131
Cheshire College of Agriculture,
Nantwich, Cheshire
Research course, approved centre
for greenkeeper training.
9 holes Par 3, 2758 yards, S.S.S.51
Founded 1987
Visitors: small parties and societies
only, min 8; by prior arrangement
(contact Dennis Motram); April-Oct
preferred
Green Fee: £3/18 holes.
Catering: at local hostelry.

K100 **Reddish Vale**
☎(061) 480 2359
Southcliffe Rd, Reddish, Stockport,
Cheshire SK5 7EE
1.5 miles N of Stockport, off Reddish
road.
Undulating course in valley.
18 holes, 6086 yards, S.S.S.69
Designed by Dr A. Mackenzie.
Founded 1912
Visitors: welcome weekdays (not
12.30-1.30pm), with member only at
weekends.
Green Fee: £20.
Societies: weekdays by prior
arrangement.
Catering: generally available during
normal bar opening hours.
Hotels: Belgrade; Old Rectory,
Haughton Green.

K101 **Ringway**
☎(061) 904 9609, 904 0940
catering
Hale Mount, Hale Barns, Altrincham,
Cheshire WA15 8SW
8 miles S of Manchester, off M56
junction 6, follow signs for Hale; just
through Hale Barns village.
Parkland course.
18 holes, 6494 yards, S.S.S.71
Founded 1909
Visitors: welcome, not Friday.
Green Fee: £22 WD.
Societies: catered for Thurs only
from May to Sept.
Catering: full, by arrangement with
Catering Manageress.
Hotels: Cresta Court; Four Seasons;
Unicorn.

K102 **Romiley**
☎(061) 430 2392
Goosehouse Green, Romiley,
Stockport SK6 4LJ
On B6104 off A560, 0.75 mile from
Romiley station.
Undulating parkland course.
18 holes, 6335 yards, S.S.S.70
Founded 1897
Visitors: welcome except Thurs
(Ladies Day).
Green Fee: on application
Societies: apply to Sec.
Catering: full service except Mon.

K103 **Royal Liverpool**
☎(051) 632 3101 Sec, 632 6757
starter
Meols Drive, Hoylake, Wirral,
Merseyside L47 4AL
A553 to Hoylake, 10 miles W of
Liverpool.
Seaside links course.
18 holes, 6804 yards, S.S.S.74
Founded 1869
Visitors: welcome weekdays with
letter of intro from club or h/cap cert;
prior booking required; very limited
weekends.
Green Fee: £32/round, £45/day WD;
£45/round, £75/day WE.
Societies: Wed and Fri.
Catering: bar snacks available every
day and lunches on Sun.
Hotels: Leasowe Castle; Thornton
Hall; Bowler Hat.

K104 **Runcorn**
☎(0928) 572093, 574214 Sec.
Clifton Rd, Runcorn, Cheshire WA7
4SU
Signposted The Heath off A557.
High parkland course.
18 holes, 6035 yards, S.S.S.69
Founded 1909
Visitors: welcome weekdays except
Tues; bona fide h/cap cert required.
Green Fee: £14/round WD,
£18/round WE & BH.
Societies: by arrangement, normally
Mon.
Catering: bar and dining room,
meals by arrangement.
Snooker.
Hotels: Crest.

K105 **St Michael Jubilee**
☎(051) 424 6230, 423 6461
Dundalk Rd, Widnes, Cheshire
Close to Widnes centre.
Public parkland course
18 holes, 5638 yards, S.S.S.67
Founded 1977

Visitors: welcome weekdays, with booking at weekends.
Green Fee: £3 WD, £3.50 WE; reductions for jnrs and OAPs WD.
Societies: welcome by arrangement; full catering facilities.
Catering: full facilities.
Practice area.
Hotels: Hillcrest.

K106 Sale
☎(061) 973 3404 or 973 1638 Sec.
Sale Lodge, Golf Rd, Sale, Cheshire M33 2LU
On the edge of Sale, 1 mile from station.
Parkland course.
18 holes, 6346 yards, S.S.S.70
Founded 1913
Visitors: welcome any day, phone for confirmation.
Green Fee: £17 WD, £25 WE and BH.
Societies: welcome by arrangement with Sec.
Catering: bar snacks, main meals every day except Mon.
Hotels: Post House; Normanhurst.

K107 Sandbach
☎(0270) 762117
117 Middlewich Rd, Sandbach, Cheshire CW11 9EA
1 mile N of town centre on A533 Middlewich Rd.
Meadowland course.
9 holes, 5614 yards, S.S.S.67
Founded 1921
Visitors: welcome weekdays; weekends and Bank Holidays by invitation only.
Green Fee: £12/round/day.
Societies: limited to a few each year.
Catering: except Mon and Thurs.
Hotels: Saxon Cross Motel; Old Hall.

K108 Sandiway
☎(0606) 883247
Chester Rd, Sandiway, Northwich, Cheshire CW8 2DJ
On A556 14 miles E of Chester, 4 miles from Northwich.
Undulating parkland course.
18 holes, 6435 yards, S.S.S.72
Designed by Ted Ray.
Founded 1921
Visitors: weekdays and certain weekends with letter of intro.
Green Fee: £30 WD, £35 WE & BH.
Societies: catered for Tues by arrangement.
Catering: meals daily by arrangement.
Hotels: Hartford Hall; Oaklands.

K109 Sandwell Park
☎(021) 553 4637 Sec, 553 4384 Pro.
Birmingham Rd, West Bromwich, W Midlands B71 4JJ
M5 junction 1, 0.25 mile from West Bromwich Albion Football Ground.
Parkland/heathland course.
18 holes, 6422 yards, S.S.S.72
Founded 1897
Visitors: weekdays unlimited; weekends with member.
Green Fee: £30/day/round.
Societies: any weekday, societies over 20 £25.
Catering: full facilities except Mon.
Hotels: Moat House.

K110 Sedgley Golf Centre
☎(0902) 880503
Sandyfields Rd, Sedgeley, Dudley, W Midlands DY3 3DL
0.5 mile from Sedgley town centre near Cotwall End Nature Centre, just off A463.
Pay-as-you-play course; wooded, undulating with extensive views.
9 holes, 3147 yards, Par 37.
Designed by W.G. Cox.
Founded Sept 1989
Visitors: book at weekends.
Green Fee: £3 (9 holes), £5 (18 holes).
Societies: weekdays preferred by prior arrangement.
Catering: none except hot drinks.
Driving range.
Hotels: Park Hall (Wolverhampton); Station, Ward Arms (Dudley).

K111 Seedy Mill
☎(0543) 417333
Elm Hurst, Lichfield, Staffs WS13 8HE
1.5 miles N of Lichfield off A515.
Undulating parkland course.
18 holes, 6247 yards, S.S.S.70
Designed by Hawtree & Sons.
Founded 1991
Visitors: welcome; pay-as-you-play.
Green Fee: £16/round WD, £20/round WE.
Societies: welcome Mon-Fri.
Catering: full facilities.
Hotels: Cedar Tree (Rugeley).

K112 Severn Meadows
☎(0746) 862212
Highley, Nr Bridgnorth, Shropshire WV16 6HZ
10 miles N of Bewdley via B4194, B4363, B4555; 8 miles S of Bridgenorth.
Hilly parkland course in Severn Valley.
9 holes, 2521 yards, S.S.S.65
Founded 1989
Visitors: welcome weekdays, pay-as-you-play, must book weekends.
Green Fee: £8 18 holes WD, £12 WE.
Societies: booking only.
Catering: clubhouse and bar, meals to order.
Putting green, practice nets.
Hotels: Bull (Chelmarsh).

K113 Shifnal
☎(0952) 460330
Decker Hill, Shifnal, Shropshire TF11 8QL
On B4379 1 mile from Shifnal; from M54 junction 4 turn left, left again, travel with motorway for 2 miles, left again, 500 yards left again.
Parkland course.
18 holes, 6422 yards, S.S.S.71
Designed by Frank Pennink.
Founded 1929
Visitors: weekdays; weekends only with member.
Green Fee: £18.50/round, £25/day WD.
Societies: Tues, Wed or Fri.
Catering: lunch and evening meals.
Hotels: Park House; Jerningham Arms.

K114 Shrewsbury
☎(0743 72) 2976 club, 2977 Sec, 3751 Pro.
Condover, Shropshire SY5 7BL
4 miles SW of Shrewsbury, follow signs for Condover and golf club.
Parkland course.
18 holes, 6212 yards, S.S.S.70
Designed by C.K. Cotton, Pennink, Lawrie & Partners.
Founded 1890
Visitors: must have h/cap certs.
Green Fee: £11/round, £16/day WD, £20/round/day WE & BH.
Societies: apply to Sec.
Catering: full facilities available.
Snooker.
Hotels: Lord Hill; Deanhurst.

K115 Shrigley Hall Hotel
☎(0625) 575757
Shrigley Park, Pott Shrigley, Macclesfield, Cheshire SK10 5SB
From M63 Stockport take A6 towards Hazel Grove and Buxton, then A523 towards Macclesfield; turn left at Lee Arms in Adlington, signposted Pott Shrigley, 2 miles.
Parkland course.
18 holes; 6305 yards, S.S.S.71
Designed by Donald Steel.

Founded 2 May 1989
Visitors: welcome.
Green Fee: £18/round, £25/day WD;
£27/round WE.
Societies: welcome.
Catering: bars and restaurants.
Pitch & Putt, swimming, tennis,
squash, fishing and other leisure
facilities.
Hotels: Shrigley Hall (weekend
golfing packages available).

K116 South Staffordshire
☎(0902) 751065
Danescourt Rd, Tettenhall,
Wolverhampton WV6 9BQ
A41 from Wolverhampton to
Tettenhall, clubhouse and course
behind cricket club.
Parkland course.
18 holes, 6653 yards, S.S.S.72
Designed by Harry Vardon (original);
H.S. Colt.
Founded 1892
Visitors: weekdays except Tues am.
Green Fee: £25/round/day.
Societies: welcome except Tues am
and weekends.
Catering: snacks, lunches, dinners.
Hotels: Mount; Connaught.

K117 Stafford Castle
☎(0785) 223821
Newport Rd, Stafford
0.5 mile from Stafford main street.
Meadowland course.
9 holes, 6347 yards, S.S.S.70
Founded 1907
Visitors: welcome weekdays.
Green Fee: £15.
Societies: welcome by prior
arrangement.
Catering: bar meals daily, others by
arrangement except Mon.
Hotels: Swan; Tillington Hall; Vine.

K118 Stamford
☎(0457) 832126, 834829 Pro.
Oakfield House, Huddersfield Rd,
Heyheads, Stalybridge, Cheshire
SK15 3PY
On B6175 Huddersfield Rd, 3 miles
from Ashton-under-Lyne off A6108.
Undulating moorland course.
18 holes, 5619 yards, S.S.S.67
Founded 1900
Visitors: welcome weekdays (Ladies
Day Tues afternoon).
Green Fee: £15 WD, £20 WE after
3pm.
Societies: weekdays except Mon
and Tues.
Catering: meals served except Mon.
Hotels: York House (Ashton-under-
Lyne).

K119 Stockport
☎(061) 427 2001
Offerton Rd, Offerton, Stockport SK2
5HL
1 mile along A627 from Hazel Grove
to Marple.
Parkland course.
18 holes, 6319 yards, S.S.S.71
Founded 1908
Visitors: members of other clubs
welcome.
Green Fee: on application
Societies: Wed and Thur.
Catering: restaurant (closed Mon).

K120 Stone
☎(0785) 813103
Filleybrooks, Stone, Staffs ST15 0NB
0.5 mile N of Stone on A34 next to
Wayfarer Hotel.
Meadowland course.
9 holes, 6140 yards, S.S.S.69
Founded 1896
Visitors: welcome weekdays.
Green Fee: £18.
Societies: welcome weekdays.
Catering: lunch and evening meal
except Mon.
Hotels: Stonehouse (on A34); Crown.

K121 Swindon
☎(0902) 897031
Bridgnorth Road, Swindon, Dudley,
W Midlands DY3 4PU
On B4176 Bridgnorth road, 5 miles
from Wolverhampton; just off A449
Stourbridge to Wolverhampton road.
Woodland/parkland course;
exceptional views.
18 holes, 6042 yards, S.S.S.69;
9 holes Par 3, 1135 yards.
Founded 1974
Visitors: welcome, booking not
required.
Green Fee: £13/round, £20/day WD;
£20/round, £30/day WE & BH.
Societies: by arrangement
weekdays only.
Catering: fully licensed bar and
restaurant.
Snooker tables, buggies for hire.

K122 Tamworth
☎(0827) 53850
Eagle Drive, Tamworth, Staffs B77
4EG
Off B5000 Tamworth-Polesworth
road, signposted from Railway
Arches at Tamworth roundabout.
Undulating moorland course.
18 holes, 6083 yards, S.S.S.72
Founded 1975
Visitors: welcome 7 days.

Green Fee: on application.
Societies: Mon-Fri advance booking.
Catering: daily, licensed.

K123 Telford Hotel G & CC
☎(0952) 585642, 586602 fax.
Great Hay, Telford, TF7 4DT
Off A442 at Sutton Hill, S of Telford.
Undulating meadowland course.
18 holes, 6274 yards, S.S.S.70
Designed by John Harris.
Founded 1981
Visitors: welcome with h/cap cert.
Green Fee: on application.
Societies: by arrangement.
Catering: meals served every day.
Driving range, squash, swimming
pool, snooker, sauna etc.
Hotels: Telford Hotel Country Club.

K124 Three Hammers Golf Complex
☎(0902) 790428
Old Stafford Rd, Coven, Staffs WV10
7PP
M54 junction 2, N on A449, course 1
mile on right.
Public 18 hole Par 3 short course.
Designed by Henry Cotton.
Visitors: welcome.
Green Fee: on application.
Societies: welcome Mon-Sat.
Catering: bar and bistro, à la carte
restaurant, private dining facilities.
Driving range.
Hotels: accommodation planned.

K125 Trentham
☎(0782) 658109
14 Barlaston Old Rd, Trentham,
Stoke-on-Trent ST4 8HB
Off M6 junction 15 towards Stoke,
follow A34 to Trentham Gardens,
turn left, 1st right.
Parkland course.
18 holes, 6644 yards, S.S.S.72
Founded 1894
Visitors: welcome with h/cap cert;
not Sat or Sun am.
Green Fee: £25.
Societies: Wed, Thurs, max 40.
Catering: bar and restaurant.
Squash, snooker.
Hotels: Post House; Clayton Lodge;
Stonehouse (Stone).

K126 Trentham Park
☎(0782) 658800
Trentham Park, Trentham,
Stoke-on-Trent ST4 8AE
4 miles S of Newcastle under Lyme
on A34, 1 mile from M6 junction 15.

Parkland course.
18 holes, 6403 yards, S.S.S.70
Founded 1936
Visitors: h/cap and club membership required.
Green Fee: £20 WD, £25 WE.
Societies: Wed and Fri.
Catering: full facilities.
Snooker.
Hotels: Clayton Lodge; Post House.

K127 The Tytherington
☎(0625) 434562
Macclesfield, Cheshire, SK10 2JB
Approx 2 miles from Macclesfield on A523 Stockport road.
Modern championship parkland course.
18 holes, 6735 yards, S.S.S.72
Designed by Dave Thomas, Patrick Dawson.
Founded Oct 1986
Visitors: h/cap certs required.
Green Fee: £22/round.
Societies: weekdays; £20 per round, £30 2 rounds; all-day catering.
Catering: bar, conservatory, restaurant, private rooms available.
Tennis, snooker, pool, health club, bowls, clay shoot.
Hotels: special arrangements with local hotels.

K128 Upton-by-Chester
☎(0244) 381183
Upton Lane, Chester CH2 1EE
Off A41 Liverpool-Chester road, near Upton zoo.
Parkland course.
18 holes, 5808 yards, S.S.S.68
Founded 1934
Visitors: unlimited except competition days.
Green Fee: £16/round, £21/day WD; £21 WE 1 round only.
Societies: Wed-Fri.
Catering: full restaurant facilities.
Hotels: Mollinston Banastre; Dene; Euro Hotel.

K129 Uttoxeter
☎(0889) 565108, 564884 Pro.
Wood Lane, Uttoxeter, Staffs ST14 8JR
Off B5017 Uttoxeter-Marchington road, about 0.5 mile along Wood Lane, just past race course.
Moorland course
18 holes, 5456 yards, S.S.S.67
Founded 1972
Visitors: welcome except invitation days etc; subject to availability.

Green Fee: £13 WD, £17 WE; half price with member and jnrs.
Societies: all year by arrangement; £21 per person, min 4.
Catering: available except Mon.
Pool.
Hotels: White Hart; Bank.

K130 Vicars Cross
☎(0244) 335174
Tarvin Rd, Great Barrow, Chester CH3 7HN
A51 3 miles E of Chester.
Meadowland course.
18 holes, 6238 yards, S.S.S.70
Designed by E. Parr.
Founded 1939
Visitors: Mon-Thurs; members guests only Fri, Sat, Sun.
Green Fee: £20/day.
Societies: Tues, Thurs only.
Catering: full facilities.
Hotels: Oaklands; Hoole Hall.

K131 Wallasey
☎(051) 691 1024
Bayswater Rd, Wallasey, Merseyside L45 8LA
From Liverpool through Wallasey Tunnel to junction 1; follow signs to New Brighton.
Seaside links course.
18 holes, 6607 yards, S.S.S.73
Designed by Tom Morris Snr.
Founded 1891
Visitors: welcome weekdays, limited weekends.
Green Fee: £25/day WD, £30/day WE & BH; half-price with member.
Societies: Mon-Fri by arrangement.
Catering: full facilities. Snooker.
Hotels: Leasowe Castle; Belvedere.

K132 Walsall
☎(0922) 613512
The Broadway, Walsall, WS1 3EY
1 mile S of Walsall centre, 400 yards from the Crest Motel; take A34 from M6 junction 7.
Parkland/meadowland course.
18 holes, 6232 yards, S.S.S.70
Founded 1907
Visitors: welcome weekdays, with member weekends.
Green Fee: on application
Societies: welcome.
Catering: full service.

K133 Walton Hall
☎(0925) 66775
Warrington Rd, Higher Walton, Warrington WA4 5LU

4 miles from Warrington along A56, 0.5 mile from M56.
Undulating parkland course.
18 holes, 6801 yards, S.S.S.73
Founded 1972
Visitors: welcome.
Green Fee: on application.
Societies: by appointment.
Catering: bar snacks available during licensed hours; meals by arrangement with Steward.
Hotels: Lord Daresbury.

K134 Warren
☎(051) 639 5730
The Grange, Grove Rd, Wallasey, Merseyside
500 yards up Grove Rd, beyond Grove Rd station.
Municipal links course.
9 holes, 2700 yards, S.S.S.34(68)
Founded 1911
Visitors: welcome weekdays; phone first at weekends.
Green Fee: on application.
Catering: lunch and tea in café.
Hotels: Grove House.

K135 Warrington
☎(0925) 65431 Pro, 61775 Sec.
London Rd, Appleton, Warrington, Cheshire WA4 5HR
On A49 from M56 or S on A49 through town, 3 miles S of Warrington.
Undulating parkland course.
18 holes, 6217 yards, S.S.S.70
Designed by James Braid.
Founded 1902
Visitors: welcome.
Green Fee: on application
Societies: apply to Sec.
Catering: available except Mon.

K136 Wergs
☎(0902) 742225
Keepers Lane, Tettenhall, Wolverhampton WV6 8UA
Follow A41 Telford road out of Wolverhampton for approx 3 miles; turn right (course signposted) into Keepers Lane, 0.5 mile on right.
Public parkland course.
18 holes, 6949 yards, S.S.S.73
Designed by C.W. Moseley.
Founded June 1990
Visitors: pay-as-you-play.
Green Fee: £14 WD, £17.50 WE & BH.
Societies: at all times.
Catering: lounge/spike bar and restaurant.
Driving range (under construction).

K137 Werneth Low
☎(061) 368 2503
Werneth Low Rd, Hyde, Cheshire
SK14 3AF
2 miles from Hyde town centre via
Gee Cross and Joel Lane.
Undulating course.
9 holes, 5734 yards, S.S.S.68
Founded 1918
Visitors: welcome except Sun.
Green Fee: on application
Societies: weekdays by
arrangement.
Catering: daily, except Wed.

K138 Westminster Park
☎(0244) 680231
Hough Green, Chester, CH4 8JQ
In Saltney on SW outskirts of Chester.
Public parkland course
9 holes Par 3, 900 yards, S.S.S.27
Visitors: welcome.
Green Fee: £1.70/round.

K139 Westwood (Leek)
☎(0583) 383060
Wallbridge, Newcastle Rd, Leek,
Staffs ST13 7AA
0.5 mile S of Leek on A53.
Moorland/parkland course.
18 holes, 6156 yards, S.S.S.67
Founded 1892
Visitors: welcome weekdays, with
member Sat; not Sun.
Green Fee: £15 (£6 with member).
Societies: Mon and Thurs.
Catering: available. Snooker, pool.

K140 Whiston Hall
☎(0538) 266260
Whiston, Nr Froghall, Staffs ST10 2HZ
A52 midway between Stoke-on-Trent
and Ashbourne, 3 miles Alton Towers.
Moorland course.
18 holes, 5675 yards, S.S.S.71
Designed by Thomas Cooper.
Founded 1971
Visitors: welcome, not before 9am
Sun.
Green Fee: £6 WD, £7 WE & BH.
Societies: welcome any time by
prior arrangement.
Catering: bar and catering at
weekends all year, some weekdays
in summer.

K141 Whittington Barracks
☎(0543) 432317 Clubhouse,
432261 Pro, 432317 Sec.
Tamworth Rd, Lichfield, WS14 9PW
On A51 2.5 miles from Lichfield
station.
Heathland course.
18 holes, 6457 yards, S.S.S.71
Founded 1886
Visitors: welcome weekdays with
h/cap cert or letter of intro.
Green Fee: £28/day/round.
Societies: Wed, Thurs max 40.
Catering: snack lunches, evening
meals available except Mon.
Hotels: George; Little Barrow; Swan.

K142 Widnes
☎(051) 424 2995
Highfield Rd, Widnes, Cheshire
Near town centre.
Parkland course.
18 holes, 5688 yards, S.S.S.67
Founded 1923/4
Visitors: welcome weekdays.
Green Fee: on application
Societies: weekdays, except Tues.
Catering: meals by arrangement.

K143 Wilmslow
☎(0565 87) 2148
Great Warford, Mobberley,
Knutsford, Cheshire WA16 7AY
2 miles from Wilmslow on B5085
Knutsford road, turn at Warford Lane.
Parkland course.
18 holes, 6607 yards, S.S.S.72
Founded 1889
Visitors: welcome Mon-Fri;
restricted weekends.
Green Fee: £22/round, £32/day WD,
£34/round, £44/day WE.
Societies: Tues and Thurs.
Catering: full facilities.
Hotels: Edge; The Belfry.

K144 Wirral Ladies
☎(051) 652 1255
93 Budston Rd, Oxton, Birkenhead,
Merseyside L43 6TS
On A41 adjacent to M53 exit 3.
Moorland course.
18 holes, 4539 yards, S.S.S.70
Designed by H. Hilton.

Founded 1894
Visitors: welcome anytime.
Green Fee: on application
Societies: apply to Sec.
Catering: meals at all times.

K145 Withington
☎(061) 445 9544, 434 8716 catering
243 Palatine Rd, West Didsbury,
Manchester M20 8UD
From Manchester S on A5103 then
B5166 through Northenden.
Parkland course.
18 holes, 6411 yards, S.S.S.71
Founded 1892
Visitors: welcome weekdays.
Green Fee: on application.
Societies: catered for weekdays
except Thurs.
Catering: full facilities; phone
caterer.

K146 Wolstanton
☎(0782) 622413 Sec, 616995 Club
Dimsdale Old Hall, Hassam Parade,
Newcastle under Lyme, Staffs ST5
9DR
1.5 miles NW of Newcastle under
Lyme on A34, turn off at Lymelight
Hotel into Dimsdale Parade, then 1st
right into Hassam Parade.
Meadowland/parkland course.
18 holes, 5807 yards, S.S.S.68
Founded 1925
Visitors: welcome weekdays.
Green Fee: on application.
Societies: welcome Mon, Wed,
Thurs and Fri.
Catering: lunches served Mon-Sat
(not Fri).
Hotels: Thomas Forshaw.

K147 Wrekin
☎(0952) 44032
Ercall Woods, Wellington, Telford TF6
5BX
Off M54 back along B5061 to Golf
Links Lane.
Parkland course.
18 holes, 5699 yards, S.S.S.67
Founded 1905
Visitors: welcome weekdays.
Green Fee: on application
Societies: weekdays except Mon.
Catering: booked in advance.

L

DERBYSHIRE, NOTTINGHAMSHIRE, LINCOLNSHIRE

Seacroft at Skegness may not be the most accessible golf course. There is a strong argument to make that that is the key to its appeal. On the other hand, there is nothing like a rave notice to start the queues forming and the ensuing disturbance of the peace will not be to the liking of the locals.

Golfers place a high premium on tranquillity, particularly when seeking a leisurely round, and Seacroft fits that bill admirably. Its true seaside qualities may be slow to blossom as the opening holes are flanked on the right by trim avenues and typically large Lincolnshire fields. Out of bounds, in fact, is an obvious threat most of the way to the turn but, from the moment that the short 10th turns back, diagonally to the line of play hitherto, there are inspiring sights of the sea and many memorable holes.

Seacroft lies on the opposite side of The Wash from Hunstanton, on the edge of the Gibraltar Point wildlife sanctuary, which epitomises its joyous remoteness. It is the only true seaside links between Hunstanton and Seaton Carew, a pick of the Eastern seaboard, but Lincolnshire has another gem in Woodhall Spa, again a peaceful retreat though widely contrasting in character. It highlights the best of British inland golf, a stout championship challenge revolving around glorious heathland, deep bunkers and handsome trees. A word too, for Luffenham Heath near Stamford which is almost as good.

Seacroft and Woodhall Spa are the perfect foil for each other but the Notts Golf Club at Hollinwell is a rival to Woodhall Spa in its severity as a test and in a pleasant setting that largely obscures evidence of the mining community that surrounds it. It lies in a gentle valley fringed by pine trees and boasts a collection of par 4s which are notably good. There is also a little climbing to be done which tends to be enlightening rather than exhausting.

Hollinwell has distinguished neighbours in Sherwood Forest and Coxmoor, courses that enjoy similarly appealing golfing terrain and problems to match.

Part of Lindrick falls in Nottinghamshire, although I am inclined to think the bulk of it is in Yorkshire — or used to be. However, wherever its loyalties are directed, it is a superb course that has rightly attracted its share of big events including victory in the 1957 Ryder Cup at a time when Great Britain and Ireland were not used to winning.

Newark is worthy of recommendation and Wollaton Park in Nottingham has also housed professional events but, if Derbyshire, the third county in this particular trinity, lacks the outstanding courses of the other two, some of them bear the signature of famous architects. Cavendish at Buxton is the work of Alister Mackenzie while James Braid and John Morrison had a hand in Kedleston Park. To Harry Colt goes credit for Chesterfield and Frank Pennink made changes at Mickleover. Since the last edition of this guide, a second course has been added to Breadsall Priory Hotel Golf and Country Club which is part of the Country Club Hotels chain that includes St Pierre and Dalmahoy.

The first course, opened in 1977, indulges in a good deal of up and down but the second course, which comes into play this summer, commands marvellous views from nicely rolling moorland with exactly the same feeling of escape that can be experienced on the distant coast at Seacroft.

L1 Alfreton
☎(0773) 832070
Highfields, Wingfield Rd, Oakthorpe,
Derbys DE5 7DH
Take the Matlock road out of
Alfreton, about 0.75 mile.
Parkland course.
9 holes, 5012 yards, S.S.S.65
Founded 1893
Visitors: welcome; Sat, Sun and
Mon with member only.
Green Fee: £12/round, £15/day.
Societies: catered for weekdays on
consultation with Sec.
Catering: full facilities except Mon.
Hotels: Swallow (S Normanton);
Granada (Swanwick).

L2 Allestree Park
☎(0332) 550616
Allestree Hall, Allestree, Derbys
Leave Derby on A6, 4 miles from city
centre, signposted Allestree Park.
Undulating parkland course.
18 holes, 5749 yards, S.S.S.68
Founded 1940
Visitors: welcome at all times,
except competition days or Sun am.
Green Fee: on application.

Societies: welcome.
Catering: by prior arrangement.
Hotels: Clovelly (Derby).

L3 Ashbourne
☎(0335) 42078
Clifton, Nr Ashbourne, Derbys DE6
4BN
1 mile S of Ashbourne on A515 to
Sudbury and Lichfield.
Undulating parkland course.
9 holes, 5359 yards, S.S.S.66
Designed by Frank Pennink.
Founded 1910
Visitors: welcome.
Green Fee: on application
Societies: small.
Catering: by arrangement, not Thurs.

L4 Bakewell
☎(062 981) 2307
Station Rd, Bakewell, Derbys DE4
1GB
0.75 mile from Bakewell Square,
cross bridge over River Wye on A619
Sheffield-Chesterfield road, right up
Station Rd, left before Industrial
Estate.

Hilly parkland course.
9 holes, 4808 yards, S.S.S.64
Designed by George Low.
Founded 1899
Visitors: welcome.
Green Fee: on application
Societies: by arrangement.
Catering: bar, meals, except Mon.

L5 Beeston Fields
☎(0602) 257062
Beeston Fields, Nottingham NG9 3DD
Off A52 4 miles W of Nottingham, 4
miles from M1 exit 25.
Parkland course.
18 holes, 6414 yards, S.S.S.71
Designed by Tom Williamson.
Founded 1922
Visitors: daily by arrangement.
Green Fee: on application.
Societies: catered for Mon and Wed.
Catering: meals served every day.
Hotels: The Priory; Novotel.

L6 Belton Park
☎(0476) 67399
Belton Lane, Londonthorpe Rd,
Grantham, Lincs NG31 9SH

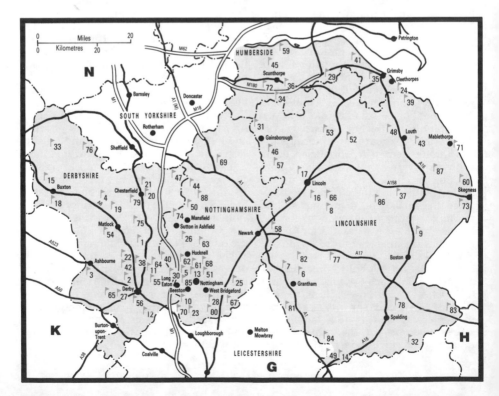

A607 from Grantham signposted to Sleaford and Lincoln, turn right at traffic lights at Park signposted Londonthorpe, club is 1 mile on left. Parkland courses.
Brownlow, 9 holes, 6420 yards, S.S.S.71; Belmont, 9 holes, 6016 yards, S.S.S.69; Ancaster, 9 holes, 6252 yards, S.S.S.70
Designed by Thomas & Alliss.
Founded 1890
Visitors: welcome, preferably with h/cap cert; no jeans or collarless shirts, proper golf shoes required.
Green Fee: £15.50 (18 holes), £20.50 (27 + holes) WD; £25 (18 holes), £30 (27 + holes) WE & BH.
Societies: not Tues or weekends.
Catering: full facilities at all times. 2 practice fairways.
Hotels: Angel & Royal; King's; Lodge (Marston); Travel Lodge.

L7 Belton Woods Hotel & Country Club
☎(0476) 593200
Belton, Nr Grantham, Lincolnshire NG32 2LN
2 miles E of A1 via Gonerby Moor services; 2 miles N of Grantham on A607 to Lincoln.
Rolling parkland courses with mature trees and adjacent woodland.
Lancaster, 18 holes, 7021 yards, S.S.S.74; Wellington, 18 holes, 6875 yards, S.S.S.73; Spitfire, 9 holes Par 3, 1184 yards
Designed by Cayford GC Construction
Founded Jan 1991
Visitors: welcome any day; max 6 visits per year; no advance booking permitted.
Green Fee: 18 holes; £12/round, £18/day WD; £16/round, £22/day WE: Par 3 course, £5 any day.
Societies: Mon-Fri by prior arrangement. Special Company and Society Golf Days.
Catering: leisure restaurant 7am-10pm, bar snacks 11am-10pm; à la carte restaurant, banqueting for 240.
Driving range, putting green, full range of health, sports, leisure and conference facilities.
Hotels: Belton Woods, golfing breaks for individuals and groups; golf tuition holidays.

L8 Blankney
☎(0526) 20263 Sec, 20202 Pro.
Blankney, Lincoln, Lincs LN4 3AZ
On B1188 10 miles from Lincoln, 1 mile past Metheringham.

Parkland course.
18 holes, 6402 yards, S.S.S.71
Designed by Cameron Sinclair.
Founded 1903
Visitors: weekdays only, phone Pro in advance.
Green Fee: £15/round, £20/day.
Societies: weekdays only.
Catering: full facilities.
Snooker.
Hotels: Moor Lodge; Golf; Petwood; Dower House.

L9 Boston
☎(0205) 362306 Club, 350589 Sec.
Cowbridge, Horncastle Rd, Boston, Lincs PE22 7EL
2 miles N of Boston on B1183, look for sign on right crossing 1st bridge. Parkland course; water on 10 holes.
18 holes, 5795 yards, S.S.S.68
Designed by B.S. Cooper, extended by Donald Steel.
Founded 1962
Visitors: welcome.
Green Fee: £14 WD, £20 WE & BH.
Societies: welcome weekdays.
Catering: full facilities except Wed when only bar snacks available.
Hotels: White Hart; Bridge Foot; New England; Wide Bargate; Boston.

L10 Bramcote Hills
☎(0602) 281880
Thoresby Rd, off Derby Rd, Bramcote, Nottingham
M1 junction 25, take A52 towards Nottingham, past Bramcote Leisure Centre, turn left 0.25 mile further on. Parkland course.
18 holes Par 3, 1501 yards
Founded 1981
Visitors: pay-as-you-play.
Green Fee: £3.40 WD, £3.90 WE & BH, reductions for jnrs.
Societies: bookings welcomed.
Catering: refreshments only.

L11 Breadsall Priory Hotel Golf & Country Club
☎(0332) 832235, 833509 fax.
Moor Rd, Morley, Derbys DE7 6DL
3 miles NE of Derby off A61, towards Breadsall, turn left into Rectory Lane and right onto Moor Rd.
Undulating parkland course.
18 holes, 6402 yards, S.S.S.71
Founded 1977
Visitors: welcome weekdays; by prior arrangement weekends.
Green Fee: on application
Societies: weekdays only; residential societies at weekends.

Catering: 5 bars, 2 restaurants; breakfast, lunch and dinner. Tennis, squash, pool, snooker, etc.
Hotels: Breadsall Priory.

L12 Breedon Priory
☎(0332) 863081
The Clubhouse, Wilson, Nr Derby, DE7 1AT
1 mile E of A 453 between E Midlands Airport and Ashby-de-la-Zouche. Parkland course.
18 holes, 5512 yards, S.S.S.66
Founded 1990
Visitors: welcome Mon-Fri; weekends pm only, by arrangement.
Green Fee: £12.
Societies: weekdays by arrangement.
Catering: Bar and snacks daily.
Hotels: Park Farmhouse.

L13 Bulwell Forest
☎(0602) 278008
Hucknall Rd, Bulwell, Nottingham NG5 9LQ
4 miles N of city centre, follow signs for Bulwell or Hucknall, 3 miles from M1 junction 26.
Moorland course.
18 holes, 5572 yards, S.S.S.67
Founded 1902
Visitors: welcome.
Green Fee: on application
Societies: by arrangement.
Catering: by arrangement.

L14 Burghley Park
☎(0780) 53789
St Martins Without, Stamford, Lincs PE9 3JX
Leave A1 at roundabout S of town, course entrance is 1st gateway on the right, 1 mile S of Stamford. Parkland course.
18 holes, 6236 yards, S.S.S.70
Founded 1890
Visitors: welcome weekdays only; h/cap certs essential.
Green Fee: £20.
Societies: welcome weekdays (preference given to Wed).
Catering: lunches and teas, dinner for Societies and by arrangement.
Hotels: George of Stamford; Crown; Cavalier; Lady Anne's; Garden House.

L15 Buxton & High Peak
☎(0298) 23453, 26263
Waterswallows Rd, Fairfield, Buxton, Derbys
1 mile from Buxton station on A6.

Meadowland course.
18 holes, 5954 yards, S.S.S.69
Founded 1887
Visitors: welcome.
Green Fee: on application.
Societies: by arrangement with House Manageress.
Catering: full facilities and supper licence.
Hotels: Buckingham; Palace; Portland; Egerton.

L16 **Canwick Park**
☎(0522) 522166
Canwick Park, Washingborough Road, Lincoln LN4 1EF
2 miles E of city centre.
Parkland course.
18 holes, 6237 yards, S.S.S.70
Designed by Hawtree & Partners.
Founded 1973
Visitors: welcome weekdays.
Green Fee: £10 Mon, £12 Tues-Fri, £13 WE & BH.
Societies: weekdays.
Catering: lunches and evening meals except Mon.
Hotels: Eastgate; Brierley House.

L17 **Carholme**
☎(0522) 523725
Carholme Rd, Lincoln LN1 1SE
On A57, 1 mile from city centre.
Parkland course.
18 holes, 6144 yards, S.S.S.69
Founded 1906
Visitors: welcome weekdays, with member weekends.
Green Fee: on application.
Societies: weekdays only.
Catering: lunch served except Mon.

L18 **Cavendish**
☎(0298) 23494, 25052 Pro.
Gadley Lane, Buxton, Derbys SK17 6XD
0.75 mile from town centre going W on A53 Leek road, right on Carlisle Rd, left on Watford Rd, signposted.
Parkland/downland course.
18 holes, 5815 yards, S.S.S.68
Designed by Dr Alistair Mackenzie.
Founded 1925
Visitors: welcome.
Green Fee: £20/day WD, £30/round WE; half price with member.
Societies: catered for weekdays by arrangement with Pro.
Catering: snacks available at all times and meals by arrangement. Snooker table.
Hotels: Lee Wood; Buckingham; Portland; Egerton.

L19 **Chatsworth**
☎(0246) 582204
Chatsworth Park, Bakewell, Derbys
Parkland course.
9 holes (18 tees), 5248 yards, S.S.S.66
Visitors: members and guests only.

L20 **Chesterfield**
☎(0246) 279256
Walton, Chesterfield, Derbys S42 7LA
2 miles from town centre on Matlock Rd A632.
Parkland course.
18 holes, 6326 yards, S.S.S.70
Designed by H. Colt.
Founded 1897
Visitors: welcome weekdays.
Green Fee: £20/round, £25/day.
Societies: catered for on weekdays if booked in advance.
Catering: lunch and dinner served every day.
Hotels: Chesterfield; Portland.

L21 **Chesterfield Municipal (Tapton Park)**
☎(0246) 273887, 239500 bookings
Murray House, Crow Lane, Chesterfield, Derbys S41 0EQ
Near centre of Chesterfield, signposted.
Municipal parkland course.
18 holes, 6013 yards, S.S.S.69; 9 holes, 2700 yards, Par 34
Founded 1934
Visitors: welcome any time; booking system all week, up to 6 days in advance.
Green Fee: on application
Societies: welcome by prior arrangement.
Catering: full bar and restaurant facilities.
Pitch & Putt.

L22 **Chevin**
☎(0332) 841864
Golf Lane, Duffield, Derbys DE6 4EE
5 miles N of Derby on A6, just outside Duffield.
Hilly parkland course.
18 holes, 6043 yards, S.S.S.69
Founded 1894
Visitors: welcome weekdays, not before 9.30am nor 12am-2pm; with member at weekends.
Green Fee: £24/day.
Societies: not weekends; no meals Mon.
Catering: meals served except Mon. Snooker.
Hotels: Strutt Arms adjacent.

L23 **Chilwell Manor**
☎(0602) 258958
Meadow Lane, Chilwell, Nottingham NG9 5AE
4 miles W of Nottingham, near Beeston, on A6005.
Parkland course.
18 holes, 6379 yards, S.S.S.69
Founded 1906
Visitors: welcome weekdays, restricted to 4 per hour.
Green Fee: £20/round/day.
Societies: catered for Mon.
Catering: lunches served weekdays; evening meals by arrangement.
Hotels: Post House; Novotel.

L24 **Cleethorpes**
☎(0472) 812059, 814060
Kings Rd, Cleethorpes, S Humberside DN35 0PN
Off A1031 1 mile S of Cleethorpes.
Meadowland course.
18 holes, 6015 yards, S.S.S.69
Designed by Harry Vardon.
Founded 1894
Visitors: must be members of recognised club (Ladies only, Wed pm).
Green Fee: £15 (£10 with member) WD, £20 (£15 with member) WE.
Societies: by arrangement.
Catering: full facilities available by arrangement with Steward.
Hotels: Kingsway; Wellow; Blundell Park.

L25 **Cotgrave Place G & CC**
☎(0602) 333349 Office, 334686 Pro.
Stragglethorpe, Nottingham NG12 3HB
Approx 3.5 miles from Nottingham on A52 Grantham road, take right turn to Cotgrave.
Parkland course, lake bestrewn.
3 x 9 holes, c. 6500 yards, S.S.S.71-72
Founded 1990, fully open May 1992
Visitors: to be decided: apply for details.
Green Fee: on application.
Societies: apply for details; company days a speciality.
Catering: full facilities.
Driving range.
Hotels: own hotel and leisure centre under construction; opening 1993.

L26 **Coxmoor**
☎(0623) 559878 Club, 557359 Office, 559906 Pro shop
Coxmoor Rd, Sutton-in-Ashfield, Notts NG17 5LF.

On A611 5 miles from M1 junction 27, 2 miles SW of Mansfield.
Heathland course.
18 holes, 6251 yards, S.S.S.70
Founded 1913
Visitors: weekdays except Tues (Ladies' Day); must book tee time in advance.
Green Fee: £22/day.
Societies: welcome Mon, Wed, Thurs, Fri.
Catering: full facilities.
Hotels: Pine Lodge; Carr Bank; Dalestorth GH; Hole in the Wall; Swallow.

L27 Derby
☎(0332) 766462 Pro shop, 766326 catering
Shakespeare St, Sinfin, Derby DE2 9HD
1 mile off A5111 at Sinfin, vehicle access via Wilmore Rd.
Municipal parkland course.
18 holes, 6183 yards, S.S.S.69
Founded 1923
Visitors: welcome.
Green Fee: on application.
Societies: weekdays by prior arrangement.
Catering: bar and catering daily.

L28 Edwalton Municipal
☎(0602) 234775
Edwalton Village, Nottingham
Left off A606 from Nottingham at Edwalton Hall Hotel.
Parkland course.
Main, 9 holes, 3336 yards, S.S.S.36;
Par 3, 9 holes, 1592 yards, S.S.S.27
Designed by Frank Pennink.
Founded 1981
Visitors: welcome.
Green Fee: on application.
Societies: weekdays.
Catering: lunches and evening meals served.
Hotels: Edwalton Hall.

L29 Elsham
☎(0652) 688382, 680291
Barton Rd, Elsham, Brigg, S Humberside DN20 0LS
Situated on E side of Brigg to Barton road, B1206, 3 miles N of Brigg.
Parkland course.
18 holes, 6411 yards, S.S.S.71
Founded 1901
Visitors: welcome weekdays.
Green Fee: on application.
Societies: welcome weekdays except Thurs.
Catering: full bar all day.

L30 Erewash Valley
☎(0602) 323258
Stanton-by-Dale, Ilkeston, Derbys
From M1 junction 25 follow signs to Stanton Ironworks Co Ltd, through Sandiacre.
Meadowland/parkland course.
18 holes, 6487 yards, S.S.S.71
Founded 1905
Visitors: welcome weekdays.
Green Fee: £20/round, £25/day WD; £25/round/day WE & BH.
Societies: catered for weekdays.
Catering: lunches, evening meals by arrangement.
Snooker, bowling green.
Hotels: Post House; Novotel.

L31 Gainsborough
☎(0427) 613088
Thonock, Gainsborough, Lincs DN21 1PZ
1 mile NE of Gainsborough.
Parkland course.
18 holes, 6515 yards, S.S.S.71
Founded 1985
Visitors: welcome weekdays.
Green Fee: £18/round, £24/day.
Societies: Mon-Fri, book in advance.
Catering: bar, restaurant, coffee shop all day.
Driving range, practice putting green, snooker.
Hotels: Hemswell Cliff; Hickman Hill.

L32 Gedney Hill
☎(0406) 330922
West Drove, Gedney Hill, Nr Holbeach, Lincs PE12 0NT
6 miles from Crowland on B1166, 6 miles from Thorney by A47/B1167.
Public links type course, reasonably flat, small greens.
18 holes, 5429 yards, S.S.S.66
Designed by C. Britton.
Founded 1988
Visitors: welcome; smart dress on and off course.
Green Fee: £5.75 WD, £8.75 WE; reductions for Jnrs and OAPs.
Societies: welcome weekdays; min 2 weeks notice.
Catering: casual bar, bar snacks; restaurant for meals and functions.
Driving range, snooker, heated swimming pool.

L33 Glossop & District
☎(0457) 853117
Hurst Lane, off Sheffield Rd, Glossop, Derbys SK13 8RH
1 mile out of town on A57 Sheffield road.

Moorland course.
11 holes, 5726 yards, S.S.S.68
Founded 1895
Visitors: welcome.
Green Fee: £10/day (£6 with member) WD, £20 (£6 with member) WE & BH.
Societies: welcome.
Catering: meals by arrangement.
Hotels: Hurst Lee Guest House.

L34 Grange Park
☎(0724) 762945
Butterwick Rd, Messingham, Scunthorpe, S Humberside DN17 3PP
Signposted from Messingham.
Public parkland course.
9 holes, 2970 yards, Par 35
Designed by Ray Price.
Founded July 1991
Visitors: welcome, no restrictions.
Green Fee: £4 WD, £6 WE; jnrs half price.
Catering: coffee bar.
Driving range.

L35 Grimsby
☎(0472) 342630 Sec, 342823 Clubhouse, 356981 Pro.
Littlecoates Rd, Grimsby, S Humberside DN34 4LU
1 mile W of town centre; turn left off A18 at 1st roundabout, 0.75 mile on left, next to Humber Royal Hotel.
Undulating parkland course.
18 holes, 6058 yards, S.S.S.69
Founded 1922
Visitors: members of golf clubs only (Ladies Day Tues).
Green Fee: £15 WD, £20 WE and BH; reduction with member.
Societies: Mon and Fri only.
Catering: available; full meals by arrangement, except Wed.
Bowls, bridge.
Hotels: Humber Royal.

L36 Holme Hall
☎(0724) 862078 office, 840909 club
Holme Lane, Bottesford, Scunthorpe, S Humberside DN16 3RF
2 miles SE of Scunthorpe near E exit of M180.
Parkland course.
18 holes, 6475 yards, S.S.S.71
Founded 1908
Visitors: welcome weekdays, not weekends or Bank Holidays.
Green Fee: £15/round/day.
Societies: not Mon.
Catering: meals by arrangement, bar snacks daily except Mon.
Hotels: Royal; Wortley; Beverley.

L37 Horncastle

☎(0507) 526800
West Ashby, Horncastle, Lincs LN9 5PP
Just off A158 between Lincoln and Skegness; down hill at Edlington, follow AA signs.
Heathland course with trees and water features.
18 holes, 5782 yards, S.S.S.70
Designed by Ernie Wright.
Founded July 1990
Visitors: welcome.
Green Fee: £10/round, £15/day.
Societies: 7 days a week.
Catering: bars and restaurant; conferences, ballroom.
Driving range, coarse fishing.
Hotels: Petwood, Golf (Woodhall Spa); Bull; Admiral Rodney.

L38 Horsley Lodge

☎(0332) 780838
Horsley Lodge, Smalley Mill Road, Horsley, Derbys DE2 5BL
4 miles from Derby on A608 Derby-Heanor road turn left at Rose & Crown then 2nd left.
Undulating parkland course.
18 holes, 6443 yards, S.S.S.71
Designed by George 'Bill' White.
Founded 1990
Visitors: welcome, not during weekend competitions.
Green Fee: £15/round, £20/day.
Societies: welcome any week day or non-competition Sat.
Catering: 2 bars, à la carte restaurant, function room, banquets.
Driving range, tennis, sauna.
Hotels: Own luxury hotel on site; free golf for residents, bargain breaks.

L39 Humberston Park

☎(0472) 210404
Humberston Ave, Humberston, S Humberside
Humberstone Avenue at back of Cherry Garth Scouts Field.
Parkland course.
9 holes, Par 30
Founded 1970
Visitors: welcome, not before 12am weekends.
Green Fee: £6 (19 holes) WD, £10 (18 holes) WE.
Societies: welcome by arrangement.
Catering: bar and snacks.

L40 Ilkeston Borough

☎(0602) 307704
West End Drive, Ilkeston, Derbyshire DE7 5GH

0.5 mile E of Ilkeston town centre.
Municipal meadowland course.
9 holes, 4002 yards, S.S.S.60
Founded 1920
Visitors: welcome.
Green Fee: £4.80/day.
Societies: welcome.

L41 Immingham

☎(0469) 575298, 575493
Church Lane, Immingham, Grimsby, S Humberside DN40 2EU
A180 Immingham exits, Pelham Rd; Bluestone Lane or Washdyke Lane both lead into Church Lane.
Part municipal parkland course.
18 holes, 5809 yards, S.S.S.68
Designed by Hawtree & Son (1st 9), F. Pennink (2nd 9).
Founded 1974
Visitors: welcome weekdays, restrictions at weekends.
Green Fee: £9/round WD.
Societies: weekdays by prior arrangement.
Catering: snacks and bar meals, arranged with Steward.

L42 Kedleston Park

☎(0332) 840035
Kedleston, Quarndon, Derby DE6 4JD
From A38 follow signs to Kedleston Hall.
Parkland course.
18 holes, 6611 yards, S.S.S.71
Designed by James Braid and Morrison & Co.
Founded 1947
Visitors: weekdays only by appointment.
Green Fee: £25/round.
Societies: weekdays only by appointment.
Catering: full restaurant and bar facilities.
Snooker.
Hotels: Kedleston; Midland; Mundy Arms.

L43 Kenwick Park

☎(0507) 605134
Kenwick, Nr Louth, Lincs LN11 8NR
On Mablethorpe road out of Louth.
Woodland/parkland course.
18 holes, 6782 yards, Par 72
Designed by Patrick Tallack.
Opening Aug 1992
Visitors: welcome; ring for details of visitor requirements, green fees, society meetings etc.
Catering: bar and restaurant.
Practice ground.
Hotels: Kenwick Hall.

L44 Kilton Forest

☎(0909) 486563 Pro.
Blyth Rd, Worksop, Notts S81 0TL
2 miles NE of town centre on B6045; on by-pass follow signs for Blyth.
Public parkland course
18 holes, 6569 yards, S.S.S.72
Founded 1978
Visitors: welcome, booking system in operation weekends and Bank Holidays.
Green Fee: £5.50 WD, £7.50 WE & BH.
Societies: welcome by arrangement, Club competitions weekends and some Bank Holidays.
Catering: bar meals; not Sun.
Bowling green adjacent.
Hotels: Regancy.

L45 Kingsway

☎(0724) 840945
Kingsway, Scunthorpe, S Humberside DN15 7ER
S of A18 between Berkeley and Queensway roundabouts.
Undulating parkland course.
9 holes, 1915 yards, S.S.S.59
Designed by R.D. Highfield.
Founded 1971
Visitors: welcome every day.
Green Fee: on application
Catering: snacks available.

L46 Lincoln

☎(042 771) 210
Torksey, Lincoln LN1 2EG
Off A156, 12 miles NW of Lincoln.
Undulating meadowland course.
18 holes, 6438 yards, S.S.S.71
Founded 1891
Visitors: welcome with reservation weekdays only.
Green Fee: £17/round, £20/day.
Societies: weekdays by arrangement.
Catering: meals by arrangement.
Hotels: White Hart; Grand; Crest.

L47 Lindrick

☎(0909) 475282
Lindrick, Worksop, Notts S81 8BH
On A57, 4 miles W of Worksop.
Heathland course.
18 holes, 6615 yards, S.S.S.72
Designed by Willie Park and N.H. Fowler.
Founded 1891
Visitors: welcome weekdays, prior notice required.
Green Fee: Nov-Mar £25/round/day WD; Apr-Oct £35/round/day WD, £40/round/day WE.

Societies: weekdays.
Catering: lunches served most days; evening meals for visiting societies/parties, prior notice required.
Hotels: Red Lion (Todwick); Fourways, Charnwood (Blyth); Olde Bell (Barnby Moor).

L48 Louth
☎(0507) 603681
Crowtree Lane, Louth, Lincs LN11 9LJ
From Lincoln or Gainsborough turn right at Trout Farm on outskirts of Louth, from Sleaford turn left by the Grammar School; course is situated in Hubbard Hills 1 mile out of Louth.
Undulating meadowland course.
18 holes, 6477 yards, S.S.S.71
Founded 1965
Visitors: welcome.
Green Fee: £13/round, £15/day WD; £15/round, £17/day WE & BH.
Societies: catered for weekdays; 4 weeks notice and deposit required.
Catering: lunches, bar snacks served daily.
Hotels: Priory; Kings Head; Masons Arms.

L49 Luffenham Heath
☎(0780) 720205
Ketton, Stamford, Lincs PE9 3UU
6 miles SW of Stamford on A6121 by Fosters Bridge, off A47 at Morcott onto A6121.
Undulating heathland course.
18 holes, 6253 yards, S.S.S.71
Designed by James Braid.
Founded 1911
Visitors: by prior arrangement; h/cap certs required.
Green Fee: £28 WD, £34 WE & BH.
Societies: welcome Wed, Thurs and Fri.
Catering: by arrangement.
Hotels: George; Kings Arms (Wing); Cavalier (Collyweston).

L50 Mansfield Woodhouse
☎(0623) 23521
Leeming Lane North, Mansfield Woodhouse, Notts NG19 9EU
On A60 Mansfield-Worksop road, 2 miles N of Mansfield.
Public parkland course.
9 holes, 2411 yards, S.S.S.65
Founded 1973
Visitors: welcome any time except Sat before 11am.
Green Fee: on application
Catering: full facilities.

L51 Mapperley
☎(0602) 265611
Central Ave, Mapperley Plains, Nottingham NG3 5RH
From Nottingham take Woodborough Rd, turn right at Speeds (Volvo) Garage c. 4 miles NE of Nottingham.
Hilly meadowland course.
18 holes, 6224 yards, S.S.S.70
Founded c. 1905
Visitors: welcome.
Green Fee: £14/round, £17/day WD; £16/round, £19/day WE; reductions for jnrs.
Societies: weekdays.
Catering: lunch and evening meals served except Wed (snacks only).

L52 Market Rasen & District
☎(0673) 842416
Legsby Rd, Market Rasen, Lincs LN8 3DZ
B1202 off A46, 1 mile S of racecourse.
Moorland course.
18 holes, 6043 yards, S.S.S.69
Founded 1922
Visitors: welcome weekdays; with member weekends.
Green Fee: on application
Societies: Tues and Fri by arrangement with Sec.
Catering: lunch except Mon.

L53 Market Rasen Race Course
☎(0673) 843434
Market Rasen Race Course, Legsby Road, Market Rasen, Lincs LN8 3EA
Off A631.
Public pay-as-you-play course.
9 holes, 2532 yards, Par 33
Founded May 1989
Visitors: welcome, not race days.
Green Fee: £4 (9 holes), £6 (18 holes) WD; £5 (9 holes), £8 (18 holes) WE; reduction for jnrs and OAPs.
Societies: welcome.
Catering: available on race course. Children's playground.
Hotels: The Limes.

L54 Matlock
☎(0629) 582191
Chesterfield Rd, Matlock, Derbys DE4 5LF
On A632 Matlock-Chesterfield road, 1.5 miles out of Matlock.
Moorland/parkland course.
18 holes, 5801 yards, S.S.S.68
Founded 1907
Visitors: welcome weekdays, weekends with member only.

Green Fee: £20 WD, £12.50 WE & BH with member only.
Societies: catered for weekdays.
Catering: snacks available, meals to order except Mon.
Hotels: Peacock; New Bath.

L55 Maywood
☎(0602) 392306
Rushy Lane, Risley, Draycott, Derbys DE7 3ST
Off A52 to Risley by Post House Hotel.
Wooded course with water features.
9 holes, 2883 yards, Par 68; further 18 holes opening April 1992.
Founded 1990
Visitors: welcome weekdays.
Green Fee: £10 (18 holes) WD.
Societies: welcome.
Catering: clubhouse, bar, snacks available.
Hotels: Post House; Novotel.

L56 Mickleover
☎(0332) 513339 Clubhouse, 518662 Pro.
Uttoxeter Rd, Mickleover, Derby
3 miles W of Derby; take A516 out of Derby, join B5020 to Mickleover.
Meadowland course.
18 holes, 5708 yards, S.S.S.68
Founded 1923
Visitors: welcome.
Green Fee: £15 WD, £20 WE & BH.
Societies: welcome Tues, Thurs, greeb fee £15.
Catering: full catering facilities available.
Hotels: Crest; International; Mickleover Court.

L57 Millfield
☎(042 771) 255
Laughterton, Torksey, Nr Lincoln, Lincs LN1 2LB
8 miles E of Lincoln between A57 and A158 on A11; 10 miles from Gainsborough.
Inland links course.
18 holes, 5986 yards, S.S.S.69; 9 holes Par 3, 1500 yards; further 15 hole intermediate course, 4100 yards, from summer 1992.
Founded 1984
Visitors: no restrictions, pay-as-you-play.
Green Fee: £5/round.
Societies: weekdays by arrangement.
Catering: light refreshments.
Driving range, tennis, bowls.
Hotels: self-catering apartments in complex.

L58 Newark

☎(0636) 626282 Sec/Manager, 626241 Club
Kelwick, Coddington, Newark, Notts NG24 2QX
On A17 between Newark and Sleaford, just past Coddington roundabout.
Parkland course.
18 holes, 6482 yards, S.S.S.71
Founded 1901
Visitors: welcome any time; h/cap cert required; Tues Ladies' Day.
Green Fee: £17/round, £22/day WD and WE.
Societies: welcome except Tues and weekends; catering with booking.
Catering: bar and meals all day. Snooker, pool.
Hotels: Robin Hood; George Inn (Leadenham).

L59 Normanby Hall

☎(0724) 720252 Clubhouse, 720226 Pro shop
Normanby Park, Normanby, Scunthorpe, S Humberside DN15 9HU
5 miles N of Scunthorpe adjacent to Normanby Hall.
Parkland course.
18 holes, 6548 yards, S.S.S.71
Designed by H.F. Jiggens, Hawtree & Sons.
Founded 1978
Visitors: welcome.
Green Fee: £8.50/round, £12.50/day WD; £10/round WE & BH.
Societies: not Fri pm, weekends or Bank Holidays.
Catering: full facilities; banqueting etc at Normanby Hall and Country Park adjacent to course.
Hotels: Royal; Wortley House.

L60 North Shore

☎(0754) 763298
North Shore Rd, Skegness, Lincs PE25 1DN
1 mile N of town on seaward side of Ingoldmells Rd.
Links/parkland course.
18 holes, 6134 yards, S.S.S.69
Designed by James Braid.
Founded 1910
Visitors: welcome if member of recognised club with current h/cap cert.
Green Fee: £12/round WD, £16/round WE.
Societies: as for visitors.
Catering: normal hotel services. Snooker, hard tennis court, banqueting.
Hotels: North Shore on site.

L61 Nottingham City

☎(0602) 278021
Lawton Drive, Bulwell, Nottingham NG6 8BL
2 miles off M1 at junction 26.
Municipal parkland course.
18 holes, 6120 yards, S.S.S.70
Founded 1910
Visitors: welcome weekdays and by booking at weekends.
Green Fee: £8/day WD, £10/day WE.
Societies: welcome weekdays except Fri.
Catering: meals served.

L62 Notts (Hollinwell)

☎(0623) 753225
Hollinwell, Derby Rd, Kirkby-in-Ashfield, Notts NG17 7QR
Leave M1 at junction 27, then 2 miles N on A611.
Undulating heathland course.
18 holes Championship, 7020 yards, S.S.S.74
Designed by Willie Park.
Founded 1887
Visitors: reserved for members 12am-1pm Mon/Tues, 12am-2pm Wed/Thurs, and until 12.30pm Fri.
Green Fee: £30/round, £38/day.
Societies: by arrangement.
Catering: full facilities every day.
Hotels: Swallow; Pine Lodge.

L63 Oakmere Park (Oxton)

☎(0602) 653545, 655628 fax.
Oaks Lane, Oxton, Notts NG25 0RH
On A614 and A6097 8 miles NE of Nottingham.
Parkland course.
18 holes, 6046 metres, S.S.S.72; 9 holes, 3193 metres, Par 37.
Designed by F. Pennink.
Founded 1974
Visitors: welcome but should make reservation at weekends.
Green Fee: 18 hole course £15 WD, £18 WE & BH; 9 hole course £6 WD, £7.50 WE.
Societies: welcome 7 days; max possible notice for weekends.
Catering: clubhouse bar, spike bar, restaurant (resident chef).
Driving range.

L64 Ormonde Fields CC

☎(0773) 42987 Pro, 44157 Club
Nottingham Rd, Codnor, Ripley, Derbys DE5 9RL
Off M1 at junction 26, take A610 towards Ripley for about 2 miles.
Undulating course.
18 holes, 6007 yards, S.S.S.69
Founded 1906
Visitors: welcome weekdays; by arrangement with Sec weekends.
Green Fee: on application
Societies: by arrangement.
Catering: full facilities.

L65 Pastures

☎(0332) 513921 extn 348
Pastures Hospital, Mickleover, Derby DE3 5DQ
On A516 4 miles W of Derby.
Undulating meadowland course.
9 holes, 5005 yards, S.S.S.64
Designed by Frank Pennink.
Founded 1969
Visitors: with member only.
Green Fee: on application.
Societies: weekdays by special arrangement.
Catering: for societies only.

L66 RAF Waddington

☎(0522) 720271 ext 955
Waddington, Lincoln, LN5 9NB
Airfield course.
18 holes, 5223 yards, S.S.S.69
Founded 1973
Visitors: if introduced by member.
Green Fee: £3.
Catering: limited bar facility.

L67 Radcliffe-on-Trent

☎(0602) 333000, 335771 Steward
Dewberry Lane, Cropwell Rd, Radcliffe on Trent, Notts NG12 2JH
Off A52 Nottingham-Grantham road, 7 miles W of Nottingham.
Undulating parkland course.
18 holes, 6434 yards, S.S.S.71
Designed by F. Pennink.
Founded 1909
Visitors: weekdays except Tues.
Green Fee: £23.50 WD, £29.50 WE.
Societies: apply in writing.
Catering: contact Steward.
Hotels: Bridgford Lodge.

L68 Ramsdale Park Golf Centre

Oxton Rd, Calverton, Notts.
N of Nottingham via A60 and A614.
Parkland course.
18 holes, c. 6500 yards, Par 72; 18 holes Par 3
Designed by Hawtree & Co.
Opening end May 1992
Visitors: welcome; apply for details of visitor requirements, green fees and society meetings.
Catering: full facilities.
Driving range.

Seacroft

For years, the temptation to get to Woodhall Spa blinded me to some of the other attractions of Lincolnshire's golf, notably the links of Seacroft which lie between Skegness and the nature reserve at Gibraltar Point. The British coastline is dotted with a profusion of courses with many qualities, although settings that are off the beaten track are denied the championship recognition of the Birkdales, Formbys and Muirfields.

However, remoteness is a characteristic to be cherished and at Seacroft it adds to the appeal of a course that typifies the virtues of seaside links.

From the clubhouse, doubts may be formed by the road and row of houses that line the opening holes, but very soon a firm impression is formed that the threat of out of bounds cannot be shirked by cowardly play to the left. Limiting factors make their appearance there, too.

A central spine of dunes divides the course at two levels and there is the added feature, one unique in my experience, of a huge host of thorn bushes that are punishing in more senses than one. The 3rd, blind from the back tee, is a short par 4 with a little pitch to an elevated green that it is unwise to miss on the right. But the 4th introduces us to a series of short holes that are first class, the 4th involving another elevated green and a tee shot that needs to be solidly hit to negotiate the hint of a valley in between.

After the 5th, where there is little fruitful option to hitting the fairway, the 6th offers the first significant change of direction but the 7th, 8th and 9th continue the journey to the furthest point from the clubhouse with sandhills offering the main hazards and providing a series of interesting shots. The second half begins with another beautifully, simple short hole, but it is the 225 yard 12th which heads towards the sea and introduces a stretch of 4 or 5 holes that are quite delightful both in the challenge and enjoyment they present and in giving us views of the sea. On a clear day, the outline of Hunstanton can be detected across the Wash, but the 13th demands the closest attention, a hole that can be approached in a number of different ways.

The green stands on a small plateau and is guarded by a big bunker in the face of the hill. It needs two of the best to get home and discretion is often the better part of valour. The more conservative way is to hit over a prominent ridge and launch a high pitch at the green.

Beyond the green is a marshy lagoon separating the course from the beach but the genuine seaside nature of the links is maintained by the 3rd par 3 in five holes and a drive over a hill at the 15th followed by a nasty second in a cross wind to a green standing back to back with the 3rd. All the attributes of a good dogleg are embraced by the 16th and the need for proper control is highlighted by the 17th and 18th which become more and more overlooked by houses.

It is no wonder that those who know Seacroft are lost in admiration of a challenge that has everything, including the essential power of enjoyment.

However, the last word must belong to Bernard Darwin who, writing in his famous book *The Golf Courses of the British Isles* reminded readers of the posters, familiar in the early years of the century, which proclaimed with more accuracy than is usual in such circumstances, "Skegness is so bracing".

In closing his chapter on East Anglia with a description of Seacroft, he lauded the fact that there was good turf and plenty of sand and the sea itself, although he added "we do not often see it. Neither do we see — and this is an unmixed blessing — the teeming swarms of trippers that come to Skegness to be braced".

THE SHERWOOD FOREST GOLF CLUB LTD

EAKRING ROAD, MANSFIELD, NOTTS. NG18 3EW
Club House Telephone No. 23327

Secretary: K. Hall   Tel: 0623 26689

Professional: K. Hall   Tel: 0623 27403

Catering Manageress D. McCart Tel: 0623 23327

Full catering service available with dining for up to 70 persons at one sitting. Course is heathland, set in the very heart of Robin Hood country, and was designed by James Braid. Yellow markers distance is 6,294 yds. SSS 71. White markers distance is 6,714 yds. SSS 73.

The Course is the venue for the
Midland region Qualifying Round for the Open Championship 1990 – 1996
Green Fees on application.
All applications to be made with the secretary.
Within a few miles of places of interest – such as the Major Oak (Robin Hood's Larder). Newstead Abbey, Thoresby Hall, Clumber Park, and 14 miles from the centre of Nottingham.

L69 Retford
☎(0777) 703733
Ordsall, Retford, Notts
S off A620.
Woodland course.
9 holes, 5697 metres, S.S.S.70
Visitors: welcome weekdays, with member at weekends.
Green Fee: on application
Catering: full meal facilities.

L70 Ruddington Grange
☎(0602) 846141, 24139 Club
Wilford Rd, Ruddington, Notts NG11 6NB
S of Nottingham via M1 junction 24, A453, A52 Grantham road.
Parkland course.
18 holes, 6496 yards, S.S.S.71
Designed by Eddie McCausland, David Johnson.
Founded 1988
Visitors: welcome with h/cap certs; not Sat.
Green Fee: £20/round, £22/day WD, £24/round, £26/day WE.
Societies: welcome, advance bookings only.
Catering: bars, restaurant, function rooms.
Practice ground, putting green.

L71 Sandilands
☎(0507) 441432, 441617
Sea Lane, Sandilands, Sutton-on-Sea, Mablethorpe, Lincs LN12 2RJ
4 miles S of Mablethorpe on A52 coast road, course next to sea wall.
Seaside links course.
18 holes, 5995 yards, S.S.S.69
Founded 1901
Visitors: welcome any time.
Green Fee: £11/round, £16/day WD; £16/round WE & BH.
Societies: on application.
Catering: bar meals except Tues.
Hotels: Grange & Links, 3-day golf breaks, societies welcome, phone (0507) 441334.

L72 Scunthorpe
☎(0724) 866561
Burringham Rd, Scunthorpe, S Humberside DN17 2AB
On B1450, adjoining Mallard Hotel.
Parkland course.
18 holes, 6281 yards, S.S.S.71
Founded 1936
Visitors: Mon to Fri.
Green Fee: £16/day.
Societies: Mon to Fri.
Catering: full facilities Mon to Fri.
Hotels: Royal.

L73 Seacroft
☎(0754) 763020
Drummond Rd, Skegness, Lincs PE25 3AU
1 mile S of Skegness alongside road to Gibraltar Road Bird Sanctuary.
Undulating seaside links course.
18 holes, 6490 yards, S.S.S.71
Founded 1895
Visitors: welcome from bona fide club with h/cap.
Green Fee: £18/round, £25/day WD; £25/round, £30/day WE.
Societies: as for visitors.
Catering: available except Tues.
Hotels: Vine; Crown.

L74 Sherwood Forest
☎(0623) 26689 Sec, 27403 Pro, 23327 Club
Eakring Rd, Mansfield, Notts NG18 3EW
M1 junction 27; Mansfield exit from roundabout, left at T-junction, left at next T-junction (5 miles), right at next T-junction, left at lights, right at 3rd mini-roundabout, course on left.
Heathland course.
18 holes, 6714 yards, S.S.S.73
Designed by H. Colt, redesigned by James Braid.

Founded 1895
Visitors: must be members of golf club with h/cap.
Green Fee: £28/round, £33/day WD; £33/round WE.
Societies: welcome Mon, Thurs and Fri.
Catering: full facilities daily.
Hotels: Pine Lodge; Midland; Swallows.

L75 Shirland
☎(0773) 834935
Lower Delves, Shirland, Derbys DE5 6AU
1 mile N of Alfreton off A61; 3 miles from M1 junction 28 via A38.
Tree-lined rolling parkland course
18 holes, 6072 yards, S.S.S.69
Founded 1976
Visitors: no restrictions weekdays, book through Pro at weekends.
Green Fee: on application
Societies: welcome weekdays.
Catering: full facilities.
3 practice grounds, county standard bowling green.

L76 Sickleholme
☎(0433) 51306
Saltergate Lane, Bamford, Sheffield S30 2BH
On A625, 14 miles W of Sheffield, near Marquis of Granby.
Hillside meadowland course.
18 holes, 6064 yards, S.S.S.69
Founded 1895
Visitors: welcome but not Wed am; preferably phoned in advance.
Green Fee: on application
Societies: catered for on weekdays.
Catering: by arrangement.

L77 Sleaford
☎(052 98) 273
Willoughby Rd, South Rauceby, Sleaford, Lincs NG34 8PL
On A153 Sleaford-Grantham road, 2 miles W of Sleaford.
Heathland course.
18 holes, 6443 yards, S.S.S.71
Designed by Tom Williamson.
Founded 1905
Visitors: welcome except winter Sun.
Green Fee: £14 WD, £22 WE & BH; reductions when playing with member.
Societies: Mon-Fri by prior arrangement.
Catering: full bar; meals and snacks available.
Hotels: Carre Arms.

L78 Spalding
☎(0775 85) 386 Sec, 234 Club, 474 Pro.
Surfleet, Spalding, Lincs PE11 4EA
4 miles N of Spalding off A16.
Meadowland course.
18 holes, 5807 yards, S.S.S.68
Founded 1908
Visitors: members of recognised clubs; h/cap cert required.
Green Fee: on application.
Societies: Thurs only on application.
Catering: full facilities except Tues.

L79 Stanedge
☎(0246) 566156
Walton Hay Farm, Stanedge, Chesterfield, Derbys S45 0LW
5 miles SW of Chesterfield, at top of long hill on A632, turn on to B5057; club 300 yards W of Red Lion Inn.
Undulating moorland course.
9 holes, 4867 yards, S.S.S.64
Founded 1931
Visitors: welcome weekdays am; with member only afternoons, weekends and Bank Holidays.
Green Fee: £10 (£5 with member) WD; £10 WE & BH with member only.
Societies: prior arrangement only.
Catering: provided for parties by prior arrangement.
Hotels: The Chesterfield; Portland; Glen Stuart; Olde House.

L80 Stanton-on-the-Wolds
☎(06077) 2044
Stanton-on-the-Wolds, Keyworth, Notts NG12 5AH
Off A606 at Blue Star Garage 8 miles SE of Nottingham.
Meadowland course.
18 holes, 6437 yards, S.S.S.71
Designed by Tom Williamson.
Founded 1906
Visitors: weekdays if no competitions in progress; weekends and Bank Holidays with member only.
Green Fee: £18/round, £20/day; societies £22/round/day.
Societies: write to Sec, H.G. Gray FCA, 2 Golf Rd, Stanton-on-the-Wolds, Notts, (06077) 2006.
Catering: ring Steward in advance.
Hotels: Edwalton (Nottingham).

L81 Stoke Rochford
☎(047 683) 275
Stoke Rochford, Grantham, Lincs
Off A1 northbound carriageway 5 miles S of Grantham, entrance at A.J.S. Service area.
Parkland course.
18 holes, 6204 yards, S.S.S.70
Designed by C. Turner.
Founded 1926
Visitors: welcome, not before 10.30am Sat or Sun unless with member; contact Pro before visiting.
Green Fee: on application.
Societies: catered for Mon, Tues, Thurs and Fri only.
Catering: lunches and evening meals served upon request. Snooker, pool.

L82 Sudbrook Moor
☎(0400) 50796
Carlton Scroop, Nr Grantham, Lincs NG32 3AT
On A607 8 miles N of Grantham.
Parkland course.
9 holes, 4712 yards, S.S.S.63
Designed by Tim Hutton.
Founded 1986
Visitors: welcome.
Green Fee: £5/day WD, £7 WE & BH.
Societies: by arrangement.
Catering: coffee shop.
Practice ground.
Hotels: phone for details.

L83 Sutton Bridge
☎(0406) 350323, 351080 Pro.
New Rd, Sutton Bridge, Spalding, Lincs
On A17 10 miles W of Kings Lynn.
Parkland course.
9 holes, 5820 yards, S.S.S.68
Founded 1914
Visitors: weekdays only.
Green Fee: £15.
Catering: meals, sandwiches; not Mon.

L84 Toft Hotel
☎(0778) 33616
Toft, Nr Bourne, Lincs PE10 0XX
6 miles N of Stamford on A6121.
Undulating parkland course with water features.
18 holes, 6355 yards, S.S.S.70
Designed by Derek and Roger Fitton.
Founded 1988
Visitors: welcome; standard dress etiquette; tees bookable 14 days in advance.
Green Fee: on application.
Societies: welcome by arrangement.
Catering: full bar, bar snack and restaurant facilities in adjacent hotel; function room (120).
Hotels: Toft, weekend/bargain breaks with reduced green fees for residents.

L85 **Wollaton Park**

☎(0602) 787574
Wollaton Park, Nottingham NG8 1BT
Parkland course.
18 holes, 6494 yards, S.S.S.71
Designed by T. Williamson.
Founded 1927
Visitors: welcome weekdays.
Green Fee: £15.50/round,
£23.50/day WD.
Societies: Tues and Fri.
Catering: daily except Mon.

L86 **Woodhall Spa**

☎(0526) 52511
The Broadway, Woodhall Spa, Lincs
LN10 6PU
On B1191 6 miles SW of Horncastle,
18 miles Lincoln or Sleaford.
Heathland course.
18 holes, 6866 yards, S.S.S.73
Designed by Col S.V. Hotchkin.

Founded 1905
Visitors: welcome all week by prior
arrangement with Sec, max h/cap
20, ladies 30.
Green Fee: £21/round, £28/day WD;
£23/round, £31/day WE & BH.
Societies: as for visitors.
Catering: full facilities 7 days.
Hotels: Golf; Petwood; Dower House.

L87 **Woodthorpe Hall**

☎(0507) 450294
Woodthorpe, Alford, Lincs LN13 0DD
3.5 miles from Alford off B1371.
Parkland course.
18 holes, 4659 yards, S.S.S.63
Founded 1986
Visitors: welcome.
Green Fee: £7/round.
Societies: by prior arrangement.
Catering: available.
Fishing, snooker, bowls.

Hotels: self-catering at Woodthorpe
Park Caravan Complex.

L88 **Worksop**

☎(0909) 477731 Sec, 477732 Pro,
472696 members
Windmill Lane, Worksop, Notts S80
2SQ
On SE of town, from new by-pass
(A57) take A6005, follow local
signposts for Sherwood Forest, turn
immediately left into Windmill Lane.
Sandy heathland course.
18 holes, 6651 yards, S.S.S.72
Founded 1904
Visitors: welcome, telephone first.
Green Fee: on application.
Societies: by arrangement, not
weekends, Bank Holidays.
Catering: full, with notice.
Hotels: Van Dyk; Regancy; Aston
Hall; Red Lion.

M

LANCASHIRE, ISLE OF MAN, CUMBRIA

Lancashire encompasses the great chain of coastal courses between Liverpool and Southport that, for the championship status many possess, is as prolific a stretch as any in the world. West Lancashire is the most senior, the modern clubhouse conveniently served by Hall Road Station on the electric railway line that gets a good view of Formby, Southport & Ainsdale, and Hillside. West Lancashire is noble seaside terrain although the rugged dimensions of the dunes grow a cubit or two as they approach Southport.

Royal Birkdale, scene of seven Opens, provides a succession of avenues between sandhills, its fairways possessing few of the eccentric humps and hollows which golfers either love or hate.

Royal Birkdale's fame is very much post-war, its reputation fairly galloping after staging its first Open in 1954, but its neighbour, Hillside, has come even more recently to the distinction of hosting championships. Jack Nicklaus made his professional debut in Britain there in 1962 but the course has undergone a major change since then, the alterations enabling it to graduate to higher realms. It needs no stressing that Birkdale and Hillside constitute mighty days' golf and that Formby, more secluded, keeps them company. Hesketh and Southport & Ainsdale should also be included in select itineraries of the Southport area, the latter having staged two pre-war Ryder Cup matches — that in 1933 resulting in a rare home victory.

Of the Lancashire courses north of Southport, Royal Lytham & St Annes is a pillar of strength, a championship links renowned for the severity of its challenge. Although its visitors invariably retire battered and bruised, it does not stop them coming. Royal Lytham is a relentless test but the Lytham area has other notable attractions.

St Annes Old Links, next to Blackpool Airport, and Fairhaven, are demanding enough to have played host to qualifying rounds for the Open but there is plenty of variety in a part of the world where golf is as popular as black pudding. Knott End, near Fleetwood, Blackpool North Shore and Lytham Green Drive offer enjoyable detours, while Ormskirk and Pleasington stand out in Lancashire's heartland.

Castletown in the Isle of Man is only a short hop from Blackpool Airport and the links and their lovely hotel only a short taxi ride from the terminal buildings at Ronaldsway, which are remarkably free of unattractive bustle.

But the Isle of Man has other golfing temptations that may be more to the liking of those less anxious to grapple with such a stern task. Not the least of the scenic delights of the island are the distant views of the lakeland hills, conjuring up thoughts of fell walkers, poets, climbers and relaxation on a boat.

Golf is secondary in the minds of the majority of Cumbria's visitors but Seascale and Silloth occupy an important place as fine seaside courses both locally and nationally. Seascale is the more remote, a small town south of Whitehaven and Workington just off the road that makes a grand coastal sweep round the Lake District. Furness and Grange over Sands are worthy of a short detour, but Seascale is true links with more undulation than some.

Then it is on up past St Bees Head to the edge of the Solway Firth and Silloth on Solway which is an authentic championship setting in a town well known for its flour mill and the little harbour that serves it.

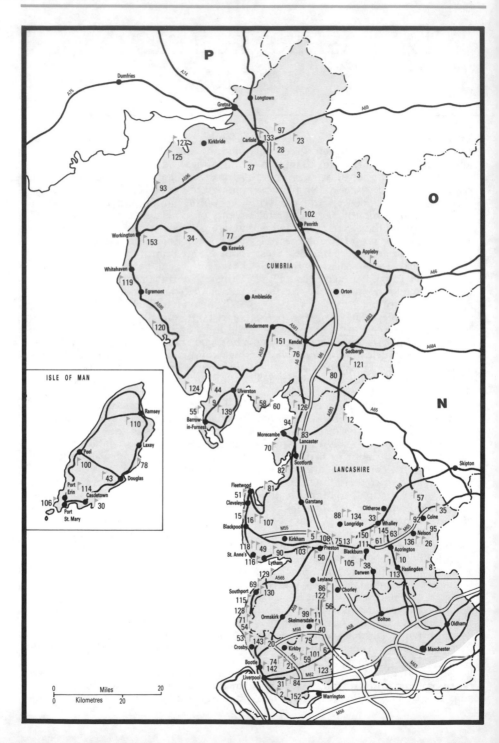

P

Dumfries

A74

A75

Gretna
Longtown

A69

Carlisle
127 Kirkbride
125
97
133 23
28

37

3

O

93
A596

102
Penrith

Workington
153 34 77
Keswick

Appleby
4

Whitehaven
CUMBRIA
A66

119
Egremont
A595

Ambleside

Orton

A684

120

Windermere
A591
151 Kendal
76
A6
80

Sedbergh
121

N

A6
A683

A65

124 44 Ulverston
9
55 139
Barrow-in-Furness
58 60 126
94
12

Morecambe
83
70 Lancaster

Scotforth
82
LANCASHIRE
Skipton

Fleetwood
81
Garstang
A59
57

Cleveleys
51
88 134 33 Whalley
Clitheroe
92 Colne 35
M65 Nelson 95
15
16 107
M55
Longridge
145
63 136 26
Blackpool
5 108
75 13
150
111 61
Kirkham
103
118
49
90
50
Preston
Blackburn
105
Accrington
10
113 Haslingden 8
St. Anne's
116
Lytham
38
Darwen
129
A565
Leyland
86
122
Chorley
56
Southport
69
130
115
A59
Bolton
Oldham
128
71
Ormskirk
99 11
54
Skelmersdale
40
M58
53
143 20
79
Kirkby
101 6
Crosby
59
Manchester
Bootle
74
142 21
123
Liverpool
31 84
M62
2 152
Warrington
M56
M63

ISLE OF MAN

Ramsey
110

Peel
Laxey
100
78
43 Douglas
Port Erin
114
Castletown
106
30
Port St. Mary

0 Miles 20
0 Kilometres 20

M1 Accrington & District

☎(0254) 232734
New Barn Farm, Devon Ave, West
End, Oswaldtwistle, Accrington,
Lancs BB5 4LR
On A679 5 miles from Blackburn.
Moorland course.
18 holes, 5954 yards, S.S.S.69
Visitors: welcome at any time.
Green Fee: on application.
Societies: by arrangement.
Catering: full facilities.
Hotels: Kendal; Moat House.

M2 Allerton Municipal

☎(051) 428 1046
Allerton, Liverpool 18
From city centre on Allerton Rd.
Undulating parkland course.
18 holes, 5494 yards, S.S.S.67
Visitors: welcome.
Green Fee: on application.
Catering: snacks served.

M3 Alston Moor

☎(0434) 381675
The Hermitage, Alston, Cumbria CA9
3DB
1.75 miles from Alston on B6277 to
Middleton in Teesdale.
Parkland course.
10 holes, 6450 yards, S.S.S.66
Founded 1906
Visitors: welcome anytime.
Green Fee: £6 WD, £7.50 WE & BH.
Societies: any time by prior
arrangement.

Catering: py prior arrangement.
Hotels: George & Dragon; Hillcrest;
Bluebell Inn; Nenthall.

M4 Appleby

☎(07683) 51432
Brackenber Moor,
Appleby-in-Westmorland, Cumbria
CA16 6LP
2 miles S of Appleby on A66.
Moorland course.
18 holes, 5913 yards, S.S.S.68
Founded 1902
Visitors: welcome at any time.
Green Fee: £11 WD, £15 WE & BH.
Societies: welcome at any time
subject to prior arrangement.
Catering: by arrangement.
Snooker.
Hotels: Tufton Arms; Royal Oak;
Appleby Manor; The Gate.

M5 Ashton & Lea

☎(0772) 726480, 735282
Tudor Ave, off Blackpool Rd, Lea,
Preston PR4 0XA
3 miles from Preston centre on
Blackpool road, turn opposite Pig &
Whistle.
Parkland course.
18 holes, 6289 yards, S.S.S.70
Designed by J. Steer.
Founded 1913
Visitors: phone (0772) 720374 for
tee reservations.
Green Fee: £18 Mon-Thurs, £20 Fri,
£24 WE & BH.

Societies: welcome Mon, Tues and
Wed on application to Sec.
Catering: full facilities daily.
Snooker.
Hotels: Crest; Tickled Trout.

M6 Ashton-in-Makerfield

☎(0942) 719330, 727267
Garswood Park, Liverpool Rd,
Ashton-in-Makerfield WN4 0YT
On A58, off M6 0.5 mile to course.
Parkland course.
18 holes, 6160 yards, S.S.S.69
Designed by F.W. Hawtree.
Founded 1902
Visitors: welcome weekdays except
Wed; with member at weekends.
Green Fee: on application.
Societies: Tues and Thurs.
Catering: meals except Mon.
Hotels: Cranberry.

M7 Ashton-under-Lyne

☎(061) 330 1537
Gorsey Way, Ashton-under-Lyne,
Lancs OL6 9HT
From Ashton take Mossley Rd, left at
Queens Rd, right St Christophers Rd.
Moorland course.
18 holes, 6209 yards, S.S.S.70
Founded 1913
Visitors: welcome if member of golf
club; Sat and Sun only with member.
Green Fee: £18/day.
Societies: by arrangement, not Wed
or weekends.
Catering: full facilities except Mon.
Snooker.
Hotels: York House; Birch Hall.

M8 Bacup

☎(0706) 873170
Maden Rd, Bacup, Lancs OL13 8HM
Off A671, 7 miles N of Rochdale, 0.5
mile from Bacup centre.
Meadowland course.
9 holes, 5652 yards, S.S.S.67
Founded 1911
Visitors: welcome weekdays, except
Mon, Tues, and at weekends after
competitions.
Green Fee: on application.
Societies: welcome weekdays
except Mon and Tues.
Catering: full facilities. Snooker.
Hotels: Royal (Waterfoot).

M9 Barrow

☎(0229) 25444
Rakesmoor Lane, Hawcoat,
Barrow-in-Furness, Cumbria LA14
4QB

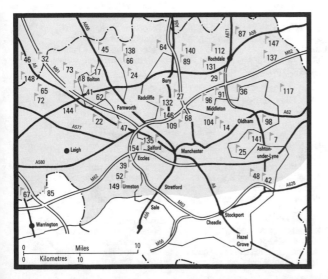

Turn right to Hawcoat off A590 on entering boundary of Barrow. Undulating meadowland course. 18 holes, 6209 yards, S.S.S.70
Founded 1922
Visitors: welcome.
Green Fee: £12 WD, £20 WE.
Societies: by arrangement.
Catering: by arrangement.
Hotels: Victoria Park; Michaelson House; Lisdoonie.

M10 **Baxenden & District**
☎(0254) 234555
Top-o'-the Meadow, Wooley Lane, Baxenden, Nr Accrington, Lancs
Take Accrington exit from M65, follow signs for Baxenden, course signposted in village.
Moorland course.
9 holes, 5702 yards, S.S.S.68
Founded 1913
Visitors: welcome weekdays, with member only weekends.
Green Fee: on application.
Societies: welcome weekdays by arrangement.
Catering: bar and bar snacks, meals if ordered in advance.

M11 **Beacon Park**
☎(0695) 622700
Beacon Lane, Dalton, Up Holland, Wigan, Lancs WN8 7RU
Signposted from centre of Up Holland on A577 and from A5209 near Parbold, located on side of Ashurst Beacon Hill overlooking Skelmersdale.
Public, hilly parkland course.
18 holes, 5996 yards, S.S.S.69
Designed by Donald Steel.
Founded 1982
Visitors: welcome at any time.
Green Fee: on application.
Societies: welcome weekdays, by arrangement weekends.
Catering: bar meals during bar hours; other meals by arrangement. Driving range.
Hotels: Balcony Farm.

M12 **Bentham**
☎(05242) 61018, 62455 Sec.
Robin Lane, Bentham, Lancaster LA2 7AG
Half way between Lancaster and Settle on B6480, 13 miles E of M6 junction 34.
Undulating meadowland course.
9 holes, 5760 yards, S.S.S.69
Founded 1922
Visitors: welcome.

Green Fee: £10/day (£5 with member) WD, £13 (£6.50 with member) WE & BH.
Societies: by arrangement.
Catering: snacks.
Hotels: Bridge; Post House.

M13 **Blackburn**
☎(0254) 51122 Sec/club, 55942 Pro.
Beardwood Brow, Blackburn, Lancs BB2 7AX
Easy access from M6, M61, M65; in W end of town off Revidge Rd, from Moat House Hotel on A677 turn left at lights, left at Dog Hotel.
Undulating meadowland course.
18 holes, 6140 yards, S.S.S.70
Founded 1894
Visitors: welcome weekdays (restricted Tues).
Green Fee: £14 (£5 with member) WD, £15 (£6 with member) WE & BH.
Societies: welcome; contact Sec for special terms.
Catering: daily except Mon. Snooker.
Hotels: Moat House; Dunkenhalgh.

M14 **Blackley**
☎(061) 654 7770 Sec, 643 2980 Club
Victoria Ave East, Blackley, Manchester M9 2HW
5 miles N of city centre.
Parkland course.
18 holes, 6237 yards, S.S.S.70
Founded 1907
Visitors: Mon, Tues, Wed, Fri; Thurs, weekends and Bank Holidays with member only.
Green Fee: £15.
Societies: Mon, Tues, Wed and Fri, all-in fee inc bar lunch and evening meal £21.
Catering: all types available.
Hotels: Bower (Chadderton).

M15 **Blackpool North Shore**
☎(0253) 51017, 52054 Sec.
Devonshire Rd, Blackpool FY2 0RD
N of town centre 0.5 mile from Promenade.
Undulating parkland course.
18 holes, 6400 yards, S.S.S.71
Founded 1906
Visitors: restricted Thurs and Sun; not Sat.
Green Fee: £21.
Societies: Mon, Tues, Wed, Fri; special package rates,
Catering: bar, full catering. Snooker.
Hotels: Sheraton; Doric.

M16 **Blackpool Stanley Park**
☎(0253) 33960
North Park Drive, Blackpool, Lancs FY3 8LS
1.5 miles E of centre of Blackpool.
Parkland course.
18 holes, 6060 yards, S.S.S.69
Designed by Dr Mackenzie.
Founded 1926
Visitors: welcome anytime.
Green Fee: on application.
Societies: welcome weekdays.
Catering: everyday except Tues.

M17 **Bolton**
☎(0204) 43067
Lostock Park, Chorley New Rd, Bolton BL6 4AJ
Leave M61 at exit 6, off main road half way between Bolton and Horwich.
Parkland course.
18 holes, 6215 yards, S.S.S.70
Founded 1891
Visitors: weekdays except Tues.
Green Fee: £24 Mon, Thurs, Fri; £28 Wed, Sat, Sun, BH.
Societies: Thurs.
Catering: all day.
Hotels: Crest.

M18 **Bolton Municipal**
☎(0204) 42336
Links Rd, off Chorley New Rd, Bolton, Lancs BL6 4AF
M61 exit 6 to Bolton.
Municipal parkland course.
18 holes, 6250 yards, S.S.S.70
Founded 1932
Visitors: welcome.
Green Fee: on application.
Societies: weekdays.
Catering: bar and restaurant.
Hotels: Crest; Swallow Field.

M19 **Bolton Old Links**
☎(0204) 42307 Office am, 40050 Club, 43089 Pro.
Chorley Old Rd, Bolton BL1 5SU
On B6226 just N of A58 from M61 junction 5.
Moorland course.
18 holes, 6406 yards, S.S.S.72
Designed by Dr A. Mackenzie.
Founded 1891
Visitors: welcome except competition days.
Green Fee: £25 WD, £30 WE & BH.
Societies: by prior arrangement on weekdays.
Catering: daily except Mon.
Hotels: Crest; Pack Horse; Last Drop.

Castletown, Isle of Man

When the weather is fine, the greens holding and there is no wind, seaside links often present fewer problems than other types of course; but the moment the wind stirs it is another matter.

Tales of the 1979 P.G.A. Cup match at Castletown in the Isle of Man centred largely on days of sunshine, the ball running a mile, and agreement that it was an idyllic spot. My baptism was a little more severe, a near gale springing up overnight and rain slanting in from the Irish Sea. The clear outline of mountain peaks disappeared and there was a remoteness, almost a loneliness, on the little peninsula. But not even a princely soaking could dampen my admiration. Castletown's position as one of the great courses of the British Isles is undoubted.

Its modern version owes everything to Mackenzie Ross whose restoration after the war was similar to the miracle he wrought at Turnberry. Good driving is essential. On such as the 7th and 8th, the fairway is the only place to be; yet the line from the championship tees involves quite a carry.

Castletown's hazards are all natural — gorse, bracken, rough, rocks and a beach which gives the course more coastal frontage than perhaps any other in the world. Apart from a clump of forlorn palms behind the 8th green, and some planting to mask the wall behind the 4th there isn't a tree to be seen. Though the golfer has nothing to shield him, there is nothing to obscure the magnificent array of views either; the sea, two great sweeps of bay, the landmark of the castle and, on a good day, the Cumbrian Hills.

In days gone by, it was the residence of the Earl of Derby who, as Lord of Man, started the Derby at Castletown prior to taking it to Epsom. The 10th was the actual site, the hole not surprisingly assuming the name 'Racecourse'.

Castletown deserves undivided attention, although the start is no indication of what lies ahead. The 1st is a short, uphill par 4, one yard, in fact, over the par 3 limit, and the 2nd a somewhat plain two

shotter. It is when you turn away down the long 5th, a dogleg round the corner of a stone wall, with a second shot (or third or fourth) between a large mound and an old pill box, that the course really begins.

The 5th, not quite such a good par 5 as the 3rd, sandwiches the 4th where the drive must be left to obtain the correct angle to negotiate the slope of the green and to miss the guardian bunkers on the right. Castletown's short holes make a wonderful set, the 6th, the shortest of them, providing an inviting shot even if the green is encircled by trouble. The same applies to the drive at the 7th and the second shot to a green typical of Mackenzie Ross's imaginative designs.

The 8th is no easier. The fairway may present a nice target at a lower level but it is also alarmingly narrow and the road is only a thin strip separating errant drives from the beach on which balls, pebbles and boulders are indistinguishable. The drive at the 9th must be aimed on the outline of King William's College, a fortress of Manx stone. And at what may have been the home turn in the first Derby down by the 10th green, Castletown Bay hoves in sight. There is no let-up.

At the delightful short 11th and the next two par 4s, it is all too simple to let a tee shot drift to the right and, if the 14th is a shade less of a threat in this regard, the tee marker tells the bad news that it is 468 yards. On the 15th, a stone wall denotes out of bounds and the contouring of the greens foil those playing too safe to the left; but the best is yet to come — notably the 17th with its gaping gorge in front of the tee and resplendent rocks to the right. The 18th is a challenging finish, set against the square form of the welcoming Links Hotel.

Those who originally spied out the land knew what they were doing; but a question must be asked of the island's emblem of the Three Legs of Man and its motto 'whichever way you throw me, I shall stand'. Did they ever experiment on the championship tee at the 17th with a gale off the sea?

M20 **Bootle**
☎(051) 928 6196
Dunnings Bridge Rd, Bootle,
Merseyside L30 2PP
A565, 5 miles from Liverpool.
Seaside/links course.
18 holes, 6362 yards, S.S.S.70
Designed by F. Stephens.
Founded 1934
Visitors: welcome.
Green Fee: on application.
Societies: by arrangement.
Catering: meals served.

M21 **Bowring**
☎(051) 489 1901
Bowring Park, Roby Rd, Huyton,
Liverpool L36 4HD
4.5 miles from city centre.
Parkland course.
9 holes, 2500 yards, S.S.S.66
Founded c. 1911
Visitors: welcome.
Green Fee: on application.

M22 **Brackley**
☎(061) 790 6076
Bullows Rd, Little Hulton, Worsley,
Manchester
9 miles from Manchester on A6, turn
right at White Lion Hotel into
Highfield Rd, left into Captain Fold
Rd, left into Bullows Rd.
Parkland course.
9 holes, 3003 yards, S.S.S.69
Founded 1976
Visitors: welcome.
Green Fee: on application.

M23 **Brampton**
☎(06977) 2255 Clubhouse, 2000
Pro.
Brampton, Cumbria CA8 1HN
1.75 miles from Brampton on B6413
Castle Carrock road.
Moorland course.
18 holes, 6420 yards, S.S.S.71
Designed by James Braid.
Founded 1907
Visitors: welcome; standard tee
bookings 9.30-10.30am Mon and
Wed, 10-11.15am Thurs.
Green Fee: £14 WD, £18 WE & BH.
Societies: by arrangement
weekdays; limited at weekends.
Catering: full bar and catering
facilities.
Snooker.
Hotels: Tarn End; Hare & Hounds;
Blacksmith's Arms; Sands House,
Kirby Moor GH; Cumbria Park;
Gosling Bride; Weary Sportsman; all
offer reduced green fees.

M24 **Breightmet**
☎(0204) 27381
Red Bridge, Ainsworth, Bolton, Lancs
BL2 5PA
From Bolton 3 miles on main road to
Bury and turn left to Red Bridge.
Parkland course.
9 holes, 6448 yards, S.S.S.71
Designed by Alliss & Thomas.
Founded 1911
Visitors: weekdays except Wed.
Green Fee: £10 WD, £12 WE & BH;
£5 with member.
Societies: welcome Tues, Thurs, Fri.
Catering: daily except Mon. Snooker.
Hotels: Pack Horse.

M25 **Brookdale**
☎(061) 681 4534 or 681 2655
Ashbridge, Woodhouses, Failsworth,
Manchester M35 9WM
5 miles N of Manchester.
Parkland, meadowland course.
18 holes, 6040 yards, S.S.S.68
Founded 1962
Visitors: welcome.
Green Fee: on application.
Societies: welcome by prior
arrangement with Sec; special
package can be arranged.
Catering: daily except Mon.

M26 **Burnley**
☎(0282) 21045
Glen View, Burnley BB11 3RW
Off A56 to Glen View Rd, after 300
yards turn right.
Moorland/meadowland course.
18 holes, 5900 yards, S.S.S.69
Founded 1905
Visitors: weekdays and Sun; limited
Sat.
Green Fee: £12/day WD, £16/day
WE & BH.
Societies: weekdays, Sun.
Catering: snacks and full meals
except Mon.
Hotels: Kierby; Rosehill House; Oaks.

M27 **Bury**
☎(061) 766 4897
Unsworth Hall, Blackford Bridge,
Bury BL9 9TJ
On A56 7 miles N of Manchester.
Undulating moorland course.
18 holes, 5961 yards, S.S.S.69
Founded 1890
Visitors: welcome with reservation;
h/cap cert required.
Green Fee: £17.50 WD.
Societies: Wed, Thurs and Fri.
Catering: daily except Mon.
Hotels: Red Hall; Village Leisure.

M28 **Carlisle**
☎(0228) 513303
Aglionby, Carlisle CA4 8AG
2 miles E of Carlisle, leave M6 at exit
43 and take A69 for about 0.75 mile.
Parkland course.
18 holes, 6278 yards, S.S.S.70
Designed by Tom Simpson,
McKenzie Ross and (latterly) Frank
Pennink.
Founded 1909
Visitors: welcome, advisable to
check availability.
Green Fee: on application.
Societies: Mon, Wed and Fri.
Catering: meals and snacks daily.
Hotels: Queens Arms; Bridge;
Kilorran; Cumbria Park.

M29 **Castle Hawk**
☎(0706) 40841
Heywood Rd, Castleton, Rochdale
Leave Rochdale on Castleton road, in
Castleton turn right directly before
railway station, follow until reach
Heywood Rd (dirt track).
Undulating parkland/meadowland
course.
18 holes, 3158 yards, S.S.S.65
Designed by T. Wilson.
Founded 1965
Visitors: welcome.
Green Fee: on application.
Societies: welcome.
Catering: snacks and lunches;
evening meals by arrangement.
Driving range.

M30 **Castletown**
☎(0624) 822201
Fort Island, Castletown, Isle of Man
1.5 miles E of Castletown.
Seaside course.
18 holes, 6804 yards, S.S.S.73
Designed by Mackenzie Ross
Founded 1 June 1892
Visitors: welcome.
Green Fee: details by request.
Societies: by arrangement.
Catering: bar snacks served all day;
full à la carte lunch and dinner.
Snooker, indoor swimming pool,
sauna, solarium.
Hotels: Castletown Golf Links
adjoining course, DBB/Golf & flight
packages available.

M31 **Childwall**
☎(051) 487 0654
Naylor's Rd, Liverpool L27 2YB
M62 junction 6, 2 miles on A5080
Huyton exit.
Parkland course.

Castletown Golf Links Hotel
PALACE HOTEL & CASINO
ISLE OF MAN

The Isle of Man's major 18-hole Championship course, 6,700 yards of pure Links golf — spectacular views of the Irish Sea from every tee and green.

The 17th is not for the faint hearted, a huge ravine eats into the fairway, making the tee shot a carry of about 180 yards.

The 18th appears straight forward, but on front of the green lurks "The Gully". This hole has been the graveyard for many a good card.

Palace Group Hotels offer warm hospitality with the finest facilities to match.

Golfing Breaks, Society Company Days and Specialised Packages including transfer and flight telephone:

Castletown Golf Links Hotel
Tel: (0624) 822201

Palace Hotel & Casino
Tel: (0624) 662662

O U R   S T A N D A R D S   A R E   H I G H E R

18 holes, 6025 yards, S.S.S.71
Designed by James Braid.
Founded 1912
Visitors: weekdays only except Tues; h/cap cert required.
Green Fee: £19.50 day.
Societies: weekdays only.
Catering: bar and restaurant.
Snooker.

M32 Chorley
☎(0257) 480263
Hall o' th'Hill, Heath Charnock, Nr Chorley, Lancs PR6 9HX
On A6 at Skew Bridge traffic lights.
Heathland course.
18 holes, 6277 yards, S.S.S.70
Designed by J.A. Steer.
Founded 1898
Visitors: welcome by prior arrangement with Sec, Tues-Fri only (not Bank Holidays).
Green Fee: £20.
Societies: welcome, restrictions as for visitors.
Catering: full bar and restaurant facilities; societies by prior arrangement.
Snooker, pool.
Hotels: Parkville; Hartwood Hall; Gladmar.

M33 Clitheroe
☎(0200) 22618 Club, 22292 Sec, 24242 Pro.
Whalley Rd, Pendleton, Clitheroe BB7 1PP
Off A59 2 miles S of Clitheroe.
Undulating parkland course.
18 holes, 6311 yards, S.S.S.71
Designed by James Braid.
Founded 1891
Visitors: welcome subject to competition days on Sat and Thurs.
Green Fee: £19 WD, £24 WE & BH.
Societies: welcome by arrangement, max 24 on Sun.
Catering: bar and restaurant.
Hotels: Post House; Swan and Royal; Brooklyn GH; Stirk House.

M34 Cockermouth
☎(07687) 76223
Embleton, Cockermouth, Cumbria CA13 9SG
4 miles E of Cockermouth.
Fell land course.
18 holes, 5496 yards, S.S.S.67
Designed by James Braid.
Founded 1896
Visitors: weekdays unrestricted before 5pm except Wed; not Sun before 11am and 2-3.15pm.
Green Fee: £9/day WD, £15 WE & BH.

Societies: apply to Sec.
Catering: snacks and meals by arrangement with Stewardess.
Snooker.
Hotels: Armathwaite Hall; Globe.

M35 Colne
☎(0282) 863391
Law Farm, Skipton Old Rd, Colne, Lancs BB8 7EB
Leave end of M65, straight on 0.75 mile to roundabout, take small road in left hand corner signposted Lothersdale; club at top of hill.
Moorland course.
9 holes, 5961 yards, S.S.S.69
Founded 1901
Visitors: welcome, not competition days; 2 balls only Thurs; no parties weekends April-Oct; normal dress and equipment requirements.
Green Fee: £11 WD, £13 WE.
Societies: by appointment.
Catering: snacks or full meals; parties (to 100) by negotiation with Steward. Snooker tables.

M36 Crompton & Royton
☎(061) 624 2154
Highbarn, Royton, Oldham, Lancs OL2 6RW

Off A627 at Royton centre.
Moorland course.
18 holes, 6222 yards, S.S.S.70
Founded 1908
Visitors: welcome.
Green Fee: £17 (£9 with member)
WD, £21 (£11 with member) WE.
Societies: welcome by arrangement.
Hotels: Periquito (Oldham).

M37 **Dalston Hall**
☎(0228) 710165
Dalston, Nr Carlisle, Cumbria CA5 7JX
From M6 junction 42 follow signs for
Dalston, through village, course 0.5
mile on right.
Parkland course.
9 holes, 5294 yards, S.S.S.67
Designed by David Pearson.
Founded May 1990
Visitors: tee booking required at
weekends and after 4pm weekdays.
Green Fee: £4 9 holes, £7 18 holes.
Societies: throughout the season,
booking required.
Catering: bar and restaurant.
Fly fishing.
Hotels: Dalston Hall caravan park,
towers and tents welcome.

M38 **Darwen**
☎(0254) 704367 Sec, 701287 Club,
776370 Pro.
Winter Hill, Darwen, Lancs BB3 0LB
1.5 miles from Darwen town centre,
off A666 Bolton-Blackburn road.
Moorland course.
18 holes, 5752 yards, S.S.S.68
Founded Sept 1893
Visitors: welcome weekdays and
with advance bookings at weekends.
Green Fee: £14 (£7 with member)
WD, £20 (£10 with member) WE.
Societies: except Mon, Tues, Sat.
Catering: full, except Mon.
Hotels: Red House Motel; Whitehall
Country Club.

M39 **Davyhulme Park**
☎(061) 748 2856 Club, 748 2260
Sec.
Gleneagles Rd, Davyhulme, Urmston,
Manchester M31 2SA
8 miles S of Manchester, adjacent to
Park Hospital, Moorside Rd.
Parkland course.
18 holes, 6237 yards, S.S.S.70
Founded 1910
Visitors: except competition days.
Green Fee: on application.
Societies: Mon, Tues, Thurs,
weekends and Bank Holidays.
Catering: except Mon.

M40 **Dean Wood**
☎(0695) 622219
Lafford Lane, Up Holland,
Skelmersdale, Lancs WN8 0QZ
Exit 26 from M6, 1.5 miles on A577
to Up Holland.
Undulating parkland course.
18 holes, 6137 yards, S.S.S.70
Designed by James Braid.
Founded 1922
Visitors: welcome weekdays,
preferably by arrangement;
weekends by introduction.
Green Fee: £21 WD, £25 WE & BH.
Societies: weekdays only by
arrangement.
Catering: daily. Snooker.
Hotels: Holland Hall.

M41 **Deane**
☎(0204) 651808 Sec, 61944 Club
and Pro.
Broadford Rd, Bolton, Lancs BL3 4NB
M61 exit 5, 1 mile towards town
centre, Dealey Rd on left leads
directly to club.
Undulating parkland course.
18 holes, 5595 yards, S.S.S.67
Founded 1906
Visitors: members of other clubs
only unless playing with member.
Green Fee: £16.50/day WD,
£22.50/day WE & BH.
Societies: Tues, Wed, Fri.
Catering: full facilities except Mon.
Hotels: Crest; Pack Horse; Moat
House.

M42 **Denton**
☎(061) 336 3218
Manchester Rd, Denton, Manchester
M34 2NU
A57, 5 miles SE of Manchester.
Parkland course.
18 holes, 6290 yards, S.S.S.70
Founded May 1909
Visitors: welcome weekdays and at
weekends with member.
Green Fee: on application.
Societies: Mon, Wed, Thurs and Fri.
Catering: lunch served except Mon.

M43 **Douglas**
☎(0624) 75952
Pulrose Rd, Douglas, Isle of Man
1 mile from Douglas town centre,
clubhouse near large cooling tower
for Electricity Dept Power Station.
Municipal parkland course.
18 holes, 6080 yards, S.S.S.69
Designed by Dr Mackenzie.
Founded 1927
Visitors: welcome.

Green Fee: on application.
Societies: welcome.
Catering: meals and snacks 11am to
11pm from May to end of Sept.

M44 **Dunnerholme**
☎(0229) 62675
Duddon Rd, Askam-in-Furness,
Cumbria LA16 7AW
A590 to Askam, turn left over railway
line into Duddin Rd, down towards
seashore over cattle grid on right.
Links course.
10 holes, 6181 yards, S.S.S.69
Founded 1905
Visitors: welcome but not Sun until
after 4.30pm.
Green Fee: £10 (£5 with member)
WD, £15 WE & BH; jnrs half-price.
Societies: welcome almost any time
if telephoned in advance.
Catering: facilities available.
Pool.
Hotels: Railway; White Water;
Clarence; Wellington; Abbey House.

M45 **Dunscar**
☎(0204) 53321 Club, 51090 Sec,
592992 Pro.
Longworth Lane, Bromley Cross,
Bolton BL7 9QY
N of Bolton about 2 miles off A666
Blackburn road, course signed to left
at Dunscar Bridge.
Parkland/moorland course.
18 holes, 6030 yards, S.S.S.70
Founded 1908
Visitors: welcome, steward's day off
Mon; weekends by special
arrangement.
Green Fee: £20 (£10 with member)
WD, £30 (£10 with member) WE & BH.
Societies: details from Sec.
Catering: lunch, dinner except Mon.
Hotels: Last Drop; Egerton House;
Moat House.

M46 **Duxbury Park**
☎(025 72) 65380
Duxbury Park, Chorley, Lancs
1.5 miles S of Chorley, off A6, 200
yards along A5106 Chorley to Wigan
road.
Municipal parkland course.
18 holes, 6390 yards, S.S.S.70
Founded 1970
Visitors: municipal course, booking
accepted by phone.
Green Fee: on application.
Societies: catered for.
Catering: separate facilities from the
club.
Hotels: Hartwood Hall; Kilhey Court.

M47 **Ellesmere**
☎(061) 790 2122 Club, 790 8591 Pro.
Old Clough Lane, Worsley, Manchester M28 5HZ
5 miles W of Manchester, on A580, adjacent to junction 14 on M62.
Undulating parkland course.
18 holes, 5954 yards, S.S.S.69
Founded 1913
Visitors: members of recognised club welcome by arrangement with Pro, except during club competitions and Bank Holidays.
Green Fee: £13.50 (£4.50 with member) WD, £17.50 (£5.50 with member) WE.
Societies: catered for weekdays; apply in writing to Hon Sec.
Catering: at all times by prior arrangement with Steward's wife.

M48 **Fairfield Golf & Sailing Club**
☎(061) 370 1641, 370 2292 Pro.
Booth Rd, Audenshaw, Manchester M34 5GA
A635 6 miles from city centre.
Meadowland course.
18 holes, 5654 yards, S.S.S.68
Founded 1892
Visitors: welcome weekdays; club competitions Wed pm, Thurs and weekends am.
Green Fee: on application.
Societies: by arrangement, preferably Tues; not Wed, Thur or weekends.
Catering: full, by arrangement.

M49 **Fairhaven**
☎(0253) 736976
Lytham Hall Park, Ansdell, Lytham-St-Annes FY8 4JU
On B5261 2 miles from Lytham, next to Fylde Rugby Ground.
Semi-links course.
18 holes, 6883 yards, S.S.S.73
Designed by James Braid.
Founded 1895
Visitors: welcome by arrangement.
Green Fee: on application.
Societies: by arrangement.
Catering: meals served except Mon (sandwiches available from bar)
Snooker, card room, banqueting.
Hotels: Clifton Arms; Grand; Dalmeney; Fearnlee.

M50 **Fishwick Hall**
☎(0772) 798300, 795870 Pro shop
Glenluce Drive, Farringdon Park, Preston, Lancs PR1 5TD

From M6 junction 31 take A59 towards Preston, past Tickled Trout, Glenluce Drive is 1st left at top of hill.
Undulating meadowland/parkland course.
18 holes, 6092 yards, S.S.S.69
Founded 1912
Visitors: welcome.
Green Fee: £20 WD, £25 WE & BH; reduction Nov-April and with member.
Societies: by arrangement weekdays; also some weekends.
Catering: full facilities.
Hotels: Tickled Trout Motel; Crest.

M51 **Fleetwood**
☎(0253) 873661
Princes Way, Fleetwood, Lancs FY7 8AF
On A587, 7 miles N of Blackpool.
Seaside links course.
18 holes, 6723 yards, S.S.S.71
Founded 1932
Visitors: members of recognised golf clubs welcome without reservation.
Green Fee: on application.
Societies: weekdays; weekends by special arrangement.
Catering: bar 7 days; catering 6 days, by special arrangement Thurs.
Hotels: Boston; North Euston.

M52 **Flixton**
☎(061) 748 2116 Club, 746 7160 Pro, 748 7545 Stewardess
Church Rd, Flixton, Urmston, Manchester
0.5 mile from Flixton village on B5213.
Meadowland course.
9 holes, 6410 yards, S.S.S.71
Founded 1896
Visitors: welcome weekdays except Wed, weekends with member only.
Green Fee: £15/day.
Societies: by arrangement weekdays except Wed.
Catering: bar snacks; full meals by arrangement except Tues. Snooker.

M53 **Formby**
☎(07048) 72164
Golf Rd, Formby, Liverpool L37 1LQ
1 mile W of A565, adjacent to Freshfield station.
Links course.
18 holes, 6871 yards, S.S.S.74
Founded 1884
Visitors: welcome weekdays except Wed with advance reservation; not weekends or public holidays.

Green Fee: £40 WD.
Societies: Tues, Thurs, Fri.
Catering: lunches except Mon.
Hotels: Tree Tops.

M54 **Formby Ladies**
☎(07048) 74127 club, 73493 Sec.
Golf Rd, Formby, Liverpool L37 1LQ
6 miles S of Southport off A565.
Seaside course.
18 holes, 5374 yards, S.S.S.71
Founded 1896
Visitors: welcome, ring first.
Green Fee: £22.50 WD, £28 WE.
Societies: by arrangement.
Catering: bar snacks and salads.
Hotels: Prince of Wales; Royal Clifton; Scarisbrick; Bold.

M55 **Furness**
☎(0229) 471232
Central Drive, Walney Island, Barrow-in-Furness, Cumbria LA14 3LN
A590 to Barrow, towards Walney Island, over bridge, through lights, 0.5 mile on right.
Seaside links course.
18 holes, 6363 yards, S.S.S.71
Founded 1872
Visitors: welcome; parties booked in advance.
Green Fee: £10/day (£8 with member).
Societies: advance booking; not competition days.
Catering: bar meals available.
Snooker, darts.
Hotels: White House; Abbey House.

M56 **Gathurst**
☎(025 75) 2861
Miles Lane, Shevington, Wigan WN6 8EW
1 mile S of M6 junction 27, 0.25 mile W of Shevington village centre.
Meadowland course.
9 holes, 6308 yards, S.S.S.70
Founded 1913
Visitors: Mon, Tues, Thurs and Fri.
Green Fee: £20/day.
Societies: by arrangement.
Catering: lunch except Mon, Tues.
Hotels: Lindley; The Beeches.

M57 **Ghyll**
☎(0282) 842466
Ghyll Brow, Barnoldswick, Colne, Lancs BB8 6JQ
M65 then A56 to Thornton-in-Craven, turn left on B6252, 1 mile on left.
Scenic parkland course.

9 holes, 5796 yards, S.S.S.68
Founded 1907
Visitors: not Tues am, not Fri after
4.30pm, not Sun.
Green Fee: £10.50 (£5.50 with
member) WD, £15.50 (£12.50 with
member) WE & BH.
Societies: daytime weekdays except
Tues.
Catering: by special arrangement.
Hotels: Stirk House; Black Horse;
Tempest.

M58 **Grange Fell**
☎(05395) 32536
Fell Rd, Grange-over-Sands,
Cumbria LA11 6HB
On main road to Cartmel from Grange
at top of the hill.
Hillside course with panoramic
Lakeland views.
9 holes, 4826 metres, S.S.S.66
Founded 1952
Visitors: welcome; closed most Sun
in the season.
Green Fee: £10 WD, £15 WE & BH.
Hotels: Grange; Netherwood;
Cumbria Grand.

M59 **Grange Park**
☎(0744) 26318
Prescot Rd, St Helens, Merseyside
WA10 3AD
On A58 1 mile from town centre
towards Prescot.
Parkland course.
18 holes, 6429 yards, S.S.S.71
Founded 1891
Visitors: welcome weekdays (Ladies
Day Tues), by arrangement
weekends.
Green Fee: £15 WD, £21.50 WE.
Societies: Mon, Wed, Thur.
Catering: full restaurant facilities.
Hotels: Post House; Cherry Tree;
Haydock Thistle.

M60 **Grange-over-Sands**
☎(05395) 33180
Meathop Rd, Grange-over-Sands,
Cumbria LA11 6QX
Leave A590 at roundabout
signposted Grange, course on left
just before entering Grange.
Flat parkland course.
18 holes, 5670 yards, S.S.S.68
Founded 1921
Visitors: welcome at any time (Thurs
Ladies day).
Green Fee: £15/day WD, £20 WE &
BH.
Societies: by arrangement
weekdays and weekends.

Catering: except Tues.
Hotels: Grange; Cumbria Grand;
Berners Close; Netherwood.

M61 **Great Harwood**
☎(0254) 884391
Harwood Bar, Great Harwood, Lancs
BB6 7TE
Between Blackburn and Burnley, off
A680 Accrington-Whalley road.
Parkland course.
9 holes, 6140 yards, S.S.S.71
Founded 1896 (1928 on present site)
Visitors: welcome any time except
competition days; must be member
of recognised club.
Green Fee: £10 (£7 with member)
WD, £12 (£8 with member) WE & BH.
Societies: on application.
Catering: bar and restaurant
facilities except Mon. Snooker.
Hotels: Duncan House.

M62 **Great Lever & Farnworth**
☎(0204) 656137
Lever Edge Lane, Bolton BL3 3EN
1.5 miles from town centre.
Meadowland course.
18 holes, 5958 yards, S.S.S.69
Founded 1917
Visitors: welcome weekdays.
Green Fee: £11 (£5 with member)
WD, £17 (£8.50 with member) WE &
BH.
Societies: weekdays by prior
arrangement.
Catering: lunch except Mon.
Hotels: Crest (Bolton).

M63 **Green Haworth**
☎(0254) 237580
Green Haworth, Accrington, Lancs
BB5 3SL
From Accrington town centre take
main road to Blackburn, turn left on
Willows Lane, follow road for 2 to 3
miles, sign just past Red Lion Hotel.
Moorland course.
9 holes, 5470 yards, S.S.S.67
Founded 1914
Visitors: welcome weekdays; Sat
with reservation.
Green Fee: on application.
Societies: catered for.
Catering: by arrangement.
Hotels: Moat House (Blackburn).

M64 **Greenmount**
☎(0204 88) 3712
Greenhalgh Fold Farm, Greenmount,
Bury BL8 4LH

Exit M66 to Ramsbottom, left at lights
towards Bolton, 2 miles turn left into
Holcombe Rd, 1 mile turn right into
Holhouse Lane, over speed bumps,
turn right approaching Convent into
clubhouse.
Undulating parkland course.
9 holes, 4920 yards, S.S.S.64
Founded 1920
Visitors: welcome weekdays and
with member at weekends.
Green Fee: £10 (£5 with member).
Societies: weekdays except Tues.
Catering: full service except Mon.
Snooker.
Hotels: Red Hall; Old Mill; Red Lion.

M65 **Haigh Hall**
☎(0942) 833337, 831107 Pro.
Haigh Country Park, Aspull, Wigan,
Lancs WN2 1PE
M6 exit 27, B5239 to Standish, 6
miles NE of Wigan.
Municipal parkland course.
18 holes, 6423 yards, S.S.S.71
Founded 1973
Visitors: welcome any time;
telephone bookings via Pro.
Green Fee: £4.25 WD, £6 WE & BH.
Societies: contact Pro.
Catering: cafeteria.
Hotels: Brocket; Oak; Almond Brook
Moathouse.

M66 **Harwood**
☎(0204) 22878
Springfield, Roading Brook Rd,
Harwood, Bolton BL2 4JD
On B6391 off A666 4 miles NE of
Bolton town centre.
Undulating parkland course.
9 holes, 5958 yards, S.S.S.69
Founded 1926
Visitors: welcome, but must be
members of recognised club.
Green Fee: £12 (£5 with member).
Catering: on request. Snooker.
Hotels: Last Drop; Grants Arms.

M67 **Haydock Park**
☎(0925) 228525 Sec, 224389
Steward
Golborne Park, Newton-le-Willows,
Merseyside WA12 0HX
M6 to A580, then 1 mile E.
Parkland course.
18 holes, 6043 yards, S.S.S.69
Founded 1877
Visitors: weekdays except Tues.
Green Fee: £16/round, £21/day.
Societies: weekdays except Tues.
Catering: on request.
Hotels: Kirkfield.

M68 **Heaton Park**
☎(061) 798 0295
Prestwich, Manchester
Leave M62 at exit 19, right at A576,
200 yards on right.
Public undulating parkland course.
18 holes, 5849 yards, S.S.S.68
Designed by C.H. Taylor.
Founded 1912
Visitors: welcome, book in advance.
Green Fee: £4/round WD,
£6.60/round WE & BH.
Societies: by arrangement.

M69 **Hesketh**
☎(0704) 36897 Sec, 30050 Pro.
Cockle Dicks Lane, off Cambridge
Rd, Southport, Merseyside PR9 9QQ
1 mile N of Southport town centre on
main Preston road, A565.
Links course.
18 holes, 6478 yards, S.S.S.72
Founded 1885
Visitors: welcome weekdays,
occasionally weekends; advance
booking for societies.
Green Fee: on application.
Societies: catered for weekdays.
Catering: bar snacks and dining
room facilities always available.

M70 **The Heysham**
☎(0524) 51011
Trumacar Park, Middleton Rd,
Heysham, Lancs LA3 3JH
3 miles from M6, 2 miles S of
Morecambe on right of road to
Middleton.
Parkland course.
18 holes, 6340 yards, S.S.S.70
Designed by H. Vardon.
Founded 1910
Visitors: welcome.
Green Fee: £16/round, £20/day WD;
£25 WE & BH; half price with
member.
Societies: by arrangement.
Catering: full facilities daily.
Snooker.
Hotels: Midland; Clarendon; Golf;
Strathmore; Post House; Grosvenor.

M71 **Hillside**
☎(0704) 67169
Hastings Rd, Hillside, Southport PR8
2LU
Take A565 Southport-Liverpool road,
turn right before Hillside railway
station, club at end of Hastings Rd.
Championship links course.
18 holes, 6850 yards, S.S.S.74
Designed by Fred Hawtree.
Founded 1909 (1923 on present site)

Visitors: by appointment.
Green Fee: on application.
Societies: by appointment.
Catering: facilities continuous.

M72 **Hindley Hall**
☎(0942) 55131, 55991 Pro.
Hall Lane, Hindley, Wigan, Lancs
WN2 2SQ
M61 exit 6 onto A6, take Dicconson
Lane, after 1 mile left at church into
Hall Lane, club just after lake.
Moorland course.
18 holes, 5875 yards, S.S.S.68
Founded 1895
Visitors: welcome if member of
recognised club, advisable to check
with Pro in advance.
Green Fee: on application.
Societies: by arrangement.
Catering: meals served by
arrangement except Mon.
Hotels: Brockett Arms (Wigan).

M73 **Horwich**
☎(0204) 696980
Victoria Rd, Horwich, Bolton BL6 5PH
1.5 miles from M61.
Parkland course.
9 holes, 5800 yards, S.S.S.67
Founded 1895
Visitors: with member only.
Green Fee: on application.
Societies: catered for weekdays
only by application.
Catering: full facilities.

M74 **Huyton & Prescot**
☎(051) 489 3948
Hurst Park, Huyton Lane, Huyton,
Liverpool L36 1UA
Approx 10 miles from Liverpool city
centre, just off M57.
Parkland course.
18 holes, 5738 yards, S.S.S.68
Founded 1905
Visitors: must be members of
recognised golf clubs.
Green Fee: on application.
Societies: by arrangement
weekdays only.
Catering: every day.
Hotels: Derby Lodge; Hillcrest.

M75 **Ingol Golf & Squash Club**
☎(0772) 734556
Tanterton Hall Rd, Ingol, Preston,
Lancs PR2 7BY
Leave M6 junction 32, turn left
towards Preston, follow signpost on
left marked Ingol.

Parkland course.
18 holes, 6225 yards, S.S.S.70
Designed by Cotton, Pennink, Lawrie
& Partners.
Founded 1980
Visitors: welcome any day.
Green Fee: on application.
Societies: by arrangement.
Catering: full facilities.
Squash, snooker, banqueting.
Hotels: Barton Grange; Broughton
Park; Fulwood Park.

M76 **Kendal**
☎(0539) 724079
The Heights, Kendal, Cumbria LA9
4PQ
To Kendal on A6, course signposted
in town.
Moorland course.
18 holes, 5483 yards, S.S.S.67
Founded 1903
Visitors: welcome any time but prior
application suggested.
Green Fee: on application.
Societies: catered for any time
subject to availability.
Catering: full catering facilities
except Mon.
Hotels: County; Woolpack.

M77 **Keswick**
☎(07687) 79324
Threlkeld Hall, Threlkeld, Keswick,
Cumbria CA12 4SX
Off A66 4 miles E of Keswick.
Moorland/parkland course.
18 holes, 6175 yards, S.S.S.72
Designed by Eric Brown.
Founded 1975
Visitors: welcome even at most
weekends and Bank Holidays.
Green Fee: £10 WD, £12 WE.
Societies: apply to sec; some
weekends and Bank Holidays.
Catering: bar and dining facilities
available.
Hotels: Ladore Swiss; Borrowdale;
Wordsworth; all have free midweek
golf.

M78 **King Edward Bay (Howstrake)**
☎(0624) 620430, 676794
Howstrake, Groudle Rd, Onchan, Isle
of Man
On A11, 2 miles NE of Douglas.
Moorland/seaside course.
18 holes, 5457 yards, S.S.S.66
Founded 1914
Visitors: welcome Mon-Sat; Sun by
arrangement.
Green Fee: £6 WD, £7 WE & BH.

Societies: weekdays; weekends by arrangement.
Catering: 10am-10pm daily.
Snooker, sauna, sunbed.
Hotels: Empress.

M79 **Kirkby**
☎(051) 546 5435
Ingoe Lane, Kirkby, Liverpool L32 4SS
M57 exit B5192.
Meadowland course.
18 holes, 6706 yards, S.S.S.72
Founded 1976
Visitors: welcome every day.
Green Fee: £4.40.
Societies: tee booking required weekends.
Catering: only at weekends.
Hotels: Golden Eagle (Liverpool).

M80 **Kirkby Lonsdale**
☎(046 836) 365, 366
Scalebar Lane, Barbon, Carnforth, Cumbria LA6 2LE
2.5 miles N of Kirkby Lonsdale on A368 to Sedbergh; Clubhouse on Backfoot Lane.
Parkland course next to River Lune.
18 holes, 6286 yards, S.S.S.70
Founded (new course) 1991
Visitors: no restrictions.
Green Fee: £15 WD, £18 WE & BH.
Societies: Tues and Thurs.
Catering: available.

M81 **Knott End**
☎(0253) 810576
Wyreside, Knott End on Sea, Blackpool FY6 0AA
Take A585 Fleetwood road off M55, and then B2588 to Knott End.
Meadowland course.
18 holes, 5852 yards, S.S.S.68
Designed by James Braid.
Founded 1911
Visitors: welcome weekdays, not before 9.30am or 12.30-1.30pm.
Green Fee: £17 WD, £21 WE.
Societies: by arrangement.
Catering: every day.
Hotels: Bourne Arms; Seven Stars.

M82 **Lancaster**
☎(0524) 751247, 751105 Caterer, 751802 Pro.
Ashton Hall, Ashton-with-Stodday, Lancaster LA2 0AJ
On A588 2.5 miles SW of Lancaster.
Undulating parkland course.
18 holes, 6282 yards, S.S.S.71
Designed by James Braid.

Visitors: welcome but restricted at weekends.
Green Fee: on application.
Societies: welcome by arrangement.
Catering: meals served.
Hotels: Post House.

M83 **Lansil**
☎(0524) 39269 Club
Caton Rd, Lancaster, Lancs LA1 3PE
2 miles E of Lancaster on A683.
Parkland/meadowland course.
9 Holes, 5608 yards, S.S.S.67
Founded 1947
Visitors: welcome but not before 1pm Sun.
Green Fee: £14 (£7 with member).
Societies: weekdays.
Catering: light refreshments only.
Hotels: Farmers Arms; Post House.

M84 **Lee Park**
☎(051) 487 3882 Sec.
Childwall Valley Rd, Gateacre, Liverpool L27 3YA
On B5171 off A562, next to Netherley Comprehensive School.
Parkland course.
18 holes, 6024 yards, S.S.S.69
Designed by Frank Pennink.
Founded 1950
Visitors: welcome with reservation.
Green Fee: on application.
Societies: by arrangement.
Catering: bar snacks served and meals by arrangement.
Hotels: Gateacre Hall.

M85 **Leigh**
☎(0925) 762943
Kenyon Hall, Broseley Lane, Culcheth, Warrington WA3 4BG
5 minutes from Culcheth centre.
Parkland course.
18 holes, 5861 yards, S.S.S.68
Founded 1906
Visitors: anytime except during club competitions.
Green Fee: £20 WD, £25 WE & BH.
Societies: Tues on application.
Catering: bar snacks/full catering.
Hotels: Greyhound Motel.

M86 **Leyland**
☎(0772) 436457
Wigan Rd, Leyland, Lancs PR5 2UD
On A49, 0.25 mile from M6 exit 28.
Meadowland course.
18 holes, 6105 yards, S.S.S.69
Founded 1923
Visitors: weekdays unrestricted, weekends with member.

Green Fee: £20.
Societies: apply to Sec.
Catering: daily except Mon.
Hotels: Ladbroke Mercury.

M87 **Lobden**
☎(0706) 343228
Lobden Moor, Whitworth, Nr Rochdale OL12 8XJ
A671 4 miles from Rochdale, 0.5 mile from centre of village.
Moorland course.
9 holes, 5750 yards, S.S.S.68
Founded 1888
Visitors: weekdays and Sun.
Green Fee: on application.
Catering: by arrangement with Steward. Snooker.

M88 **Longridge**
☎(0772) 783291
Fell Barn, Jeffery Hill, Longridge, Preston, Lancs PR3 2TU
Off B6243 8 miles NE of Preston, follow signs to Jeffery Hill.
Moorland course, panoramic views.
18 holes, 5800 yards, S.S.S.68
Founded 1877
Visitors: welcome; check by phone or letter.
Green Fee: £13/day Mon-Thurs, £16 Fri, Sat, Sun and BH.
Societies: apply in writing.
Catering: bar and meals at reasonable times. Snooker.
Hotels: Shireburn Arms; Gibbon Bridge; Black Moss GH.

M89 **Lowes Park**
☎(061) 764 1231, (0706) 67331 Sec.
Hill Top, Bury, Lancs BL9 6SU
A56 Walmersley Rd, right into Lowes Rd, follow signs to club; approx 1.5 miles from Bury centre, right at General Hospital.
Moorland course (usually windy).
9 holes, 6009 yards, S.S.S.69
Founded 1914
Visitors: welcome weekdays, except Wed (Ladies Day), Sat and competition days; Sun by appointment only.
Green Fee: £10 WD, £15 Sun.
Societies: contact Sec.
Catering: full facilities except Mon.
Hotels: Woolfield House.

M90 **Lytham Green Drive**
☎(0253) 737390
Ballam Rd, Lytham, Lancs FY8 4LE
0.75 mile from Lytham centre.

Parkland course.
18 holes, 6159 yards, S.S.S.69
Founded 1922
Visitors: weekdays only, h/cap cert required.
Green Fee: £24.
Societies: apply to Sec.
Catering: full service daily.
Hotels: Clifton Arms.

M91 **Manchester**
☎(061) 643 3202
Hopwood Cottage, Rochdale Rd, Middleton, Manchester M24 2QP
7 miles N of city on A664, 2 miles from exits 19 and 20 off M62.
Undulating moorland course.
18 holes, 6540 yards, S.S.S.72
Designed by J.H. Taylor.
Founded 1882
Visitors: weekdays only, h/cap certs required.
Green Fee: £25/day.
Societies: weekdays.
Catering: full facilities available.
Driving range, snooker, banqueting.
Hotels: Normandy; Norton Grange; Midway.

M92 **Marsden Park**
☎(0253) 67525
Downhouse Rd, Belson, Lancs BB9 8GD
Off A56, 8 miles N of Burnley.
Undulating meadowland course.
18 holes, 5806 yards, S.S.S.68
Designed by C.K. Cotton & Partners.
Founded 1968
Visitors: welcome.
Green Fee: on application.
Societies: by arrangement.
Catering: snacks in evenings, all day at weekends.

M93 **Maryport**
☎(0900) 812605
Bank End, Maryport, Cumbria CA15 6PA
N of Maryport, turn left off A596 onto B5300 (Silloth), course 1 mile.
Seaside links course.
18 holes, 6272 yards, S.S.S.71
Founded 1905
Visitors: welcome at any time.
Green Fee: on application.
Societies: catered for.
Catering: by prior arrangement.
Hotels: Ellenbank; The Waverley.

M94 **Morecambe**
☎(0524) 412841 Sec, 418050 Members, 415596 Pro.

Bare, Morecambe, Lancs LA4 6AJ
5 miles from M6 at Carnforth, follow signs to Morecambe.
Seaside/parkland course.
18 holes, 5766 yards, S.S.S.68
Designed by Dr Clegg.
Founded 1922
Visitors: welcome by arrangement.
Green Fee: on application.
Societies: welcome by arrangement with Sec, if members of recognised golf clubs.
Catering: full catering available except Mon when bar snacks only.
Hotels: Elms; Strathmore.

M95 **Nelson**
☎(0282) 64583
King's Causeway, Brierfield, Belson, Lancs BB9 0EU
Off A682 2 miles E of Brierfield.
Moorland course.
18 holes, 5967 yards, S.S.S.69
Founded 1902
Visitors: welcome weekdays except Thurs afternoons; weekends and Bank Holidays by application.
Green Fee: £16 (£8 with member) WD, £18 (£9 with member) WE.
Societies: by arrangement.
Catering: lunches except Mon, evening meals except Mon or Fri.
Hotels: Kierby; Oaks.

M96 **New North Manchester**
☎(061) 643 2941 Clubhouse, 643 9033 Sec, 643 7094 Pro Shop
Rhodes House, Manchester Old Rd, Middleton, Manchester M24 4PE
5 miles N of Manchester, M62 exit 18.
Moorland/parkland course.
18 holes, 6527 yards, S.S.S.72
Founded 1894
Visitors: welcome weekdays and by arrangement at weekends.
Green Fee: on application.
Societies: weekdays.
Catering: full service except Tues.
Hotels: Bower; Birch.

M97 **Newby Grange Hotel**
☎(0228) 573645
Newby Grange, Carlisle, Cumbria
A69 to Newcastle, turn left to Little Corby, through village, take road to Carlisle, course on right.
Riverbank parkland course.
18 holes, 6973 yards, S.S.S.75
Designed by Eddie MacCauslin.
Opening April 1992
Visitors: welcome.
Green Fee: £14/round WD, £18 WE.

Societies: welcome.
Catering: full bar and restaurant.
Driving range.
Hotels: Newby Grange.

M98 **Oldham**
☎(061) 624 4986 or 626 8346
Lees New Rd, Oldham OL4 5EN
Just off minor road between Oldham and Ashton-under-Lyne or on A669 turn right at Lees.
Moorland/parkland course.
18 holes, 5045 yards, S.S.S.65
Registered 1891
Visitors: unlimited, but phone for arrangements on competitions.
Green Fee: on application.
Societies: by arrangement.
Catering: full facilities.
Hotels: Birch Hall.

M99 **Ormskirk**
☎(0695) 572112
Cranes Lane, Lathom, Ormskirk, Lancs L40 5UJ
2 miles E of Ormskirk.
Parkland course.
18 holes, 6358 yards, S.S.S.70
Founded 1899
Visitors: advanced booking advised.
Green Fee: £25/round, £30/day Mon, Tues, Thurs, Fri; £30/round, £35/day Wed, Sun and BH.
Societies: book in advance.
Catering: daily except Mon.

M100 **Peel**
☎(0624) 843456 (Mon-Fri am)
Rheast Lane, Peel, Isle of Man
On A1, signposted on outskirts of Peel, coming from Douglas.
Moorland course.
18 holes, 5914 yards, S.S.S.68
Designed by A. Herd.
Founded 1895
Visitors: welcome weekdays; by arrangement weekends (after 10.30am).
Green Fee: £14/day WD, £18/day WE & BH.
Societies: apply to Sec.
Catering: meals and snacks to order by arrangement with Steward.

M101 **Pennigton**
☎(0942) 607278
Pennigton Country Park, St Helen's Road, Leigh, Greater Manchester
Off A572 to S of town centre; M6 junctions 22/23.
Public parkland course with ponds and streams.

9 holes, 2929 yards, S.S.S.34
Visitors: welcome.
Green Fee: on request.
Catering: snack bar.
Fishing, bird watching.

M102 **Penrith**
☎(0768) 62217
Salkeld Rd, Penrith, Cumbria CA11 8SG
0.5 mile NE of Penrith.
Parkland course.
18 holes, 6026 yards, S.S.S.69
Founded 1890
Visitors: must have current h/cap; only by prior arrangement Sat/Sun.
Green Fee: £12 WD, £15 WE & BH.
Societies: by arrangement.
Catering: full except Mon and Tues; normal bar facilities.
Hotels: George; Edenhill.

M103 **Penwortham**
☎(0772) 744630
Blundell Lane, Penwortham, Preston, Lancs PR1 0AX
Off A59 at Penwortham traffic lights, 1 mile from Preston.
Parkland course.
18 holes, 5915 yards, S.S.S.68
Founded 1908
Visitors: weekdays (not Tues).
Green Fee: £20 (£7 with member) WD, £25 (£9 with member) WE & BH.
Societies: weekdays (not Tues).
Catering: lunches and evening meals except Mon.
Hotels: Crest.

M104 **Pike Fold**
☎(061) 740 1136
Cooper Lane, Victoria Ave, Blackley, Manchester M9 2QQ
4 miles N of city centre off Rochdale road; off Victoria Ave from M62 junction 18.
Undulating meadowland course.
9 holes, 5789 yards, S.S.S.68
Founded 1909
Visitors: welcome weekdays.
Green Fee: £12/round/day WD (£5 with member), £7/round WE with member only.
Societies: welcome by appointment.
Catering: full facilities by prior arrangement with Steward. Snooker.
Hotels: Piccadilly; Midland.

M105 **Pleasington**
☎(0254) 202177
Pleasington, Blackburn, Lancs BB2 5JF

3 miles from Blackburn off A674.
Undulating parkland course.
18 holes, 6417 yards, S.S.S.71
Founded 1891
Visitors: Mon, Wed, Fri by prior arrangement; h/cap cert required.
Green Fee: £22.50 WD, £27.50 WE & BH.
Societies: Mon, Wed, Fri.
Catering: full facilities.
Hotels: Moat House Motel.

M106 **Port St Mary Golf Pavilion**
☎(0624) 834932
Port St Mary, Isle of Man
Just outside Port St Mary towards the sea, signposted.
Public seaside links course
9 holes, 5454 yards, S.S.S.66
Visitors: welcome any time.
Green Fee: on application.
Societies: welcome, discount for 10 or more.
Catering: bar, cafeteria (closed Mon and Tues until May).
Putting green, outdoor chessboard.
Hotels: Point; Bay View.

M107 **Poulton-le-Fylde.**
☎(0253) 893150/892444
Myrtle Farm, Breck Rd, Poulton-le-Fylde, Lancs
0.5 mile N of Poulton town centre.
Municipal meadowland course.
9 holes, 2779 yards, S.S.S.69
Founded 1974
Visitors: welcome, no restrictions.
Green Fee: on application.
Societies: by arrangement.
Catering: bar, snacks, lunches daily.
Snooker, games room.
Hotels: Imperial; Pembroke.

M108 **Preston**
☎(0772) 700011
Fulwood Hall Lane, Fulwood, Preston, Lancs PR2 4DD
From M6 junction 31 take Blackpool Rd, turn right at Deepdale Rd, turn left at Watling Street Rd, turn right at Fulwood Hall Lane.
Undulating course.
18 holes, 6233 yards, S.S.S.71
Designed by James Braid.
Founded 1892
Visitors: welcome weekdays.
Green Fee: £17.50/round, £20.50/day WD.
Societies: Mon, Wed, Fri (max 48); Tues (max 16); Thurs (max 32); no visiting parties weekends or Bank Holidays.

Catering: lunches, breakfast, dinner, snacks.
Hotels: Broughton Park.

M109 **Prestwich**
☎(061) 773 4578
Hilton Lane, Prestwich, Manchester M25 8SB
On A4066 0.25 mile W of junction with A56.
Parkland course.
18 holes, 4712 yards, S.S.S.63
Founded 1908
Visitors: h/cap certs required.
Green Fee: on application.
Societies: welcome except Tues
Catering: by arrangement with Steward, except Mon.
Hotels: Village Squash; Hazel Dean.

M110 **Ramsey**
☎(0624) 812244
Brookfield, Ramsey, Isle of Man
12 miles N of Douglas, 5 minutes walk from town centre.
Parkland course.
18 holes, 6019 yards, S.S.S.69
Designed by James Braid.
Founded 1890
Visitors: welcome; phone in advance.
Green Fee: £10/day WD, £12 WE.
Societies: apply to Sec.
Catering: lunches daily; dinner Thurs, Fri, Sat (bookings).
Hotels: Grand Island.

M111 **Rishton**
☎(0254) 884442
Eachill Links, Rishton, Blackburn, Lancs BB1 4HG
Signposted from church in village.
Undulating meadowland course.
9 holes, 6094 yards, S.S.S.69
Designed by Allis & Thomas.
Founded 1928
Visitors: welcome weekdays; weekends and Bank Holidays with member.
Green Fee: £10 (£5 with member) WD.
Societies: welcome with prior arrangement with Sec.
Catering: by prior arrangement.
Hotels: Dunkenhalgh.

M112 **Rochdale**
☎(0706) 43818 Sec, 46024 Club, 522104 Pro.
Edenfield Rd, Bagslate, Rochdale OL11 5YR
3 miles from M62 exit 20 on A680.

Parkland course.
18 holes, 6002 yards, S.S.S.69
Founded 1888
Visitors: welcome but restricted.
Green Fee: on application.
Societies: Wed and Fri.
Catering: coffee, lunch and evening meals served except Mon. Snooker.
Hotels: Crimble; Midway.

M113 Rossendale
☎(0706) 831339 Sec.
Ewood Lane Head, Haslingden, Rossendale, Lancs BB4 6LH
16 miles from Manchester off M66.
Moorland/meadowland course.
18 holes, 6267 yards, S.S.S.70
Founded 1903
Visitors: welcome except Sat.
Green Fee: £18 WD, £22 Sun & BH.
Societies: welcome.
Catering: full facilities except Mon. Snooker, banqueting.
Hotels: Queen's; Royal.

M114 Rowany
☎(0624) 834108
Rowany Drive, Port Erin, Isle of Man
4 miles W of Castletown.
Parkland/seaside course.
18 holes, 5840 yards, S.S.S.69
Founded 1895
Visitors: welcome, no restrictions.
Green Fee: £10/day WD, £15 WE; 25% discount for groups (8+) and visitors staying locally.
Catering: bar, bar snacks, restaurant (evening meals, lunches).

M115 Royal Birkdale
☎(0704) 69913, 67920 Sec.
Waterloo Rd, Birkdale, Southport, Merseyside PR8 2LX
1.5 miles S of Southport on A565.
Seaside course.
18 holes, 6703 yards, S.S.S.73
Designed by Hawtree & Taylor.
Founded 1889
Visitors: letter of intro required from home club with confirmation of h/cap.
Green Fee: winter, £35 WD; summer, £46/round, £67/day.
Societies: welcome weekdays by arrangement.
Catering: light lunches, teas; full meals by arrangement for societies.

M116 Royal Lytham & St Annes
☎(0253) 724206
Links Gate, St Annes on Sea, Lancs
FY8 3LQ

1 mile from centre of St Annes.
Links course.
18 holes, 6673 yards, S.S.S.73
Founded 1886
Visitors: weekdays by arrangement; weekends, dormy visitors only.
Green Fee: on application.
Societies: by arrangement.
Catering: full catering and bar facilities. Snooker.
Hotels: 16-bed dormy house, gentlemen only, by arrangement.

M117 Saddleworth
☎(0457) 873653
Mountain Ash, Ladcastle Rd, Uppermill, Oldham OL3 6LT
5 miles from Oldham, signposted off A670 Ashton-Huddersfield road at bend where road crosses railway.
Scenic moorland course.
18 holes, 5976 yards, S.S.S.69
Designed by Dr Mackenzie.
Founded 1904
Visitors: welcome.
Green Fee: on application.
Societies: catered for weekdays.
Catering: facilities daily.
Hotels: Old Bell Inn (Delph).

M118 St Annes Old Links
☎(0253) 723597 Sec, 722432 Pro.
Highbury Rd, St Annes, Lytham St Annes, Lancs FY8 2LD
M6 to junction 32; M55 to junction 4, follow signs to Blackpool Airport; past airport, left at A584 coast road to St Annes; 1 mile to lights, left into Highbury Rd, course immediately over railway bridge.
Championship links course.
18 holes, 6616 yards, S.S.S.72
Designed by James Herd.
Founded 1901
Visitors: welcome weekdays; restricted Tues and weekends.
Green Fee: £25 WD, £30 WE & BH.
Societies: apply to Sec.
Catering: lunches, teas, dinner daily. Men's bar, snooker, practice ground.
Hotels: St Ives; Warwick (Blackpool).

M119 St Bees
☎(0946) 822695
Station Rd, St Bees, Cumbria
On B5345, 4 miles S of Whitehaven.
Seaside course.
9 holes, 5097 yards, S.S.S.65
Founded 1942/43
Visitors: welcome except on competition days in summer.
Green Fee: on application.
Catering: none available.

M120 Seascale
☎(09467) 28202
The Banks, Seascale, Cumbria CA20 1QL
On coast to N of village; clubhouse at top of hill.
Seaside links course.
18 holes, 6416 yards, S.S.S.71
Founded 1893
Visitors: unrestricted.
Green Fee: £18 WD, £22 WE & BH.
Societies: apply to Sec, terms for parties of 12 or more.
Catering: full facilities except Mon, Tues (by arrangement).
Hotels: Scawfell; Calder House; 3-day bargain breaks available.

M121 Sedbergh
☎(05396) 20993 Hon Sec.
Catholes-Abbot Holme, Dent Rd, Sedbergh, Cumbria LA10 5SS
1.5 miles S of Sedbergh on road to Dent.
Scenic undulating parkland course.
9 holes; temporary greens 1992, full new course 1993.
Designed by Maxel Golf.
Founded 1896 (new site 1991)
Visitors: welcome except Sun am; advisable to phone.
Green Fee: £8 WD, £12 WE & BH.
Societies: welcome by arrangement.
Catering: good local facilities.
Hotels: bargain breaks being arranged.

M122 Shaw Hill Hotel G & CC
☎(0257) 269221, 261223 fax.
Preston Rd, Whittle-le-Woods, Nr Chorley, Lancs PR6 7PP
From M6 exit 28, just off A6 towards Chorley; from M61 exit 8, just off A6 towards Preston.
Parkland course.
18 holes, 6467 yards, S.S.S.71
Designed by T. McCauley.
Founded 1925
Visitors: welcome with proof of h/cap.
Green Fee: £20/round, £30/day WD; £30/round, £40/day WE.
Societies: weekdays only.
Catering: bar, full à la carte restaurant and function rooms. Sauna, solarium, snooker room.
Hotels: own 3 star hotel, golf inclusive packages available.

M123 Sherdley Park
☎(0744) 815518 Club, 813149 Pro.
Sherdley Park, St Helens, Merseyside

2 miles S of town centre on Warrington road.
Public undulating parkland course.
18 holes, 5941 yards, S.S.S.69
Designed by P.R. Parkinson.
Founded 1973
Visitors: welcome.
Green Fee: £5/round.
Societies: by arrangement.
Catering: bar and cafeteria.
Hotels: Post House; Thistle.

M124 Silecroft
☎(0229) 774250
Silecroft, Cumbria LA18 4NX
On A5093 3 miles N of Millom, through Silecroft village towards shore.
Seaside course.
9 holes (18 tees), 5712 yards, S.S.S.68
Founded 1903
Visitors: normally unrestricted weekdays; weekends and Bank Holidays often restricted 12am-5.30pm.
Green Fee: £10/round/day WD or WE.
Societies: by arrangement.
Catering: by prior arrangement for visiting groups.
Hotels: Bankfield; Miners Arms.

M125 Silloth on Solway
☎(06973) 31304
Silloth on Solway, Carlisle, Cumbria CA5 4AT
B5302 at A596 at Wigton, 18 miles W of Carlisle.
Undulating seaside course.
18 holes, 6343 yards, S.S.S.71
Designed by Dr Leach.
Founded 1892
Visitors: welcome any time.
Green Fee: £18/day WD, £23/round WE & BH.
Societies: welcome.
Catering: full facilities except Mon.
Hotels: Golf; Queens; Skinburness.

M126 Silverdale
☎(0524) 701300
Redbridge Lane, Silverdale, Carnforth, Lancs LA5 0SP
Off M6 at Carnforth, course opposite Silverdale railway station via Carnforth and Warton.
Hilly heathland course.
9 holes, 5262 yards, S.S.S.67
Founded 1906
Visitors: welcome, not competition days (Sun Men, Wed Ladies).
Green Fee: £10 WD, £15 WE & BH; (£5 with member).

Societies: by arrangement.
Catering: usually, by special arrangement.
Hotels: Wheatsheaf; Silverdale.

M127 Solway Village Golf Centre
☎(06973) 32544
Solway Village, Silloth-on-Solway, Cumbria CA5 4QQ
Easily located in village of Silloth.
Scenic parkland course.
9 holes, 2000 yards, Par 32
Founded 1988
Visitors: welcome any time.
Green Fee: £5/day.
Catering: bar and restaurant.
Driving range, swimming pool, indoor bowls.
Hotels: Skinburness; Golf.

M128 Southport & Ainsdale
☎(0704) 78000
Bradshaws Lane, Ainsdale, Southport, Merseyside PR8 3LG
3 miles S of Southport on A565, 0.5 mile from Ainsdale station.
Championship links course.
18 holes, 6612 yards, S.S.S.73
Designed by James Braid.
Founded 1907
Visitors: weekdays only, must be members of a golf club; advance booking recommended.
Green Fee: £25/round, £35/day.
Societies: as for visitors.
Catering: full facilities. Snooker.
Hotels: Prince of Wales; Scarisbrick; Royal Clifton.

M129 Southport Municipal
☎(0704) 535286, (530133 Park Golf Club)
Park Rd West, Southport, Merseyside PR9 0JS
N end of Promenade.
Public seaside course.
18 holes, 5953 yards, S.S.S.69
Founded 1914 (Park Golf Club)
Visitors: welcome.
Green Fee: £4.40/round (£2.20 jnrs) WD; £6.05 WE; booking required.
Societies: by arrangement.
Catering: meals served.

M130 Southport Old Links
☎(0704) 28207
Moss Lane, Southport, Merseyside PR9 7QS
From town centre take Lord St to

roundabout at Law Courts, turn right into Manchester Rd, into Roe Lane and into Moss Lane.
Seaside course.
9 holes, 6486 yards, S.S.S.72
Founded 1920
Visitors: preferably not Wed or weekends.
Green Fee: on application.
Societies: by arrangement if party of 12 or more.
Catering: snacks or light cooked meals as arranged with Steward.
Hotels: Bold.

M131 Springfield Park
☎(0707) 56401 (weekends only)
Springfield Park, Bolton Rd, Rochdale, Lancs
3 miles from M62.
Parkland course.
18 holes, 5337 yards, S.S.S.66
Founded 1927
Visitors: welcome anytime.
Green Fee: £4.30 WD, £5.10 WE.
Hotels: Midway (Castleton).

M132 Stand
☎(061) 766 3197 Sec, 766 2388 Club
The Dales, Ashbourne Grove, Whitefield, Manchester M25 7NL
1 mile N of M62, exit 17.
Undulating parkland course.
18 holes, 6426 yards, S.S.S.71
Designed by Alex Herd.
Founded 1904
Visitors: welcome weekdays.
Green Fee: £18 (£7 with member) WD, £20 (£10 with member) WE & BH.
Societies: weekdays; Mon, Wed and Fri preferred.
Catering: lunch/snacks except Mon.

M133 Stonyholme Municipal
☎(0228) 34856 Pro, 33208 Club
St Aidans Rd, Carlisle, Cumbria
Off A69, 1 mile W of M6, junction 43.
Flat meadowland course.
18 holes, 5773 yards, S.S.S.68
Designed by Frank Pennink.
Founded 1974
Visitors: welcome.
Green Fee: on application.
Societies: welcome.
Catering: meals served.

M134 Stonyhurst Park
☎(0254) 822351 Sec.
Stonyhurst, Via Hurst Green, Blackburn, Lancs BB6 9PZ

On B6243 Clitheroe-Longridge road.
Moorland course.
9 holes, 5246 yards, S.S.S.66
Founded 1979 (born 1892)
Visitors: welcome except Wed; book
in at Bayley Arms.
Green Fee: on application.
Catering: at Bayley Arms; snacks, à
la carte always available.
Hotels: Bayley Arms.

M135 **Swinton Park**
☎(061) 794 1785
East Lancashire Rd, Swinton,
Manchester M27 1LX
On A580 Manchester-Liverpool road,
about 4 miles from Manchester.
Parkland course.
18 holes, 6675 yards, S.S.S.72
Designed by Braid & Taylor.
Founded 1926
Visitors: welcome weekdays only.
Green Fee: on application.
Societies: by arrangement Tues,
Wed and Fri.
Catering: bar snacks, meals all day
(excluding Mon). Snooker.

M136 **Towneley**
☎(0282) 38473 bookings, 51636
bar and catering
Todmorden Rd, Burnley, Lancs BB11
3ED
Off Todmorden Rd approx 2 miles
from town centre.
Public parkland course.
18 holes, 5900 yards, S.S.S.68;
9 holes Par 3
Designed by Burnley Council
Founded 1932
Visitors: welcome anytime; normal
dress rules; booking required.
Green Fee: £4 WD, £5 WE & BH.
Societies: any weekday.
Catering: bar 12am-4pm, 7.30-
11pm; restaurant 12am-2pm daily or
by arrangement with Steward.
Snooker table.

M137 **Tunshill**
☎(0706) 342095
Kiln Lane, Milnrow, Lancs
M62 junction 21 to Milnrow; follow
Kiln Lane out of Milnrow town centre
and along narrow lane to clubhouse.
Moorland course.
9 holes, 2902 yards, S.S.S.68
Founded 1943
Visitors: welcome weekdays except
Tues evening; with special
permission at weekends.
Green Fee: on application.
Societies: welcome weekdays.

Catering: by prior arrangement.
Snooker, pool.
Hotels: Midway (Castleton).

M138 **Turton**
☎(0204) 852235
Wood End Farm, Chapeltown Rd,
Bromley Cross, Bolton BL7 9QH
3 miles N of Bolton on A676, adjacent
to Last Drop Hotel.
Moorland course.
9 holes, 5894 yards, S.S.S.68
Designed by James Braid.
Founded 1908
Visitors: welcome except Wed
12.30-4pm, Sat, Sun and special
competition days.
Green Fee: £10/day WD.
Societies: welcome by prior
arrangement.
Catering: every day except Mon,
resident Steward and Stewardess.
Hotels: Last Drop; Egerton House.

M139 **Ulverston**
☎(0229) 52824
The Club House, Bardsea Park,
Ulverston, Cumbria LA12 9QJ
From Ulverston town centre to
Bardsea on B5087.
Parkland course.
18 holes, 6142 yards, S.S.S.69
Designed by W.H. Colt.
Founded 1896 (present course 1910)
Visitors: welcome; introduction card
or h/cap cert preferred; Tues Ladies
Day; not Sat if Men's Competition.
Green Fee: £20 WD, £25 WE & BH
Mar-Oct inclusive; £15 WD, £18 WE
Nov-Feb.
Societies: welcome by prior
arrangement.
Catering: full meals and bar snacks
available daily except Mon; full time
Steward.
Hotels: Virginia House; Sefton
House; White Water (Backbarrow).

M140 **Walmersley**
☎(061) 764 5057
Garretts Close, Walmersley, Bury
On A56 about 2.5 miles N of Bury;
M66 junction 1, then 0.5 mile S.
Moorland course.
9 holes, 3057 yards, S.S.S.70
Founded 1906
Visitors: Wed, Thur and Fri; Sun with
member.
Green Fee: £12/day.
Societies: by arrangement
weekdays.
Catering: available with prior notice.
Hotels: Old Mill; Red Hall.

M141 **Werneth (Oldham)**
☎(061) 624 1190
Green Lane, Garden Suburb,
Oldham, Lancs OL8 3AZ
5 miles from Manchester, take A62
to Hollinwood and then A6104.
Moorland course.
18 holes, 5363 yards, S.S.S.66
Founded 1908
Visitors: welcome weekdays only.
Green Fee: £14 WD.
Societies: weekdays.
Catering: lunch served except Mon.
Hotels: Bower; Hollinwood.

M142 **West Derby**
☎(051) 254 1034 Sec, 220 5478 Pro.
Yew Tree Lane, Liverpool L12 9HQ
4 miles E of Liverpool centre, 1 mile S
of West Derby village.
Parkland course.
18 holes, 6333 yards, S.S.S.70
Founded 1896
Visitors: welcome weekdays.
Green Fee: on application.
Societies: by arrangement.
Catering: facilities.
Hotels: Derby Lodge.

M143 **West Lancashire**
☎(051) 924 1076
Hall Rd West, Blundellsands,
Liverpool L23 8SZ
M57 to Aintree, A5036 to Seaforth,
then A565 to Crosby, follow signs to
club, by Hall Rd station.
Seaside links course.
18 holes, 6756 yards, S.S.S.73
Designed by C.K. Cotton.
Founded 1873
Visitors: welcome with h/cap cert
except competition days.
Green Fee: £20/round, £30/day WD,
£35 WE.
Societies: Mon, Wed, Thurs, Fri.
Catering: lunch daily, other by
arrangement.
Hotels: Blundellsands.

M144 **Westhoughton**
☎(0942) 811085
Long Island, Westhoughton, Bolton,
Lancs BL5 2BR
4 miles SW of Bolton on A58.
Meadowland course.
9 holes, 5834 yards, S.S.S.68
Founded 1929
Visitors: welcome weekdays, with
member only at weekends.
Green Fee: on application.
Societies: by arrangement.
Catering: except Mon. Snooker.
Hotels: Mercury.

M145 **Whalley**
☎(0254) 822236
Portfield Lane, Whalley, Blackburn,
Lancs BB6 9DR
A59 to Whalley, course on left of road
to Accrington.
Parkland course.
9 holes, 5953 yards, S.S.S.69
Founded 1912
Visitors: welcome except Thurs
12.30-4pm (Ladies Day) and Sat
during April-Sept.
Green Fee: £12 (£5 with member)
WD, £20 (£8 with member) WE & BH.
Societies: by arrangement.
Catering: lunches, teas and dinners
except Mon.
Snooker.
Hotels: Moat House; Dunkenhalgh.

M146 **Whitefield**
☎(061) 766 2904
81/83 Higher Lane, Whitefield,
Manchester M25 7EZ
Leave M62 at exit 17 onto A56, club
is 200 yards on left in Higher Lane.
Parkland course.
18 holes, 5714 yards, S.S.S.68
Founded 1932
Visitors: welcome.
Green Fee: on application.
Societies: Tues-Fri, special rates on
application.
Catering: meals served.
Hotels: Bolton Crest; Hazeldean.

M147 **Whittaker**
☎(0706) 378310
Shore Lane, Littleborough, Lancs
OL15 0LH
1.5 miles from town centre.
Moorland course.
9 holes, 5576 yards, S.S.S.67
Founded 1906
Visitors: welcome except Sun and
Tues pm.
Green Fee: £8 (£4 with member)
WD, £10 (£5 with member) WE.
Societies: apply to Sec.
Catering: none, bar can be
arranged.

M148 **Wigan**
☎(0257) 421360
Arley Hall, Haigh, Wigan WN1 2UH

Leave M6 at exit 27, through
Standish on B5239, turn left at traffic
lights at Canal Bridge, opposite
Crawford Arms public house.
Parkland course.
9 holes, 6058 yards, S.S.S.69
Founded 1898
Visitors: welcome any day except
Tues and Sat.
Green Fee: £13 WD, £18 WE.
Societies: on application.
Catering: available.
Hotels: Bellingham; Brockett Arms;
Kilhey Court.

M149 **William Wroe**
☎(061) 748 8680, 748 1226 (Acre
Gate GC)
Penny Bridge Lane, Flixton,
Manchester 31
M63 exit 4, B5124, then B5158 to
Flixton road.
Municipal parkland course.
18 holes, 4395 yards, S.S.S.61
Visitors: welcome.
Green Fee: on application.

M150 **Wilpshire**
☎(0254) 248260
72 Whalley Rd, Wilpshire, Blackburn,
Lancs BB1 9LF
On A666 4 miles N of Blackburn.
Moorland course.
18 holes, 5911 yards, S.S.S.69
Founded 1890
Visitors: welcome weekdays.
Green Fee: on application.
Societies: catered for weekdays.
Catering: lunches daily, except Mon.
Hotels: Moat House; Trafalgar.

M151 **Windermere**
☎(05394) 43123
Cleabarrow, Windermere, Cumbria
LA23 3NB
1.25 miles from Bowness on Kendal
road B5284.
Undulating parkland course.
18 holes, 5006 yards, S.S.S.65
Designed by George Low.
Founded 1891
Visitors: members of recognised
golf clubs with official h/caps.
Green Fee: £18/day WD, £25/day
WE & BH.

Societies: by arrangement, numbers
12-60.
Catering: bar daily, bar meals
12am-2.00pm, 6.30-9pm except
Mon. Snooker.
Hotels: Wild Boar (Crook).

M152 **Woolton**
☎(051) 486 2298, 486 1298 Pro.
Doe Park, Speke Rd, Woolton,
Liverpool L25 7TZ
6 miles from City centre.
Parkland course.
18 holes, 5706 yards, S.S.S.68
Founded 1901
Visitors: welcome.
Green Fee: £17.50 WD, £25 WE.
Societies: weekdays; not Tues.
Catering: by arrangement.

M153 **Workington**
☎(0900) 603460 Steward, 67828
Pro.
Branthwaite Rd, Workington,
Cumbria CA14 4SS
Off A595 2 miles SE of town centre.
Undulating meadowland course.
18 holes, 6100 yards, S.S.S.70
Designed by James Braid.
Founded 1893
Visitors: welcome, must be
members of golf club and hold
current h/cap cert.
Green Fee: £15 WD, £20 WE & BH.
Societies: apply to Sec.
Catering: full except Mon, Thurs pm.
Hotels: Westlands; Cross Barrow;
Hunday Manor.

M154 **Worsley**
☎(061) 789 4202
Stableford Ave, Monton, Eccles,
Manchester M30 8AP
1 mile from junction of M62/M63.
Parkland course.
18 holes, 6217 yards, S.S.S.70
Designed by James Braid.
Founded 1894
Visitors: welcome if member of golf
club with official h/cap.
Green Fee: £20/day.
Societies: Mon, Wed and Thurs.
Catering: available from 12am.
Snooker.
Hotels: Wendover.

YORKSHIRE

Crossing the Pennines and approaching Yorkshire on the M62 gives a perfect impression of the remoteness of some of the countryside, an impression that can only be reinforced as you travel north.

Nevertheless, the area around Leeds is the one most blessed with the quality of its golf and its courses. Few courses, if any, are as much dominated by a river as Ilkley, particularly the opening holes which have a habit of destroying a score before it has taken shape. For all its modest length, Ilkey is quite a handful.

Alwoodley, Moor Allerton, Moortown and Sand Moor formed a distinguished cluster until Moor Allerton sold up and moved out towards Wike. The development of houses on the old course and on part of Sand Moor meant that Moortown became so surrounded that a redesign of their layout was essential. Sand Moor relocated their clubhouse on the other side of Alwoodley Lane and added several new holes but both Moortown and Sand Moor have preserved their considerable reputations.

Alwoodley, handiwork of the legendary Alister Mackenzie, is undoubtedly one of his finest, an elegant, demanding course in a wonderfully natural setting that is not as well known as it should be. The latest version of Moor Allerton lies close by, the creation of Robert Trent Jones, while the outlying districts of Yorkshire's county town have pleasant golfing attractions, notably Headingley, Scarcroft and Garforth.

Neighbouring Bradford boasts West Bowling and the Bradford Club while Halifax is well served and Huddersfield claims Crosland Heath, Woodsome Hall and the Huddersfield GC at Fixby which is probably the pick. Bradley Park, on the edge of the M62 is a well used public course. Moving south-east, the Sheffield district is full of good things. Hallamshire, Hallowes, Dore & Totley, Abbeydale, Lees Hall and Phoenix constitute the pick; nor must one forget Doncaster Town Moor, Wheatley and the Doncaster Club as thoughts move to the East Riding. Doncaster Town Moor is close to the racecourse and Doncaster Rovers FC, a real sporting cocktail.

Of the old North Riding courses, Ganton surely wears the crown. Lying in the midst of the lovely Vale of Pickering, it is without doubt one of the finest inland courses in Britain and the only one to have housed the British Amateur championship, which it did for the first time in 1964. Michael Bonallack's "impertinence" in going round in 61 in the final of the 1968 English Championship should not deceive anyone into thinking that it is short or straightforward.

A round at Ganton is always a boost to the spirits, a reminder that it is good to be alive but Pannal at Harrogate and Fulford, York, are other courses that have welcomed their share of professional tournaments. From a clubhouse position close to the Leeds/Harrogate road, Pannal rises onto higher ground but Fulford is almost entirely flat, the stiffest climb being over the bridge that crosses the York by-pass. It splits the course virtually in two, a layout more on the lines of ancient seaside links which take the golfer straight out for six holes, then, after a pleasant loop, straight back.

Scarborough has both North Cliff and South Cliff, the one designed by James Braid, the other by Alister Mackenzie. North Cliff is the sterner but Braid also had a hand in Bridlington, and Filey is a course of which I retain happy memories of a pleasant round many years ago.

Further south, Beverley & East Riding and Driffield form convenient stopping-off spots for travellers to the area of Hull which has a municipal course at Springhead Park, plus the Hull GC and Hessle. Boothferry is another municipal course while up in the north of the county Catterick Garrison and Richmond stand out along with Bedale and, just to the south, the pleasant 9 holes of Ripon City.

N1 Abbeydale

☎(0742) 360763
Twentywell Lane, Dore, Sheffield
S17 4QA
Off A621 5 miles S of Sheffield.
Parkland course.
18 holes, 6419 yards, S.S.S.71
Founded 1895
Visitors: welcome by arrangement;
not before 9.30am, or 12am-1.30pm.
Green Fee: £25 WD, £30 WE & BH.
Societies: Tues and Fri by
arrangement.
Catering: bar snacks and restaurant
throughout the day. Snooker.
Hotels: Beauchief; Sheffield Moat
House.

N2 Aldwark Manor

☎(03473) 353
Aldwark, Alne, York YO6 2NF
12 miles N of York in village of
Aldwark off A19; 5 miles SE of
Boroughbridge off A1.
Parkland course.
9 holes, 5120 yards, S.S.S.66; (18
holes, 6075 yards, Par 71 from June
1992)
Founded 1978

Visitors: welcome weekdays,
weekends by arrangement.
Green Fee: from June 1992, £15
WD, £19 WE & BH.
Societies: welcome by prior
arrangement.
Catering: snacks and full restaurant
service; banqueting and private
parties.
Hotels: Aldwark Manor on course.

N3 Alwoodley

☎(0532) 681680
Wigton Lane, Alwoodley, Leeds LS17
8SA
5 miles N of Leeds on A61
Leeds-Harrogate road.
Heathland/moorland course.
18 holes, 6686 yards, S.S.S.72
Designed by Dr A. Mackenzie/H. Colt.
Founded 1907
Visitors: weekdays only by
arrangement.
Green Fee: £35 WD.
Societies: welcome by prior
arrangement.
Catering: bar and restaurant
facilities by arrangement.
Hotels: Harewood Arms.

N4 Ampleforth College

☎(0439) 70678
c/o Sec, Beckdale Cottage, 56 High
St, Helmsley, York YO6 5AE
In village of Gilling East, 20 miles N of
York on Helmsley road B1363.
Parkland course.
10 holes, 4018 yards, S.S.S.63
Designed by Ampleforth College.
Founded 1962
Visitors: welcome but must give way
to College pupils 2-4pm during term
time; apply for play and pay green
fees at Fairfax Arms in Gilling East.
Green Fee: £6/day WD, £12/day WE
& BH.
Societies: apply to Sec.
Catering: at Fairfax Arms in village.

N5 Austerfield Park

☎(0302) 710841, 710850
Cross Lane, Austerfield, Nr Bawtry, S
Yorks DN10 6RF
On roundabout, A614 2 miles N of
Bawtry.
Moorland course.
18 holes, 6828 yards, S.S.S.73
Designed by E. and M. Baker Ltd.
Founded 1974

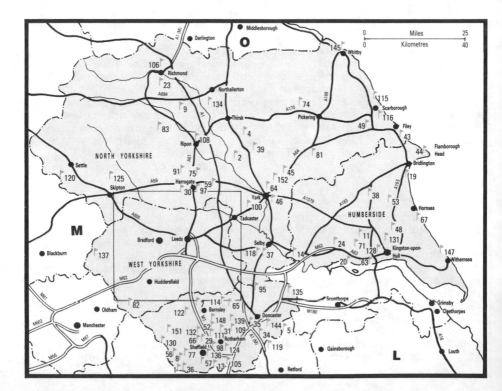

Visitors: welcome any day.
Green Fee: £12, £6 Eurogolf and guest WD; £16, £8 Eurogolf and guest WE.
Societies: welcome, packages from £14.
Catering: full bar and restaurant. Driving range, flat green bowls.
Hotels: Crown; Mount Pleasant; Punches.

N6 Baildon
☎(0274) 584266
Moorgate, Baildon, Shipley, W Yorks BD17 5PP
5 miles N of Bradford, A6037 to Shipley, 0.75 mile NE on A6038, left at Junction Hotel.
Moorland course.
18 holes, 6278 yards, S.S.S.70
Founded 1896
Visitors: welcome weekdays and at weekends by arrangement.
Green Fee: on application.
Societies: welcome.
Catering: lunches except Mon.
Hotels: Bankfield (Cottingley).

N7 Barnsley
☎(0220) 382850
Wakefield Rd, Staincross, Nr Barnsley, S Yorks S75 6JZ
On A61 3 miles from Barnsley.
Public undulating meadowland course.
18 holes, 6048 yards, S.S.S.69
Founded 1928
Visitors: welcome.

Green Fee: £6 WD, £7 WE.
Societies: arrange with Pro.
Catering: bar meals.
Hotels: Queens; Ardley Moat House.

N8 Beauchief
☎(0742) 620040, 367274
Abbey Lane, Sheffield S8 0DB
5 miles from city centre, Abbeydale Rd is on A625 to Baslow.
Municipal meadowland course.
18 holes, 5452 yards, S.S.S.66
Founded 1925
Visitors: welcome.
Green Fee: £6.50/round; day tickets not available.
Societies: weekdays only, by arrangement with City of Sheffield Recreation Dept, Meersbrook Park, Sheffield S8 9FL.
Catering: meals served except Tues.
Hotels: Beauchief adjacent to course.

N9 Bedale
☎(0677) 422568
Leyburn Rd, Bedale, N Yorks DL8 1EZ
On A684 immediately on leaving Bedale.
Parkland course.
18 holes, 5599 yards, S.S.S.68
Founded 1894
Visitors: welcome.
Green Fee: £16 WD, £24 WE.
Societies: weekdays only.
Catering: served daily except Mon.
Hotels: Old Vicarage (Bedale); Leeming Motel (Northallerton).

N10 Ben Rhydding
☎(0943) 608759
High Wood, Ben Rhydding, Ilkley, W Yorks LS29 8SB
Keep left after passing Wheatley Hotel to top of hill.
Moorland course.
9 holes, 4711 yards, S.S.S.64
Founded 1947
Visitors: welcome; not weekends.
Green Fee: £7.50 WD.
Hotels: Wheatley; Craiglands.

N11 Beverley & East Riding
☎(0482) 868757
Ante Mill, The Westwood, Beverley HU17 8RG
On Beverley-Walkington road.
Undulating course.
18 holes, 5937 yards, S.S.S.69
Designed by Dr J.J. Fraser.
Founded 1889
Visitors: welcome weekdays.
Green Fee: £10 WD, £12.50 WE & BH.
Societies: weekdays.
Catering: lunch, evening meals.
Hotels: Beverley Arms; Lairgate.

N12 Bingley St Ives
☎(0274) 562436
The Mansion, St Ives Estate, Bingley, W Yorks BD16 1AT
Turn off A650 in Bingley town centre onto Harden-Cullingworth road; 0.5 mile on right, turn right into Estate.
Wooded parkland/moorland course.
18 holes, 6480 yards, S.S.S.71
Founded 1931
Visitors: welcome weekdays.
Green Fee: on application.
Societies: weekdays.
Catering: meals daily except Mon.
Hotels: Bankfield.

N13 Birley Wood
☎(0742) 647262, 471258 Sec.
Birley Lane, Sheffield S12 3BP
4 miles S of Sheffield off A616 heading towards Mosborough.
Public open course.
18 holes, 5700 yards, S.S.S.66
Founded 1974
Visitors: no restrictions.
Green Fee: variable.
Catering: at Fairways Inn adjacent.
Hotels: Grosvenor (Sheffield).

N14 Boothferry
☎(0430) 430364
Spaldington, Howden, Goole DN14 7NG

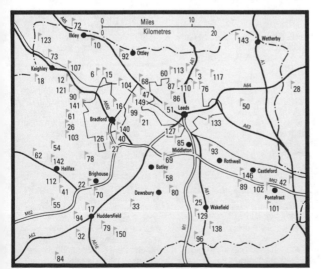

A63 towards Howden then B1228 to Bubwith for 3 miles.
Public meadowland course.
18 holes, 6651 yards, S.S.S.72
Designed by Cotton, Pennink, Lawrie & Partners.
Founded 1982
Visitors: welcome any time except Christmas Day.
Green Fee: on application.
Societies: catered for any day except certain club competitions days; reduced rates for 12 or more.
Catering: meals and snacks served lunchtimes except Christmas Day, and summer season evenings except Mon.

N15 Bradford
☎(0943) 875570 Sec, 873719 Pro.
Hawksworth Lane, Guiseley, Leeds LS20 8NP
From Shipley 3.5 miles NE on A6038, left to Hawksworth Lane.
Moorland/parkland course.
18 holes, 6259 yards, S.S.S.71
Founded 1891
Visitors: weekdays unlimited; weekends not before noon.
Green Fee: £22 WD, £30 WE.
Societies: weekdays.
Catering: full facilities; functions. Snooker.
Hotels: Chevin Lodge; Hollins Hall.

N16 Bradford Moor
☎(0274) 638313
Scarr Hall, Pollard Lane, Bradford BD2 4RW
2 miles from Bradford.
Undulating meadowland course.
9 holes, S.S.S.68
Founded 1907
Visitors: welcome.
Green Fee: on application.
Catering: meals served.

N17 Bradley Park
☎(0484) 539988
Bradley Rd, Huddersfield, W Yorks HD2 1PZ
M62 runs alongside course between junctions 24 and 25, boundary borders on A6107 Bradley Rd, entrance to course signposted midway along Bradley Rd.
Public undulating parkland course.
18 holes, 6202 yards, S.S.S.70;
9 holes Par 3
Designed by C.K. Cotton, Pennink, Lawrie & Partners.
Founded 1977
Visitors: welcome anytime.

Green Fee: £8.25/round WD, £9.75 WE.
Societies: Mon-Fri, not weekends.
Catering: full facilities.
Driving range.
Hotels: Ladbroke; George.

N18 Branshaw
☎(0535) 643235
Branshaw Moor, Oakworth, Keighley, W Yorks BD22 7ES
B6143 2 miles SW of Keighley.
Moorland course.
18 holes, 5858 yards, S.S.S.69
Founded 1912
Visitors: welcome weekdays.
Green Fee: £12 WD, £17 WE.
Societies: weekdays except Mon; not weekends.
Catering: meals except Mon; prior notice required for larger parties.
Hotels: Old Hall & White Lion.

N19 Bridlington
☎(0262) 672092, 606367
Belvedere Rd, Bridlington, N Humberside YO15 3NA
1.5 miles S of Bridlington station, off A165 from Hull.
Seaside course.
18 holes, 6491 yards, S.S.S.71
Designed by James Braid.
Founded 1905
Visitors: welcome.
Green Fee: £12 WD, £18 WE & BH.
Societies: welcome by arrangement with Hon Sec.
Catering: full facilities.
Hotels: Marine; The Spa; Monarch.

N20 Brough
☎(0482) 667291 Sec, 667374 Club, 667483 Pro.
Cave Rd, Brough, N Humberside HU15 1HB
10 miles W of Hull off A63.
Parkland course.
18 holes, 6035 yards, S.S.S.69
Founded 1893
Visitors: weekdays only; Wed after 2.30pm only.
Green Fee: on application.
Societies: Tues and Fri.
Catering: available.
Hotels: Cave Castle; Crest (Hull).

N21 Calverley
☎(0532) 569244 Pro, 564362 Club
Woodhall Lane, Pudsey, Leeds LS28 5QY
7 miles from Leeds centre, 4 miles from Bradford centre.

Parkland course, 18 holes private, 9 holes public.
18 holes, 5527 yards, S.S.S.67;
9 holes, 2581 yards, Par 34
Founded 1983
Visitors: welcome; h/cap cert required for 18 hole course; 9 hole course unrestricted.
Green Fee: 18 hole course, £8.50 WD, £12.50 WE; 9 hole course, £5 any day (for 18 holes).
Societies: any time by arrangement.
Catering: bar and restaurant.

N22 Castle Fields
☎(0484) 712108
Rastrick Common, Rastrick, Brighouse, W Yorks
Parkland course.
6 holes, 2406 yards, S.S.S.50
Founded 1903
Visitors: only with member.
Green Fee: £3/round.

N23 Catterick Garrison
☎(0748) 833268
Leyburn Rd, Catterick Garrison, N Yorks DL9 3QE
6 miles S of Scotch Corner, turn off A1 at Catterick Garrison and follow signs (2.5 miles).
Undulating moorland/parkland course.
18 holes, 6332 yards, S.S.S.70
Designed by Arthur Day.
Founded 1932
Visitors: welcome.
Green Fee: £14 (£8 with member) WD, £22 (£10 with member) WE & BH.
Societies: on application.
Catering: restaurant and snacks except Mon.
Hotels: Bridge House (Catterick Bridge); Golden Lion (Leyburn).

N24 Cave Castle Hotel
☎(0430) 421286 Golf, 422245 Hotel
South Cave, Brough, E Yorks HU15 2EU
10 miles from city of Kingston upon Hull, junction of A63/M62 East.
Parkland course.
18 holes, 6900 yards, S.S.S.73
Founded July 1989
Visitors: welcome at all times.
Green Fee: £12.50/round, £18/day WD; £18/round, £25/day WE.
Societies: weekdays and weekends, special rates by arrangement.
Catering: full facilities; conference and banqueting up to 300, à la carte.
Hotels: Cave Castle, weekday and weekend golfing breaks.

Alwoodley

Alwoodley is a course of unsuspected beauty. It lies a shortish bus ride from the centre of Leeds suggesting a setting within sight and sound of urban outline and bustle, but those familiar with the glorious Dales country to the north will know how quickly it can be reached and that the Club's attractive name is remarkably descriptive and apt.

For much of its existence, Alwoodley has been one of the most private clubs in the country where a round for the visitor was very much a privilege. There was no wish or need for the club to seek attention and nobody could blame them for that. But in 1965, they acted as host to the Yorkshire Amateur Championship for what, according to *The Golfers Handbook*, was the first time and in 1966 the English Women had the pleasure of holding their Championship there.

Alwoodley is a close neighbour of Moortown and Sand Moor, Alwoodley's first secretary being the eminent golf course architect, Dr Alister Mackenzie who had a hand in the present layout.

Golf at Alwoodley, on part of Lord Harewood's Estate, had, before my first visit, been described to me in enthusiastic terms but, even so, I confess surprise at finding what must surely rank as one of the finest inland courses in Britain. Its admirers had not done it justice.

It was my good luck to have Rodney Foster, winner of the 1965 Yorkshire Amateur at Alwoodley, as my guide and we were fortunate in having a glorious day for our round but the immediate impression was of the number of challenging strokes to be met. From the back tees in any sort of wind, a scratch man could be delighted with a score of 75.

In appearance, the course is a little like Woodhall Spa with an added hint of Walton Heath. Its character is moorland with plenty of heather, gorse, bushes, trees and consuming undergrowth and there is a constant feeling of escape from the city. There is even a fair chance of completing a premature introduction to agricultural surroundings by driving over the hedge on the left of the first tee which is an alarmingly full view of the charming clubhouse but, for all the excellence of the drive and pitch 2nd hole, the course really starts after crossing the road to the 3rd.

This is a five for most people's money and, by the time the first short hole is reached at the 7th, other fives at the 4th, 5th and 6th may also have to be marked down. However, nobody need ever be ashamed of a five at the 8th (543 yards), a magnificent hole curving around a wood into which it is so easy to hook. Not that one's troubles end with the drive. The second shot must make a formidable carry or else find a narrow elbow of fairway.

After such a severe beginning, there are mercifully three short ones among five holes around the turn but the 10th is another of Alwoodley's classic doglegs where nobody is quite happy until he has left it behind. This a sharp left-hander where a long drive is needed to negotiate what can be a full second shot to a green in a hidden dell.

The other is the 15th, with danger this time awaiting the slicer, and a superb approach to an unusually shaped green awaiting everyone; but in between, are two grand fours and the longest short hole (211 yards), a testing stroke in a cross wind. These holes provide perfect balance to the round which ends with three more par 4s, the shortest of which is 435 yards.

No matter how one plays them, or has scored as a whole, three strong impressions remain. Enjoyment will have been increased by the excellence of the lies on springy turf. There will undoubtedly be an urge to return and the completeness of the examination faced is confirmed by the fact that you will probably have used, at sometime, every club in the bag. Not many courses can make claims such as these but an interesting tailpiece is contained in Mackenzie's book on Golf Architecture which informs the reader that at Alwoodley and Moortown "practically every green and every hummock has been artificially made, and yet it is difficult to convince the stranger that this is so".

N25 **City of Wakefield**
☎(0924) 360282 Pro shop
Lupset Park, Horbury Rd, Wakefield,
W Yorks WF2 8QS
Approx 2 miles from M1 junctions 39
or 40, on A642 Huddersfield road,
turn at Empire Mail Order Stores.
Public parkland course.
18 holes, 6299 yards, S.S.S.70
Founded 1936
Visitors: welcome.
Green Fee: £4.75 WD, £7.20 WE &
BH.
Societies: apply to Pro.
Catering: meals and snacks for
groups, arrange with Stewardess.
Hotels: Swallow; Post House; Cedar
Court.

N26 **Clayton**
☎(0274) 880047
Thornton View Rd, Clayton, Bradford,
W Yorks BD14 6JX
On A647 from Bradford, then turn
right and follow signs to Clayton.
Moorland course.
9 holes, 5407 yards, S.S.S.67
Founded 1906
Visitors: welcome weekdays and Sat
unless tee closed for competition.
Green Fee: £8 WD, £10 Sun (not
before 4pm) and Bank Holidays.
Societies: apply to Sec.
Catering: bar and bar snacks except
Mon; other by arrangement. Snooker.
Hotels: Guide Post.

N27 **Cleckheaton & District**
☎(0274) 874118
Bradford Rd, Cleckheaton, W Yorks
BD19 6BU
Exit 26 from M62 onto A638 towards
Bradford.
Parkland course.
18 holes, 5847 yards, S.S.S.69
Founded 1900
Visitors: welcome.
Green Fee: on application.
Societies: catered for weekdays.
Catering: full facilities available;
morning coffee, lunches, afternoon
teas, dinner every day except Mon.
Hotels: Novotel (Bradford).

N28 **Cocksford**
☎(0937) 834253
Stutton, Tadcaster, N Yorkshire LS24
9NG
1.5 miles S of Tadcaster near village
of Stutton.
Parkland course.
18 holes, 5566 yards, S.S.S.69

Designed by Townend and Brodigan.
Founded 1991
Visitors: contact Pro.
Green Fee: £15 WD, £20 WE.
Societies: by arrangement; phone
(0937) 530344/834253.
Catering: bar and restaurant;
banqueting.
Hotels: 4 luxury holiday cottages on
site; phone as for societies.

N29 **Concord Park**
☎(0742) 456806 Sec.
Shiregreen Lane, Sheffield, S Yorks
Off A6135, 3.5 miles N of Sheffield,
next to Concord Sports Centre.
Public undulating parkland course.
18 holes, 4321 yards, S.S.S.62
Founded 1952
Visitors: welcome.
Green Fee: £5.20.
Catering: in adjacent sports centre.

N30 **Crimple Valley**
☎(0423) 883485
Hookstone Wood Rd, Harrogate,
N Yorks HG2 8PN
1 miles S of town centre; turn off A61
at crossroads at Appleyards Garage,
after 0.75 mile signposted to right.
Gently sloping fairways in rural
setting.
9 holes, 2500 yards, S.S.S.33
Founded 1976
Visitors: welcome at all times.
Green Fee: on application.
Catering: licensed bar, lunches
weekdays, breakfasts at weekends.

N31 **Crookhill Park**
☎(0709) 862979
Conisbrough, Nr Doncaster, S Yorks
DN12 2AH
Between Conisbrough and Edlington;
turn off A630 Doncaster-Rotherham
road onto B6094, signposted.
Public parkland course.
18 holes, 5839 yards, S.S.S.68
Founded 1975
Visitors: welcome, no restrictions.
Green Fee: £6.50/round all week.
Societies: any time by arrangement;
written confirmation required.
Catering: bar and bar snacks.
Hotels: Consort Suite (Thurcroft);
Moat House (Doncaster).

N32 **Crosland Heath**
☎(0484) 653216
Felk Stile Rd, Crosland Heath,
Huddersfield HD4 7AF
Take A62 Huddersfield-Oldham road

for 3 miles, then follow signs for
Goodalls Caravans.
Moorland course.
18 holes, 5962 yards, S.S.S.70
Visitors: welcome by arrangement;
h/cap cert required.
Green Fee: on application.
Societies: welcome except Sat;
contact Sec.
Catering: full facilites except Mon.
Hotels: Dryclough (Crosland Moor);
Durker Roods (Meltham).

N33 **Dewsbury District**
☎(0924) 492399, 496030 Pro.
The Pinnacle, Sands Lane, Mirfield,
W Yorks WF14 8HJ
Off A644, 2.5 miles from Dewsbury,
at Swan Hotel turn left into Steanard
Lane, sign at Sands Lane.
Undulating meadowland/moorland
course.
18 holes, 6256 yards, S.S.S.71
Re-designed Allis & Thomas (1970).
Founded 1891
Visitors: welcome weekdays by
arrangement, weekends after 4pm.
Green Fee: on application.
Societies: welcome.
Catering: full facilites except Mon.
Hotels: Flowerpot Motel; The
Woolpack.

N34 **Doncaster**
☎(0302) 865632 Office
278 Bawtry Rd, Bessacarr,
Doncaster, S Yorks DN4 7PD
Easy to locate between Doncaster
and Bawtry on A638.
Undulating heathland course.
18 holes, 6015 yards, S.S.S.69
Founded 1894
Visitors: welcome with or without
member, not weekends.
Green Fee: on application.
Societies: weekdays except Wed by
prior arrangement with Sec.
Catering: main meals available by
prior arrangement daily except Wed.
Hotels: Punch's; Danum.

N35 **Doncaster Town Moor**
☎(0302) 535286
Belle Vue Club, Belle Vue, Doncaster,
S Yorks DN4 5HT
400 yards S of racecourse
roundabout on A638 travelling
towards Bawtry; entrance as for
Doncaster Rovers Football Ground.
Parkland course.
18 holes, 6094 yards, S.S.S.69
Visitors: welcome except Sun before
11.30am.

Green Fee: £12/round, £14/day WD; £14/round, £16/day WE & BH; reduction of £4 with member.
Societies: welcome on application to Sec.
Catering: available; contact Steward at Belle Vue Club (0302) 531000.
Hotels: Danum; Earl of Doncaster; Punches; Rockingham.

N36 Dore & Totley
☎(0742) 360492
Bradway Rd, Sheffield, S Yorks S17 4QR
Off A61 Sheffield-Chesterfield road on Holmesfield Rd.
Parkland course.
18 holes, 6301 yards, S.S.S.70
Founded 1913
Visitors: welcome by prior arrangement.
Green Fee: £20.
Societies: welcome weekdays except Wed.
Catering: full catering facilities except Mon.
Snooker.
Hotels: Beauchief.

N37 Drax
☎(0405) 860533
Drax, Nr Sowerby, N Yorks
6 miles S of Selby, opposite Power Station.
Parkland course.
9 holes, 5454 yards, S.S.S.66
Designed by John Scott.
Founded 1989
Visitors: only if introduced by member.
Green Fee: on application.
Catering: at Drax Sports and Social Club.

N38 Driffield
☎(0377) 43116
Sunderlandwick, Driffield, N Humberside
1 mile from Driffield town centre towards Hull on A164.
Parkland course.
18 holes, 6227 yards, S.S.S.70
Founded 1935
Visitors: welcome, h/cap certs required.
Green Fee: £10/round, £15/day WD; £15/round, £20/day WE.
Societies: catered for weekdays; parties of 12 or more £8 plus £8 for day's catering.
Catering: not Mon, except parties by arrangement.
Hotels: Bell.

N39 Easingwold
☎(0347) 21486, 21964 Pro.
Stillington Rd, Easingwold, N Yorks YO6 3ET
0.75 mile off A19, entering Easingwold from York turn right immediately past garage.
Parkland course.
18 holes, 6262 yards, S.S.S.70
Founded 1930
Visitors: welcome.
Green Fee: £20/day WD, £25/day WE & BH.
Societies: by arrangement (not weekends or Bank Holidays).
Catering: bar lunches, lunches, dinners except Mon.
Hotels: George.

N40 East Bierley
☎(0274) 681023
South View Rd, Bierley, Bradford, W Yorks
3 miles SE of Bradford on Wakefield-Heckmondwike Rd.
Undulating moorland course.
9 holes, 4692 yards, S.S.S.62
Founded 1909
Visitors: no restrictions except Mon evening and Sun.
Green Fee: £9/round WD, £11 WE.
Societies: write for details.
Catering: bar and restaurant daily.
Snooker.

N41 Elland
☎(0422) 372505
Hammerstones, Leach Lane, Elland, W Yorks HX5 0TA
Leave M62 at junction 24, look for Blackley sign, approx 1 mile.
Parkland course.
18 holes, 5630 yards, S.S.S.66
Founded 1912
Visitors: welcome weekdays.
Green Fee: £10 WD, £15 WE.
Societies: by arrangement.
Catering: meals, bar snacks except Mon.
Hotels: Hilton National; The Rock.

N42 Ferrybridge 'C'
☎(0977) 674188 extn 2852
P.O. Box 39, Strangland Lane, Knottingley, W Yorks WF11 8SQ
400 yards to W side of A1, on Castleford-Knottingley road.
9 holes, 5138 yards, S.S.S.65
Designed by N.E. Pugh.
Founded 1976
Visitors: with member only.
Green Fee: £3/day WD, £4 WE & BH.
Societies: by arrangement.

N43 Filey
☎(0723) 513293
West Ave, Filey, N Yorks YO14 9BQ
Private road off end of West Ave in S end of town.
Seaside course.
18 holes, 6030 yards, S.S.S.69
Founded 1897
Visitors: unaccompanied with proof of membership of a golf club and/or h/cap cert.
Green Fee: winter, £12.50 WD, £15.50 WE; summer, £16.50 WD, £20.50 WE.
Societies: by arrangement, not Bank Holidays.
Catering: all year. Snooker.
Hotels: White Lodge.

N44 Flamborough Head
☎(0262) 850333
Lighthouse Rd, Flamborough, Bridlington, N Humberside YO15 1AR
5 miles NE of Bridlington on B1255, near lighthouse on headland at Flamborough.
Undulating course.
18 holes, 5438 yards, S.S.S.66
Founded 1932
Visitors: welcome; restricted Sun am, Wed 10.30am-1.30pm.
Green Fee: £12 WD, £16 WE & BH.
Societies: apply to Sec.
Catering: full facilities except Mon.
Snooker table.
Hotels: Flaneburg; Timoneer.

N45 Forest Park
☎(0904) 400425
Stockton on Forest, York, N Yorks YO3 9UW
2 miles from E end of York by-pass, in village of Stockton on Forest.
Parkland course.
18 holes, 6211 yards, S.S.S.70
Founded 1991
Visitors: welcome, phone for tee times.
Green Fee: £12/round, £18/day WD; £18 WE.
Societies: weekdays by arrangement.
Catering: bar, bar meals.
Driving range.

N46 Fulford
☎(0904) 413579
Heslington Lane, Heslington, York YO1 5DY
Off A19 from York, follow signs to University.
Parkland course.
18 holes, 6779 yards, S.S.S.72

Designed by Dr A. Mackenzie.
Founded 1906
Visitors: by prior arrangement.
Green Fee: on application.
Societies: contact Sec at above address and telephone number.
Catering: morning coffee, lunch and evening meal.
Hotels: Alfreda.

N47 Fulneck

☎(0532) 565191
The Clubhouse, Fulneck, Pudsey, W Yorks LS28 8NT
Between Leeds and Bradford.
Undulating wooded parkland course.
9 holes, 5432 yards, S.S.S.67
Founded 1892
Visitors: welcome weekdays, with member only weekends.
Green Fee: £10 (£5 with member).
Societies: by arrangement.
Catering: by arrangement.

N48 Ganstead Park

☎(0482) 811280 Sec, 811121 Pro.
Longdales Lane, Coniston, Hull HU11 4LB
On A165 2 miles E of Hull boundary.
Parkland course.
18 holes, 6801 yards, S.S.S.73
Designed by Peter Green.
Founded 1976
Visitors: any day except Sun am.
Green Fee: £12/round, £15/day (£8 with member) WD; £20 (£10 with member) WE.
Societies: by arrangement.
Catering: lunches, evening meals.
Hotels: Hull Marina; Beverley Arms.

N49 Ganton

☎(0944) 70329
Ganton, Scarborough, N Yorks YO12 4PA
11 miles from Scarborough on A64.
Heathland course.
18 holes, 6720 yards, S.S.S.73
Designed by Dunn, Vardon, Colt, C.K. Cotton.
Founded 1891
Visitors: by prior arrangement.
Green Fee: on application.
Societies: by prior arrangement.
Catering: available.

N50 Garforth

☎(0532) 862021
Long Lane, Garforth, Leeds LS25 2DS
6.5 miles E of Leeds on A63, then left onto A642.
Parkland course.

18 holes, 6296 yards, S.S.S.70
Founded 1913
Visitors: welcome weekdays.
Green Fee: on application.
Societies: during the week.
Catering: all days except Tues.
Hotels: Ladbroke.

N51 Gott's Park

☎(0532) 310492
Armley Ridge Rd, Leeds LS12 2QX
About 3 miles W of city centre.
Public parkland course.
18 holes, 4960 yards, S.S.S.64
Visitors: welcome.
Green Fee: on application.
Societies: apply to Council.
Catering: meals served.
Hotels: Queens; Dragonara.

N52 Grange Park

☎(0709) 559497 Pro.
Upper Wortley Rd, Rotherham S61 2SJ
2 miles W of town on A629.
Municipal parkland course.
18 holes, 6461 yards, S.S.S.71
Founded 1971
Visitors: no restrictions.
Green Fee: on application.
Catering: available on request (private clubhouse).

N53 Hainsworth Park

☎(0964) 542362
Brandesburton, Driffield, E Yorks YO25 8RT
On A165 8 miles N of Beverley.
Parkland course.
18 holes, 5950 yards, S.S.S.69
Founded 1983
Visitors: restricted weekends.
Green Fee: £8 WD, £10 WE & BH.
Societies: any time.
Catering: bar and restaurant.
Hotels: Burton Lodge on course.

N54 Halifax

☎(0422) 244171
Union Lane, Ogden, Halifax HX2 8XR
4 miles from town centre on A629 Halifax-Keighley road.
Moorland course.
18 holes, 6037 yards, S.S.S.70
Designed by W.H. Fowler, James Braid.
Founded 1895
Visitors: welcome weekdays.
Green Fee: £20/day WD, £30/day WE & BH.
Societies: weekdays and limited weekends.

Catering: full range, à la carte and table d'hôte, except Mon.
Hotels: Holdsworth House (Holmfield); Princess (Halifax).

N55 Halifax Bradley Hall

☎(0422) 374108
Stainland Rd, Holywell Green, Halifax, W Yorks HX4 9AN
Half way between Halifax and Huddersfield on B6112.
Moorland course.
18 holes, 6213 yards, S.S.S.70
Founded 1924
Visitors: welcome.
Green Fee: £14 WD, £22 WE & BH.
Societies: on application.
Catering: full except Mon and Tues.
Snooker.
Hotels: Old Golf House (Outlane).

N56 Hallamshire

☎(0742) 302153 Sec, 301007 Clubhouse, 305222 Pro.
The Clubhouse, Sandygate, Sheffield S10 4LA
A57 from centre of Sheffield, left fork at Crosspool (3 miles), 1 mile to club.
Moorland course.
18 holes, 6396 yards, S.S.S.71
Founded 1898
Visitors: weekdays and limited weekends.
Green Fee: £27 WD, £33 WE & BH.
Societies: weekdays except Tues and Wed.
Catering: full facilities.
Snooker.
Hotels: Hallam Tower; Rutland.

N57 Hallowes

☎(0246) 413734 Sec, 411196 Pro.
Hallowes Lane, Dronfield, Sheffield S18 6UA
A61 Sheffield-Chesterfield road into Dronfield (not by-pass), sharp right under railway bridge, signposted.
Undulating moorland course.
18 holes, 6134 yards, S.S.S.71
Founded 1892
Visitors: check with Pro.
Green Fee: on application.
Societies: limited.
Catering: by arrangement with the Stewardess.

N58 Hanging Heaton

☎(0924) 461606
White Cross Rd, Bennett Lane, Dewsbury, W Yorks WF12 7DT
On A653 1 mile from Dewsbury centre.

Parkland course.
9 holes, 5874 yards, S.S.S.67
Visitors: welcome weekdays.
Green Fee: on application.
Societies: welcome weekdays.
Catering: lunch except Mon.

N59 **Harrogate**
☎(0423) 862999
Forest Lane Head, Harrogate,
N Yorks HG2 7TF
On right of A59, 2.5 miles from
Harrogate towards Knaresborough.
Undulating parkland course.
18 holes, 6241 yards, S.S.S.69
Designed by Sandy Herd.
Founded 1892
Visitors: welcome.
Green Fee: £22 WD, £32 WE & BH.
Societies: weekdays only by
arrangement, parties over 12.
Catering: bar and restaurant.
Snooker.
Hotels: Dower House; Newton House
(Knaresborough).

N60 **Headingley**
☎(0532) 679573 Sec, 675100 Pro.
Back Church Lane, Adel, Leeds LS16
8DW
At roundabout on Leeds ring road
take A660 towards Otley, turn right
after 1 mile at lights, then left, course
is just past Adel Church.
Undulating parkland course.
18 holes, 6298 yards, S.S.S.70
Founded 1892
Visitors: members of other clubs
welcome, prior reservation
preferred.
Green Fee: £22/round, £27.50/day
WD; £36/round/day WE & BH.
Societies: recognised societies
welcome if previous arrangements
made with Sec.
Catering: full facilities (not Fri).
2 snooker tables.
Hotels: Post House; Parkway.

N61 **Headley**
☎(0274) 833481
Headley Lane, Thornton, Bradford,
W Yorks BD13 3AJ
4 miles W of Bradford, on B6145
Thornton road, in village of Thornton.
Moorland course.
9 holes, 2457 yards, S.S.S.64
Founded 1906
Visitors: unlimited, not Sun.
Green Fee: £6/day, £10 WE.
Societies: by arrangement.
Catering: by arrangement.
Hotels: Norfolk Gardens.

N62 **Hebden Bridge**
☎(0422) 842896
Wadsworth, Hebden Bridge, W Yorks
HX7 8PH
1 mile N of Hebden Bridge past
Birchcliffe Centre.
Moorland course.
9 holes, 5114 yards, S.S.S.65
Founded 1930
Visitors: weekdays no restrictions,
weekends check first.
Green Fee: £7.50 WD, £10 WE.
Societies: welcome by arrangement.
Catering: meals and bar snacks
except Mon.
Hotels: Carlton (reduced green fees);
Hebden Lodge; Old Civic Hall.

N63 **Hessle**
☎(0482) 650171
Westfield Rd, Cottingham, Hull,
N Humberside HU16 5YL
3 miles SW of Cottingham, off A164.
Undulating meadowland course.
18 holes, 6638 yards, S.S.S.72;
18 holes, 6290 yards, S.S.S.70
Designed by Allis & Thomas.
Founded 1906; new course 1975
Visitors: not Tues, 9.15am-1pm.
Green Fee: on application.
Societies: recognised golfing
societies welcome by prior
arrangement with Sec.
Catering: all days during summer.
Hotels: Willerby Manor; Grange
Park; Beverley Arms.

N64 **Heworth**
☎(0904) 424618, 422389 Pro.
Muncaster House, Muncastergate,
York YO3 9JX
1.5 miles from city centre, on A1036
York-Scarborough road.
Meadowland/parkland course.
11 holes, 6078 yards, S.S.S.69
Founded 1911
Visitors: weekdays, weekends
restricted availability.
Green Fee: on application.
Societies: weekdays.
Catering: lunches except Mon.

N65 **Hickleton**
☎(0709) 896081 Sec, 892496 Club,
895170 Pro.
Hickleton, Nr Doncaster, S Yorks DN5
7BE
7 miles out of Doncaster on B6411,
off A635 to Barnsley.
Undulating parkland course.
18 holes, 6403 yards, S.S.S.71
Designed by Huggett, Coles & Dyer.
Founded 1909

N66 **Hillsborough**
☎(0742) 349151 Sec, ££2666 Pro.
Worrall Rd, Sheffield S6 4BE
Moorland/parkland course.
18 holes, 5518 metres, S.S.S.69
Founded 1920
Visitors: welcome weekdays.
Green Fee: £20/round/day WD, £30
WE & BH.
Societies: by arrangement.
Catering: soup/sandwiches every
lunchtime except Fri; full meals by
prior arrangement.
Snooker.
Hotels: Grosvenor; Rutland.

N67 **Hornsea**
☎(0964) 532020 Sec, 534989 Pro.
Rolston Rd, Hornsea, N Humberside
HU18 1XG
Follow sign for Hornsea Pottery in
Hornsea, clubhouse is approx 600
yards further on road to Withernsea.
Parkland/moorland course.
18 holes, 6450 yards, S.S.S.71
Designed by Sandy Herd.
Founded 1910
Visitors: every day; after 3pm Sat
and Sun, after 2pm Tues.
Green Fee: £16.50/round,
£21.50/day WD; £26.50/round WE.
Societies: by arrangement with Sec,
not weekends.
Catering: Steward's day off Mon,
catering by arrangement.
Snooker.
Hotels: Tickton Grange; Burton
Lodge.

N68 **Horsforth**
☎(0532) 586819
Layton Rd, Horsforth, Leeds, W Yorks
LS18 5EX
On A65 Leeds-Ilkley road, Layton Rd
is on right after crossing A6120
Leeds ring road, and after passing
Rawdon Crematorium on left.
Undulating pastureland course.
18 holes, 6243 yards, S.S.S.70
Founded 1905
Visitors: welcome, not weekends.
Green Fee: £20/day, £25 WE.
Societies: weekdays and Sun.
Catering: full service available.
Hotels: Post House (Bramhope).

Top right column intro:
Visitors: welcome if members of
recognised club; after 2.30 pm
weekends and Bank Holidays.
Green Fee: £17 WD, £25 WE & BH.
Societies: weekdays; annual society
open day.
Catering: available except Mon.

N69 Howley Hall
☎(0924) 472432
Scotchman Lane, Morley, Leeds
LS27 0NX
From A650 Bradford-Wakefield road,
take B6123, situated in Morley.
Parkland course.
18 holes, 6420 yards, S.S.S.71
Founded 1900
Visitors: welcome except Sat.
Green Fee: £18/round, £22/day WD;
£25/round/day WE.
Societies: weekdays.
Catering: every day except Mon.
Snooker.
Hotels: Post House(Ossett).

N70 Huddersfield (Fixby)
☎(0484) 426203 Sec, 420110
Clubhouse, 426463 Pro.
Fixby Hall, Lightridge Rd, Fixby,
Huddersfield HD2 2EP
M62 exit 24 to Huddersfield, to
roundabout, 3rd exit A643
signposted Brighouse, 1 mile to
traffic lights (Sun Inn), turn right,
after 0.75 mile, right on Lightridge
Rd, club 500 yards on right.
Heathland course.
18 holes, 6364 yards, S.S.S.71
Designed by Herbert Fowler,
amendments by Hawtree.
Founded 1891
Visitors: welcome; societies and
companies must book in advance;
starting sheets operate; tee
reservation recommended.
Green Fee: £25/round, £35/day WD;
£35/round, £45/day WE.
Societies: Mon-Fri, weekends
limited.
Catering: lunch, à la carte
restaurant; exclusive bar catering for
societies (over 40). Snooker.
Hotels: Pennine Hilton; TH Forte.

N71 Hull
☎(0482) 658919
The Hall, 27 Packman Lane, Kirkella,
Hull HU10 7TJ
5 miles W of Hull, off A164.
Parkland course.
18 holes, 6242 yards, S.S.S.70
Designed by James Braid.
Founded 1921
Visitors: Mon to Fri only.
Green Fee: £22/day or round.
Societies: Tues and Thurs by prior
arrangement.
Catering: prior arrangement if
possible, lunches served Mon to Fri.
Snooker.
Hotels: Willerby Manor; Grange
Park.

N72 Ilkley
☎(0943) 600214 Sec, 607277
Steward, 607463 Pro.
Myddleton, Ilkley, W Yorks LS29 0BE
On A65 18 miles NW of Leeds.
Parkland course.
18 holes, 6262 yards, S.S.S.70
Founded 1890
Visitors: welcome by arrangement.
Green Fee: £28 WD, £35 WE & BH.
Societies: by arrangement
weekdays only.
Catering: full facilities.
Hotels: Rombalds; Grove.

N73 Keighley
☎(0535) 604778, 603179
Howden Park, Utley, Keighley,
W Yorks BD20 6DA
1 mile W of Keighley on A650 Skipton
road.
Parkland course.
18 holes, 6139 yards, S.S.S.70
Founded 1904
Visitors: not Sat, limited Sun.
Green Fee: £20/round £24/day WD.
Societies: by arrangement.
Catering: available every day except
Mon.
Hotels: Dalesgate; Beeches.

N74 Kirkbymoorside
☎(0751) 31525
Manor Vale, Kirkbymoorside, N Yorks
YO6 6EG
On A170 Thirsk to Scarborough road;
Helmsley 7 miles, Pickering 7 miles.
Undulating moorland course.
18 holes, 6027 yards, S.S.S.69
Founded 1905
Visitors: welcome, advisable to
telephone first.
Green Fee: £15 (£7.50 with
member) WD, £20 (£10 with
member) WE & BH.
Societies: by arrangement with
Steward.
Catering: meals and snacks daily
except Mon.
Hotels: George & Dragon; Feversham
Arms; Feathers (Helmsley); Worsley
Arms (Hovingham).

N75 Knaresborough
☎(0423) 862690, 863219
Butterhills, Boroughbridge Rd,
Knaresborough HG5 0QQ
1.5 miles N of Knaresborough off
main Boroughbridge road.
Parkland course.
18 holes, 6232 yards, S.S.S.70
Designed by Hawtree & Son.
Founded 1920

Visitors: welcome, few restrictions.
Green Fee: £18 WD, £24 WE.
Societies: catered for.
Catering: available every day except
Mon.
Hotels: Dower House.

N76 Leeds
☎(0532) 658775
Elmete Lane, Leeds LS8 2LJ
Off A58 4 miles from Leeds.
Parkland course.
18 holes 6097 yards, S.S.S.69
Founded 1896
Visitors: weekdays only, weekends
only with member.
Green Fee: £18/round, £24/day.
Societies: weekdays.
Catering: as required except Mon.
Snooker.
Hotels: Queens; Hotel Metropole.

N77 Lees Hall
☎(0742) 554402 Club, 552900 Sec,
551526 Steward
Hemsworth Rd, Norton, Sheffield S8
8LL
3 miles S of Sheffield, A61 then
A6054 towards Gleadless, 1st exit at
roundabout, follow road to next
roundabout passing water tower on
left, take 1st exit, course 300 yards
on right.
Parkland course.
18 holes, 6137 yards, S.S.S.69
Founded 1907
Visitors: always welcome.
Green Fee: £16/round, £20/day WD;
£25/round WE & BH.
Societies: weekdays subject to prior
booking.
Catering: no catering on Tues.
Snooker.
Hotels: Grosvenor House; Hallam
Towers; Sheffield Moat House.

N78 Lightcliffe
☎(0422) 202459
Knowle Top Rd, Lightcliffe, Halifax
On A58 Leeds-Halifax road, on left
entering Lightcliffe/Hipperholme
village 4 miles E of Halifax.
Parkland course.
9 holes, 5388 yards, S.S.S.68
Founded 1907
Visitors: welcome apart from Wed
and Sat.
Green Fee: on application.
Societies: catered for on weekdays
except Wed.
Catering: lunch and evening meals
except Tues.
Hotels: Clifton Trust House.

N79 Longley Park
☎(0484) 422304
Maple St, off Somerset Rd,
Huddersfield HD5 9AX
0.5 mile from town centre.
Parkland course.
9 holes, 5269 yards, S.S.S.66
Founded 1911
Visitors: welcome weekdays except
Wed, Thurs; restricted weekends.
Green Fee: £11 WD, £13.50 WE.
Societies: by arrangement except
Wed, Thurs and Sat.
Catering: except Mon by
arrangement.

N80 Low Laithes
☎(0924) 273275 Club, 274667 Pro.
Parkmill Lane, Flushdyke, Ossett,
W Yorks WF5 9AP
Leave M1 at exit 40, signposted on
Dewsbury road, 1st turning from
northbound exit M1.
Parkland course.
18 holes, 6463 yards, S.S.S.71
Designed by McKenzie.
Founded 1925
Visitors: dress rules and reasonable
golfers.
Green Fee: £15 WD, £18 WE & BH.
Societies: by prior arrangement, not
weekends.
Catering: full facilities daily.
Hotels: Post House; Mews; Swallow.

N81 Malton & Norton
☎(0653) 692959 Clubhouse,
697912 Sec, 693882 Pro.
Welham Park, Malton, N Yorks YO17
9QE
From Malton & Norton level crossing,
S on Welham road for 0.75 mile, turn
right.
Parkland course.
18 holes, 6411 yards, S.S.S.71
Designed by Hawtree & Son.
Founded 1910
Visitors: welcome, restricted on club
competition days.
Green Fee: £17 WD, £22 WE & BH.
Societies: apply to Sec.
Catering: full facilities, breakfast by
arrangement.
Hotels: Talbot; The Mount.

N82 Marsden
☎(0484) 844253
Mount Rd, Hemplow, Marsden,
Huddersfield HD7 6NN
Off A62 8 miles out of Huddersfield
towards Manchester.
Moorland course.
9 holes, 5702 yards, S.S.S.68

Designed by Dr Mackenzie.
Founded 1920
Visitors: welcome weekdays.
Green Fee: on application.
Societies: catered for by
arrangement weekdays.
Catering: lunches except Tues,
evening meals by arrangement.
Hotels: Durker Roods (Meltham).

N83 Masham
☎(0765) 689379, 689491 Sec.
Swinton Rd, Masham, Ripon, N Yorks
HG4 4HT
9 miles N of Ripon on A6108.
Parkland course.
9 holes, 5244 yards, S.S.S.66
Founded 1900
Visitors: welcome weekdays,
weekends and Bank Holidays with
member only.
Green Fee: £15/day.
Societies: apply to Sec.
Catering: bar all day, catering
daytime only.
Hotels: Kings Head.

N84 Meltham
☎(0484) 850227, 851521 Pro.
Thick Hollins, Meltham, Huddersfield
HD7 3DQ
5 miles from Huddersfield on B6108,
in Meltham take B6107.
Moorland/parkland course.
18 holes, 6145 yards, S.S.S.70
Founded 1908
Visitors: any day except Wed, Sat.
Green Fee: on application.
Societies: weekdays.
Catering: all days except Tues.
Hotels: Durker Roods; Old Bridge.

N85 Middleton Park
☎(0532) 700449
Ring Rd, Beeston, Leeds 10
3 miles S of city centre.
Public parkland course.
18 holes, 5233 yards, S.S.S.69
Designed by Leeds City Council.
Founded 1932
Visitors: welcome.
Green Fee: on application.
Societies: can be booked.

N86 Moor Allerton
☎(0532) 661154, 661155
Coal Rd, Wike, Leeds LS17 9NH
Take A61 Harrogate Rd, about 1 mile
past intersection with A6120 ring
road turn right onto Wigton Lane, at
T-junction take 1st left, then 1st right
then signposted.

Undulating parkland course.
1-18 The Lakes, 6045 yards,
S.S.S.71; 10-27 Blackmoor, 6222
yards, S.S.S.72; 1-9/19-27 High
Course, 6930 yards, S.S.S.75
Designed by Robert Trent Jones.
Founded 1923
Visitors: welcome weekdays.
Green Fee: on application.
Societies: any weekday.
Catering: lunches every day; dinner
Tues, Wed, Thurs, unlimited
numbers; Mon, Fri min 40 required.

N87 Moortown
☎(0532) 686521 Sec, 681682 Club,
683636 Pro.
Harrogate Rd, Leeds LS17 7DB
On A61 main Leeds-Harrogate road.
Moorland course.
18 holes, 6544 yards, S.S.S.72
Designed by Dr Mackenzie.
Founded 1909
Visitors: welcome weekdays, apply
to Sec/Pro weekends.
Green Fee: on application.
Societies: weekdays.
Catering: lunches served except
Mon; other meals by arrangement.
Snooker.
Hotels: Harewood Arms; Post House.

N88 Mount Skip
☎(0422) 842896
Greater Mount, Wadsworth, Hebden
Bridge, W Yorks HX7 8PH
1 mile N of Hebden Bridge on
Birchcliffe Rd.
Moorland course.
9 holes, 5112 yards, S.S.S.66
Founded 1930
Visitors: welcome.
Green Fee: on application.
Societies: welcome except Mon.
Catering: restaurant and bar service
available except Mon.
Hotels: Hebden Lodge; Carlton.

N89 Normanton
☎(0924) 892943
Syndale Rd, Normanton, Wakefield,
W Yorks WF6 1PA
Off M62 at junction 31, 0.5 mile from
Normanton centre.
Flat meadowland course.
9 holes, 5184 yards, S.S.S.66
Founded 1903
Visitors: weekdays and Sat,
members only Sun.
Green Fee: on application.
Societies: weekdays, £13 package.
Catering: full facilities.
Hotels: Village Motel.

N90 **Northcliffe**
☎(0274) 584085 Clubhouse,
596731 Sec, 587193 Pro.
High Bank Lane, Shipley, W Yorks
BD18 4LJ
Take A650 Bradford-Keighley road to
Saltaire roundabout, turn up
Moorhead Lane, leading to High Bank
Lane, club 0.5 mile on left.
Parkland course.
18 holes, 6104 yards, S.S.S.69
Designed by James Braid and Harry
Vardon.
Founded 1920
Visitors: welcome except Sat and
Sun; (Tues Ladies Day).
Green Fee: £15.50 WD, £22.50 WE
& BH.
Societies: welcome Wed-Fri.
Catering: bar, snacks except Mon;
dinner by arrangement with Steward.
Hotels: Bankfield; Regency.

N91 **Oakdale**
☎(0423) 567162
Oakdale, Harrogate HG1 2LN
From Ripon Rd, Harrogate, turn into
Kent Rd, follow signs.
Undulating parkland course with
panoramic views.
18 holes, 6456 yards, S.S.S.71
Designed by Dr Mackenzie.
Founded 1914
Visitors: welcome.
Green Fee: £18/round, £25/day.
Societies: weekdays.
Catering: full facilities except Mon
lunchtime, dinner by arrangement.
Hotels: Crown; Fern; Majestic;
Studley; Old Swan; Balmoral.

N92 **Otley**
☎(0943) 465329 Sec, 461015 Club,
463403 Pro.
West Busk Lane, Otley, W Yorks LS21
3NG
On Otley-Bradford road 1.5 miles
from Otley.
Parkland course.
18 holes, 6225 yards, S.S.S.70
Founded 1906
Visitors: welcome.
Green Fee: £20 WD, £25 WE.
Societies: by arrangement.
Catering: full facilities except Mon.
Hotels: Post House; Devonshire
Arms.

N93 **Oulton Park**
☎(0532) 823152 (may change in
1992)
Oulton, Leeds LS26
M62 junction 30, A642 to Rothwell,
over 1st roundabout (1 mile),
immediately left at 2nd roundabout.
Public parkland course.
18 holes, c. 6,500 yards, S.S.S.71
Designed by Allis & Thomas.
Founded 1990
Visitors: no restrictions, book in
advance.
Green Fee: £5.25/round WD,
£6.15/round WE.
Societies: by arrangement.
Catering: bar, bar meals.
Driving range

N94 **Outlane**
☎(0422) 74762
Slack Lane, Outlane, Huddersfield,
W Yorks
Off A640 Rochdale road, 4 miles out
of Huddersfield, through village of
Outlane, turn left under motorway.
Moorland course.
18 holes, 6000 yards, S.S.S.68
Founded 1906
Visitors: welcome.
Green Fee: £12 (£5 with member)
WD, £20 (£8 with member) WE.
Societies: by arrangement.
Catering: meals daily except Mon.
Hotels: Old Golf House; Ladbroke
Mercury.

N95 **Owston Park**
☎(0302) 330821
Owston Hall, Owston, Nr Carcroft,
Doncaster, S Yorks DN6 9JF
Off A19, 10 mins N of Doncaster.
Parkland course.
9 holes, 3042 yards, S.S.S.71
Designed by Michael Parker.
Founded 1988
Visitors: welcome, pay-as-you-play.
Green Fee: £2.50 (9 holes), £2 jnrs
and OAPs.
Societies: welcome.

N96 **Painthorpe House
G & CC**
☎(0924) 255083
Painthorpe Lane, Crigglestone,
Wakefield, W Yorks WF4 3HE
2 mins from M1 junction 39.
Parkland course.
9 holes, 4250 yards, S.S.S.62
Founded 1961
Visitors: welcome Mon–Fri only.
Green Fee: £5.
Societies: by arrangement.
Catering: 4 bars, dining room, 2 ball
rooms.
Exhibitions, conferences, dinner
dances (max 450), bowls.
Hotels: Cedar Court (Durkar).

N97 **Pannal**
☎(0423) 872628 Sec.
Follifoot Rd, Pannal, Harrogate HG3
1ES
Just off A61 Leeds-Harrogate road at
Pannal.
Parkland/moorland championship
course.
18 holes, 6659 yards, S.S.S.72
Designed by Sandy Herd.
Founded 1906
Visitors: welcome weekdays.
Green Fee: £26/round/day WD;
£31/round WE & BH.
Societies: weekdays by
arrangement with Sec.
Catering: meals, bar snacks daily.

N98 **Phoenix**
☎(0709) 382624
Pavilion Lane, Brinsworth,
Rotherham, W Yorks
1 mile along Bawtry turning from
Tinsley roundabout on M1.
Undulating meadowland course.
18 holes, 6145 yards, S.S.S.69
Founded 1932
Visitors: welcome if member of
recognised golf club.
Green Fee: £15/day (£6 with
member) WD, £20 (£8 with member)
WE & BH.
Societies: welcome.
Catering: full on request.
Hotels: Moat House; Brecon.

N99 **Phoenix Park**
☎(0274) 667178, 662369 Sec.
Phoenix Park, Dick Lane, Thornbury,
Bradford, W Yorks
From Bradford take Leeds road for
2.5 miles to Thornbury roundabout,
course situated at side of
roundabout.
Undulating parkland course.
9 holes, 4776 yards, S.S.S.63
Visitors: welcome weekdays only.
Green Fee: on application.
Societies: by prior arrangement with
Sec.
Catering: by arrangement with
Steward prior to visit.

N100 **Pike Hills**
☎(0904) 706566
Tadcaster Rd, Askham Bryan, York
YO2 3UW
Turn left towards York off A64
Leeds-Scarborough road
immediately after by-pass flyover.
Parkland course.
18 holes, 6121 yards, S.S.S.69
Founded 1920

Visitors: weekdays before 4.30pm; weekends and Bank Holidays only with member.
Green Fee: £18/round/day summer, £14/round/day winter (Oct-Mar).
Societies: parties of 12+ welcome if previously booked, correct dress essential, each member must have recognised h/cap.
Catering: full facilities except Mon.

N101 Pontefract & District

☎(0977) 792241
Park Lane, Pontefract, W Yorks WF8 4QS
M62 exit 32, situated on B6134.
Parkland course.
18 holes, 6227 yards, S.S.S.70
Founded 1900
Visitors: welcome weekdays.
Green Fee: £20 WD, £25 WE & BH.
Societies: catered for weekdays except Wed.
Catering: daily, except Mon.
Hotels: Red Lion; Wentbridge House; Park Side Inne.

N102 Pontefract Park

☎(0977) 702799
Park Road, Pontefract, W Yorkshire
0.5 mile from M62 towards Pontefract beside race course.
Public parkland course.
9 holes, 2034 yards, Par 31
Visitors: welcome.
Green Fee: £3.35/round (18 holes) WD, £4.75/round WE.

N103 Queensbury

☎(0274) 882155
Brighouse Rd, Queensbury, Bradford, W Yorks BD13 1QF
4 miles from Bradford on A647.
Undulating parkland course.
9 holes, 5102 yards, S.S.S.65
Founded 1923
Visitors: bona fide golfers welcome.
Green Fee: on application.
Societies: by arrangement.
Catering: during normal licensing hours.
Hotels: Norfolk Gardens; White Swan.

N104 Rawdon

☎(0532) 506040
Buckstone Drive, Rawdon, Leeds LS19 6BD
On A65 6 miles from Leeds.
Undulating parkland course.
9 holes, 5964 yards, S.S.S.69
Founded 1896

Visitors: welcome weekdays.
Green Fee: on application.
Societies: welcome weekdays by arrangement.
Catering: lunch except Mon.
3 all-weather tennis courts, 4 grass.
Hotels: Peas Hill; Robin Hood.

N105 Renishaw Park

☎(0246) 432044
Station Rd, Renishaw, Sheffield S31 9UZ
M1 junction 30, take sign for Eckington, club 1.5 miles on right.
Parkland course.
18 holes, 6253 yards, S.S.S.70
Designed by R. Sitwell.
Founded 1911
Visitors: welcome weekdays; ring club for dress rule.
Green Fee: on application.
Societies: by arrangement.
Catering: full bar and restaurant.
Hotels: Sitwell Arms; Mosborough Hall.

N106 Richmond

☎(0748) 822457
Bend Hagg, Richmond, N Yorks DL10 5EX
A6108 from Scotch Corner, turn right at traffic lights after 4 miles.
Parkland course.
18 holes, 5704 yards, S.S.S.68
Designed by Frank Pennink.
Founded 1892
Visitors: welcome; not before 11.30am on Sun.
Green Fee: £11/round, £13/day WD; £17/round, £22/day WE & BH.
Societies: catered for.
Catering: daily except Mon.
Hotels: Frenchgate.

N107 Riddlesden

☎(0535) 602148
Howden Rough, Riddlesden, Keighley, W Yorks
A650 Keighley-Bradford road, left into Bar Lane, left into Scott Lane for 2 miles.
Moorland course.
18 holes, 4185 yards, S.S.S.61
Founded 1927
Visitors: unlimited weekdays; after 2pm Sat and Sun.
Green Fee: £8/round/day (£5 with member) WD, £12 (£8 with member) WE.
Catering: 12am-2pm and 6-10pm weekdays,, 12am-5.30pm weekends.
Hotels: Dalesway.

N108 Ripon City

☎(0765) 603640 Sec/Clubhouse, 600411 Pro.
Palace Rd, Ripon, N Yorks HG4 3HH
1 mile N on A6108 towards Leyburn.
Undulating parkland course.
9 holes, 5752 yards, S.S.S.68
Founded 1905
Visitors: any day.
Green Fee: £10/day WD, £15/day WE & BH.
Societies: by prior arrangement.
Catering: only for parties, by prior arrangement.
Hotels: Ripon Spa; Unicorn.

N109 Rotherham

☎(0709) 850812 Sec, 850466 Pro.
Thrybergh Park, Thrybergh, Rotherham S65 4NU
On A631 Doncaster-Rotherham road, from A1M, 3 miles from M18 at Bramley, 7 miles from M1 junction 35.
Parkland course.
18 holes, 6324 yards, S.S.S.70
Founded 1903
Visitors: by arrangement with Pro.
Green Fee: £20/round/day.
Societies: parties of 16+ to book with Sec; not Wed, weekends or Bank Holidays.
Catering: full facilities every day.
Hotels: Beeches; Moat House; Limes; Brecon.

N110 Roundhay

☎(0532) 662695, 661686 Pro shop
Park Lane, Leeds LS8 2EJ
A58 to Oakwood Clock, then Princes Ave, Street Lane, right at Park Lane, 4 miles from city centre.
Municipal parkland course.
9 holes, 5322 yards, S.S.S.65
Founded 1921
Visitors: unrestricted.
Green Fee: £4.90 WD, £5.35 WE.
Societies: by arrangement with Leeds City Council.
Catering: restaurant Tues-Sun evenings; snacks available Sat, Sun.
Hotels: Beech Wood.

N111 Roundwood

☎(0709) 523471
Off Green Lane, Rawmarsh, Rotherham, S Yorks S62 6LA
2.5 miles N of Rotherham on A633.
Parkland course.
9 holes, 5600 yards, S.S.S.67
Founded 1977
Visitors: welcome.
Green Fee: £10/day (£5 with member).

Societies: welcome.
Catering: bar and snacks, not Sun, Mon, Tues.
Practice putting green.
Hotels: Marquis; Guest House.

N112 **Ryburn**
☎(0422) 831355
The Shaw, Norland, Sowerby Bridge, W Yorkshire
3 miles S of Halifax.
Moorland course.
9 holes, 5002 yards, S.S.S.65
Founded 1910
Visitors: welcome, no restrictions.
Green Fee: £11 (£8 with member).
Societies: welcome by application only.
Catering: available.

N113 **Sand Moor**
☎(0532) 685180
Alwoodley Lane, Leeds LS17 7DJ
A61 N from Leeds city centre 6 miles, turn left into Alwoodley Lane, 0.5 mile on right.
Undulating parkland/moorland course.
18 holes, 6429 yards, S.S.S.71
Designed by N. Barnes.
Founded 1926
Visitors: welcome weekdays; members reserved times 12am-1.30pm; Tues 9.30-10.30am; Thurs 8.30-12am.
Green Fee: £25/round WD; WE & BH by arrangement with Sec.
Societies: weekdays.
Catering: full facilities weekdays except Mon (lunches and snacks only).
Hotels: Harewood Arms; Parkway; Forte Crest.

N114 **Sandhill**
☎(0226) 751775
c/o Colliery Farm, Little Houghton, Barnsley, S Yorks
Off A635 1 mile E of Darfield, 6 miles E of Barnsley.
Meadowland course.
18 holes, 6211 yards, S.S.S.70
Designed by John Royston.
Founded Oct 1991
Visitors: welcome; course due to open Sept 1992 for limited play, April 1993 unlimited; ring to check in advance.
Green Fee: £10 WD, £12 WE.
Societies: by arrangement, phone for details.
Catering: by arrangement.
Driving range.

N115 **Scarborough North Cliff**
☎(0723) 360786
North Cliff Ave, Burniston Rd, Scarborough YO12 6PP
2 miles N of town centre on coast road (Burniston Rd), turn right along North Cliff Ave.
Seaside/parkland course.
18 holes, 6425 yards, S.S.S.71
Designed by James Braid.
Founded 1928
Visitors: no restrictions except before 10am Sun; must be recognised golfers.
Green Fee: £18/day WD; £24/day WE & BH.
Societies: mainly weekdays by prior arrangement with Sec, parties of 12 to 36.
Catering: soup and sandwiches available to 5.30pm; bar snacks lunchtime and 7-10pm.
Hotels: Clifton; Majestic; Overdale.

N116 **Scarborough South Cliff**
☎(0723) 374737
Deepdale Ave, Scarborough YO11 2UE
1 mile S of Scarborough on main Filey road.
Parkland/seaside course.
18 holes, 6085 yards, S.S.S.69
Designed by Dr Mackenzie.
Founded 1903
Visitors: welcome.
Green Fee: £19 WD, £22 WE & BH.
Societies: weekdays and weekends.
Catering: full catering facilities.
Hotels: Royal; Crown; St Nicholas; Brooklands; Southlands; Holbeck Hall.

N117 **Scarcroft**
☎(0532) 892263, 892311
Syke Lane, Leeds LS14 3BQ
On A58 NE of Leeds in Scarcroft village, immediately after the New Inn on the left is Syke Lane.
Parkland course.
18 holes, 6426 yards, S.S.S.71
Designed by Major C. Mackenzie.
Founded 1937
Visitors: welcome weekdays, weekends by prior arrangement only.
Green Fee: £25/round, £30/day WD; £35/round WE by prior arrangement with Sec.
Societies: welcome Tues-Thurs by arrangement.
Catering: meals daily except Mon.
Hotels: Harewood Arms; Swan; Talbot.

N118 **Selby**
☎(0757) 228622
Mill Lane, Brayton Barff, Selby, N Yorks YO8 9LD
3 miles SW of Selby, 1 mile E of A19 at Brayton village; from M62 junction 34, A19 (Selby-Doncaster) for 5 miles N towards Selby, 1st left in Brayton into Mill Lane, 1 mile on right.
Flat inland links type course.
18 holes, 6246 yards, S.S.S.70
Founded 1907
Visitors: welcome weekdays with h/cap certs; members and guests only at weekends.
Green Fee: £18/round, £20/day.
Societies: Wed, Thurs and Fri.
Catering: every day except Mon. Snooker, large practice ground.
Hotels: Londesborough; Selby Fork Motel.

N119 **Serlby Park**
☎(0777) 818268
Serlby, Doncaster, S Yorks DN10 6BA
3 miles S of Bawtry.
Parkland course on Galway Estate.
9 holes, 5370 yards, S.S.S.66
Designed by Viscount Galway.
Founded 1895
Visitors: only with member.
Green Fee: £7 WD, £10 WE.
Societies: selected few.
Catering: available.
Hotels: Crown (Bawtry); Mount Pleasant, Olde Bell (Barnby Moor).

N120 **Settle**
☎(07292) 3912
Buckhaw Brow, Settle, N Yorks BD24
Main A65 Settle-Kendal road, opposite Giggleswick Quarry.
Parkland/moorland course.
9 holes, 4600 yards, S.S.S.62
Founded 1891
Visitors: welcome, restricted Sun.
Green Fee: £7.50/day.
Hotels: Falcon Manor.

N121 **Shipley**
☎(0274) 563212 Clubhouse, 563674 Pro, 568652 Sec.
Beckfoot Lane, Cottingley Bridge, Bingley, W Yorks BD16 1LX
Situated on A650 Bradford-Keighley road at Cottingley Bridge, Bingley.
Parkland course.
18 holes, 6218 yards, S.S.S.70
Designed by Colt, Alison and Mackenzie assisted by James Braid.
Founded 1896
Visitors: welcome except Tues before 2pm, Sat before 4pm.

Green Fee: £22.50/day WD, £29 WE & BH (£10 with member).
Societies: by arrangement with Sec.
Catering: except Mon, bar snacks and evening meals by arrangement with Steward. Snooker.
Hotels: Bankfield; Oakwood Hall; Hall Bank.

N122 Silkstone
☎(0226) 790328, 790128 Pro.
Field Head, Silkstone, Barnsley, S Yorks S75 40D
1 mile from M1 on A628 towards Manchester.
Undulating meadowland course.
18 holes, 6045 yards, S.S.S.70
Founded 1893
Visitors: welcome weekdays.
Green Fee: on application.
Societies: catered for weekdays.
Catering: full facilities except Mon.
Hotels: Ardsley Moat House; Brooklands Motel.

N123 Silsden
☎(0525) 652998
High Brunthwaite, Silsden, Keighley BD20 0NH
A629, 4 miles from Keighley, on to A6034 to Silsden town centre, turn E at canal.
Moorland/meadowland course.
14 holes, 4870 yards, S.S.S.64
Founded 1913
Visitors: welcome; restrictions Sat pm and Sun am.
Green Fee: £10 WD, £15 WE; (£5 with member).
Hotels: Steeton Hall.

N124 Sitwell Park
☎(0709) 541046, 540961 Pro, 700799 Stewardess
Shrogswood Rd, Rotherham, S Yorks S60 4BY
From M1 exit 31, take A630 and A631 to Bawtry; from M18 exit 1, follow A631 Sheffield road; club 2 miles SE of Rotherham.
Undulating parkland course.
18 holes, 6203 yards, S.S.S.70
Designed by Dr Mackenzie.
Founded 1913
Visitors: welcome.
Green Fee: £17/round, £21/day WD; £20/round, £24/day WE & BH.
Societies: welcome weekdays; book through Sec.
Catering: meals booked through Stewardess.
Hotels: Moat House; Brecon; Brentwood; Limes.

N125 Skipton
☎(0756) 793922
North-West By-Pass, Skipton, N Yorks BD23 1LL
Off NW by-pass (A59 and A65) 1 mile from town centre.
High fell land course.
18 holes, 6191 yards, S.S.S.70
Founded 1905
Visitors: welcome; phone Pro beforehand.
Green Fee: winter (Nov-Mar) £12 WD, £20 WE & BH; summer (April-Oct) £17 WD, £22 WE & BH.
Societies: welcome, special terms for parties of 12 or more; contact general manager.
Catering: every day except Mon.

N126 South Bradford
☎(0274) 679195
Pearson Rd, Odsal, Bradford BD6 1BH
From Odsal roundabout take Stadium Rd (1st road left down Cleckheaton Rd) then Pearson Rd to club.
Undulating meadowland course.
9 holes, 6004 yards, S.S.S.69
Founded 1906
Visitors: welcome weekdays.
Green Fee: £10 (£6 with member) WD, £15 (£8 with member) WE.
Societies: weekdays.
Catering: lunches and evening meals served except Mon.
Hotels: Guide Post.

N127 South Leeds
☎(0532) 700479
Gipsy Lane, Beeston Ring Rd, Leeds LS11 5TU
From M62 junction 28 take Leeds-Dewsbury road to lights at Tommy Wass Hotel, ring road for 100 yards then left into Gipsy Lane; c. 2 miles.
Parkland course.
18 holes, 5890 yards, S.S.S.68
Founded 1914
Visitors: welcome any time (reduced green fees if playing with member).
Green Fee: £17/day/round WD, £22 WE & BH.
Societies: apply to Sec.
Catering: every day except Mon. Snooker.
Hotels: Dragonara; Queens; Red Lion.

N128 Springhead Park
☎(0482) 656309
Willerby Rd, Hull, Yorks HU5 5JE
3 miles W of Hull centre.
Municipal parkland course
18 holes, 6402 yards, S.S.S.71

Founded 1930
Visitors: welcome, no restrictions.
Green Fee: £2.85/round WD, £4/round WE (to be revised); reductions for jnrs and OAPs.
Societies: on application.
Catering: light snacks; bar for members and guests only.
Hotels: Willerby Manor; Grange Park.

N129 Springmill
☎(0924) 272515
Queens Drive, Osset, W Yorks
M1 junction 40, 1 mile out of Osset towards Wakefield.
Public parkland course.
9 holes Par 3, 1165 yards.
Visitors: welcome.
Green Fee: £1.50 (9 holes).
Societies: welcome.

N130 Stocksbridge & District
☎(0742) 882003
30 Royd Lane, Townend, Deepcar, Sheffield S30 5RZ
A616 into Deepcar, 1st left into Carr Rd, course 1 mile on left.
Moorland course.
18 holes, 5221 yards, S.S.S.66
Designed by Allis & Thomas.
Founded 1924
Visitors: welcome any time.
Green Fee: £12/day WD, £18 WE.
Societies: on request, not weekends.
Catering: on request except Mon.
Hotels: Grosvenor; Hallam Towers.

N131 Sutton Park
☎(0482) 74242
Saltshouse Rd, Holderness Rd, Hull, N Humberside HU8 9HF
4 miles E of city centre on A165 (B1237).
Public parkland course.
18 holes, 6251 yards, S.S.S.70
Founded 1935
Visitors: unlimited.
Green Fee: £2.50/round.
Societies: on application to Hull City Council Leisure Services.
Catering: bar snacks lunchtime, full meals by arrangement. Snooker.
Hotels: Royal Station.

N132 Tankersley Park
☎(0742) 468247
High Green, Sheffield S30 4LG
Close M1 between junctions 35A (northbound only) or 36, on A616.
Parkland course.
18 holes, 6212 yards, S.S.S.70

Designed by Hawtree.
Founded 1907
Visitors: weekdays unlimited, Sat and Sun after 3pm; must be bona fide golfers with club h/cap.
Green Fee: £15.50/round (£6 with member), £20/day.
Societies: Mon-Fri only.
Catering: bar and restaurant.
Snooker.

N133 **Temple Newsam**
☎(0532) 645624
Temple Newsam Rd, Leeds LS15
On A63 Selby road, 5 miles from Leeds centre, follow signs for Temple Newsam House.
Public undulating parkland course.
18 holes, 6448 yards, S.S.S.71;
18 holes, 6029 yards, S.S.S.70
Founded 1923
Visitors: welcome.
Green Fee: municipal rates.
Societies: by arrangement.
Catering: bar 7 days, carvery Sat, Sun.
Hotels: Windmill; Mercury.

N134 **Thirsk & Northallerton**
☎(0845) 522170
Thornton-le-Street, Thirsk, N Yorks YO7 4AB
2 miles N of Thirsk on A168, the Northallerton spur, 0.5 mile from dual carriageway A19.
Meadowland course.
9 holes, 6257 yards, S.S.S.70
Founded 1914
Visitors: welcome.
Green Fee: on application.
Societies: catered for weekdays except Tues and Wed pm; must be members of recognised golf club; book in writing well in advance.
Catering: full facilites except Tues.
Hotels: Golden Fleece; Three Tuns.

N135 **Thorne**
☎(0405) 812084
Kirton Lane, Thorne, Doncaster, S Yorks DN8 5RJ
Follow signposts to Thorne from M18 junction 6 or M180 junction 1.
Public parkland course.
18 holes, 5500 yards, S.S.S.65
Designed by Richard Highfield.
Founded 1980
Visitors: welcome, no restrictions.
Green Fee: £6/round WD, £7 WE.
Societies: book in advance.
Catering: full facilities.
Hotels: Belton.

N136 **Tinsley Park**
☎(0742) 560237
High Hazel Park, Darnall, Sheffield S9
Take A57 off M1 at junction 33, at traffic lights turn right on Greenland Rd and right by bus depot.
Parkland course.
18 holes, 6064 yards, S.S.S.69
Founded 1921
Visitors: unrestricted.
Green Fee: £6.60/round WE, reduction WD.
Societies: cannot book block times.
Catering: any day except Tues.
Hotels: Royal Victoria.

N137 **Todmorden**
☎(0706) 812986
Rive Rocks, Cross Stone Rd, Todmorden OL14 7RD
From town centre proceed c. 1.5 miles along Halifax road, turn right.
Moorland course.
9 holes, 5858 yards, S.S.S.68
Founded 1895
Visitors: Tues-Fri no restrictions (Thurs Ladies' Day); weekends by prior arrangement.
Green Fee: £10/day WD, £15/day WE.
Societies: Tues-Fri.
Catering: full facilities except Mon.
Hotels: Scaitliffe Hall; Brandschatter Berghoff.

N138 **Wakefield**
☎(0924) 255104 Club, 255380 Pro, 258778 Sec.
Woodthorpe Lane, Sandal, Wakefield WF2 6JH
3 miles S of Wakefield on A61, from M1 exit 39.
Parkland course.
18 holes, 6611 yards, S.S.S.72
Designed by Alex (Sandy) Herd.
Founded 1891
Visitors: by arrangement.
Green Fee: £22 WD, £25 WE.
Societies: apply to Sec.
Catering: except Mon. Snooker.
Hotels: Cedar Court; Swallow.

N139 **Wath**
☎(0709) 878677
Abdy, Blackamoor, Rotherham, S Yorks S62 7SJ
Off A633 in Wath, 7 miles N of Rotherham.
Meadowland course.
18 holes, 5857 yards, S.S.S.68
Founded 1904
Visitors: welcome weekdays, with member at weekends.

Green Fee: £14/day (£7 with member).
Societies: welcome by arrangement; special package.
Catering: snacks and bar food.
Hotels: Marquis Hotel.

N140 **West Bowling**
☎(0274) 724449 Clubhouse, 393207 Sec, 728036 Pro.
Newall Hall, Rooley Lane, Bradford, W Yorks BD5 8LB
Corner of M606 and Bradford ring road East.
Parkland course.
18 holes, 5570 yards, S.S.S.67
Founded 1898
Visitors: welcome weekdays, restricted weekends.
Green Fee: £20/round/day WD; £25 WE.
Societies: not weekends; apply to manager.
Catering: full catering facilities except Mon.
Hotels: Novotel; Norfolk Gardens; Guide Post; Tong Village; Victoria.

N141 **West Bradford**
☎(0274) 542767
Chellow Grange, Haworth Rd, Bradford, W Yorks BD9 6NP
B6144 3 miles from Bradford on Haworth Rd.
Meadowland course.
18 holes, 5752 yards, S.S.S.68
Founded 1900
Visitors: welcome weekdays.
Green Fee: £14.50 WD, £20.50 WE & BH.
Societies: weekdays.
Catering: meals served except Mon.
Hotels: Norfolk Gardens.

N142 **West End (Halifax)**
☎(0422) 353608 Clubhouse, 363293 Pro.
Paddock Lane, Highroad Well, Halifax, W Yorks HX2 0NT
Leave Halifax on Burnley/Rochdale road, turn right at 1st lights by People's Park (Parkinson Lane), over crossroads to T-junction, turn right to next T-junction and turn left, take 2nd on right (Court Lane) to junction and turn left into Paddock Lane.
Parkland course.
18 holes, 6003 yards, S.S.S.69
Founded 1906
Visitors: welcome.
Green Fee: £12.50/round, £15.50/day WD; £15.50/round, £20.50/day WE.

Societies: to be booked through Sec; not Sat.
Catering: full facilities except Mon. Snooker.
Hotels: Tower House; Holdsworth House.

N143 Wetherby
☎(0937) 63375
Linton Lane, Wetherby, LS22 4JF
Off A1 at Wetherby.
Parkland course.
18 holes, 6235 yards, S.S.S.70
Founded 1910
Visitors: welcome at all times except 12.15-1.15pm (members only).
Green Fee: on application.
Societies: Wed, Thurs, Fri; 9.30am and 2pm starting times.
Catering: lunch served except Mon.
Hotels: Wetherby Resort.

N144 Wheatley
☎(0302) 831655
Armthorpe Rd, Doncaster, S Yorks DN2 5QB
Follow S ring road from old A1 E along boundary of St Leger racecourse to next crossroads, clubhouse is on right opposite large water tower.
Undulating parkland course.
18 holes, 6345 yards, S.S.S.70
Designed by George Duncan.
Founded 1913 (relocated 1933)
Visitors: welcome.
Green Fee: £14.50/round, £18.50/day WD; £18.50/round, £22.50/day WE & BH.
Societies: weekdays only by arrangement.
Catering: restaurant facilities.
Hotels: Balmoral; Earl of Doncaster; Punches.

N145 Whitby
☎(0947) 602768 Club, 600660 Sec.
Low Straggleton, Whitby, N Yorks YO21 3SR
On main coast road between Whitby and Sandsend.
Seaside course.
18 holes, 5706 yards, S.S.S.69
Founded 1892.
Visitors: welcome.
Green Fee: on application.
Societies: parties over 12 by prior arrangement (experienced golfers).
Catering: available except Mon.
Hotels: Saxonville; White House; Royal.

N146 Whitwood
☎(0977) 512835
Altofts Lane, Whitwood, Castleford, W Yorkshire WF10 5PZ
M62 junction 31, 0.5 mile towards Castleford.
Public parkland course.
9 holes, 6282 yards, S.S.S.70
Designed by Steve Wells (Wakefield Council).
Founded April 1986
Visitors: Welcome at all times, booking system at weekends.
Green Fee: £3.35/18 holes WD, £4.75 WE; half-price OAPs and jnrs.

N147 Withernsea
☎(0964) 612258
Chestnut Ave, Withernsea, N Humberside HU19 2PG
20 miles NE of Hull at S end of town.
Seaside course.
9 holes, 5112 yards, S.S.S.66
Founded 1909
Visitors: welcome weekdays, with member only at weekends.
Green Fee: £8/day (£5 with member) WD.
Societies: apply to Sec.
Catering: evening meals weekdays; breakfast, lunch, evening meal weekends; private functions by arrangement with Sec.
Hotels: Queen's.

N148 Wombwell (Hillies)
☎(0226) 754433
Wentworth View, Wombwell, Barnsley, S Yorkshire S73 0LA
4 miles SE fof Barnsley, 10 miles M1 junction 36.
Municipal meadowland course.
9 holes, 2095 yards, S.S.S.60
Founded 1981
Visitors: no restrictions.
Green Fee: £2.60 (9 holes), £5.10 (18 holes) WD; £3.40 (9 holes), £6.70 (18 holes) WE; reductions for jnrs.
Societies: by arrangement.
Catering: bar, evenings only.
Hotels: Tankersley Lodge; Churchill.

N149 Woodhall Hills
☎(0532) 554594 Sec, 562857 Pro.
Woodhall Rd, Calverley, Pudsey, W Yorks
Turn off A647 Leeds-Bradford road to Calverley, 1 mile.
Undulating parkland course.
18 holes, 6102 yards, S.S.S.69
Founded 1905

Visitors: welcome most days, restricted Sat.
Green Fee: on application.
Societies: contact Sec.
Catering: full except Mon.

N150 Woodsome Hall
☎(0484) 602971, 602739 Sec.
Fenay Bridge, Huddersfield, W Yorks HD8 0LQ
5 miles SE of Huddersfield off A629 Sheffield-Penistone road.
Parkland course.
18 holes, 6080 yards, S.S.S.69
Founded 1922
Visitors: welcome weekdays with h/cap cert, jackets and ties; not before 4pm Tues; limited at weekends.
Green Fee: £25 WD, £30 WE & BH.
Societies: weekdays.
Catering: full facilities except Mon.
Hotels: George; Ladbroke Mercury.

N151 Wortley
☎(0742) 885294 Sec, 882139 Steward, 886490 Pro.
Hermit Hill Lane, Wortley, Sheffield S30 4DF
Off M1 at junction 35A (from S) or 36 (from N), take A629 through Wortley village, course 1st right.
Undulating wooded parkland course.
18 holes, 5983 yards, S.S.S.69
Founded 1894
Visitors: no restrictions.
Green Fee: £16.50 WD, £24 WE & BH.
Societies: Wed and Fri by arrangement.
Catering: by arrangement.
Hotels: Hallam Towers (Sheffield); Brooklands (Barnsley).

N152 York
☎(0904) 490304 Pro, 491840 Sec.
Lords Moor Lane, Strensall, York YO3 5XF
2 miles N of A1234 (York Ring Road), exit at Earswick/Strensall roundabout.
Woodland course.
18 holes, 6285 yards, S.S.S.70
Designed by J.H. Taylor (1904).
Founded 1890
Visitors: ring beforehand.
Green Fee: £24 WD, £28 Sun.
Societies: catered for except Fri and Sat.
Catering: full catering facilities except Fri.

O

NORTHUMBERLAND, DURHAM, CLEVELAND, TYNE & WEAR

Northumberland is one of the most lovely counties, a rich tapestry of seascape, woodland, lonely moor and fertile farmland. Since the last edition of the Golf Course Guide, a welcome addition to the golfing map has been the extravagant development at Slaley Hall near Hexham, a comfortable drive west of Newcastle. A man-sized course is an attractive adjunct to housing plans although the long stretch of Northumberland's coastline, running parallel to the A1, makes it an obvious target for those who like sea air in their nostrils and golf that can be described, in the most complimentary of veins, as off the beaten track.

The best is Berwick-upon-Tweed at Goswick, a true links approached along a quiet lane that crosses the main railway line and goes no further when the entrance to the Club is reached. The course divides itself neatly into two, the best and most enchanting being the few holes that nestle between the dunes and open up views of the hallowed, ancient ground of Holy Island.

It is the second oldest place in the county where golf is played, the distinction of being the oldest belonging to the little village 9-hole course at Alnmouth. For the golfer travelling along the coast, there are several pleasant stopping-off spots, notably at Bamburgh Castle, Dunstanburgh, Warkworth, Newbiggin-by-the-Sea and Seahouses. I have particularly happy memories of a game at Dunstanburgh, a course that is certainly great fun in an ancient setting.

The northern outskirts of Newcastle boast Ponteland, Gosforth and the Northumberland Club in High Gosforth Park, much of which is confined within the white rails of the racecourse. It is a Club that has housed the men's English championship and the Women's Commonwealth tournament, testimony to its quality as a test of golf and to its convenience as a location.

Crossing the Tyne into Durham marks a distinct change of scenery although there are two outstanding courses in Seaton Carew, a magnificent links even if its backcloth is industrial, and Brancepeth Castle south west of Durham, designed by the master, Harry Colt, and of which Leonard Crawley was inordinately fond. That is enough of a recommendation and it is ideally situated for anyone intent on breaking the journey to Scotland. Crook and Bishop Auckland, both great names in the heyday of amateur football, are close by and Durham City was founded in 1887.

Again, however, there is a natural inclination to head from Durham towards the sea and sample the coastal chain of courses starting with Hartlepool, the handiwork of James Braid, and then sandwiching Seaton Carew between Hartlepool and the ancient Cleveland Club at Redcar.

Seaton Carew, host to a variety of national championships is magnificent, one of the very few seaside links on the East of England coast north of Norfolk but there are other good ports of call.

Eaglescliffe and Middlesborough are two more courses out of the Braid stable. Moving west towards Darlington, there are Teeside, Billingham, Dinsdale Spa, and in or near Darlington itself are Stressholme and Blackwell Grange.

Somewhat more remote are Barnard Castle and Allendale; but a final word for Hexham, just north of Allendale. Designed in 1907 by Harry Vardon, it occupies pleasant, undulating parkland.

O1 Allendale
☎(091) 267 5875 Sec.
Thornley Gate, Allendale, Hexham,
N'umberland NE47 9LG
10 miles SW of Hexham on Nenthead
road (B6305/B6295).
Meadowland course.
9 holes, 4488 yards, S.S.S.63;
relocating to new site Sept 1992.
Founded 1907
Visitors: no restrictions but
competitions have preference, no
visitors Aug Bank Holiday Mon.
Green Fee: £4 WD, £5 WE & BH.
Societies: by arrangement.
Catering: kettle and cooker
provided; charge for electricity.
Hotels: Hotspur.

O2 Alnmouth
☎(0665) 830231
Foxton Hall, Lesbury, Alnwick,
N'umberland NE66 3BE
Alnmouth road from Alnwick, left at
Alnmouth, Foxton 1 mile on right.
Seaside meadowland course.
18 holes, 6414 yards, S.S.S.71
Founded 1869
Visitors: welcome Mon, Tues and
Thurs; h/cap cert required.
Green Fee: £20/day.
Societies: by arrangement; max 30.
Catering: available at all times.
Hotels: Marine House; Schooner.

O3 Alnmouth Village
☎(0665) 830370
Marine Rd, Alnmouth, N'umberland
From Alnwick on A1 to Alnmouth on
A1068.
Undulating seaside course.
9 holes, 6078 yards, S.S.S.70
Founded 1869
Visitors: welcome.
Green Fee: £10 WD, £20 WE & BH.
Catering: by arrangement.
Hotels: Marine.

O4 Alnwick
☎(0665) 602632, 602499 Sec.
Swansfield Park, Alnwick,
N'umberland
From S, 1st left off A1, into
Willowburn Ave, 3rd left into
Swansfield Park Rd, carry on to top of
hill, follow signs Alnwick Golf Club.
Parkland course.
9 holes (18 tee blocks), 5387 yards,
S.S.S.66
Founded 1907
Visitors: except competition days;
allowed most Sun 11.30am-12.30pm
in 3 balls, should contact Sec.

Green Fee: £10/round, £15/day WD;
£15/round, £20/day WE & BH.
Societies: apply to Sec.
Catering: limited catering service.
Hotels: White Swan; The Oaks.

O5 Arcot Hall
☎(091) 236 2794
Dudley, Cramlington, N'umberland
NE23 7QP
1 mile E of A1 off A1068 near Holiday
Inn.
Parkland course.
18 holes, 6389 yards, S.S.S.70
Designed by James Braid.
Founded 1910
Visitors: weekdays and
non-competition weekends.
Green Fee: £20 WD, £25 WE.
Societies: not weekends.
Catering: lunches and teas.
Hotels: Holiday Inn; Gosforth Park;
Metro Park.

O6 Aycliffe
☎(0325) 310820
Sports and Leisure Complex, School
Aycliffe Lane, Newton Aycliffe,
Durham DL5 6QZ
Take A68 from A1(M), then turn off
for Aycliffe.
Public parkland course.
9 holes, 2981 yards, S.S.S.69
Visitors: welcome.
Green Fee: £3.60 (18 holes) WD,
£4.60 WE.
Catering: available.
Driving range; sports and leisure
complex.
Hotels: Redworth Hall.

O7 Backworth
☎(091) 268 1048
Backworth Welfare, The Hall,
Backworth, Shiremoor, Tyne & Wear
NE27 0AH
Off Tyne Tunnel link road at
Holystone roundabout.
Parkland course.
9 holes, 5930 yards, S.S.S.69
Founded 1937
Visitors: welcome with restrictions,
ring for details.
Green Fee: on application.
Catering: bar, snacks; catering by
arrangement.
Pool, bowls, banqueting.

O8 Bamburgh Castle
☎(06684) 378 Steward, 321 Sec.
The Wynding, Bamburgh,
N'umberland NE69 7DE

Turn off A1 between Alnwick and
Berwick on B1341 or B1342 and
proceed to Bamburgh village, turn
left opposite Lord Crewe Arms and
travel along The Wynding.
Seaside course.
18 holes, 5465 yards, S.S.S.67
Founded 1896
Visitors: welcome, restricted, Bank
Holidays, weekends and competition
days; h/cap certs required.
Green Fee: April-Oct, £15/day/round
WD; £25/day, £20/round WE & BH;
Oct-Mar, £15/day/round WD,
£13/day/round WE & BH.
Societies: by arrangement.
Catering: lunches, teas and evening
meal except Tues.
Hotels: Sunningdale; Mizen Head;
Victoria; Lord Crewe Arms.

O9 Barnard Castle
☎(0833) 38355
Harmire Rd, Barnard Castle, Co
Durham DL12 8QN
On N boundary of town on B6278
Barnard Castle-Eggleston road.
Undulating parkland course
18 holes, 5838 yards, S.S.S.68
Visitors: welcome except on
competition days.
Green Fee: £12 WD, £18 WE & BH.
Societies: welcome, max 40.
Catering: meals and bar snacks.
Snooker.
Hotels: Rose & Crown (Romaldkirk);
Jersey Farm Hotel; Montalbo.

O10 Beamish Park
☎(091) 370 1382
The Clubhouse, Beamish, Stanley,
Co Durham DH9 0RH
Take Chester-le-Street turn-off from
A1(M), follow signs for Beamish
Museum.
Parkland course.
18 holes, 6205 yards, S.S.S.70
Designed by Henry Cotton (part).
Founded c. 1925
Visitors: not Sun, not before 9am on
any day.
Green Fee: £14/day.
Societies: not Sat, Sun.
Catering: bar and restaurant;
banqueting.

O11 Bedlingtonshire
☎(0670) 822457 Sec, 822087 Pro.
Acorn Bank, Bedlington, N'umberland
0.5 mile W of Bedlington on A1068.
Public meadowland/parkland
course.
18 holes, 6224 metres, S.S.S.73

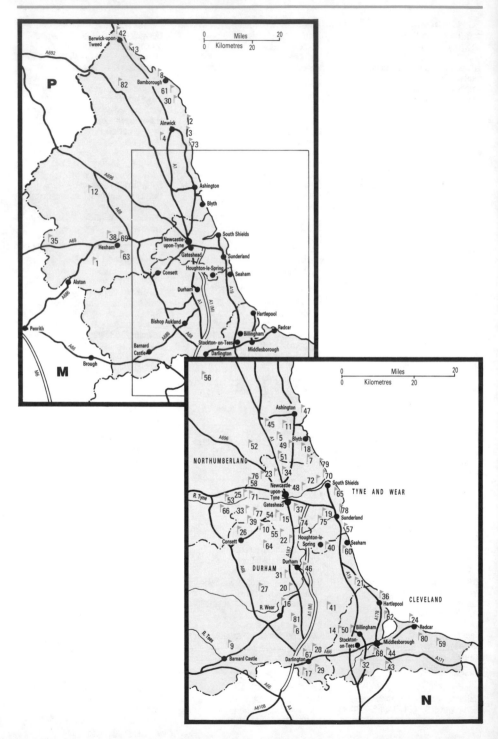

Designed by Frank Pennink.
Founded April 1972
Visitors: welcome weekdays 9am to sunset, weekends from 9.30am to sunset, except on competition days.
Green Fee: on application.
Societies: on application.
Catering: on request.
Hotels: Holiday Inn; Red Lion; Ridge Farm; North Seaton (Ashington).

O12 Bellingham

☎(0660) 20530
Boggle Hole, Bellingham, Hexham, N'umberland NE48 2DT
Off B6320, 16 miles NE of Hexham, easy access from A68.
Parkland/moorland course.
9 holes (18 tees), 5245 yards, S.S.S.66.
Designed by Edward Johnson.
Founded 1893
Visitors: welcome, limited Sun.
Green Fee: £6 WD, £8 WE & BH.
Societies: welcome, limited to 18 holes on Sat, limited Sun.
Catering: parties welcome, individuals by arrangement.
Hotels: Riverdale Hall.

O13 Berwick-upon-Tweed (Goswick)

☎(0289) 87256
Beal, Berwick-upon-Tweed, N'umberland TD15 2RW
Off A1 approx 3 miles S of Berwick-upon-Tweed.
Links course.
18 holes, 6425 yards, S.S.S.71
Designed by James Braid.
Founded 1890
Visitors: welcome after 10am weekdays, after 12am weekends.
Green Fee: £15/round, £18/day WD; £18/round, £25/day WE & BH.
Societies: any day.
Catering: bar and dining room except Mon.

O14 Billingham

☎(0642) 554494
Sandy Lane, Billingham, Cleveland TS22 5NA
E of A19 Billingham by-pass, near town centre.
Undulating parkland course.
18 holes, 6334 yards, S.S.S.71
Designed by Frank Pennink.
Founded 1967
Visitors: weekdays after 9.30am and 1.30pm, with member only at weekends and Bank Holidays.
Green Fee: £16.50/day.

Societies: weekdays only after 9.30am and 1.30pm.
Catering: daily except Mon.
Hotels: Billingham Arms.

O15 Birtley

☎(091) 410 2207
Portobello Rd, Birtley, Co Durham
A6127 off A1, 6 miles S of Newcastle.
Parkland course.
9 holes, 5154 yards, S.S.S.67
Founded 1921
Visitors: welcome weekdays only unless accompanied by member.
Green Fee: on application.
Societies: by arrangement.
Catering: bar facilities, evenings.
Hotels: Post House; Coach & Horses.

O16 Bishop Auckland

☎(0388) 602198 Club, 663648 Sec.
High Plains, Durham Rd, Bishop Auckland, Co Durham DL14 8DL
Leave Market Place, up Durham Rd towards Spennymoor and Durham; course on left half-way up the bank.
Parkland course.
18 holes, 6420 yards, S.S.S.71
Founded 1894
Visitors: welcome.
Green Fee: £16/round/day WD, £20/round/day WE.
Societies: best days Wed, Thurs, Fri (Ladies Day Tues); not Sat or Sun.
Catering: full except Mon. Snooker
Hotels: Park Head; Queens Head.

O17 Blackwell Grange

☎(0325) 464464 Clubhouse, 464458 Sec, 462088 Pro.
Briar Close, Blackwell, Darlington, Co Durham DL3 8QX
1 mile S of Darlington, 0.25 mile W off A66.
Undulating parkland course.
18 holes, 5621 yards, S.S.S.67
Designed by Frank Pennink.
Founded 1930
Visitors: welcome except Wed pm.
Green Fee: £18/day WD, £20/round WE & BH.
Societies: by arrangement on weekdays.
Catering: full service Tues-Sat.
Hotels: Blackwell Grange.

O18 Blyth

☎(0670) 367728
New Delaval & Newsham, Blyth, N'umberland NE24 4DB
11 miles N of Newcastle, 6 miles N of Whitley Bay.

Parkland course.
18 holes, 6533 yards, S.S.S.72
Designed by Hamilton Stutt & Co.
Founded 1905
Visitors: weekdays only before 3pm, unless with member.
Green Fee: £12/round, £14/day (£6 with playing member).
Societies: welcome by arrangement (28 days in advance).
Catering: full facilities.

O19 Boldon

☎(091) 536 5360 Sec/Office, 536 4182 Clubhouse, 536 5385 Pro
Dipe Lane, East Boldon, Tyne & Wear NE36 0PQ
On A184, 1 mile E of A19/A1 junction.
Parkland course.
18 holes, 6362 yards, S.S.S.70
Founded 1912
Visitors: welcome weekdays, weekends and Bank Holidays restricted.
Green Fee: £16 WD (£9 with member), £20 WE (£11 with member).
Societies: by arrangement.
Catering: bar snacks all day; meals by arrangement. Snooker table.
Hotels: George Washington; Friendly.

O20 Brancepeth Castle

☎(091) 378 0075
Brancepeth Village, Durham DH7 8EA
4 miles W of Durham city on A690 to Crook; left at crossroads in village of Brancepeth and take slip road to left immediately before Castle gates.
Parkland course.
18 holes, 6415 yards, S.S.S.71
Designed by H.S. Colt.
Founded 1924
Visitors: weekdays only for parties, individuals at weekends.
Green Fee: casual £24 WD, £30 WE & BH.
Societies: weekdays, reduced green fees dependent on numbers in party.
Catering: lunches and bar snacks pm, dinners by prior booking.
Hotels: Bridge (Croxdale).

O21 Castle Eden & Peterlee

☎(0429) 836220, 836510 Sec.
Castle Eden, Hartlepool, Cleveland TS27 4SS
Durham-Hartlepool road off A19, follow signs to Castle Eden, course opposite Whitbread Brewery.
Parkland course.
18 holes, 6293 yards, S.S.S.70
Designed by Henry Cotton (2nd 9)

Founded 1927
Visitors: welcome at all times.
Green Fee: £18/day WD, £23 WE;
(£9 with member).
Societies: weekdays.
Catering: every day.
Hotels: Crossways; Peterlee Lodge;
Hardwick Manor.

O22 Chester-le-Street
☎(091) 388 3218, 389 0157 Pro.
Lumley Park, Chester-le-Street, Co
Durham DH3 4NS
Leave A1(M) to Chester-le-Street,
follow A167 signposted Durham,
course 0.25 mile E of Chester-le-
Street, beside Lumley Castle.
Parkland course.
18 holes, 6054 yards, S.S.S.69
Designed by J.H. Taylor (original 9).
Founded 1909
Visitors: welcome weekdays, not
before 9.30am or 12am-2pm
weekends; must have letter of intro
or h/cap cert.
Green Fee: £18 WD, £25 WE & BH.
Societies: welcome; not weekends.
Catering: bar 11am-11pm Mon-Sat;
snacks, lunches and evening meals.
Snooker.
Hotels: Lumley Castle; Lambton
Arms.

O23 City of Newcastle
☎(091) 285 1775
Three Mile Bridge, Gosforth,
Newcastle upon Tyne NE3 2DR
3 miles N of Newcastle city centre on
main A1; opposite Three Mile Inn.
Parkland course.
18 holes, 6508 yards, S.S.S.71
Designed by Harry Vardon.
Founded 1892
Visitors: welcome except Men's
competitions days.
Green Fee: £14.50 (£5.50 with
member) WD, £18.50 (£7.50 with
member) WE & BH.
Societies: Tues, Wed, Thurs and
exceptionally other days.
Catering: lunches, bar snacks,
sandwiches every day except Mon.
Snooker, pool.
Hotels: Gosforth Park.

O24 Cleveland
☎(0642) 483693 Club, 471798 Sec.
Queen St, Redcar, Cleveland TS10
1BT
From A174 to A1042 to Coatham.
Championship links course.
18 holes, 6707 yards, S.S.S.72
Founded 1887

Visitors: welcome.
Green Fee: £14.50/round WD,
£20/round WE & BH.
Societies: welcome weekdays,
brochure from Sec.
Catering: excellent.
Hotels: The Park; The Royal.

O25 Close House
☎(0661) 852953
Close House, Heddon-on-the-Wall,
Newcastle-upon-Tyne NE15 0HT
9 miles W of Newcastle off A69.
Parkland course.
18 holes, 5506 yards, S.S.S.67
Founded 1968
Visitors: societies only accepted, by
prior arrangement with Sec.

O26 Consett & District
☎(0207) 502186
Elmfield Rd, Consett, Co Durham
DH8 5NN
Off A68 2 miles from Castleside or
Allensford; 12 miles from Durham
(A691) and Newcastle (A694).
Undulating parkland course.
18 holes, 6001 yards, S.S.S.69
Designed by Harry Vardon.
Founded 1911
Visitors: welcome; prior
confirmation at weekends advisable.
Green Fee: £15 WD, £20 WE & BH.
Societies: by arrangement, max 40.
Catering: full by arrangement,
limited Mon. Snooker.

O27 Crook
☎(0388) 762429
Low Jobs Hill, Crook, Co Durham
DL15 9AA
On A689 6 miles W of Durham city
between Willington and Crook.
Moorland/parkland course.
18 holes, 6089 yards, S.S.S.69
Founded 1919
Visitors: welcome all times.
Green Fee: £10/day WD (£5 with
member), £15/day WE & BH (£7 with
member).
Societies: by appointment.
Catering: daily except Thurs.
Hotels: Kensington Hall; Uplands;
Matthews Motel.

O28 Darlington
☎(0325) 463936
Haughton Grange, Darlington, Co
Durham DL1 3JD
NE of town on A1150.
Parkland course.
18 holes, 6032 yards, S.S.S.70

Designed by Mackenzie.
Founded 1908
Visitors: welcome
Green Fee: £15.50/round,
£21.50/day.
Societies: welcome, max 40.
Catering: excellent bar and
restaurant except Mon. Snooker.
Hotels: Kings Head; White Horse;
Blackwell Grange.

O29 Dinsdale Spa
☎(0325) 332297 Sec, 332515 Pro,
332222 Clubhouse
Middleton-St-George, Darlington, Co
Durham DL2 1DW
From A66 or A19 follow signs for
Teeside Airport until Middleton-St-
George, club is 1.5 miles from village
on Neasham road.
Parkland course.
18 holes, 6078 yards, S.S.S.69
Founded 1906
Visitors: welcome weekdays.
Green Fee: £15, £18.
Societies: by arrangement.
Catering: facilities available.
Hotels: Devenport.

O30 Dunstanburgh
☎(0665) 576562
Embleton, Alnwick, N'umberland
NE66 3XQ
Off A1, 8 miles NE of Alnwick.
Seaside course.
18 holes, 6298 yards, S.S.S.70
Visitors: welcome.
Green Fee: on application.
Societies: by arrangement.
Catering: meals by arrangement.
Hotels: Dunstanburgh Castle.

O31 Durham City
☎(091) 378 0069
Littleburn Farm, Langley Moor,
Durham DH7 8HL
Off A690 2 miles SW of Durham City.
Meadowland course.
18 holes, 6326 yards, S.S.S.70
Designed by C.C. Stanton.
Founded 1887
Visitors: welcome weekdays.
Green Fee: £14 WD, £18 WE.
Societies: weekdays.
Catering: daily except Mon.
Hotels: Royal County; Three Tuns;
Duke of Wellington.

O32 Eaglescliffe
☎(0642) 780098
Yarm Rd, Eaglescliffe, Stockton-on-
Tees, Cleveland TS16 0DQ

On the left of A135 from Stockton-on-Tees to Yarm.
Undulating parkland course.
18 holes, 6045 yards, S.S.S.69
Designed by James Braid, modification by H. Cotton.
Founded 1914
Visitors: welcome weekdays, restricted Tues and Fri (Ladies Days).
Green Fee: £16 WD, £22 WE.
Societies: catered for weekdays.
Catering: full except Mon.
Hotels: Parkmore; Swallow.

O33 Garesfield
☎(0207) 561278, 561309
Chopwell, Tyne & Wear, NE17 7AP
A694 Newcastle-Consett road to Rowlands Gill, take B6315 to High Spen, then take Chopwell road, 1 mile on left.
Parkland course.
18 holes, 6603 yards, S.S.S.72
Designed by William Woodend.
Founded 1922
Visitors: weekdays unrestricted, weekends and Bank Holidays not before 4.30pm unless with member.
Green Fee: £9/round, £11/day.
Societies: by arrangement.
Catering: full facilities.

O34 Gosforth (Bridlepath)
☎(091) 285 3495
Broadway East, Gosforth, Newcastle-upon-Tyne NE3 5ER
3 miles N of city centre; turn right at 1st main roundabout after Regent Centre metro station.
Meadowland course.
18 holes, 6043 yards, S.S.S.69
Founded 1905
Visitors: welcome weekdays; members' guests only before 4pm weekends and Bank Holidays.
Green Fee: £14.50 WD, £15.50 WE & BH after 4pm.
Societies: weekdays.
Catering: full facilities except Mon.
Hotels: Gosforth Park.

O35 Haltwhistle
☎(06977) 47364
Banktop, Greenhead, Via Carlisle, N'umberland
3 miles W of Haltwhistle, 0.25 mile off A69 on road to Gilsland.
Undulating parkland course.
12 holes, 5968 yards, S.S.S.69
Founded 1968
Visitors: any day except Sun am.
Green Fee: £7.50/day May-Sept, £5/day Oct-April.

Societies: welcome except Sun; contact W.E. Barnes, Secretary, Croftlynn, Haltwhistle NE49 9JR, (0434) 320337
Catering: bar; catering by prior arrangement.
Hotels: beneficial arrangements for golfers at Greenhead Hotel and Gilsland Spa.

O36 Hartlepool
☎(0429) 274398
Hart Warren, Hartlepool, Cleveland TS24 9QF
N boundary of Hartlepool off A1086.
Seaside links course.
18 holes, 6255 yards, S.S.S.70
Designed by James Braid.
Founded 1906
Visitors: weekdays unrestricted, weekends limited.
Green Fee: £14 WD, £20 WE.
Societies: weekdays.
Catering: by arrangement with Steward. Snooker.
Hotels: Grand; Staincliffe.

O37 Heworth
☎(091) 469 2137
Gingling Gate, Heworth, Tyne & Wear NE10 8XY
Parkland course.
18 holes, 6437 yards, S.S.S.71
Founded 1922
Visitors: not before 10am at weekends.
Green Fee: £13 WD, £16 WE.
Societies: by arrangement.
Catering: bar and restaurant.

O38 Hexham
☎(0434) 603072
Spital Park, Hexham, N'umberland NE46 3RZ
On A69, 1 mile W of Hexham centre.
Undulating parkland course.
18 holes, 6026 yards, S.S.S.68
Designed by Harry Vardon.
Founded 1907
Visitors: welcome any day.
Green Fee: £18/round, £24/day.
Societies: by arrangement, not Sat or Sun.
Catering: full facilities every day.
Hotels: Beaumont; Royal.

O39 Hobson Municipal
☎(0207) 570189 Sec, 70941 catering, 71605 Pro.
Burnopfield, Newcastle-upon-Tyne, Tyne & Wear
On main Newcastle-Consett road.

Municipal parkland course
18 holes, 6582 yards, S.S.S.71
Founded 1980
Visitors: restricted Sat (Club competitions).
Green Fee: on application.
Societies: apply to Pro.
Catering: bar, lounge, restaurant.
Hotels: Harperley.

O40 Houghton-le-Spring
☎(091) 584 1198
Copt Hill, Houghton-le-Spring DH5 8LU
0.5 mile from Houghton-le-Spring on A1085 Seaham Harbour road.
Undulating hillside course.
18 holes, 6450 yards, S.S.S.71
Founded 1912
Visitors: welcome, restrictions at weekends and competition days.
Green Fee: on application.
Societies: welcome, prior arrangement for meals.
Catering: available most days.
Hotels: White Lion; Ramside Hall; Rainton Lodge.

O41 Knotty Hill Golf Centre
☎(0740) 20320
Sedgefield, Stockton-on-Tees, Cleveland TS21 2BB
2 miles off A1(M) on A689 Teeside road.
Undulating lowland course.
18 holes, 6700 yards, S.S.S.73
Designed by Denis Craggs.
Opening Sept 1992
Visitors: welcome; phone for details of green fees, society meetings etc.
Catering: temporary facilities, coffee shop, bar. Driving range.

O42 Magdalene Fields
☎(0289) 306384
Berwick-upon-Tweed
5 minutes walk from town centre.
Seaside course (parkland fairways).
18 holes, 6551 yards, S.S.S.71
Visitors: welcome.
Green Fee: on application.
Societies: by arrangement.
Catering: meals during summer, at other times by arrangement.

O43 Middlesbrough
☎(0642) 311515, 316430
Brass Castle Lane, Marton, Middlesbrough, Cleveland TS8 9EE
5 miles S of Middlesbrough, 1 mile W of A172.

Parkland course.
18 holes, 6106 yards, S.S.S.69
Designed by James Braid.
Founded 1908
Visitors: weekdays except Tues.
Green Fee: £18.50 (£5.15 with member) WD, £22.50 (£10.25 with member) WE & BH.
Societies: Wed, Thurs and Fri.
Catering: full facilities except Mon.
Hotels: Marton Hotel & Country Club; Blue Bell Inn (Acklam).

O44 Middlesbrough Municipal

☎(0642) 315533
Ladgate Lane, Middlesbrough, Cleveland TS5 7YZ
Access from A19 via A174 to Acklam.
Undulating parkland course.
18 holes, 6314 yards, S.S.S.70
Designed by Middlesborough Borough Council Planning Dept.
Founded 1977
Visitors: welcome but need a starting time.
Green Fee: £5.10 WD, £7.15 WE & BH.
Catering: lunches and evening meals, open to the public.
Driving range.
Hotels: Blue Bell Inn.

O45 Morpeth

☎(0670) 504942 Sec, 519980 Club, 515675 Pro.
The Common, Morpeth, NE61 2BT
On A197 1 mile S of Morpeth.
Parkland course.
18 holes, 6215 yards, S.S.S.70
Designed by Harry Vardon (1922).
Founded 1906
Visitors: welcome.
Green Fee: on application.
Societies: catered for weekdays, apply to Sec.
Catering: snacks, bar lunches, dinners; booking advisable.
Hotels: Waterford Lodge.

O46 Mount Oswald

☎(091) 386 7527
Mount Oswald Manor, South Rd, Durham DH1 3TQ
SW of Durham on A1050.
Parkland course.
18 holes, 6162 yards, S.S.S.69
Visitors: welcome any time; members only until 10am Sun.
Green Fee: £10 WD, £12 WE.
Societies: welcome any time; special rates for 12 or more inc weekends.

Catering: meals 9.30am-9.30pm; Sun lunch; function room (75-80).
Hotels: Royal County; Bridge; Three Tuns.

O47 Newbiggin-by-the-Sea

☎(0670) 817344
Clubhouse, Newbiggin-by-the-Sea, N'umberland NE64 6DW
Off A197 16 miles N of Newcastle, 8 miles E of Morpeth; at easternmost point of village adjacent Church Point Caravan Park.
Seaside links course.
18 holes, 6423 yards, S.S.S.71
Founded 17 July 1884
Visitors: welcome after 10am; not competition days.
Green Fee: on application.
Societies: apply to Sec.
Catering: bar meals, lunch, dinner except Tues. Snooker.

O48 Newcastle United

☎(0632) 864693
Ponteland Rd, Cowgate, Newcastle-upon-Tyne, N'umberland NE5 3JW
1 mile W of city centre.
Moorland course.
18 holes, 6498 yards, S.S.S.71
Founded 1892
Visitors: welcome weekdays.
Green Fee: £9.50.
Societies: by arrangement.
Catering: meals by arrangement.

O49 Northumberland

☎(091) 236 2009 Steward, 236 2498 Sec.
High Gosforth Park, Newcastle-upon-Tyne NE3 5HT
Situated off A6125 4 miles N of Newcastle-upon-Tyne city centre.
Undulating parkland course.
18 holes, 6640 yards, S.S.S.72
Designed by H.S. Colt & James Braid.
Founded 1898
Visitors: weekdays by reservation with Sec and letter of intro.
Green Fee: on application.
Societies: Tues, Thurs and Fri only.
Catering: lunch served except Mon.
Hotels: Gosforth Park; Holiday Inn.

O50 Norton Golf Course

☎(0642) 676385
Junction Rd, Stockton-on-Tees, Cleveland TS20 1SU
Parkland course.
18 holes, 6100 yards, Par 71
Founded 1989

Visitors: no jeans, correct footwear, half set of clubs each player.
Green Fee: £6.50/round.
Societies: welcome by arrangement.
Catering: bar and bar meals.

O51 Parklands

☎(091) 236 4480, 417 2626
High Gosforth Park, Newcastle-upon-Tyne NE3 5HQ
N of Newcastle on A1.
Parkland course.
18 holes, 6060 yards, S.S.S.69
Founded 1971
Visitors: no restrictions.
Green Fee: £9/round WD, £11 WE.
Societies: welcome.
Catering: bar and restaurant.
Driving range, 9-hole Pitch & Putt.
Hotels: Gosforth Park.

O52 Ponteland

☎(0661) 22689
53 Bell Villas, Ponteland, Newcastle-upon-Tyne NE20 9BD
On A696 road to Jedburgh, 1.5 miles N of Newcastle Airport.
Parkland course.
18 holes, 6512 yards, S.S.S.71
Designed by Harry Ferney.
Founded 1927
Visitors: Mon to Fri.
Green Fee: £18.50/day/round.
Societies: Tues and Thurs.
Catering: full in bar hours, by prior arrangement at other times.

O53 Prudhoe

☎(0661) 32466
Eastwood Park, Prudhoe, N'umberland NE42 5DX
12 miles W of Newcastle on A695.
Parkland course.
18 holes, 5812 yards, S.S.S.68
Founded 1930
Visitors: welcome weekdays.
Green Fee: on application.
Societies: welcome weekdays.
Catering: bar snacks and meals.

O54 Ravensworth

☎(091) 487 6014
Moss Heaps, Wrekenton, Gateshead, Tyne & Wear NE9 7UU
Off A1, 2 miles S of Gateshead.
Moorland/parkland course.
18 holes, 5872 yards, S.S.S.68
Founded 1906
Visitors: welcome.
Green Fee: £13/round (£7 with member) WD, £21/round (£11 with member) WE & BH.

Societies: weekdays.
Catering: any day but Mon.
Hotels: Springfield.

O55 Roseberry Grange
☎(091) 370 2047 office, 370 0660
Pro, 370 0670 Club
Grange Villa, Chester-le-Street,
Durham DH2 3NF
Off A693 from Chester-le-Street to
Stanley, turn left before Beamish
Museum.
Parkland course.
18 holes, 5892 yards, S.S.S.68
Founded 1986
Visitors: welcome.
Green Fee: £6.50/round WD,
£9/round WE; reductions for jnrs,
OAPs and unemployed.
Societies: welcome, book in writing
via District Council.
Catering: bar, snacks daily.
Driving range, putting green.

O56 Rothbury
☎(0669) 20718 after 6pm.
Old Race Course, Rothbury, Morpeth,
N'umberland NE65 7UB
Off A697, 15 miles NE of Morpeth.
Meadowland course.
9 holes, 5146 metres, S.S.S.67
Founded 1891
Visitors: welcome weekdays and
most Sun.
Green Fee: £9 WD, £14 WE.
Hotels: Coquetvale; Queens Head;
Newcastle.

O57 Ryhope
☎(091) 523 7333
c/o Mr Winfield, 30 Rosslyn Ave,
Ryhope, Sunderland SR2 0SB
Turn off A19 at Ryhope village
towards Hollycarrside.
Municipal parkland course.
9 holes, 5510 yards, S.S.S.69
Designed by Sunderland Council.
Founded March 1991
Visitors: unrestricted.
Green Fee: summer greens £4 WD,
£5 WE; temp greens £2 WD, £2.50
WE.
Catering: temporary club house.

O58 Ryton
☎(091) 413 3737
Dr Stanners, Clara Vale, Ryton, Tyne
& Wear NE40 3TD
Off A695 8 miles from Newcastle,
follow signs from Ryton to Wylam
then Clara Vale.
Moorland/parkland course.

18 holes, 6034 yards, S.S.S.69
Founded 1891
Visitors: welcome weekdays, by
arrangement weekends.
Green Fee: on application.
Societies: welcome by arrangement.
Catering: full facilities every day.
Hotels: Ryton Country Club.

O59 Saltburn-by-the-Sea
☎(0287) 622812
Hob Hill, Saltburn-by-the-Sea,
Cleveland TS12 1NJ
1 mile from Saltburn on A1268
Guisborough road on left.
Parkland course.
18 holes, 5846 yards, S.S.S.68
Founded 1894
Visitors: welcome; h/cap cert
preferred.
Green Fee: £15.50 WD, £17.50 WE.
Societies: by arrangement, not
Thurs or Sat.
Catering: full facilities except Mon.
Snooker.
Hotels: Royal York; Park.

O60 Seaham
☎(091) 581 2354
Dawdon, Seaham, Co Durham SR7
7RD
Off A19, 6 miles S of Sunderland,
take road to Seaham.
Heathland course.
18 holes, 5972 yards, S.S.S.69
Designed by Dr A. Mackenzie.
Founded May 1911
Visitors: welcome.
Green Fee: on application.
Societies: to be booked through Sec.
Catering: meals to be booked.
Snooker.
Hotels: Harbour View.

O61 Seahouses
☎(0665) 720794
Beadnell Rd, Seahouses,
N'umberland NE68 7XT
Off A1 5 miles N of Alnwick; B1340.
Seaside course.
18 holes, 5387 yards, S.S.S.66
Founded 1913
Visitors: welcome at all times; at
weekends please contact club
beforehand for availability of starting
times.
Green Fee: on application.
Societies: weekdays and most
weekends.
Catering: lunches, bar meals etc,
except Tues.
Hotels: White Swan; Bamburgh
Castle; Beach House.

O62 Seaton Carew
☎(0429) 266249
Tees Rd, Seaton Carew, Hartlepool,
Cleveland TS25 1DE
Off A178 3 miles S of Hartlepool.
Championship seaside links course.
Old, 18 holes, 6604 yards, S.S.S.72;
Brabazon, 18 holes, 6849 yards,
S.S.S.73
Designed by Duncan McCuaig.
Founded 1874
Visitors: on application to Hon Sec.
Green Fee: £20 WD, £28 WE.
Societies: apply to Hon Sec.
Catering: full facilities.
Snooker.
Hotels: Grand; Staincliffe Marine.

O63 Slaley Hall
☎(0434) 673691, 673350 club
Slaley, Hexham, N'umberland NE47
0BY
Off A68 near Corbridge.
Mainly heathland course with lakes
and woods.
18 holes, 7038 yards, S.S.S.73
Designed by Dave Thomas.
Founded 1989
Visitors: welcome with h/cap cert;
bookings only.
Green Fee: £30/round, £40/day.
Societies: welcome by appointment.
Catering: full facilities.
Driving range (from July 1992),
practice ground, leisure complex.
Hotels: 145-bed hotel on site
(opening spring 1992).

O64 South Moor
☎(0207) 232848, 283525
The Middles, Craghead, Stanley, Co
Durham DH9 6AG
2 miles from Stanley on B6313; 8
miles NW of Durham.
Moorland course.
18 holes, 6445 yards, S.S.S.71
Designed by Dr Mackenzie.
Founded 1923
Visitors: welcome.
Green Fee: £11/round, £16/day WD;
£16/round, £21/day WE & BH.
Societies: all week.
Catering: lunches and evening
meals served all week. Snooker.
Hotels: Post House; Lumley Castle;
Imperial; Beamish Park; Royal
County.

O65 South Shields
☎(091) 456 0475 Club, 456 8942
Office
Cleadon Hills, South Shields, Tyne &
Wear NE34 8EG

Seaton Carew

One of the great joys of golf in the West of Ireland is the feeling of spaciousness and the fact that the views from the links are dominated by natural beauty. For those who never venture further from Donegal than Rosses Point, it might be thought such beauty is an integral part of all courses but one of the game's great strengths is the number of contrasting settings in which it is played.

It seems to me, therefore, that the citizens of Hartlepool are every bit as justified in their ardent counting of their blessings over Seaton Carew as the Irish are in their admiration for Tralee or Lahinch.

Modern Seaton Carew is set in surroundings of industrial chimneys and chemical production plants but that has never been, and never will be, a deterrent to golfers. It is something to which you get used in the same way that, by the end of a round at Royal Mid-Surrey, you never notice the aeroplanes or, at West Hill, the trains.

Courses are judged by the challenge and enjoyment they provide and both are high on the list at Seaton Carew, whose distinction is heightened by being one of the few outstanding links on the seaboard of eastern England. Its championship qualities have been recognised by the staging of the English Amateur strokeplay and British Boys' championships, events that enhanced the course's admirable and deserved reputation.

All the same, one view from the course is of the swings and roundabouts of the amusement park, a reminder that Seaton Carew's attractions are not all confined to golf. Nevertheless, Seaton Carew, founded in 1874 as the Durham and Yorkshire GC, is the oldest in either county and its seniority undoubtedly adds to its eminence.

The current course is one of 22 holes, a convenient method of giving members playing options rather than an attempt to set new fashions, although the Old Course at St Andrews started as 22 holes. Some prefer Seaton Carew's old course which plays more or less out and back although with more variation in direction than on many seaside links, but Frank Pennink's design of four new holes gave rise to the championship version of the course, as well as making it significantly more formidable.

An opening hole named "Rocket" calls to mind that Seaton Carew is very much in railway country but the tempo rises with the long 2nd and the short 3rd which turns back towards the clubhouse. The short 6th also follows the line of the 3rd but the new 10th is the only hole that runs east, a timely signal that the flavour of the golf gains a piquant touch as it nears the sea.

The 10th is a straight par 4 but the dogleg 11th leads on to another fine par 4 aptly named "Beach" on account of its proximity to the fence guarding the shore.

By now, the sea buckthorn has begun to dominate and the 13th and 14th, both par 5s, are flanked on the right by a hazard that is statistically punishing and physically painful. There is relief from it at the 208 yard 15th but there is no escaping the buckthorn on the last three holes, which constitute quite a finish. It is particularly easy to become engulfed by it on the right of the 18th, a hole with an unusually contoured fairway, but the most renowned hole is the 17th, its title of "Snag" carrying more than a hint of understatement. It is the second shot and, more especially, the distinctive green which make demands on our cunning, although the drive can become entangled with the same central spine of hillocks encountered on the way out; and the drive can err a little too safely the other way. However, a correct angle for the second shot is essential to hold a green shaped like a scallop shell, bunkered all around and contoured ingeniously on several levels.

It wouldn't do if all greens presented such problems but golf would be duller without its teasers and the 17th green at Seaton Carew is as notable an instrument of torture as man can devise.

INTERNATIONAL HOTELIERS

WASHINGTON MOAT HOUSE
STONE CELLAR ROAD, HIGH USWORTH,
DISTRICT 12, WASHINGTON,
TYNE & WEAR, NE37 1PH.
Telephone Tyneside (091) 417 2626
Telex 537143 WSHMH

The **WASHINGTON MOAT HOUSE** extends a stylish welcome, with a warmth that's special to the North East, and offers a combination of first class business and leisure facilities.

★ 18 hole Championship Golf Course
★ 9 hole Par 3 ★ Floodlit Driving Range
★ Snooker Tables ★ Squash ★ Sauna
★ Solarium ★ Indoor Pool ★ Spa Bath ★ Gym
★ Restaurant ★ Bars ★ Conference facilities

For further details telephone Reservations
091 4172626

Near Cleadon Chimney, prominent landmark.
Seaside course.
18 holes, 6264 yards, S.S.S.70
Founded 1893
Visitors: welcome at all times.
Green Fee: £18 WD, £25 WE & BH.
Societies: by arrangement.
Catering: meals any time; bar from 11am (12am Sun).
Hotels: New Crown; Marsden Inn; Sea Hotel.

O66 Stocksfield
☎(0661) 843041
New Ridley, Stocksfield, N'umberland NE43 7RE
On A695 between Corbridge and Prudhoe.
Parkland/wooded course.
18 holes, 5594 yards, S.S.S.68
Designed by Pennink Associates.
Founded 1912
Visitors: welcome any time weekdays, after 4.30pm weekends.
Green Fee: on application.
Societies: by arrangement.
Catering: sandwiches, meals by prior booking.
Hotels: Broomhaugh (Riding Mill).

O67 Stressholme
☎(0325) 461002
Snipe Lane, Darlington, Co Durham
About 8 miles N of Scotch Corner.
Municipal parkland course.
18 holes, 6511 yards, S.S.S.71
Founded 1976
Visitors: welcome.
Green Fee: on application.
Societies: by arrangement with Pro.
Catering: lunches daily.

O68 Teesside
☎(0642) 676249 Club, 616516 Sec.
Acklam Rd, Thornaby, Cleveland
TS17 7JS

Off A19 take A1130 to Stockton, course 1 mile from A19 on right.
Meadowland course.
18 holes, 6472 yards, S.S.S.71
Founded 1901
Visitors: welcome weekdays before 4.30pm, Bank Holidays after 11am, unless with member.
Green Fee: on application.
Societies: weekdays.
Catering: full catering facilities except Mon.
Hotels: Post House; Golden Eagle.

O69 Tynedale
☎(0434) 608154
Tyne Green, Hexham, N'umberland
From A69 take road into Hexham, turn right into Countryside Park, course 500 yards on S side of River Tyne.
Public parkland course.
9 holes, 5643 yards, S.S.S.67
Founded 1907
Visitors: welcome; not Sun am.
Green Fee: £7/day WD, £8/day WE.
Societies: welcome, prior bookings only.
Catering: bar and bar snacks.
Hotels: Beaumont; County; Royal.

O70 Tynemouth
☎(091) 257 4578
Spital Dene, Tynemouth, North Shields, Tyne & Wear NE30 2ER
On A695.
Parkland course.
18 holes, 6403 yards, S.S.S.71
Designed by Willie Park.
Founded 1913
Visitors: welcome weekdays.
Green Fee: £15 (£6 with member)/day WD, £6 with member only WE.
Societies: weekdays.
Catering: lunches, teas and snacks served except Mon.
Hotels: Moat House; Park.

O71 Tyneside
☎(091) 413 2742 Sec, 413 2177 Clubhouse
Westfield Lane, Ryton, Tyne & Wear NE40 3QE
7 miles W of Newcastle upon Tyne on S side of Tyne, on A695, turn N at Ryton down to Old Ryton village, turn left, past Cross Inn, and then right at end of row of old houses on right.
Parkland course.
18 holes, 6055 yards, S.S.S.69
Designed by H.S. Colt (1910).
Founded 1879
Visitors: welcome.
Green Fee: £16/day WD, £20 WE.
Societies: weekdays only by prior arrangement with Sec.
Catering: bar, tea/coffee, bar snacks, lunch, high tea, dinner (service 8am-10pm).
Hotels: Ryton Park Country House.

O72 Wallsend
☎(091) 262 1973
Bigges Main, Wallsend-on-Tyne, N'umberland NE28 8SX
E of Newcastle on coast road to Whitley Bay.
Public parkland course.
18 holes, 6608 yards, S.S.S.72
Founded 1905
Visitors: not before 12.30pm weekends.
Green Fee: £8 WD, £10 WE.
Societies: on written request.
Catering: hot or cold snacks.

O73 Warkworth
☎(0665) 711596
The Links, Warkworth, Morpeth, N'umberland NE65 0SW
Off A1068 to Warkworth, 10 miles N of Morpeth, 7 miles SE of Alnwick.
Seaside course.
9 holes, 5856 yards, S.S.S.68
Designed by Tom Morris.
Founded 1891

Visitors: welcome except Tues and Sat (competitions).
Green Fee: £10 WD, £15 WE & BH.
Societies: apply to Sec.
Catering: by arrangement with Stewardess.
Hotels: Sun; Warkworth House.

O74 Washington Moat House

☎(091) 417 2626
Stone Cellar Rd, High Usworth, District 12, Washington, Tyne & Wear NE37 1PH
A1M/A194M, well signposted.
Parkland course.
18 holes, 6261 yards, S.S.S.72
Founded 1990
Visitors: by appointment.
Green Fee: £12 WD, £19 WE.
Societies: by appointment.
Catering: full facilities.
Driving range, Pitch & Putt, snooker.
Hotels: Washington Moat House.

O75 Wearside

☎(091) 534 2518 Clubhouse, 534 1193 Sec, 534 4269 Pro.
Coxgreen, Sunderland SR4 9JT
Take A183 direction Chester-le-Street from A19, after 400 yards turn right at Coxgreen sign, left at small T-junction, follow road down hill to clubhouse, (4 mins from A19).
Meadowland/parkland course.
18 holes, 6343 yards, S.S.S.70
Founded 1892
Visitors: welcome; unaccompanied visitors must show h/cap cert.
Green Fee: on application.
Societies: on application to Sec; weekends only during month of Aug.
Catering: full facilities, except Mon during winter.
Hotels: George Washington Sports Centre; Seaburn; Ramside Hall; Rainton Motel.

O76 Westerhope

☎(091) 286 9125
Whorlton Grange, Westerhope, Newcastle-upon-Tyne NE5 1PP
5 miles W of Newcastle; Airport Rd for 3 miles then follow signs to Westerhope.
Parkland course.
18 holes, 6407 yards, S.S.S.71
Founded 1941

Visitors: Mon to Thurs.
Green Fee: on application.
Societies: catered for Mon to Thurs.
Catering: yes except Mon.

O77 Whickham

☎(091) 488 7309
Hollinside Park, Whickham, Newcastle-upon-Tyne NE16 5BA
5 miles W of Newcastle.
Undulating parkland course.
18 holes, 6129 yards, S.S.S.69
Founded 1911
Visitors: unrestricted weekdays, by arrangement weekends.
Green Fee: on application.
Societies: weekdays only.
Catering: snacks, cooked meals by arrangement.
Snooker.
Hotels: Gibside (Whickham).

O78 Whitburn

☎(091) 529 2144, 529 4210 Pro.
Lizard Lane, South Shields, Tyne & Wear NE34 7AH
Half way between Sunderland and South Shields off coast road.
Parkland course.
18 holes, 6046 yards, S.S.S.69
Founded 1932
Visitors: welcome weekdays (restricted Tues); at weekends phone Pro beforehand.
Green Fee: £15/round/day WD, £20/round/day WE.
Societies: weekdays except Tues by arrangement.
Catering: full facilities.
Hotels: Seaburn; Roker; Sea Hotel.

O79 Whitley Bay

☎(091) 252 0180
Claremont Rd, Whitley Bay, Tyne & Wear NE26 3UF
On A183, 10 miles NE of Newcastle; at N end of town.
Links/parkland course.
18 holes, 6617 yards, S.S.S.72
Founded 1890
Visitors: not weekends.
Green Fee: £17/round, £24/day.
Societies: weekdays by arrangement.
Catering: full bar and restaurant facilities except Mon.
Hotels: Gosforth Park; Holiday Inn; Windsor.

O80 Wilton

☎(0642) 465265, 454626 Members
Wilton Castle, Redcar, Cleveland TS10 4QY
8 miles E of Middlesborough; 4 miles W of Redcar, on A174.
Parkland course.
18 holes, 6104 yards, S.S.S.69
Founded 1952
Visitors: welcome; not Sat.
Green Fee: £15 WD, £17 WE & BH.
Societies: welcome by prior arrangement.
Catering: evening meals by arrangement.
Hotels: Park; Hotel Royal York.

O81 Woodham G & CC

☎(0325) 318346
Burnhill Way, Newton Aycliffe, Durham DL5 4PM
2 miles A1(M), 1 mile N of Newton Aycliffe.
Parkland course with lakes.
18 holes, 6727 yards, S.S.S.72
Designed by J. Hamilton Stutt.
Founded 1983
Visitors: unlimited weekdays, by appointment weekends.
Green Fee: £16.50/round, £20/day WD; £20/round, £25/day WE & BH.
Societies: by appointment.
Catering: à la carte restaurant; ring (0325) 301551
Hotels: Redworth Hall.

O82 Wooler

☎(0668) 81956 Sec.
Dod Law, Doddington, Wooler, N'umberland NE71 6EA
Signposted from B6525 Wooler-Berwick road.
Moorland course with heather and bracken and panoramic views.
9 holes (18 tees), 6358 yards, S.S.S.70
Designed by club members.
Founded 1970 (present course 1976)
Visitors: welcome, usually no restrictions.
Green Fee: £6/round/day WD, £8/round/day WE & BH.
Societies: apply to Sec (23 Ryecroft Crescent, Wooler, NE71 6EA).
Catering: bar every night 8-11pm; catering by arrangement.
Hotels: Ryecroft; Tankerville Arms; Black Bull; Angel Inn; Red Lion; Anchor Inn; Wheatsheaf; Loretto GH.

P

LOTHIAN, BORDERS, DUMFRIES & GALLOWAY

This is an area embracing the south-west of Scotland, the Borders (more famous for rugby than golf), and the part of central Scotland which incorporates East Lothian, one of the oldest and most famous regions in the expanding world of golf.

Until Muirfield was opened in 1892, Musselburgh was a regular home of the Open championship between 1874 and 1889 while North Berwick staged many challenge matches that are part of the game's folklore.

Nowadays, you could stay for a week and play a different course of championship standard each day without having to drive for more than about twenty minutes. The old Musselburgh course, enveloped by Edinburgh racecourse, is the place to start on historical grounds, although Royal Musselburgh has a more sheltered parkland home a mile or two down the road to North Berwick which bristles with golfing retreats.

Longniddry, and the shorter Kilspindie at Aberlady, provide contrasting pleasures but the true heart of East Lothian lies around Gullane Hill and the incomparable stretch of natural terrain that houses Luffness New and Gullane Nos 1, 2 and 3. From a distance, they are indistinguishable the one from the other, green ribbons of fairway lined by taller grass running down to the edge of Aberlady Bay — a bird sanctuary and nature reserve that profits rather than suffers from its proximity to golf.

Luffness is enchanting, neither stern nor straightforward with magnificently true, small greens, but Gullane Hill is a dominant feature of all these Gullane courses, hiding the road from the holes bordering the Firth of Forth and a series of resplendent views. Everyone has courses for which he feels unreasoning affection, and Luffness and Gullane No. 1 are two of my particular favourites.

The incomparable stretch of country on which they stand was introduced to me by a kind uncle during my time at school in Edinburgh, when a day at Luffness really was an escape from Plato and Pythagoras; my memories are of gloriously smooth, fast putting greens, a blind short hole across a quarry — and a magnificent and very welcome lunch.

On the other side of the hill lies Muirfield, third home of the Honourable Company of Edinburgh Golfers and invariably placed top in polls on British courses. It has no enemies, a noble combination of ancient and modern that never disappoints. North Berwick, on the other hand, has changed very little through the years in spite of the advance in manufacture of equipment which has softened some of its terrors. The last of the coastal courses is Dunbar which, too, has many admirers.

As well as East Lothian, there are Midlothian and West Lothian which, though full of good courses, are less remarkable. Boyhood memories compel me to single out Bruntsfield, Dalmahoy and the Royal Burgess at Barnton, a mile or two from the Forth Bridge.

The Border country has several 9-hole courses in scenic settings and two or three of grander dimensions. However, the county of Dumfries & Galloway deserves greater recognition than it invariably receives, particularly around the countryside fringing the Solway Firth. Southerness is the flagship, a championship test which Mackenzie Ross designed and built at about the time he was resurrecting Turnberry after the war, and where heather and gorse put a heavy onus on fine driving.

Other recommendations must include Powfoot, Thornhill and, working a path westward, the courses of Wigtownshire County, Stranraer and, last but not least, Portpatrick (Dunskey).

P1 **Baberton**

☎(031) 453 4911
Baberton Ave, Juniper Green,
Edinburgh EH14 5DU
5 miles W of Edinburgh on A70
Lanark road.
Parkland course.
18 holes, 6140 yards, S.S.S.69
Designed by Willie Park.
Founded 1893
Visitors: on introduction by member.
Green Fee: £15/round, £22/day.
Societies: Mon-Fri only by
arrangement with Sec.
Catering: full facilities.

P2 **Bathgate**

☎(0506) 52232 Club, 630553 Pro,
630505 Sec.
Edinburgh Rd, Bathgate, W Lothian
EH48 1BA
400 yards E from town centre.
Parkland course.
18 holes, 6328 yards, S.S.S.70
Designed by Willie Park.
Founded 1892
Visitors: unrestricted.
Green Fee: on application.
Societies: welcome by prior
arrangement with Sec.
Catering: coffee, lunch, high tea.
Hotels: Golden Circle; Dreadnought.

P3 **Braid Hills**

☎(031) 452 9408, 445 2044 Sec
(Braids United), 447 6666 starter
Braid Hills Approach Rd, Edinburgh
EH10 6JY
A702 from city centre S.
Public hillside courses with
panoramic views.
18 holes, 5731 yards, S.S.S.68; 18
holes, 4832 yards, S.S.S.64
Founded 1897
Visitors: unrestricted.
Green Fee: £6/round.
Societies: by prior arrangement.
Catering: by prior arrangement.
Hotels: Braid Hills.

P4 **Broomieknowe**

☎(031) 663 9317
36 Golf Course Rd, Bonnyrigg,
Midlothian EH19 2HZ
About 0.5 mile into Bonnyrigg from
Eskbank Rd roundabout on A7.
Gently undulating parkland course.
18 holes, 5754 yards, S.S.S.68
Designed by James Braid.
Founded 1906
Visitors: welcome weekdays.
Green Fee: £14/round, £20/day WD;
£20/round WE.

Societies: Mon-Thurs.
Catering: bar lunches, evening
meals by arrangement with Steward.
Hotels: Dalhousie Castle.

P5 **Bruntsfield Links**

☎(031) 336 1479 Sec, 2006
Clubhouse
32 Barnton Ave, Davidsons Mains,
Edinburgh EH4 6JH
Off A90 in Davidsons Mains 2 to 3
miles W of Edinburgh city centre.
Parkland course.
18 holes, 6407 yards, S.S.S.71
Designed by Willie Park.
Founded 1761
Visitors: welcome weekdays by
appointment.
Green Fee: on application.
Societies: by appointment.
Catering: luncheon daily, evening
meals during playing season.
Hotels: Barnton.

P6 **Carrickknowe**

☎(031) 337 1096
Glendevon Park, Edinburgh EH12 5VZ
Opposite the Post House Hotel, down
Balgreen Rd.
Public meadowland course.
18 holes, 6299 yards, S.S.S.70
Founded 1933
Visitors: welcome.
Green Fee: £6/round.
Societies: by arrangement.
Catering: by arrangement with Sec.
Hotels: Post House.

P7 **Castle Douglas**

☎(0556) 2801
Abercromby Rd, Castle Douglas,
Kirkcudbrightshire
400 yards on Ayr road from town
clock.
Parkland course.
9 holes, 5408 yards, S.S.S.66
Visitors: welcome.
Green Fee: on application.
Catering: bar facilities in evenings.

P8 **Cogarburn**

☎(031) 333 4718/4110
Handley Lodge, Newbridge,
Edinburgh, Midlothian EH28
1st entrance past Gogarburn Hospital
on left hand side.
Parkland course.
12 holes, 5070 yards, S.S.S.66
Founded 1975
Visitors: welcome at any time.
Green Fee: £4/round, £6/day WD;
£6/round WE.

Societies: welcome.
Catering: bar and snacks.
Hotels: Royal Scotch.

P9 **Colvend**

☎(055 663) 398, (0556) 610878 Sec
Sandyhills, by Dalbeattie,
Kirkcubrightshire DG5 4PY
6 miles from Dalbeattie on A710
Solway coast road.
Undulating meadowland course.
9 holes, 2322 yards, S.S.S.63
Designed by Willie Fernie (Troon)
1905; extended 1982 with advice
from Dave Thomas.
Founded 1905
Visitors: welcome; course closed
April-Sept at 2pm Tues, 5.30pm
Thurs.
Green Fee: £10/day; under 18
half-price except Sat and Sun.
Societies: apply to Sec.
Catering: April-Oct full lunches and
dinners; winter weekends only.
Hotels: Clonyard House.

P10 **Craigentinny**

☎(031) 554 7501 Starter
143 Craigentinny Ave, Edinburgh
1 mile from Meadowbank Stadium,
2.5 miles E of city centre.
Public links course.
18 holes, 5418 yards, S.S.S.66
Founded 1891
Visitors: welcome.
Green Fee: £6/round.
Societies: welcome by appointment.

P11 **Craigmillar Park**

☎(031) 667 2837 Clubhouse, 667
0047 Office
1 Observatory Rd, Edinburgh EH9 3HG
Approx 3 miles from city centre close
to Royal Observatory, Blackford Hill.
Parkland course.
18 holes, 5859 yards, S.S.S.68
Designed by James Braid.
Founded 1895
Visitors: with h/cap cert, letter of
intro or proof of club membership; off
first tee by 3.30pm weekdays; not
weekends or Bank Holidays.
Green Fee: £12/round, £18/day WD.
Societies: on application.
Catering: bar lunches, high teas on
request.
Hotels: Iona.

P12 **Dalmahoy**

☎(031) 333 4105
Kirknewton, Midlothian EH27 8EB
7 miles W of Edinburgh centre on A71.

Rolling parkland course.
East, 18 holes, 6664 yards, S.S.S.72;
West, 18 holes, 5121 yards, S.S.S.66
Designed by James Braid.
Founded 1922
Visitors: welcome weekdays,
weekends by application.
Green Fee: East £30 WD, £40 WE;
West £20 WD, £30 WE.
Societies: every day.
Catering: extensive facilities;
Country club with tennis, squash,
swimming pool, snooker, health and
beauty facilities.
Hotels: Dalmahoy; golf and leisure
breaks available.

P13 Deer Park G & CC
☎(0506) 38843
Golf Course Rd, Knightsbridge,
Livingston, W Lothian EH54 8BP
Leave M8 at Livingston interchange,

follow signposts to Knightsbridge,
club signposted from there.
Championship meadowland course.
18 holes, 6775 yards, S.S.S.72
Designed by Charles Lawrie.
Founded 1978
Visitors: welcome.
Green Fee: on application.
Societies: welcome.
Catering: meals served.
Swimming pool, squash, snooker,
pool, 10-pin bowling, saunas etc.
Hotels: Hilton; Houston House.

P14 Duddingston
☎(031) 661 7688 or 661 4301 Pro.
Duddingston Rd, W Edinburgh EH15
3QD
3 miles from city centre E of A1.
Parkland course.
18 holes, 6647 yards, S.S.S.72
Designed by Capability Brown.

Founded 1895
Visitors: Mon-Fri only.
Green Fee: £18/round, £24/day.
Societies: Tues, Thurs only; £15 per
round, £21.50 per day.
Catering: lunch, high teas, bar daily.
Hotels: Lady Nairne; King's Manor;
Duddingston Mansion House.

P15 Dumfries & County
☎(0387) 53585
Edinburgh Rd, Dumfries DG1 1JX
1 mile N of Dumfries centre on A701.
Parkland course.
18 holes, 5928 yards, S.S.S.68
Designed by Willie Fernie.
Founded 1912
Visitors: welcome except Sat.
Green Fee: £14 WD, £17 WE.
Societies: apply to Sec.
Catering: full facilities every day.
Hotels: Station; Moreig; Cairndale.

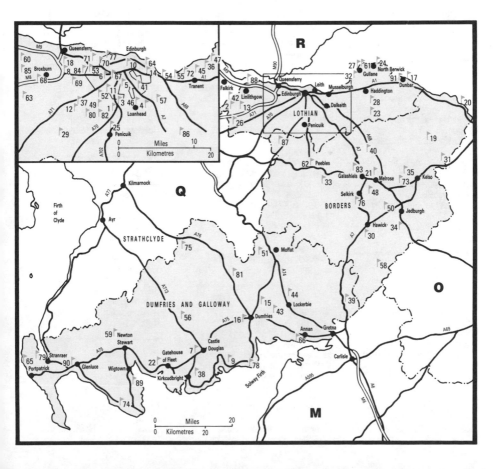

P16 **Dumfries & Galloway**
☎(0387) 53582
Laurieston Ave, Dumfries DG2 7NY
On A75 W of Dumfries.
Parkland course.
18 holes, 5782 yards, S.S.S.68
Founded 1880
Visitors: welcome without
reservation.
Green Fee: on application.
Societies: catered for.
Catering: full facilities except Mon.

P17 **Dunbar**
☎(0368) 62317
East Links, Dunbar EH42 1LT
0.5 mile from Dunbar centre.
Seaside course.
18 holes, 6426 yards, S.S.S.71
Founded 1794
Visitors: unrestricted except Thurs.
Green Fee: £20/day WD, £35/day
WE & BH.
Societies: by arrangement with Sec
in writing.
Catering: full facilities 7 days.
Hotels: Royal Mackintosh;
Battleblent; Hillside; Goldenstones.

P18 **Dundas Park**
☎(031) 331 1416
c/o Sec, 3 Loch Rd, South
Queensferry, W Lothian EH30 9LS
1 mile S of Queensferry, on right of
A8000.
Parkland course (good practice
course).
9 holes, 6024 yards, S.S.S.69
Founded 1957
Visitors: with member only.
Green Fee: £8.
Societies: welcome, written request
to Sec.
Catering: self-catering snacks in
clubhouse.

P19 **Duns**
☎(0361) 82717 Sec.
Hardens Rd, Duns, Berwicks
1 mile W of Duns off A6105.
Undulating meadowland course.
9 holes, 5826 yards, S.S.S.68
Founded 1894
Visitors: unrestricted.
Green Fee: £8/round, £12/day; 50%
reduction 1st Nov-15th Mar.
Societies: welcome if previously
arranged with Sec.
Catering: limited bar facilities,
mainly at weekends.
Hotels: "Freedom of the Fairways"
package from Scottish Borders
Tourist Board.

P20 **Eyemouth**
☎(08907) 50551
Gunsgreen House, Eyemouth TD14
4DW
2.5 miles E of Burmouth, off A1,
signposted on A1107.
Seaside course.
9 holes, 5446 yards, S.S.S.66
Founded 1880
Visitors: unrestricted weekdays,
after 10.30am Sat, 12am Sun.
Green Fee: £7/day (£3 jnrs);
£28/week (£12 jnrs).
Societies: by arrangement.
Catering: bar open evenings and
lunchtime weekends.
Snooker, pool.
Hotels: Home Arms; Contented Sole.

P21 **Galashiels**
☎(0896) 3724
Ladhope Recreation Ground,
Galashiels, Selkirkshire TD1 2NJ
At N end of town off A7.
Public, hilly course.
18 holes, 5309 yards, S.S.S.67
Designed by James Braid.
Founded 1884
Visitors: no restrictions.
Green Fee: £5.65/round Mon-Sat,
£6.45 Sun.
Catering: bar, evenings, weekends.
Hotels: Douglas (Kingsknowes).

P22 **Gatehouse**
☎(0557) 814281 Sec.
Laurieston Rd, Gatehouse-of-Fleet
Turn right at War Memorial on
entering town from E.
Public, undulating course with gorse
in places.
9 holes, 4796 yards, S.S.S.63
Founded 1921
Visitors: welcome any time.
Green Fee: £8/day.
Societies: apply to Sec.
Hotels: Cally; Murray Arms; both
offer free golf.

P23 **Gifford**
☎(062 081) 267
c/o Sec, Calroust, Tweeddale Ave,
Gifford, E Lothian, EH41 4QN
4.5 miles S of Haddington off A6137.
Meadowland/woodland course.
9 holes, 6138 yards, S.S.S.69
Founded 1904
Visitors: welcome, except Tues and
Wed from 4pm or Sat/Sun from 12am.
Green Fee: on application.
Societies: catered for on weekdays
by arrangement with Sec.
Hotels: Goblin Ha'; Tweeddale Arms.

P24 **Glen**
☎(0620) 2221
Tantallon Terrace, North Berwick,
E Lothian EH39 4LE
22 miles NE of Edinburgh on A198,
follow road along E beach, clubhouse
is last building on right.
Seaside/parkland course.
18 holes, 6098 yards, S.S.S.69
Designed by Mackenzie Ross.
Founded 1906
Visitors: no restrictions.
Green Fee: £6.50/round WD,
£8.50/round WE.
Societies: by arrangement with
clubmaster.
Catering: bar lunch, high tea, coffee.
Hotels: Royal; Blenheim House;
Nether Abbey.

P25 **Glencorse**
☎(0968) 77189
Milton Bridge, Pencuik, Midlothian
EH26 0RD
On A701, 9 miles S of Edinburgh.
Parkland course, burns on 10 holes.
18 holes, 5205 yards, S.S.S.66
Designed by Willie Park Jnr.
Founded 1890
Visitors: welcome most weekdays
and weekends if no competitions.
Green Fee: £12/round, £16/day WD;
£16/round WE.
Societies: most weekdays.
Catering: full facilities.
Hotels: Inveravon House (Loanhead);
Original, Royal (Roslin).

P26 **Greenburn**
☎(0501) 70292
6 Greenburn Rd, Fauldhouse, W
Lothian EH47 9HG
Between Edinburgh and Glasgow, off
M8 at Whitburn, 3 miles.
Moorland course.
18 holes, 6210 yards, S.S.S.70
Founded 1953
Visitors: weekdays.
Green Fee: on application.
Societies: by prior booking.
Catering: weekends and midweek
when societies are booked in.
Hotels: Hillcroft (Whitburn).

P27 **Gullane**
☎(0620) 842255
Gullane, East Lothian EH31 2BB
Off A1, on A198 to Gullane.
Links courses.
No. 1, 18 holes, 6466 yards,
S.S.S.71; No. 2, 18 holes, 6244
yards, S.S.S.70; No. 3, 18 holes,
5166 yards, S.S.S.65

Founded 1882
Visitors: welcome on No. 1 course Mon-Fri and on Nos 2 & 3 at all times.
Green Fee: No. 1 course £31/round, £43/day WD; £40/round WE; No. 2 course £14/round, £20/day WD; £17/round, £25/day WE; No. 3 £10/round, £13/day WD; £12/round, £16/day WE.
Societies: by arrangement (except No. 1 at weekends).
Catering: lunch every day except Mon; other meals by arrangement.
Hotels: Grey Walls; Golf Inn; Mallard; Queens; Marine (N Berwick); Open Arms (Dirleton).

P28 Haddington
☎(062 082) 3627
Amisfield Park, Whittinghame Drive, Haddington, E Lothian
17 miles E of Edinburgh on A1, cross Victoria Bridge on E edge of town, golf course is 500 yards on left.
Public parkland course.
18 holes, 6280 yards, S.S.S.70
Founded 1865
Visitors: welcome with pre-booking, Sat and Sun 7-10am, 12am-2pm.
Green Fee: £8.50/round, £10.50/day.
Societies: welcome.
Catering: lunches, bar snacks, bar meals, high tea, except Tues.
Hotels: Mercat; Railway; Browns; Maitland Field.

P29 Harburn
☎(0506) 871131 Sec, 871256 Pro.
West Calder, West Lothian EH55 8RS
Turn S at West Calder off A70 Lanark to Edinburgh road.
Parkland course.
18 holes, 5853 yards, S.S.S.68
Founded 1933
Visitors: welcome.
Green Fee: £11/round, £16/day WD; £16/round, £22/day WE.
Societies: by arrangement.
Catering: bar snacks; full facilities by arrangement.
Hotels: Harburn House; West End.

P30 Hawick
☎(0450) 72293
Vertish Hill, Hawick, Roxburgh TD9 0NY
SE of Edinburgh on A7.
Parkland course.
18 holes, 5927 yards, S.S.S.69
Founded 1877
Visitors: welcome.
Green Fee: on application.

Societies: apply to Sec.
Catering: full facilities.
Hotels: Kirklands; Elm House; Mansfield Park.

P31 Hirsel
☎(0890) 2678
Kelso Rd, Coldstream, Berwickshire TS12 4LG
W end of Coldstream on A697, Edinburgh-Newcastle road.
Parkland course.
9 holes, 2828 yards, S.S.S.67
Founded 1948
Visitors: any time.
Green Fee: on application.
Societies: by arrangement.
Catering: Apr-Sept or by arrangement.
Hotels: Tillmouth Park; Victoria; Newcastle Arms.

P32 Honourable Company of Edinburgh Golfers
☎(0620) 842123
Muirfield, Gullane, E Lothian EH31 2EG
Last road on left leaving Gullane for North Berwick on A198, approx 18 miles from Edinburgh.
Links course.
Medal, 18 holes, 6941 yards, S.S.S.73
Designed by Tom Morris.
Founded 1744
Visitors: Tues, Thurs and Fri am (not July/Aug); must be members of recognised golf club with h/cap of 18 or better if gentlemen, 24 if Ladies.
Green Fee: £45/round, £60/day.
Societies: no reduced rates or packages; same as for visitors.
Catering: morning coffee, lunch, tea; there are limited changing facilities for Ladies, but they are not allowed to eat in the Clubhouse.
Hotels: Greywalls; Open Arms.

P33 Innerleithen
☎(0896) 830951
Leithen Water, Leithen Road, Innerleithen EH44
1 mile from Innerleithen on Heriot road.
Heathland course.
9 holes, 5868 yards, S.S.S.60
Designed by Willie Park.
Founded 1886
Visitors: no restrictions.
Green Fee: £7 WD, £9 WE; day ticket only.
Societies: by arrangement.
Catering: by arrangement.

P34 Jedburgh
☎(0835) 63587
Dunion Rd, Jedburgh, TD8 6DQ
0.75 mile W of Jedburgh.
Undulating parkland course.
9 holes, 5555 yards, S.S.S.67
Founded 1892
Visitors: welcome except competition days at weekends.
Green Fee: £7 WD, £8 WE.
Societies: booked at least 2 weeks in advance.
Catering: bar and meals April-Oct.
Hotels: Royal; Jedforest.

P35 Kelso
☎(0573) 23009, 23259 Sec.
Racecourse Rd, Kelso, TD5 7SL
1 mile N of town centre within National Hunt Racecourse.
Flat parkland course.
18 holes, 6066 yards, S.S.S.69
Designed by James Braid.
Founded 1887
Visitors: welcome.
Green Fee: on application.
Societies: by arrangement.
Catering: not Mon or Tues; societies on these days by prior arrangement.

P36 Kilspindie
☎(0875) 358, 216
Aberlady, East Lothian EH32 0QD
Immediately E of Aberlady village, private road to left leading to club.
Seaside course.
18 holes, 5410 yards, S.S.S.66
Designed by Ross & Sayers, extended by Willie Park.
Founded 1867
Visitors: welcome subject to members' demands; advisable to enquire in advance.
Green Fee: £15/round, £21/day WD; £18/round, £24/day WE.
Societies: welcome weekdays if booked in advance.
Catering: full facilities except Fri.
Hotels: Kilspindie House (Aberlady).

P37 Kingsknowe
☎(031) 441 4030
326 Lanark Rd, Edinburgh EH14 2JD
W of Edinburgh on A71.
Parkland course.
18 holes, 5979 yards, S.S.S.69
Designed by J.C. Stutt.
Founded 1908
Visitors: welcome weekdays.
Green Fee: £11.50/round, £16.50/day WD.
Catering: bar, lunch, high tea except Mon. Snooker.

P38 **Kirkcudbright**
☎(0557) 30314
Stirling Crescent, Kirkcudbright
Turn left off A75 into town from
Castle Douglas.
Hilly parkland course.
18 holes, 5598 yards, S.S.S.67
Founded 1893
Visitors: welcome except on
competition days.
Green Fee: £15/day.
Societies: 1st Mon of each month by
arrangement.
Catering: available.
Hotels: Arden House; Royal; Selkirk;
Gordon House.

P39 **Langholm**
☎(03873) 80878 Sec.
Whitaside, Langholm, Dumfriesshire
DG13 0JR
Between Carlisle and Hawick on A7,
400 yards E of Market Place.
Hillside course.
9 holes, 5744 yards, S.S.S.68
Founded 1892
Visitors: welcome weekdays and
weekends except competitions.
Green Fee: £6/round/day.
Societies: apply to Sec.
Catering: can be arranged.

P40 **Lauder**
☎(05782) 526
Galashiels Rd, Lauder, Berwickshire
Off A68, 0.5 mile from Lauder.
Undulating course.
9 holes, 6002 yards, S.S.S.70
Designed by W. Park of Musselburgh.
Founded 1896
Visitors: welcome.
Green Fee: on application.
Societies: book in advance.

P41 **Liberton**
☎(031) 664 3309
297 Gilmerton Rd, Edinburgh EH16
5UJ
S of Edinburgh on A7.
Parkland course.
18 holes, 5299 yards, S.S.S.66
Founded 1920
Visitors: welcome except after 5pm
on Mon, Wed, Fri.
Green Fee: on application.
Societies: welcome weekdays.
Catering: full facilities available.

P42 **Linlithgow**
☎(0506) 842585
Braehead, Linlithgow, W Lothian
EH49 6QF

M9 from Edinburgh, SW of Linlithgow.
Undulating parkland course.
18 holes, 5729 yards, S.S.S.68
Founded 1913
Visitors: welcome except Sat.
Green Fee: £10/round, £14/day WD;
£14/round, £17/day Sun.
Societies: prices on request.
Catering: full catering available.
Hotels: Star & Garter.

P43 **Lochmaben**
☎(0387) 810552
Castlehill Gate, Lochmaben,
Dumfries DG11 1NT
On A709 between Dumfries and
Lockerbie.
Undulating parkland course.
9 holes, 5304 yards, S.S.S.66
Designed by James Braid.
Founded 1926
Visitors: welcome except
competition days.
Green Fee: on application.
Societies: catered for on weekdays.
Catering: by arrangement for
meetings.
Fishing, sailing.
Hotels: Balcastle; Queens.

P44 **Lockerbie**
☎(05762) 3363
Corrie Rd, Lockerbie, Dumfriesshire
DG11 2ND
A74 to Lockerbie, take Langholm
road, turn left at T-junction towards
Corrie, club 0.25 mile on right;
signposted from town centre.
Parkland course.
18 holes, 5327 yards, S.S.S.66
Designed by James Braid (original 9).
Founded 1889
Visitors: welcome Mon-Sat, Sun
pm.
Green Fee: £12 Mon-Fri, £15 Sat
and Sun.
Societies: by arrangement.
Catering: full bar and catering
service during summer.
Hotels: Queens; Lockerbie Manor;
Blue Bell; Kings Arms; Ravenshill.

P45 **Longniddry**
☎(0875) 52141, 52228 starter
Links Rd, Longniddry, E Lothian
EH32 0NL
A1 from Edinburgh, at Wallyford
roundabout take A198, turn left at
Longniddry down Links Rd.
Links/parkland course.
18 holes, 6219 yards, S.S.S.70
Designed by Harry Colt.
Founded 1921

Visitors: welcome excluding
competition days and public
holidays; phone starter.
Green Fee: £20/round, £30/day WD.
Societies: Mon to Thurs.
Catering: dining room excluding Fri,
bar service, snacks available.
Hotels: Marine (N Berwick);
Kilspindie House (Aberlady).

P46 **Lothianburn**
☎(031) 445 2206 Clubhouse, 445
5067 Sec, 445 2288 Pro.
106 Biggar Rd, Edinburgh EH10 7DU
S boundary of Edinburgh, adjacent to
Edinburgh by-pass.
Panoramic hillside course.
18 holes, 5750 yards, S.S.S.69
Designed by James Braid.
Founded 1893
Visitors: welcome weekdays only.
Green Fee: £8/round, £12/day.
Societies: welcome by arrangement
with Sec on weekdays.
Catering: lunch, bar meals, high tea;
dinners by arrangement (not Wed).

P47 **Luffness New**
☎(0620) 843114 or 843376
Clubmaster, 843336 Sec.
Aberlady, E Lothian EH32 0QA
E of Edinburgh, follow trunk road
A198 along coast, club lies between
Aberlady and Gullane.
Undulating links course.
18 holes, 6122 yards, S.S.S.69
Designed by Tom Morris (1894).
Founded 1894
Visitors: by members introduction or
by arrangement except Sat, Sun and
public holidays.
Green Fee: on application.
Societies: weekday bookings.
Catering: luncheon, high tea and
dinner except Mon.
Hotels: Greywalls (Gullane); Marine
(N Berwick).

P48 **Melrose**
☎(089 682) 2855, 2391 Sec.
Dingleton, Melrose, Roxburghshire
Off A68 Carlisle-Edinburgh road, 0.5
mile S of Melrose.
Parkland course.
9 holes, 5464 yards, S.S.S.68
Founded 1880
Visitors: April-Oct, weekdays before
4pm and some Sun; Oct-Mar virtually
any day.
Green Fee: £10/day.
Societies: by arrangement.
Catering: snacks available; by
arrangement for parties. Pool.

P49 Merchants of Edinburgh

☎(031) 447 1219
10 Craighill Gardens, Edinburgh
EH10 5PY
S side of Edinburgh off A701.
Hilly parkland course.
18 holes, 4889 yards, S.S.S.64
Founded 1907
Visitors: must be introduced by member, but parties may apply in writing for reservation to Sec.
Green Fee: £8/round; £12/day weekday parties.
Societies: welcome on weekdays by arrangement with Sec.
Catering: meals served if ordered in advance (except Wed and Thurs).
Hotels: Braid Hills.

P50 Minto

☎(0450) 87220
Minto Village, by Denholm, Hawick, Roxburghshire
5 miles NE of Hawick off A698, turn left in Denholm for Minto.
Parkland course.
18 holes, 5460 yards, S.S.S.68
Founded 1926
Visitors: welcome at all times.
Green Fee: £10 WD, £12 WE & BH.
Societies: by arrangement.
Catering: bar and catering available.
Hotels: Elm House; Kirklands.

P51 Moffat

☎(0683) 20020
Coatshill, Moffat, DG10 9SB
On A701 between Moffat and Beattock, 1 mile off A74.
Moorland course.
18 holes, 5218 yards, S.S.S.66
Designed by Ben Sayers.
Founded 1884
Visitors: welcome; not Wed pm.
Green Fee: £12/day WD, £22/day WE.
Societies: welcome except Wed.
Catering: bar, bar lunches, coffee daily.
Hotels: Moffat House; Balmoral; Annandale Arms; Beechwood Country House; Auchen Castle.

P52 Mortonhall

☎(031) 447 6974 Sec.
231 Braid Rd, Edinburgh EH10 6PB
2 miles S of city centre on A702, situated on S of Braid Hills.
Moorland course.
18 holes, 6557 yards, S.S.S.71
Designed by Braid & Hawtree.
Founded 1892

Visitors: welcome weekdays.
Green Fee: on application.
Societies: welcome weekdays by arrangement.
Catering: bar and catering facilities.
Hotels: Braid Hills.

P53 Murrayfield

☎(031) 337 3478
Murrayfield Rd, Edinburgh EH12 6EU
2 miles W of city centre.
Parkland course.
18 holes, 5727 yards, S.S.S.68
Founded 1896
Visitors: welcome weekdays with letter of intro.
Green Fee: on application.
Societies: by arrangement.
Catering: meals served except Sun.
Hotels: Ellersly House; Murrayfield; Post House.

P54 Musselburgh

☎(031) 665 2005
Monktonhall, Musselburgh, E Lothian EH21 6SA
1 mile S of Edinburgh off A1.
Parkland course.
18 holes, 6623 yards, S.S.S.72
Designed by James Braid.
Founded 1938
Visitors: on application.
Green Fee: on application.
Catering: bar and restaurant.

P55 Musselburgh Old Course

☎(031) 665 6981
Silver Ring Clubhouse, 3b Mill Hill, Musselburgh, East Lothian EH21 7RG
7 miles E of Edinburgh.
Public seaside course.
9 holes, 5380 yards, S.S.S.67
Visitors: welcome weekdays and Bank Holidays; weekends after 1pm.
Green Fee: £5 for 18 holes.
Societies: by arrangement.

P56 New Galloway

☎(06443) 455
New Galloway, Castle Douglas, Kirkcudbrightshire DG7 3RN
Easily located leaving village on A762.
Hilly panoramic moorland course.
9 holes, 5058 yards, S.S.S.65
Founded 1902
Visitors: welcome.
Green Fee: £8/day WD, £10/day WE.
Societies: apply to Sec.
Catering: bar; meals in village.
Hotels: Kenmure Arms; Kenbridge; Cairn Edward.

P57 Newbattle

☎(031) 663 2123
Abbey Rd, Dalkeith, Midlothian
7 miles SW of Edinburgh on A7, take Newbattle exit at Esbank roundabout, turn left opposite police station, club 300 yards on right.
Undulating parkland course.
18 holes, 6012 yards, S.S.S.69
Founded 1934
Visitors: Mon-Fri except Public and Local Holidays up to 4pm.
Green Fee: £12/round, £20/day.
Societies: Mon-Fri except holidays, 9-10am and 2-3pm.
Catering: full facilities on request.
Hotels: Lugton Inn; Stair Arms; County.

P58 Newcastleton

☎(03873) 75257
Holm Hill, Newcastleton, Roxburgh TD9 0QD
25 miles N of Carlisle; turn right off A7 to Canonbie, 10 miles to Newcastleton on B6357.
Hillside course.
9 holes, 5748 yards, S.S.S.68
Designed by J. Shade.
Founded 1894
Visitors: No restrictions.
Green Fee: £3.50/round.
Societies: welcome.
Catering: can be arranged.
Hotels: Grapes; Liddesdale.

P59 Newton Stewart

☎(0671) 2172
Kirroughtree Ave, Minnigaff, Newton Stewart, DG8 6PF
Off A75.
Parkland course.
9 holes, 5500 yards, S.S.S.67
Founded 1981
Visitors: welcome.
Green Fee: £8/day WD, £12 WE & BH.
Societies: by prior arrangement.
Catering: meals and bar lunches during bar hours; other by arrangement with Steward.
Hotels: Kirroughtree; Cally Palace; Bruce.

P60 Niddry Castle

☎(0506) 891097
Castle Rd, Winchburgh, W Lothian EH52 6RQ
2 miles NE of Broxburn.
Parkland course with large burn.
9 holes, 2757 yards, S.S.S.67
Designed by Derek Smith.
Founded 1984

Visitors: welcome except weekend competition days.
Green Fee: £5/day WD, £7.50/day WE.
Societies: booking only.
Catering: clubhouse.
Putting green, practice net.
Hotels: South Queensferry.

P61 North Berwick
☎(0620) 2135
Beach Rd, North Berwick EH39 4BB
23 miles E of Edinburgh on A198.
Seaside course.
18 holes, 6315 yards, S.S.S.70
Designed by Mackenzie Ross.
Founded 1832
Visitors: unrestricted.
Green Fee: £20/round, £30/day WD (£15/day Nov-Feb); £30/round, £40/day WE & BH (£20/day Nov-Feb); under 16 half-price.
Societies: unrestricted weekdays.
Catering: except Thurs.
Hotels: Marine; Royal; Point Gary; Nether Abbey.

P62 Peebles
☎(0721) 20197
Kirkland St, Peebles EH45 8EU
NW of town off A72, signposted on main roads into town.
Undulating parkland course.
18 holes, 6137 yards, S.S.S.69
Designed by James Braid, with alterations by H.S. Colt.
Founded 1892
Visitors: welcome; no denim in clubhouse.
Green Fee: £11/round, £15/day WD; £16/round, £22/day WE.
Societies: max 24.
Catering: bar and restaurant.
Hotels: Peebles Hydro; Park; Kingsmuir.

P63 Polkemmet Country Park
☎(0501) 43905
Park Centre, Polkemmet Country Park, Whitburn, Bathgate, W Lothian EH47 0AD
On N side of B7066, midway between Harthill and Whitburn; signs from Whitburn exit M8.
Public parkland course (old private estate).
9 holes, 2969 metres, S.S.S.37
Designed by W Lothian District Council.
Founded 1981
Visitors: no restrictions; players must have own clubs.

Green Fee: up to £2.45/9 holes depending on season/day.
Societies: weekdays only.
Catering: bar snacks/meals, all day license; restaurant lunches/evening meals.
Driving range, bowls, play area and fort, riverside and woodland walks.
Hotels: Whitdale, (Whitburn); Golden Circle, Dreadnought, Fairweigh, (Bathgate).

P64 Portobello
☎(031) 669 4361
Stanley St, Portobello, Edinburgh EH15 1JJ
E of Edinburgh on A1 to Milton Road.
Public parkland course.
9 holes, 2400 yards, S.S.S.32
Founded 1826
Visitors: no restrictions except for Sat in summer (Medal Days).
Green Fee: £3 (9 holes).
Societies: no restrictions except Sat in summer (Medal Days).
Hotels: Kings Manor.

P65 Portpatrick (Dunskey)
☎(0776 81) 273
Portpatrick, Stranraer, Wigtownshire DG9 8TB
A77 follow signs to Stranraer, then follow signs to Portpatrick, fork right at War Memorial, 300 yards on right signpost to club.
Links type course set on high cliffs.
18 holes, 5732 yards, S.S.S.68; 9 holes, 1442 yards, S.S.S.27
Designed by Dunskey Estate.
Founded 1903
Visitors: welcome with h/cap cert except competition days; best to book.
Green Fee: £12/round, £18/day WD; £15/round, £22/day WE; 9 hole course £4/round, £8/day.
Societies: welcome, must book in advance with Sec at club or home (0776 81) 231.
Catering: all meals in season; Mon soups and snacks.
Hotels: Fernhill; Portpatrick; Roslin; all offer concessionary golf rates.

P66 Powfoot
☎(0461) 202866
Cummertrees, Annan, Dumfriesshire 3 miles W of Annan, off B724.
Seaside course.
18 holes, 6266 yards, S.S.S.70
Designed by James Braid.
Visitors: welcome weekdays, restricted weekends.

Green Fee: £23/day WD (£14/round after 2.45pm), £15 Sun after 2.45pm only.
Societies: welcome weekdays only by arrangement.
Catering: full bar facilities; lunches and teas by arrangement.
Hotels: Powfoot Golf; Queensberry Arms; Cairndale (Dumfries).

P67 Prestonfield
☎(031) 667 1273, 667 9665
6 Priestfield Rd N, Edinburgh EH16 5HS
Near to Commonwealth Pool, Dalkeith Rd.
Parkland course.
18 holes, 6216 yards, S.S.S.70
Designed by James Braid.
Founded 1920
Visitors: welcome any weekday; not 12am-1.30pm Sat; not before 11.30am Sun.
Green Fee: £15/round, £22/day WD; £22/round, £30/day WE & BH.
Societies: weekdays starting from 9.30am and 2pm.
Catering: full facilities daily.
Hotels: Rosehall; March Hall.

P68 Pumpherston
☎(0506) 32869
Drumshoreland Rd, Pumpherston, Livingston EH53 0LF
1 mile S of Uphall off A89.
Undulating parkland course.
9 holes, 5154 yards, S.S.S.65
Founded 1895
Visitors: only with member.
Green Fee: £3 WD, £4.50 WE.
Societies: welcome weekdays only, max 24.
Catering: bar snacks.
Hotels: Houston House.

P69 Ratho Park
☎(031) 333 1752 Sec, 333 1252
Ratho, Newbridge, Midlothian EH28 8NX
8 miles W of Edinburgh on Glasgow road, adjacent to Edinburgh Airport.
Parkland course.
18 holes, 5996 yards, S.S.S.68
Designed by James Braid.
Founded 1928
Visitors: any day by arrangement with Pro.
Green Fee: £15/round, £22/day WD; £30 WE.
Societies: welcome Tues, Wed, Thurs.
Catering: bars and restaurant.
Snooker.

Southerness

Nothing like enough golfers are acquainted with the delights of Southerness which lies on the silent, sandy stretches of the Solway Firth about 15 miles south of Dumfries. This is largely because the south-west corner of Scotland is not the best known golfing area of a country that has so much to offer, although those aware of its charm find it rich in quality and enjoyment and, like me, hard to believe that its reputation has not spread further.

As with so many courses around our shores, much of its appeal lies in its out of the way position, but it still makes a convenient beginning or end to any golfing tour. The drive from Carlisle is by no means arduous but, by the time that one turns off the main road down a long, narrow lane towards the sea, there is a growing impatience to see what lies beyond.

Before the days of a new clubhouse built in 1974 close to the position of the old 6th hole, journey's end was less imposing. The small community dominated by the Paul Jones Hotel consisted of a field of caravans, a few shops and a clubhouse which had more the look of some rustic cricket pavilion. A notice invited visitors to settle green fees with the caretaker in the village shop across the road and the path to the first tee was through a quaint little paddock.

However, one round on the course laid out by Mackenzie Ross shortly after the last war, is sufficient to appreciate its merit and indicate, rather like Dornoch at the opposite end of the country, that it is well worthy of having won its championship spurs.

By a happy coincidence, Dornoch was awarded the British Amateur Championship in 1985, the same year in which the Scottish Golf Union took the Scottish Amateur to Southerness (which was constructed for a mere £2000 around 1947). The staging of the championship bestowed a posthumous tribute on Mackenzie Ross, who resurrected Turnberry at more or less the same time as he paid his regular visits to Southerness.

It is a course that would be well worthy of a professional tournament — an intriguing prospect to see Nick Faldo or Severiano Ballasteros pitting their wits against holes stiffened by a fresh wind.

There is a pleasant variety of shots to be played and nothing slavish about their pattern. There are days when shots can be pitched up to the flag, and others when the only means of holding a green is to chip and run.

By the current rating, there is only one par 5 but the weight of the challenge is marked by having eight holes between 405 and 470 yards, many with fine natural greens angled to ensure that the best chance of finishing near the hole comes from drives correctly positioned. There is no great feeling that the fairways are narrow but gorse and heather can swallow up wayward shots and there is a tough start including the longest hole, the 5th, with its elevated and quaintly shaped green.

The 8th, taking aim on the lighthouse, begins the stretch along the shore but the pick of the holes are the dogleg 12th and the 13th and the old 18th, a formidable 467 yards. The 17th green, perched above the beach, also gives the best view of the splendour of the setting. Leagues of golden sand slip westwards along the coast of Kirkcudbright and the peaks of Cumberland stand strong against the peaceful waters of the Firth. Inland, the simple green landscape completes a feeling of escape that causes as much surprise as finding a golf course to match its majestic surroundings.

P70 Ravelston

☎(031) 315 2486
24 Ravelston Dykes Rd, Blackhall,
Edinburgh EH4 5NZ
Turn S off A90 Queensferry road at
Blackhall.
Parkland course.
9 holes, 5200 yards, S.S.S.66
Designed by James Braid.
Founded 1912
Visitors: allowed during quiet
periods; h/cap certs preferred.
Green Fee: £12.50 (18 holes).
Catering: light snacks only.

P71 Royal Burgess Golfing Society of Edinburgh

☎(031) 339 2075
181 Whitehouse Rd, Edinburgh EH4
6BY
W side of Edinburgh on Queensferry
road, 100 yds N of Barton roundabout.
Parkland course.
18 holes, 6494 yards, S.S.S.71
Designed by Tom Morris.
Founded 1735
Visitors: weekdays only.
Green Fee: on application.
Societies: weekdays only.
Catering: lunches and bar snacks.
Hotels: Barnton; Royal Scot.

P72 Royal Musselburgh

☎(0875) 810276 Clubhouse,
810139 Pro.
Prestongrange House, Prestonpans,
E Lothian EH32 9RP
7 miles E of Edinburgh, 1 mile from
Wallyford roundabout on A1, take
A198 North Berwick road.
Parkland course.
18 holes, 6237 yards, S.S.S.70
Designed by James Braid.
Founded 1774
Visitors: weekdays welcome, very
limited weekends.
Green Fee: £15/round, £25/day WD;
£25/round WE.
Societies: book in writing in advance.
Catering: coffee, lunches, high teas,
snacks; dinner by advance booking.
Snooker.
Hotels: Woodside; Ravelston House;
Kings Manor; Kilspindie House;
Maitland Field; Golf Inn; Marine.

P73 St Boswells

☎(0835) 22359
Ashleabank, St Boswells,
Roxburghshire TD6 0AT
A68 junction with B6404 opposite
Buccleuch Hotel, 0.25 mile along
banks of River Tweed.

Flat parkland course.
9 holes, 2625 yards, S.S.S.65
Designed by William Park, altered by
John Shade (1956).
Founded 1899
Visitors: unrestricted except for
competition days.
Green Fee: £6/round/day WD, £8 WE.
Societies: by prior booking.
Catering: at Buccleuch Hotel.
Hotels: Buccleuch; Dryburgh Abbey.

P74 St Medan

☎(098 87) 358
Monreith, Newton Stewart,
Wigtownshire DG8 8NJ
3 miles S of Port William on A747.
Seaside links course.
9 holes, 4452 yards, S.S.S.62
Founded 1905
Visitors: no restrictions except
during competitions.
Green Fee: £5 (9 holes), £9 (18
holes), £40 weekly (7 days).
Societies: welcome any day.
Catering: full bar and catering
except Tues, Mar-Sept.
Hotels: Steam Packet; Corsemalzie.

P75 Sanquhar

☎(0659) 50577
Old Barr Rd, Sanquhar, Dumfries
DG4 6JZ
Off A76 0.5 mile from Sanquhar.
Parkland course.
9 holes, 2572 yards, S.S.S.68.
Founded 1894
Visitors: welcome.
Green Fee: on application.
Societies: by prior arrangement.
Catering: by prior arrangement.
Snooker.
Hotels: Blackaddie House; Glendyne;
Nithsdale; Mennock Lodge.

P76 Selkirk

☎(0750) 20621, 20427
The Hill, Selkirk
1 mile S of Selkirk on A7 to Hawick.
Moorland course.
9 holes, 5640 yards, S.S.S.67
Founded 1883
Visitors: welcome.
Green Fee: day ticket £9.
Societies: by arrangement.
Catering: parties by arrangement.
Hotels: Woodburn House.

P77 Silverknowes

☎(031) 336 5359
Silverknowes, Parkway, Edinburgh
EH4 5ET

W end of Edinburgh, off Cramond
Foreshore.
Municipal course.
18 holes, 6210 yards, S.S.S.70
Founded 1958
Visitors: with reservation only.
Green Fee: on application.
Hotels: Commodore, adjacent.

P78 Southerness

☎(0387 66) 677
Southerness, Dumfries DG2 8AZ
16 miles SW of Dumfries off A710.
Links course.
18 holes, 6554 yards, S.S.S.72
Designed by Mackenzie Ross.
Founded 1947
Visitors: members of recognised
clubs only; 10-12am and 2-4pm
weekdays, 10.30-12am and
2.30-4pm weekends.
Green Fee: £20/day WD, £26/day
WE; £80/week (Mon-Fri).
Societies: apply to Sec.
Catering: full bar and catering.
Hotels: Baron's Craig; Abbey Arms;
Criffel Inn; Station; Cairndale;
Clonyard; Cavenshouse.

P79 Stranraer

☎(0776) 87245
Creachmore, Stranrear DG9 0LF
Take A718 from Stranraer towards
Leswalt, club is well signposted on
right.
Parkland course.
18 holes, 6300 yards, S.S.S.71
Designed by James Braid.
Founded 1905
Visitors: welcome.
Green Fee: £15/day WD, £20.50/day
WE.
Societies: catered for.
Catering: not Mon.
Hotels: North West Castle; Fernhill.

P80 Swanston

☎(031) 445 2239
111 Swanston Rd, Edinburgh EH10
70S
S side of city on lower slopes of
Pentland Hills.
Hillside course.
18 holes, 5024 yards, S.S.S.65
Designed by Herbert More.
Founded 1927
Visitors: welcome weekdays and
with restrictions at weekends.
Green Fee: £8/round, £12/day WD;
£10/round, £15/day WE.
Societies: by arrangement.
Catering: meals served except Tues.
Hotels: Braid Hills.

P81 Thornhill

☎(0848) 30546
Blacknest, Thornhill, Dumfries-shire
14 miles N of Dumfries on A76 to
Thornhill, turn right at cross, 1 mile
on right.
Moorland/parkland course.
18 holes, 6011 yards, S.S.S.69
Founded 1893
Visitors: welcome without
reservation except on Open
Competition days.
Green Fee: on application.
Societies: welcome; contact Club
Steward.
Catering: bar facilities available;
catering except Mon.
Hotels: Buccleuch & Queensberry;
George; Elmarglen.

P82 Torphin Hill

☎(031) 441 1100
Torphin Rd, Colinton, Edinburgh
EH13 0PG
SW of Colinton, follow signposts.
Hillside course.
18 holes, 5030 yards, S.S.S.66
Founded 1895
Visitors: restricted during
competitions; no 4-balls at
weekends.
Green Fee: £8.50 WD, £12.50 WE.
Societies: welcome weekdays.
Catering: full facilities except Tues.
Hotels: Braid Hills.

P83 Torwoodlee

☎(0896) 2660
Galashiels, Selkirkshire
On A7 Galashiels-Edinburgh road, 1
mile from town centre.
Parkland course.
9 holes, 5800 yards, S.S.S.68
Designed by James Braid.
Founded 1895
Visitors: welcome, restricted Sat
and Thurs after 1pm.
Green Fee: on application.
Societies: weekdays.
Catering: full facilities except Tues.
Hotels: Burts; George & Abbotsford.

P84 Turnhouse

☎(031) 339 1014
154 Turnhouse Rd, Edinburgh EH12
0AD
W of city on A9080 near airport.
Parkland/heathland course.
18 holes, 6171 yards, S.S.S.69

Founded 1909
Visitors: only visiting clubs; not
weekends; Hotel visitors contact Pro.
Green Fee: £12/round, £18/day.
Catering: lunch, high tea except
Mon.
Hotels: Royal Scot.

P85 Uphall

☎(0506) 856404
Uphall, W Lothian
Off M8, 14 miles W of Edinburgh.
Meadowland course.
18 holes, 6250 yards, S.S.S.68
Visitors: welcome.
Green Fee: on application.
Societies: by arrangement.
Catering: bar snacks, meals by
arrangement.
Hotels: Houston House; Golden
Circle.

P86 Vogrie

☎(0875) 21716
Vogrie Estate Country Park,
Gorebridge, Lothian
Off A68 Jedburgh road.
Public parkland course.
9 holes, 2530 yards, Par 33
Founded 1989
Visitors: welcome.
Green Fee: on application.

P87 West Linton

☎(0968) 60463
West Linton, Peebleshire
15 miles from Edinburgh on A702.
Moorland course.
18 holes, 6132 yards, S.S.S.69
Founded 1890
Visitors: welcome weekdays and
after 1pm weekends.
Green Fee: £13/round, £18/day WD;
£20/round WE.
Societies: weekdays except Tues.
Catering: full facilities except Tues.
Hotels: Gordon Arms; Raemartin.

P88 West Lothian

☎(0506) 826030 Clubhouse,
826049 Pro shop
Airngath Hill, Linlithgow, W Lothian
On hill separating Bo'ness and
Linlithgow, marked by Hope
Monument.
Undulating meadowland course.
18 holes, 6578 yards, S.S.S.71
Designed by Fraser Middleton.

Founded 1892
Visitors: no restrictions weekdays
before 4pm; after 4pm and at
weekends by arrangement only.
Green Fee: on application.
Societies: catered for weekdays and
at weekends.
Catering: meals as requested.
Hotels: Earl O'Murray.

P89 Wigtown & Bladnoch

☎(09884) 3354
Lightlands Terrace, Wigtown,
Galloway DG8 9EF
0.25 mile from town centre on A746,
signposted Whithorn.
Parkland course, part hilly.
9 holes, 2731 yards, S.S.S.67
Founded 1960
Visitors: no restrictions.
Green Fee: £7/day WD, £10 (18
holes) WE; jnrs and OAPs half price.
Societies: by prior arrangement.
Catering: bar and snacks
12am-2.30pm (June-Sept); evening
meals and groups by arrangement.
Hotels: Conifers Leisure Park; Bruce;
Hill o'Burns; all offer free golf.

P90 Wigtownshire County

☎(05813) 420
Mains of Park, Glenluce, Newton
Stewart, Wigtownshire DG8 0QN
8 miles E of Stranraer on A75, 2 miles
W of Glenluce.
Links course.
18 holes, 5715 yards, S.S.S.68
Designed by Gordon Cunningham.
Founded 1894
Visitors: unrestricted.
Green Fee: £11/round, £14/day WD;
£13/round, £16/day WE.
Societies: catered for.
Catering: available all year.
Hotels: North West Castle.

P91 Winterfield

☎(0368) 62280
North Rd, Dunbar, E Lothian
W side of Dunbar.
Seaside course.
18 holes, 5035 yards, S.S.S.65
Founded 1935
Visitors: welcome.
Green Fee: on application.
Societies: welcome by arrangement
with Pro.
Catering: meals served except
Thurs.

STRATHCLYDE

Strathclyde casts a comprehensive net over the golfing scene as well as providing more than its share of Britain's great courses. It encompasses the remote outposts of Machrie and Machrihanish, the whole of the area around Glasgow and the veritable treasure trove of Ayrshire, a county many claim possesses more glittering golfing jewels than any other in Britain.

Prime among its southern defences is Turnberry, one of the world's most spectacular settings for golf and for a hotel that shares its splendours. There are few more stirring stretches than that between the short 4th and the short 11th, a testing clutch of holes graduating from the relative shelter of the dunes to the rugged, rocky promontory alongside the lighthouse. Wild westerly winds can be more than flesh, blood and balance can stand, one solution lying on the Arran, the Ailsa's neighbour, which is flatter, less exposed and little inferior.

Together, they comprise a wonderful day's golf, a comment pretty commonplace in Ayrshire. How about Old Prestwick and Royal Troon, Western Gailes and Glasgow Gailes, Barassie and Irvine or Ayr Belleisle together with Prestwick St Nicholas?

As the birthplace of championship golf, Old Prestwick commands eminence, a course that has proved its freshness time and again in spite of accusations of being a relic of the past. There are few more daunting opening tee shots, few better dogleg holes than the 4th and few more sporting tests than the 13th and 17th. It faded as a staging ground for the Open championship on account of its difficulty in handling big crowds. Its demise coincided with the rise of Troon, although 27 years separated Troon's first and second Opens, a gap attributable in part to the war.

There are five or six courses in Troon, or on its doorstep, many shrewd judges rating Western Gailes on a par with Royal Troon. It certainly ranks extremely highly, with a greater share perhaps of spectacular holes and of interesting greens. At one end, it is possible to hit a shot over the railway onto Kilmarnock (Barassie) and, at the other, onto Glasgow Gailes, the country "seat", so to speak, of the Glasgow GC in the city district of Killermont.

On one of the approach roads to Glasgow from the south, Eastwood, East Renfrewshire and Whitecraigs are encountered in quick succession but Glasgow is surrounded on all sides by good golf. Names to note are West Kilbride, Renfrew, Gleddoch, Old Ranfurly, Ranfurly Castle, Helensburgh, Balmore and Cawder.

Nor must the other courses overlooking the Clyde be forgotten or those of Arran, an island once described to me as "paradise". But, if it is romance that you seek, head for Machrie on the Isle of Islay or Machrihanish on the Mull of Kintyre, both reachable by air on a short hop from Glasgow airport.

Machrie is an authentic links full of hidden dells and high hills — bordered on one side by lonely, sandy beaches and on the other by moor and hill.

Back on the mainland at Machrihanish, the beach comes into play on the opening drive, and a notice for non-golfers proclaims "Danger, First Tee Above, please move further along the beach"; an invigorating introduction to another superb tract of natural land which many regard as the only true setting to the game.

For those choosing the lengthy and circuitous route by road, Machrihanish rarely disappoints but journey's end is Dunaverty ten miles south of Campbeltown and home of Belle Robertson, who brought it fame and distinction. Its raw charm is hard to better, although its modest length can be dramatically magnified by the breezes that frequently graduate to raging winds.

Q1 Airdrie
☎(0236) 762195
Rochsoles, Airdrie ML6 0PQ
From Airdrie Cross in centre of town
travel N on Glenmavis Rd.
Parkland course.
18 holes, S.S.S.69
Designed by James Braid.
Founded 1877
Visitors: welcome with introduction
from own Sec.
Green Fee: £12/round, £18/day.
Societies: contact Sec, not
weekends or Bank Holidays.
Catering: full catering.
Snooker.
Hotels: Tudor; Kenilworth.

Q2 Alexandra Park
☎(041) 556 3711
Alexandra Parade, Glasgow G31 8SE
M8 cut off before fruit market.
Parkland course.
9 holes, 5000 yards, S.S.S.60
Designed by Graham McArthur.
Founded 1818
Visitors: welcome at all times.
Green Fee: on application.
Societies: by arrangement
Catering: facilities available
Bowling
Hotels: Holiday Inn.

Q3 Annanhill
☎(0563) 21644
Irvine Rd, Kilmarnock KA1 4UW
Off main Kilmarnock-Irvine road.
Parkland course.
18 holes, 6118 yards, S.S.S.70
Designed by J. McLean.
Founded 1957
Visitors: welcome except Sat.
Green Fee: £6.20 WD, £9.45 WE.
Societies: by arrangement.
Catering: snacks at weekends; full
meals, breakfast, lunch, dinner or
high tea by arrangement.
Hotels: Howard Park.

Q4 Ardeer
☎(0294) 64542
Greenhead, Stevenston, Ayrshire
Follow A78 (signs for Largs and
Greenock), on High Rd by-passing
Stevenston, turn right into Kerelaw
Rd and continue for 1 mile.
Parkland course.
18 holes, 6630 yards, S.S.S.72
Founded 1880
Visitors: welcome except Sat.
Green Fee: on application.
Societies: catered for Mon-Sat.
Catering: full facilities available.

Q5 Auchenharvie Golf Complex
☎(0294) 603103
Moor Park Rd West, Brewery Park,
Stevenston, Ayrshire KA20 3HU
Public links/parkland course.
9 holes, 2642 yards, S.S.S.33
Visitors: welcome.
Green Fee: £2.25 (90p jnrs) WD,
£4.10 (£1 jnrs) WE.
Catering: clubhouse bar.
Driving range.

Q6 Ayr Belleisle
☎(0292) 41258
Belleisle Park, Doonfoot Rd, Ayr
1.5 miles S of Ayr on A719.
Parkland course.
18 holes, 6540 yards, S.S.S.71
Designed by James Braid & Stutt.
Founded 1927
Visitors: welcome.
Green Fee: on application.
Societies: apply to Course
Administrator at address above.
Catering: meals and snacks
available in hotel.
Hotels: Belleisle House; Balgarth;
Old Racecourse.

Q7 Ayr Dalmilling
☎(0292) 263893
Westwood Ave, Ayr, Strathclyde
1.5 miles from town centre on NE
boundary off A77.
Municipal meadowland course.
18 holes, 5752 yards, S.S.S.69
Founded 1960
Visitors: unrestricted.
Green Fee: £8.20/round,
£14.30/day.
Societies: catered for.
Catering: tea, coffee, lunches, high
teas, snacks daily except Tues.
Hotels: Racers.

Q8 Ayr Seafield
☎(0292) 41258
Belleisle Park, Doonfoot Rd, Ayr
1.5 miles S of Ayr on A719.
Parkland/seaside course.
18 holes, 5650 yards, S.S.S.68
Founded 1927
Visitors: welcome.
Green Fee: on application.
Societies: as Ayr Belleisle above.
Catering: meals and snacks in hotel.

Q9 Ballochmyle
☎(0290) 50469
Ballochmyle, Mauchline, Ayrshire
KA5 6RR
1 mile S of Mauchline on B705, off
A76(T) Dumfries-Kilmarnock road.
Parkland course.
18 holes, 5952 yards, S.S.S.69
Founded 1937
Visitors: welcome weekdays.
Green Fee: on application.
Societies: weekdays.
Catering: bar and restaurant.
Snooker, squash.

Q10 Balmore
☎(0360) 2120240
Balmore, Torrance, Stirlingshire
2 miles N of Glasgow on A803 and
then A807.
Parkland course.
18 holes, 5516 yards, S.S.S.67
Designed by James Braid.
Founded 1906
Visitors: welcome with introduction
from member.
Green Fee: on application.
Catering: full catering facilities.
Hotels: Black Bull.

Q11 Barshaw
☎(041) 889 2908, 889 5400, 884
2533 Sec.
Barshaw Park, Glasgow Rd, Paisley,
Renfrewshire
A737 from Glasgow W to Paisley, 1
mile before Paisley Cross.
Municipal meadowland course.
18 holes, 5703 yards, S.S.S.67
Founded 1920
Visitors: welcome all week.
Green Fee: £4.50/round.
Hotels: Water Mill; Brablock.

Q12 Bearsden
☎(041) 942 4480
Thorn Rd, Bearsden, Glasgow G61
4BP
1 mile N from Bearsden Cross on
Thorn Rd.
Parkland course.
9 holes, 6020 yards, S.S.S.69
Founded 1891
Visitors: to be introduced by and
play with member.
Green Fee: on application.
Catering: light meals, snacks.
Hotels: Black Bull; Burnbrae.

Q13 Beith
☎(05055) 3166
Threepwood Rd, Bigholm, Beith
Situated about 1 mile E of Beith.
Hilly course.
9 holes, 5488 yards, S.S.S.67
Founded 1896

Visitors: welcome weekdays and Sun am.
Green Fee: on application.
Societies: committee meetings monthly, functions welcome.
Catering: snacks 7 days.

Q14 Bellshill

☎(0698) 745124
Orbiston, Bellshill, Lanarkshire ML4 2RZ
Right turn off Bellshill/Motherwell road 10 miles SE of Glasgow.
Parkland course.
18 holes, 6604 yards, S.S.S.72
Founded 1905
Visitors: not between 4pm and 7pm, May-Aug inclusive; otherwise welcome.
Green Fee: £11/day WD, £15/day WE & BH.
Societies: by prior arrangement; not Sun.
Catering: licensed bar and lounge; meals and snacks available.

Q15 Biggar

☎(0899) 20618
The Park, Broughton Rd, Biggar, Lanarkshire ML12
1 mile E of Biggar on Broughton Rd, opposite police station.
Public parkland course.
18 holes, 5416 yards, S.S.S.67
Designed by Willie Park.
Founded 1895
Visitors: unrestricted but telephone (0899) 20319 in advance.
Green Fee: £5 WD, £8.50 WE & BH.
Societies: welcome 36 max, advance booking essential.
Catering: all day licence and catering except Mon.
All weather tennis, boating, childrens' play area, caravan park.
Hotels: Toftcombs; Elphinstone (Biggar); Tinto (Symington).

Q16 Bishopbriggs

☎(041) 772 1810 Club, 772 8938 Sec.
Brackenbrae Rd, Bishopbriggs, Glasgow G64 2DX
4 miles N of Glasgow on A803, left 200 yds before Bishopbriggs Cross.
Parkland course.
18 holes, 6041 yards, S.S.S.69
Founded 1906
Visitors: welcome with member or by application to Committee.
Green Fee: on application.
Societies: Tues, Wed, Thurs; apply to Sec at least 1 month in advance.
Catering: meals and snacks served.

Q17 Blairbeth

☎(041) 634 3355
Fernhill, Rutherglen, Glasgow
2 miles S of Rutherglen via Stonelaw road, follow road signs.
Parkland course.
18 holes, 5448 yards, S.S.S.67
Founded 1910
Visitors: welcome with member.
Green Fee: £3/day WD, £5 WE.
Catering: by arrangement.

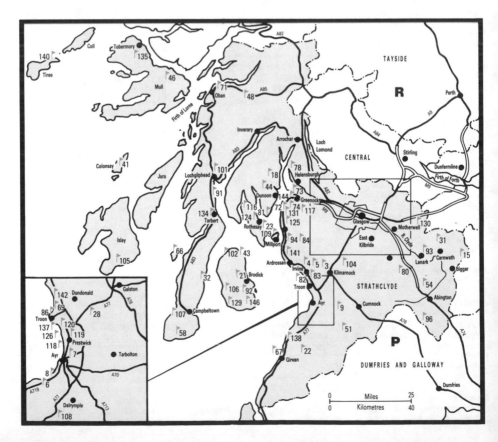

Q18 Blairmore & Strone

☎(036 984) 217
Strone, By Dunoon, Argyll PA23 8TJ
0.75 mile N of Strone on A880.
Undulating parkland/moorland
course.
9 holes, 2112 yards, S.S.S.62
Founded 1896
Visitors: welcome; some delays Sat
afternoons and Mon evenings.
Green Fee: on application.
Hotels: Kilmun.

Q19 Bonnyton

☎(03553) 2781
Eaglesham, Glasgow G76 0QA
City centre S of Eaglesham.
Moorland course.
18 holes, 6252 yards, S.S.S.71
Founded 1957
Visitors: welcome weekdays.
Green Fee: on application.
Societies: catered for by prior
arrangement.
Catering: bar, lunches, high tea
daily; dinner Sat.

Q20 Bothwell Castle

☎(0698) 853177
Blantyre Rd, Bothwell, Glasgow G71
M74 junction 5 to A9071, 3 miles N of
Hamilton.
Parkland course.
18 holes, 6240 yards, S.S.S.70
Founded 1922
Visitors: welcome weekdays
9.30am-3.30pm.
Green Fee: £12/round, £18/day.
Societies: weekdays by written
application.

Catering: snacks, lunches, high
teas, dinners daily.
Hotels: Silvertrees; Bothwell Bridge.

Q21 Brodick

☎(0770) 2349, 2513 Pro.
Brodick, Isle of Arran
By car ferry from Ardrossan, Ayrshire
(55 min); 0.5 mile from Brodick pier.
Seaside course.
18 holes, 4404 yards, S.S.S.62
Founded 1897
Visitors: welcome all week.
Green Fee: £9/day.
Societies: by letter to Sec, catered
for at all times.
Catering: light lunches, contact
Steward (0770) 2349.

Q22 Brunston Castle

Dailly, Nr Girvan, Ayrshire
35 mins from Prestwick Airport, S of
Ayr and Turnberry (4 miles).
Parkland course by Water of Girvan.
18 holes, 6790 yards, S.S.S.72
Designed by Donald Steel.
Opening Aug 1992
Visitors: welcome.
Green Fee: apply for details.
Societies: welcome.
Catering: clubhouse, bar lunches.
Driving range, putting green.
Hotels: Kings Arms (Girvan), Marine
Highland (Troon), Fairfield House
(Ayr).

Q23 Bute

☎(070 083) 648 Sec.
Kingarth, Isle of Bute, Strathclyde

In Stravanan Bay off A845
Rothesay-Kilchattan Bay road.
Links course.
9 holes, 2497 yards, S.S.S.64
Founded 1888
Visitors: welcome, not before
12.30pm Sat.
Green Fee: £3/day.
Hotels: Kingarth; St Blanes.

Q24 Calderbraes

☎(0698) 813425
57 Roundknowe Rd, Uddingston G71
7TS
Start of M74 to Carlisle, 4 miles from
Glasgow.
Hilly parkland course.
9 holes, 5046 yards, S.S.S.67
Founded 1891
Visitors: weekdays only, off course
by 5pm.
Green Fee: £6.50/round/day.
Societies: weekdays, max 20.
Catering: bar and catering available.
Hotels: Redstones.

Q25 Caldwell

☎(050 585) 329 Clubhouse, 616 Pro.
Uplawmoor, Renfrewshire
Off A736 5 miles SW of Barrhead, 12
miles NE of Irvine.
Moorland course.
18 holes, 6102 yards, S.S.S.69
Founded 1903
Visitors: welcome weekdays but
advisable to check in advance.
Green Fee: on application.
Societies: catered for on weekdays.
Catering: welcome weekdays.
Hotels: Uplawmoor; Dalmeny.

Q26 Cambuslang

☎(041) 641 3130
30 Westburn Drive, Cambuslang,
Glasgow
Off main Glasgow to Hamilton road at
Cambuslang.
Parkland course.
9 holes, 6072 yards, S.S.S.69
Founded 1891
Visitors: apply in writing to Sec.
Green Fee: on application.
Societies: weekdays except Tues.
Catering: full facilities.
Hotels: Cambus Court.

Q27 Campsie

☎(0360) 310244
Crow Rd, Lennoxtown, Glasgow G65
7HX
N of Lennoxtown on B822.
Hillside course.

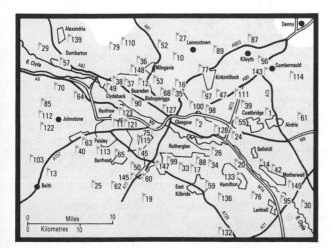

18 holes, 5517 yards, S.S.S.67
Founded 1897
Visitors: welcome weekdays and by prior arrangement at weekends.
Green Fee: on application.
Societies: apply to Sec.
Catering: bar snacks available; meals by prior arrangement.
Hotels: Glazertbank; Kincaid House.

Q28 Caprington
☎(0563) 23702
Ayr Rd, Kilmarnock KA1 4UW
S of Kilmarnock on Ayr Rd.
Municipal parkland course.
18 holes, S.S.S.68
Visitors: welcome.
Green Fee: on application.

Q29 Cardross
☎(0389) 841213 Club, 841754 Sec, 841350 Pro.
Main Rd, Cardross, Dumbarton G82 5LB
Between Dumbarton and Helensburgh on A814.
Parkland course.
18 holes, 6466 yards, S.S.S.71
Designed by Willie Fernie of Troon and James Braid.
Founded 1895
Visitors: welcome weekdays, weekends introduced by member.
Green Fee: £13/round, £20/day.
Societies: by arrangement with Sec, weekdays only.
Catering: bar snacks, teas except Mon.
Hotels: Dumbuck; Commodore; Lomond Castle.

Q30 Carluke
☎(0555) 71070
Hallcraig, Mauldslie Rd, Carluke ML8 5HG
1.5 miles from lights at town centre on road to Hamilton and Larkhall.
Tree-lined parkland course with views over Clyde valley.
18 holes, 5800 yards, S.S.S.68
Founded 1894
Visitors: weekdays only until 4.30pm.
Green Fee: £10/round, £15/day.
Societies: by written request to Sec.
Catering: full except Thurs.
Hotels: Popinjay (3 memberships).

Q31 Carnwath
☎(0555) 840251
1 Main St, Carnwath, Strathclyde
5 miles NE of Lanark.

Undulating course.
18 holes, 5860 yards, S.S.S.69
Founded 1907
Visitors: Mon, Wed, Fri and Sun.
Green Fee: £15 WD, £18 Sun and BH.
Societies: catered for.
Catering: meals except Tues, Thurs.
Hotels: Tinto (Symington).

Q32 Carradale
☎(05833) 387
Carradale, Campbeltown, Argyll PA28 6QX
In Kintyre, Argyll, off B842 from Campbeltown.
Difficult, scenic seaside course.
9 holes, 2392 yards, S.S.S.63
Founded 1906
Visitors: welcome at all times, no introduction necessary.
Green Fee: £5/day; extended terms on application.
Catering: at both hotels (below).
Hotels: Carradale; Ashbank.

Q33 Cathcart Castle
☎(041) 638 9449
Mearns Rd, Clarkston, Glasgow G76 7YL
1 mile from Clarkston on B767.
Undulating parkland course.
18 holes, 5832 yards, S.S.S.68
Founded 1895
Visitors: introduced by member.
Green Fee: on application.
Societies: by arrangement.
Catering: snacks, meals.
Hotels: Redhurst; McDonald.

Q34 Cathkin Braes
☎(041) 634 6605
Cathkin Rd, Rutherglen, Glasgow G73 4SE
SE of Glasgow on B759 between A749 and B766.
Moorland course.
18 holes, 6266 yards, S.S.S.71
Designed by James Braid.
Founded 1888
Visitors: Mon-Fri by prior arrangement.
Green Fee: £12/round, £17/day.
Catering: full catering to order.
Hotels: Stuart; Bruce; Burnside; Busby.

Q35 Cawder
☎(041) 772 5167
Cadder Rd, Bishopbriggs, Glasgow G64 3QD
0.5 mile E of Bishopbriggs cross.
Parkland course.

Cawder, 18 holes, 6229 yards, S.S.S.71; Keir, 18 holes, 5877 yards, S.S.S.68
Designed by Donald Steel (Cawder course), James Braid (Keir course).
Founded 1933
Visitors: welcome weekdays by arrangement with Sec.
Green Fee: on application.
Societies: welcome weekdays by arrangement with Sec.
Catering: full catering facilities.
Hotels: Black Bull; Glazertbank; Crowood House.

Q36 Clober
☎(041) 956 1685
Craigton Rd, Milngavie G62 7HP
7 miles NW of Glasgow.
Parkland course.
18 holes, 5068 yards, S.S.S.65
Designed by Lyle Family.
Founded 1952
Visitors: weekdays before 4.30pm.
Green Fee: on application.
Societies: weekdays by prior arrangement.
Catering: available Tues, Wed, Fri, Sat and Sun; snacks Mon and Thurs.
Hotels: Black Bull; Thistle.

Q37 Clydebank & District
☎(0389) 72389
Hardgate, Clydebank, Dunbartonshire G81 5QY
8 miles NW of Glasgow via Great Western Rd.
Parkland course.
18 holes, 5825 yards, S.S.S.68
Founded 1905
Visitors: welcome weekdays, weekends with member only.
Green Fee: on application.
Societies: welcome by prior arrangement.
Catering: meals served.
Hotels: Cameron House; Boulevard; Pine Trees.

Q38 Clydebank Overtoun
☎(041) 952 6372 Pro shop
Overtoun Rd, Clydebank, Dunbartonshire
5 minutes from Dalmuir station.
Municipal parkland course.
18 holes, 5643 yards, S.S.S.66
Founded 1928
Visitors: welcome, municipal rules apply.
Green Fee: on application.
Societies: first Mon evening of every month.
Catering: café attached to Pro Shop.

Q39 **Coatbridge**
☎(0236) 428975
Townhead Rd, Coatbridge, Lanark
ML5 2HX
In Coatbridge town.
Public parkland course.
18 holes, 6026 yards, S.S.S.69
Founded 1971
Visitors: welcome.
Green Fee: £3.50/day WD, £5 WE.
Societies: welcome.
Catering: full facilities.
Driving range, putting green.
Hotels: Jordanian.

Q40 **Cochrane Castle**
☎(0505) 20146
Scott Ave, Craigston, Johnstone PA5
0HF
0.25 mile off Johnstone-Beith road to
S of town, Bird in the Hand Hotel is
good landmark near turning to club.
Parkland course.
18 holes, 6226 yards, S.S.S.70
Designed by Charles Hunter of
Prestwick, altered by James Braid.
Founded 1895
Visitors: weekdays unrestricted,
introduced by member weekends.
Green Fee: £10/round, £15/day.
Societies: max 32 players.
Catering: full facilities except Mon.
Pool, darts.
Hotels: Lynhurst.

Q41 **Colonsay**
☎(09512) 316
Isle of Colonsay, Argyll, PA61 7Y
Ferry from Oban Mon/Wed/Fri (2.5
hrs); course is 2 miles W of pier.
Primitive and challenging public
course on natural Hebridean
machair, bearing no resemblance to
modern or mainland courses.
18 holes, 4775 yards, S.S.S.72
Founded pre 1880 (reputedly over
200 years old)
Visitors: membership open to all at
£5 per family per year.
Green Fee: none.
Hotels: membership available
through Colonsay Hotel; farm
guesthouse and self-catering details
on request.

Q42 **Colville Park**
☎(0698) 63017
Jerviston Estate, Motherwell,
Lanarkshire ML1 4UG
On left hand side of A723, 1 mile N of
Motherwell Cross.
Parkland course.
18 holes, 6280 yards, S.S.S.70

Designed by James Braid.
Founded 1922
Visitors: accompanied by member.
Green Fee: £12/day.
Societies: weekdays only by prior
arrangement.
Catering: full facilities.
Hotels: Old Mill; Garrion.

Q43 **Corrie**
☎(077 081) 223
Sannox, Isle of Arran
By A84 coast road from Brodick.
Undulating course.
9 holes, 3896 yards, S.S.S.61
Founded 1892
Visitors: welcome.
Green Fee: on application.
Catering: light meals and snacks.

Q44 **Cowal**
☎(0369) 5673 or 2216
Ardenslate Rd, Kirn, Dunoon, Argyll
PA23 8LT
0.25 mile from A815 at Kirn.
Moorland course.
18 holes, 6250 yards, S.S.S.70
Designed by James Braid.
Founded 1890
Visitors: welcome.
Green Fee: on application.
Societies: catered for at special
rates, details from Sec.
Catering: full catering available
during season.

Q45 **Cowglen**
☎(041) 632 0556
301 Barrhead Rd, Glasgow G43
S side of Glasgow, following signs to
Burrell Collection, opposite Pollok
golf club.
Undulating parkland course.
18 holes, 6006 yards, S.S.S.69
Founded 1906
Visitors: introduced by member or
by letter to Sec.
Green Fee: £14/round, £21/day.
Societies: apply to Sec.
Catering: lunch, dinner, bar snacks.
Hotels: Tinto Firs.

Q46 **Craignure**
☎(06802) 370 Sec.
Scallastle, Graignure, Isle of Mull
PA64 5AP
1 miles from ferry at Craignure.
Links course.
9 holes, 2218 metres, S.S.C.32
Founded 1980
Visitors: welcome, no restrictions.
Green Fee: £6.

Q47 **Crow Wood**
☎(041) 779 4954 Sec, 779 2011
Club, 779 1943 Pro.
Garnkirk House, Cumbernauld Rd,
Muirhead, Glasgow G69 9JF
1 mile N of Stepps on A80.
Parkland course.
18 holes, 6249 yards, S.S.S.70
Designed by James Braid
Founded 1925
Visitors: with member only.
Green Fee: £14/round, £21/day.
Societies: weekdays by prior
arrangement.
Catering: meals served daily.
Snooker.
Hotels: Garfield; Crow Wood House;
Moodiesburn House.

Q48 **Dalmally**
☎(08382) 216, 370
Dalmally, Argyll, Strathclyde
1 mile W of Dalmally on A85.
Public flat parkland course by River
Orchy.
9 holes, 2277 yards, S.S.S.62
Founded 1987
Visitors: welcome.
Green Fee: £5/round.
Hotels: Glen Orchy Lodge.

Q49 **Dalmuir Municipal**
☎(041) 952 8698 bookings.
Overtoun Rd, Dalmuir, Clydebank,
Strathclyde
8 miles W of Glasgow.
Public parkland course.
18 holes, 5349 yards, S.S.S.67
Visitors: welcome.
Green Fee: £3.20 Mon-Sat, £3.50
Sun; unemployed and jnrs £1.25
Mon-Fri.
Catering: café.
Practice nets.
Hotels: Radnor.

Q50 **Deaconsbank**
☎(041) 638 7044
Stewarton Rd, Thornliebank,
Glasgow G46
5 miles S of Glasgow near
Thornliebank.
Public parkland course.
18 holes, 4800 yards, S.S.S.63
Founded 1922
Visitors: welcome.
Green Fee: £4.75/round, £8/day
WD; £6/round, £10/day WE.
Societies: welcome.
Catering: full facilities.
Driving range, putting green, pool
tables.
Hotels: The MacDonalds.

Q51 Doon Valley
☎(0292) 531607
Hillside Park, Patna, Strathclyde
10 miles S of Ayr on A713,
signposted from village of Patna.
Municipal meadowland course.
9 holes, 5592 yards, S.S.S.67
Founded 1927
Visitors: welcome.
Green Fee: £1/round (annual
membership £20).
Societies: by arrangement.
Catering: bar; catering by
arrangement. Pool.

Q52 Dougalston
☎(041) 956 5750
Strathblane Rd, Milngavie, Glasgow
G62
7 miles N of Glasgow city centre on
A879 and A81.
Public parkland course.
18 holes, 6683 yards, S.S.S.72
Designed by John Harris.
Founded 1976
Visitors: no restrictions.
Green Fee: £9 WD, £10 WE & BH.
Societies: with advance booking at
any time.
Catering: all types of catering.
Hotels: Burnbrae, 1 mile.

Q53 Douglas Park
☎(041) 942 2220
Hillfoot, Bearsden, Glasgow G61 2SJ
20 minutes by rail and road from
centre of Glasgow; course adjacent
to to Hillfoot Station.
Parkland course.
18 holes, 5957 yards, S.S.S.68
Visitors: with member only.
Green Fee: on request.
Societies: apply to Sec.
Catering: meals by arrangement.

Q54 Douglas Water
☎(055 588) 361
Ayr Rd, Rigside, Lanark ML11 9NY
7 miles SW of Lanark on A70, 2 miles
E of A74, signposted Rigside.
Undulating parkland course.
9 holes, 2947 yards, S.S.S.69
Designed by striking coal miners
1921.
Founded 1922
Visitors: welcome.
Green Fee: £4/day WD, £6 WE & BH.
Catering: by arrangement.

Q55 Drumpellier
☎(0236) 24139 Pro, 28723
Clubmaster

Drumpellier Ave, Coatbridge ML5 1RX
8 miles E of Glasgow on A89, 1 mile
from Coatbridge.
Parkland course.
18 holes, 6227 yards, S.S.S.70
Designed by W. Fernie.
Founded 1894
Visitors: welcome weekdays
excluding Bank Holidays.
Green Fee: £20/day, £14/round.
Societies: weekdays.
Catering: full catering except Thurs.
Pool.
Hotels: Coatbridge.

Q56 Dullatur
☎(02367) 23230
Dullatur, Glasgow G68 0AR
1.5 miles from Cumbernauld village.
Undulating moorland course.
18 holes, 6195 yards, S.S.S.70
Founded 1897
Visitors: welcome weekdays by
arrangement.
Green Fee: £16/day, £10/round,
from 1.30pm, WD only.
Societies: weekdays.
Catering: full facilities available.

Q57 Dumbarton
☎(0389) 32830
Broadmeadows, Dumbarton,
Dumbartonshire G82 2BQ
15 miles NW of Glasgow off A82.
Meadowland course.
18 holes, 5981 yards, S.S.S.69
Founded 1888
Visitors: welcome weekdays.
Green Fee: on application.
Societies: by arrangement.
Catering: lunches, snacks etc
except Tues.
Hotels: Dumbuck.

Q58 Dunaverty
Southend, Campbeltown, Argyll
PA28 6RF
On B842, 10 miles S of Campbeltown.
Undulating seaside course.
18 holes, 4597 yards, S.S.S.63
Founded 1889
Visitors: welcome.
Green Fee: on application.
Catering: snacks available.
Hotels: Keil; Argyll Arms.

Q59 East Kilbride
☎(03552) 20913
Chapelside Rd, Nerston, East Kilbride
G74 4PF
On Glasgow to East Kilbride road turn
off at Nerston by Borlands Cars.

Undulating meadowland course.
18 holes, 6384 yards, S.S.S.71
Designed by Fred Hawtree.
Founded 1900
Visitors: accompanied by member
or by prior arrangement.
Green Fee: £12/round, £18/day.
Societies: Mon and Fri.
Catering: full catering except Tues
and Thurs pm.
Hotels: Bruce; Stuart.

Q60 East Renfrewshire
☎(03555) 258 Clubhouse, 206 Pro.
Loganswell, Pilmuir, Newton
Mearns, Glasgow
A77, 1 mile from Mearns Cross.
Moorland course with panoramic
views.
18 holes, 6097 yards, S.S.S.70
Designed by James Braid.
Founded 1926
Visitors: welcome by prior telephone
call.
Green Fee: on application.
Societies: by arrangement.
Catering: meals served.
Hotels: MacDonalds.

Q61 Easter Moffat
☎(0236) 842878
Mansion House, Plains, by Airdrie,
Lanarkshire
2 miles E of Airdrie on the old
Edinburgh-Glasgow road.
Moorland/parkland course.
18 holes, 6221 yards, S.S.S.70
Founded 1922
Visitors: welcome.
Green Fee: £10/round, £15/day.
Societies: weekdays.
Catering: in playing season
(Mar-Sept), otherwise by
arrangement.

Q62 Eastwood
☎(03555) 261
Loganswell, Newton Mearns,
Glasgow G77 6RX
On A77 from Glasgow, 3 miles S of
Newton Mearns Cross at junction of
Old Mearns Rd.
Moorland course.
18 holes, 5886 yards, S.S.S.68
Designed by J. Moon.
Founded 1893
Visitors: welcome by prior
appointment.
Green Fee: £12/round, £18/day.
Societies: parties welcome by prior
arrangement with Sec.
Catering: full facilities.
Hotels: Redhurst; Giffnock.

Q63 **Elderslie**
☎(0505) 22835, 23956
63 Main Rd, Elderslie, Renfrewshire
PA5 9AZ
On A737 between Paisley and
Johnstone.
Undulating parkland course.
18 holes, 6004 yards, S.S.S.69
Founded 1909
Visitors: full facilities Mon to Fri only.
Green Fee: £15.50/round, £21/day.
Societies: Mon, Wed, Fri by
arrangement.
Catering: full facilities.
Hotels: Excelsior, Glasgow Airport.

Q64 **Erskine**
☎(0505) 863327
Bishopton, Renfrewshire PA7 5PH
N of M8 leave Erskine Toll Bridge and
turn left along B815 for 1.5 miles.
Parkland course.
18 holes, 6287 yards, S.S.S.70
Founded 1903
Visitors: welcome if introduced by or
playing with a member.
Green Fee: on application.
Societies: by arrangement.
Catering: meals served to members
and guests only, or by arrangement.
Hotels: Bishopton; Crest.

Q65 **Fereneze**
☎(041) 881 1519, 221 6394 Sec,
881 7058 Pro.
Fereneze Ave, Barrhead, Glasgow
G78 1HJ
9 miles SW of Glasgow near
Barrhead station.
Moorland course.
18 holes, 5821 yards, S.S.S.68
Founded 1904
Visitors: by application to Pro, Sec,
or accompanied by member.
Green Fee: £16/day (£2 with
member); visitor's package (golf and
catering) from £21.50.
Societies: weekdays only, apply to
Sec.
Catering: lunches, bar snacks,
evening meals all day Sat/Sun,
usually by booking weekdays.
Hotels: Dalmeny Park.

Q66 **Gigha**
☎(05835) 287
Isle of Gigha, Kintyre, Argyll
By ferry from Tayinloan (ring (088
073) 253/4 for times); 2.5 hours
drive from Glasgow.
Links course.
9 holes, Par 33
Visitors: welcome.

Green Fee: £5 day (honesty box).
Catering: at Boat House and Gigha
Hotel.
Hotels: Gigha.

Q67 **Girvan**
☎(0465) 4346
Girvan, Ayrshire KA26 9HW
Off A77.
Seaside/meadowland course.
18 holes, 5078 yards, S.S.S.65
Founded pre-1877
Visitors: welcome.
Green Fee: on application.
Societies: welcome by arrangement.
Catering: meals served by
arrangement (0465) 4272.

Q68 **Glasgow**
☎(041) 942 2011 Sec.
Killermont, Bearsden, Glasgow G61
2TW
6 miles NW of Glasgow near
Killermont Bridge on A81 or A806.
Parkland course.
18 holes, 5968 yards, S.S.S.69
Designed by Tom Morris Snr.
Founded 1787
Visitors: catered for by application.
Green Fee: £30/round.
Societies: on application.
Catering: lunches, high teas served
by prior arrangement.
Hotels: Grosvenor; Burnbrae; Black
Bull; Stakis Pond.

Q69 **Glasgow (Gailes)**
☎(0294) 311347
Gailes, by Irvine, Ayrshire KA11 5AE
2 miles S of Irvine on road to Troon.
Seaside links course.
18 holes, 6493 yards, S.S.S.71
Designed by Willie Park Jr.
Founded 1787 (Gailes 1892)
Visitors: on application, or
introduction by member.
Green Fee: £25/round, £30/day.
Societies: on application.
Catering: lunches and high teas;
also bar snacks.
Hotels: Hospitality Inn; Royal Marine.

Q70 **Gleddoch CC**
☎(047 554) 304, 704 Pro.
Langbank, Renfrewshire PA14 6YE
M8 to Greenock, first turning to
Langbank Houston.
Parkland/moorland course.
18 holes, 5661 yards, S.S.S.67
Designed by Hamilton Stutt.
Founded 1975
Visitors: by arrangement with Pro.

Green Fee: on application.
Societies: welcome.
Catering: meals and snacks.

Q71 **Glencruitten**
☎(0631) 62868
Glencruitten Rd, Oban, Argyll PA34
5PU
1 mile from town centre off A816;
follow signs for Rare Breeds Park.
Hilly parkland/moorland course.
18 holes, 4452 yards, S.S.S.63
Designed by James Braid.
Founded 1908
Visitors: welcome weekdays, with
restrictions on Thurs and Sat.
Green Fee: on application.
Societies: limited number of
societies accepted.
Catering: meals and snacks.

Q72 **Gourock**
☎(0475) 31001
Cowal View, Gourock, Renfrewshire
PA19 6HD
2 miles up hill from Gourock station.
Moorland course.
18 holes, 6492 yards, S.S.S.71
Designed by Henry Cotton.
Founded 1896
Visitors: by letter to Sec, weekdays
only.
Green Fee: £10/round, £15/day.
Societies: by arrangement.
Catering: bar lunches, high teas,
dinner by arrangement.
Hotels: Queens; Ashton; Gantock;
Castle Levan.

Q73 **Greenock**
☎(0475) 20793
Forsyth St, Greenock, Renfrewshire
PA16 8RE
1 mile SW of town centre, main road
to Gourock away from River Clyde.
Moorland course.
27 holes, 5346 yards, S.S.S.68
Founded 1890
Visitors: welcome except Sat.
Green Fee: on application.
Catering: full service except Mon.
Hotels: Tontine.

Q74 **Greenock Whinhill**
☎(0475) 24694
Beith Rd, Greenock, Renfrewshire
23 miles W of Glasgow,
Renfrewshire.
Moorland course.
18 holes, 5454 yards, S.S.S.68
Founded 1908
Visitors: welcome.

Green Fee: on application.
Societies: by arrangement.
Catering: meals by arrangement.

Q75 Haggs Castle
☎(041) 427 1157
70 Dumbreck Rd, Glasgow G41 4SN
At end of M77 off M8.
Parkland course.
18 holes, 6466 yards, S.S.S.71
Designed by Allis & Thomas.
Founded 1910
Visitors: only with member.
Green Fee: £24/round, £32/day.
Societies: Wed only by prior
arrangement.
Catering: all types available.
Snooker.
Hotels: Sherbrooke Castle.

Q76 Hamilton
☎(0698) 282872, 286131 Sec.
Riccarton, Ferniegair, Hamilton,
Lanarkshire
Off A74 between Larkhill and
Hamilton.
Parkland course.
18 holes, 6264 yards, S.S.S.70
Designed by James Braid
Founded 1892
Visitors: welcome with member,
others by arrangement.
Green Fee: on application.
Societies: by arrangement with Sec.
Catering: snacks daily, meals
served by arrangement.
Hotels: Royal; Avonbridge.

Q77 Hayston
☎(041) 776 1244
Campsie Rd, Kirkintilloch, Glasgow
G66 1RN
NE from Glasgow via Bishopbriggs,
1 mile N of Kirkintilloch.
Parkland course.
18 holes, 6042 yards, S.S.S.69
Designed by James Braid.
Founded 1926
Visitors: weekdays only with letter
of intro.
Green Fee: on application.
Societies: Tues and Thurs.
Catering: full service from 9am;
lunch, bar snacks, high tea, dinner if
ordered in advance.

Q78 Helensburgh
☎(0436) 74173
25 East Abercromby St,
Helensburgh, Dunbartonshire G84
9JD
21 miles W of Glasgow on A82.

Moorland course.
18 holes, 6053 yards, S.S.S.69
Designed by Tom Morris.
Founded 1893
Visitors: welcome weekdays.
Green Fee: £12/round, £18/day; jnrs
£6/round.
Societies: by arrangement.
Catering: bar lunches, evening
meals by arrangement.
Hotels: Commodore.

Q79 Hilton Park
☎(041) 956 4657
Stockiemuir Rd, Milngavie, Glasgow
G62 9HB
8 miles N of Glasgow on A809.
Moorland courses.
Allander, 18 holes, 5374 yards,
S.S.S.69; Hilton, 18 holes, 5563
yards, S.S.S.70
Designed by James Braid.
Founded 1927
Visitors: welcome weekdays by
prior arrangement.
Green Fee: £16.50/round, £22.50/2
rounds.
Societies: catered for on weekdays
by arrangement.
Catering: full facilities.
Hotels: Kirkhouse; Black Bull;
Country Club.

Q80 Hollandbush
☎(0555) 893484
Acretophead, Lesmahagow,
Strathclyde
Off A74 between Lesmahagow and
Coalburn.
Parkland/moorland course.
18 holes, 6110 yards, S.S.S.70
Designed by Ken Pate.
Founded 1954
Visitors: welcome.
Green Fee: on application.
Catering: full catering facilities.
Hotels: Station (Coalburn).

Q81 Innellan
☎(0369) 3546
Knockamillie Rd, Innellan, Argyll
4 miles S of Dunoon.
Parkland course.
9 holes, 4878 yards, S.S.S.63
Founded 1891
Visitors: anytime except Mon
evenings.
Green Fee: £5 WD, £6 Sun.
Societies: catered for weekdays by
arrangement.
Catering: available.
Hotels: Esplanade; Slatefield;
Rosscairn.

Q82 Irvine
☎(0294) 75626
Bogside, Irvine KA12 8SN
On road from Irvine to Kilwinning, left
after Ravenspark Academy, straight
on for 0.5 mile over railway bridge.
Links course.
18 holes, 6454 yards, S.S.S.71
Designed by James Braid.
Founded 1887
Visitors: welcome weekdays.
Green Fee: on application.
Catering: meals and snacks served.
Hotels: Hospitality Inn; Redburn;
Eglinton Arms.

Q83 Irvine Ravenspark
☎(0294) 71293
13 Kidsneuk Lane, Irvine KA12 8SR
On A78 midway between Irvine and
Kilwinning.
Public parkland course.
18 holes, 6496 yards, S.S.S.71
Founded 6 June 1907
Visitors: welcome every day.
Green Fee: on application.
Societies: catered for on weekdays
and Sun by arrangement with Sec.
Catering: bar open all day every day;
lunches and high teas.
Hotels: Hospitality Inn; Annfield;
Redburn.

Q84 Kilbirnie Place
☎(0505) 683398
Largs Rd, Kilbirnie, Ayrshire
On outskirts of Kilbirnie on main
Largs road.
Parkland course.
18 holes, 5511 yards, S.S.S.67
Founded 1922
Visitors: weekdays and Sun.
Green Fee: on application.
Societies: weekdays and Sun, apply
in writing to Sec.
Catering: every day.

Q85 Kilmacolm
☎(050 587) 2139
Porterfield Rd, Kilmacolm,
Renfrewshire PA13 3PD
A740 to Linwood, then A761 to
Bridge of Weir.
Moorland course.
18 holes, 5964 yards, S.S.S.68
Designed by James Braid.
Founded 1890
Visitors: weekdays; weekends
accompanied by member only.
Green Fee: £15/round, £20/day.
Societies: by arrangement.
Catering: available.
Hotels: Gryffe (Bridge of Weir).

Q86 **Kilmarnock (Barassie)**
☎(0292) 311077 Club, 313920
Sec's office
29 Hillhouse Rd, Barassie, Troon,
Ayrshire KA10 6SY
Off A78 just N of Troon opposite
Barassie station.
Seaside course.
18 holes, 6473 yards, S.S.S.71
Designed by Matthew M. Monie.
Founded 1887
Visitors: Mon, Tues, Thurs, Fri only.
Green Fee: on application.
Societies: Tues and Thurs by prior
arrangement.
Catering: full facilities available.
Hotels: Marine (Troon).

Q87 **Kilsyth Lennox**
☎(0236) 822190
Tak-Ma-Doon Rd, Kilsyth, Glasgow
G65 0HX
12 miles from Glasgow on A80.
Moorland/parkland course.
9 holes, 5944 yards, S.S.S.69; 18
holes from Aug 1992
Founded 1907
Visitors: welcome until 5pm
weekdays, after 4pm Sat; Sun with
member only.
Green Fee: £8/day WD, £8/round WE.
Societies: weekdays.
Catering: bar snacks available.
Hotels: Coachman.

Q88 **Kirkhill**
☎(041) 641 3083
Greenlees Rd, Cambuslang, Glasgow
G72 8YN
Follow East Kilbride road from
Burnside, take first turning on left
past Cathkin by-pass roundabout.
Meadowland course.
18 holes, 5862 yards, S.S.S.69
Designed by James Braid.
Founded 1910
Visitors: by arrangement with Sec.
Green Fee: £12/round, £16/day.
Societies: welcome by prior
arrangement in writing.
Catering: bar snacks, full meals by
arrangement with Clubmistress.
Hotels: Kings Park; Burnside.

Q89 **Kirkintilloch**
☎(041) 776 1256 Club, 775 2387
Sec.
Todhill, Campsie Rd, Kirkintilloch,
Glasgow G66 1RN
1 mile from Kirkintilloch on road to
Lennoxtown.
Meadowland course.
18 holes, 5900 yards, S.S.S.66

Designed by James Braid.
Founded 1893
Visitors: only if introduced.
Green Fee: on application.
Societies: by advance booking.
Catering: full except Mon and Tues.
Hotels: Garfield (Stepps).

Q90 **Knightswood**
☎(041) 959 2131
Lincoln Ave, Knightswood, Glasgow
Off Dumbarton Rd from city centre.
Parkland course.
9 holes, 2717 yards, S.S.S.64
Founded 1920s
Visitors: welcome.
Green Fee: on application.
Societies: welcome by arrangement.
Hotels: Pond.

Q91 **Kyles of Bute**
☎(0700) 811601
Tighnabruaich, Argyll
B836 from Dunoon to Tighnabruaich,
through village to Kames Cross, then
B8000 to Millhouse, club entrance on
left at top of 1st rise.
Undulating moorland course.
9 holes, 2389 yards, S.S.S.32
Founded 1907
Visitors: welcome except Sun am.
Green Fee: £5/day; £2.50 under 18.
Societies: by arrangement.
Catering: tea, coffee, snacks only.
Hotels: Royal; Kames; Kyles of Bute.

Q92 **Lamlash**
☎(07706) 296
Lamlash, Brodick, Isle of Arran KA27
8JU
3 miles S of Brodick on Lamlash to
Whiting Bay road.
Undulating moorland course.
18 holes, 4681 yards, S.S.S.63
Founded 1889
Visitors: welcome.
Green Fee: on application.
Societies: welcome.
Catering: licenced bar, tearoom.

Q93 **Lanark**
☎(0555) 3219
The Moor, Whitelees Rd, Lanark
ML11 7RX
Off A73 or A72, turn left in Lanark
into Whitelees Rd, for 0.5 mile.
Moorland course.
18 holes, 6423 yards, S.S.S.71
Designed by Ben Sayers and James
Braid.
Founded 1851
Visitors: welcome weekdays.

Green Fee: on application.
Societies: weekdays.
Catering: full, resident chef.
Hotels: Tinto; The Popinjay.

Q94 **Largs**
☎(0475) 673594
Irvine Rd, Largs, Ayrshire KA30 8EU
1 mile S of Largs on A78, 28 miles
from Glasgow.
Parkland course.
18 holes, 6220 yards, S.S.S.70
Founded 1891
Visitors: welcome.
Green Fee: £18/round, £22/day.
Societies: Tues and Thurs.
Catering: full facilities.
Hotels: Elderslie; Haylie; Glen Eldon;
South Bay.

Q95 **Larkhall**
☎(0698) 881113
Burnhead Rd, Larkhall, Lanarkshire
SW on B7019.
Municipal course.
9 holes, 6236 yards, S.S.S.70
Visitors: all welcome.
Green Fee: on application.
Societies: by arrangement.

Q96 **Leadhills**
☎(0659) 74222
Leadhills, Biggar, Lanarkshire ML12
6XR
On B797, 6 miles from A74 at
Abington, course behind hotel within
Leadhills village.
Moorland course; highest course in
Great Britain.
9 holes, 4100 yards, S.S.S.62
Founded 1935
Visitors: welcome anytime.
Green Fee: £3 WD, £4 WE.
Societies: welcome.
Catering: at local hotel.
Hotels: Hopetoun Arms.

Q97 **Lenzie**
☎(041) 776 1535
19 Crosshill Rd, Lenzie, Glasgow G66
3DA
A80 to Stepps, Lenzie road turn left at
traffic lights.
Moorland course.
18 holes, 5984 yards, S.S.S.69
Founded 1889
Visitors: welcome with member.
Green Fee: on application.
Societies: welcome weekdays by
arrangement.
Catering: meals and snacks
available except Mon.

Q98 Lethamhill
☎(041) 770 6220
Cumbernauld Rd, Glasgow G33 1AH
On A80 adjacent Hogganfield Loch.
Municipal course.
18 holes, 6073 yards, S.S.S.69
Visitors: welcome.
Green Fee: on application.
Catering: tea room at club
April-Sept.

Q99 Linn Park
☎(041) 637 5871
Simshill Rd, Glasgow G44
Off M74 S of Glasgow.
Public parkland course.
18 holes, 4952 yards, S.S.S.65
Designed by Glasgow Parks.
Founded 1925
Visitors: welcome.
Green Fee: on application.
Catering: teas and snacks.
Wildlife park 200 yards from
clubhouse.
Hotels: King's Park.

Q100 Littlehill
☎(041) 772 1916
Auchinairn Rd, Bishopbriggs,
Glasgow
3 miles N of city centre.
Municipal parkland course.
18 holes, 6228 yards, S.S.S.70
Designed by James Braid.
Founded 1924
Visitors: no restrictions.
Green Fee: on application.
Societies: apply to Glasgow
Corporation Parks Dept.
Catering: lunches except Mon.

Q101 Lochgilphead
☎(0546) 2340
Blarbuie Road, Lochgilphead, Argyll
PA31 8LD
A82 and A83 from Glasgow to
Lochgilphead; 1 mile from parish
church on Hospital Rd.
Hilly parkland course.
9 holes, 4484 yards, S.S.S.63
Designed by Dr Ian MacCammond
Founded 1891
Visitors: welcome weekdays,
members competitions weekends.
Green Fee: £5/day WD, £7/day WE;
£20/week (Mon-Fri); jnrs and OAPs
half price.
Societies: by arrangement.
Catering: bar available evenings and
weekends; catering by arrangement.
Hotels: Stag; Argyll; Lochgair;
Castleween Caravan Park: all
advertise free golf.

Q102 Lochranza
☎(077 083) 273
Lochranza, Isle of Arran, KA27 8HL
In village of Lochranza at N of island.
Grassland course with river and
trees, 3 holes adjacent seashore.
9 holes (18 tees), 5560 yards, Par 69
Designed by Ian M. Robinson.
New course laid 1991.
Visitors: welcome 7 days.
Green Fee: £4.50/round (9 holes),
£7 (18 holes), £9.50/day.
Societies: welcome any time.
Catering: tea room, home cooking;
not licensed.
Hotels: caravan park adjacent (vans
for hire); weekly golf packages;
hotel/guest house packages on
request.

Q103 Lochwinnoch
☎(0505) 842153
Burnfoot Rd, Lochwinnoch,
Renfrewshire
On A760 about 10 miles S of Paisley,
1st on right after Struthers Garage,
400 yards along Burnfoot Rd.
Parkland course.
18 holes, 6202 yards, S.S.S.70
Founded 1897
Visitors: weekdays until 4pm,
weekends only with member.
Green Fee: on application.
Societies: by arrangement.
Catering: full meals except Mon.
Hotels: Lindhurst.

Q104 Loudoun
☎(0563) 821993 Sec, 820551 Club
Galston, Ayrshire KA4 8PA
A77 to Kilmarnock, take Edinburgh
road, club lies on main road between
Galston and Newmilns.
Parkland course.
18 holes, 5824 yards, S.S.S.68
Founded 1909
Visitors: welcome weekdays.
Green Fee: on application.
Societies: welcome.
Catering: facilities available.
Hotels: Broomhill; Foxbar.

Q105 Machrie
☎(0496) 2310, 2404 fax.
The Machrie Hotel & Golf Course,
Port Ellen, Isle of Islay, PA42 7AN
30 mins by air from Glasgow, 4 miles
from Port Ellen.
Traditional links course.
18 holes, 6226 yards, S.S.S.70
Designed by Willie Campbell,
redesigned by Donald Steel.
Founded 1891

Visitors: welcome.
Green Fee: £22.50.
Societies: at any time by
arrangement.
Catering: bar lunches, grill, table
d'hôte, à la carte.
Banqueting, conferences, company
days, own beach, salmon/sea trout
fishing, snooker.
Hotels: Machrie Hotel; leisure/golf
packages on request.

Q106 Machrie Bay
☎(077 084) 261
c/o Sec, Oakdene, Pirnmill, Brodick,
Isle of Arran, KA27 8HP
Ferry to Brodick and via String Rd to
Machrie.
Fairly flat seaside course.
9 holes, 2123 yards, S.S.S.32
Designed by William Fernie.
Founded 1900
Visitors: welcome.
Green Fee: on application.
Catering: snacks served June-Aug.
Tennis.

Q107 Machrihanish
☎(0586 81) 213
Machrihanish, Campbeltown, Argyll
5 miles W of Campbeltown on B843.
Seaside links course.
18 holes, 6228 yards, S.S.S.70; also
9 hole course
Founded 1876
Visitors: welcome at all times;
golf/flight day package available
through Logan Air, Glasgow.
Green Fee: £13.50/round, £18/day.
Societies: welcome, certain
weekends available also.
Catering: full facilities.
Hotels: White Hart; Seafield; Royal;
Argyll; Balgreggan House; Warren;
Knockstaplemore Farm Cottages.

Q108 Maybole
Memorial Park, Maybole, Ayrshire
KA19
9 miles S of Ayr on main Stranraer
route.
Public hillside course with splendid
views.
9 holes, 2652 yards, S.S.S.65
Founded 1905
Visitors: no restrictions; booking
available through Kyle and Carrick
Parks Recreation and Leisure Dept
tourist schemes.
Green Fee: £4.10.
Societies: booking as for visitors.
Hotels: many in Ayr offering golf
packages.

Machrie

Machrie's charm lies in its out of the way setting. Lapped on one side by the Atlantic and separated from the mainland by a sea voyage (or a short aeroplane hop from Glasgow), its delights are little known.

They are certainly not as well known as they deserve to be, because the course is in the very best tradition of seaside links. However, by developing its assets a little more than in the past, the Island of Islay is putting itself far more on the map; and without wishing to spoil a way of life by causing a golfing invasion to its shores, the recommendation for its golf is based on happy personal experience that it would be churlish not to pass on.

After years of acting as co-tenants to grazing sheep and cattle, golfers owe something of a transformation to the former owners of Bowmore Distillery, who bought the course and hotel, and added a cluster of cottages alongside which are an ideal base for whatever form of holiday you seek on Islay.

It is a wide choice but, as golfers have supported the distillers' product ever since man first took three putts, there is a delicious aptness about the change. However, Machrie's new look was not confined to new management. It has six new holes which add enormously to its rating as a test of golf. Some of the eccentricities that grew up before there was much in the way of machinery or golf course architects have been reduced; gone are one or two, though not all, of the blind shots into crater-like greens — a type of hole not so favourably looked upon as it once was; in their place have arisen a new 2nd, 10th, 11th, 12th, 13th and 14th that offer, in distillers' language, a smoother blend.

The 1st, a gentle opener, has an inviting drive from a raised tee, but the 2nd quickly gets down to the real golfing business. The first of the alterations, it is a winding dogleg to the left, the dogleg taking the form of a fast flowing brook; there are plans for extending the hole to par 5.

Anyone with aspirations of getting home in two will need a strong nerve as well as two good shots, although the 3rd and 4th are less stern. The 5th is a fine short hole and the 6th typical of Machrie's natural blessings with a drive to the left providing the correct approach and view of a green in a dell.

In its early days in the last century, the drive at the 7th over a vast sandhill was rather more formidable than it is now; all the same, it can still strike fear at the beginning of a stretch of three holes, all par 4s, which follow the line of a glorious sandy beach. These emphasise the remoteness and the beauty and the fact that, unlike many famous seaside courses, here is the opportunity really to see the sea.

The 10th tee is a notable example, even if it is not the time to be distracted. A marvellous natural short hole at the furthest limit of the course marks the introduction to the new golfing country; this is nicely demanding but, at the same time, there is a pleasant scenic change to the hills and the lonely peat moors.

The 11th requires a strong second to a long green with a heathery drop to the left, and the not so short par 3 12th is even tougher. The main feature of the 13th, a par 5 bending left, is the amphitheatre in which the green is situated, while the 14th is perhaps the hardest of all the par 4s. A long drive is necessary for the proper view of the flag outlined against the skyline.

After a spell where stout hitting is essential, the last four holes are not quite as severe; nevertheless, the need for good judgment is paramount and, against any sort of wind, the 16th and 18th, in particular, can pose considerably greater problems. However, if your score doesn't turn out quite the way you planned (how many do?), there are ample consolations.

There is no shortage of spirituous assistance to help forget the bad round — and celebrate the good — and the atmosphere of the Club and hotel, as of the island as a whole, is wonderfully friendly and informal.

Q109 Millport
☎(0475) 530311
Golf Rd, Millport, Isle of Cumbrae
KA28 0BA
Cal-Mac car ferry Largs Slip to
Cumbrae (7 minutes), thence 3 miles
by car or public transport.
Seaside moorland course.
18 holes, 5831 yards, S.S.S.68
Founded 1888
Visitors: welcome at all times.
Green Fee: £12.50/day max.
Societies: welcome, including
weekends.
Catering: full facilities.
Hotels: Royal George; Millerston;
Islands.

Q110 Milngavie
☎(041) 956 1619
Laighpark, Milngavie, Glasgow G62
8EP
Off A809 NW of Glasgow.
Moorland course.
18 holes, 5818 yards, S.S.S.68
Founded 1895
Visitors: only with member any time.
Green Fee: £14/round, £23/day.
Societies: catered for weekdays
except Mon and Tues.
Catering: by arrangement.
Hotels: Black Bull; Burnbrae.

Q111 Mount Ellen
☎(0236) 872277
Johnstone Rd, Johnstone House,
Gartcosh, Glasgow
Off A80 Glasgow-Stirling road.
Parkland course.
18 holes, 5525 yards, S.S.S.68(66)
Founded 1905
Visitors: by appointment.
Green Fee: on application.
Catering: full facilities. Pool.
Hotels: Garfield (Moodiesburn).

Q112 Old Course Ranfurly
☎(0505) 461 3612 Club, 461 3214
office
Ranfurly Place, Bridge of Weir,
Renfrewshire PA11 3DE
7 miles W of Paisley, 10 mins from
Glasgow airport.
Moorland course.
18 holes, 6089 yards, S.S.S.69
Founded 1905
Visitors: weekdays by introduction,
weekends with member.
Green Fee: on application.
Societies: by special arrangement.
Catering: morning coffee, bar
lunches, high tea, dinner.
Hotels: Gryffe Arms.

Q113 Paisley
☎(041) 884 4114 Pro shop
Braehead, Paisley PA2 8TZ
From Glasgow, A737 to Paisley, 3
miles S of Paisley centre.
Moorland course.
18 holes, 6424 yards, S.S.S.71
Founded 1895.
Visitors: weekdays before 4pm,
letter of intro or prior arrangement
with Sec.
Green Fee: £13/round, £17/day.
Societies: by arrangement; not
weekends or Bank Holidays.
Catering: full catering available.
Snooker.
Hotels: Watermill; Excelsior.

Q114 Palacerigg
☎(0236) 734969
Palacerigg Country Park,
Cumbernauld G67 3HU
Take A80 to Cumbernauld, follow
signs to Country Park.
Parkland course.
18 holes, 6408 yards, S.S.S.71
Founded 1976
Visitors: welcome weekdays.
Green Fee: £4 WD, £5 WE.
Catering: lunches and high teas
except Mon, Tues.
Hotels: Castlecary.

Q115 Pollok
☎(041) 632 1080
90 Barrhead Rd, Glasgow G43 1BG
On A736, 4 miles S of city centre.
Wooded parkland course.
18 holes, 6257 yards, S.S.S.70
Founded 1892
Visitors: men only Mon-Fri.
Green Fee: £26/round, £33/day.
Societies: by letter to Sec.
Catering: full dining facilities.
Hotels: Albany; Macdonald; Holiday
Inn; Forum.

Q116 Port Bannatyne
☎(0700) 502009
Bannatyne Mains Rd, Port
Bannatyne, Isle of Bute
2 miles N of Rothesay on A845.
Hilly seaside course.
13 holes, 4654 yards, S.S.S.63
Designed by James Braid.
Founded 1968
Visitors: unrestricted.
Green Fee: £6.50/day, £25/week;
jnrs £3.50/day, £15/week.
Societies: welcome.
Catering: by arrangement.
Hotels: Ardmory House; Glenburn;
Port Royal.

Q117 Port Glasgow
☎(0475) 704181
Devol Farm Industrial Estate, Port
Glasgow, Renfrewshire PA14 5XE
SW of Glasgow on M8 towards
Greenock; in town of Port Glasgow.
Undulating course.
18 holes, 5712 yards, S.S.S.68
Founded 1895
Visitors: weekdays until 3.55pm; at
all other times only with introduction.
Green Fee: £8/round, £12/day.
Societies: catered for on
non-competition days (Sun-Fri).
Catering: meals served on request.
Hotels: Clune Brae; Star.

Q118 Prestwick
☎(0292) 77404
2 Links Rd, Prestwick, Ayrshire KA9
1QG
1 mile from Prestwick Airport
adjacent to Prestwick station.
Seaside links course.
18 holes, 6544 yards, S.S.S.72
Founded 1851
Visitors: by arrangement; prior
booking essential.
Green Fee: on application.
Societies: by arrangement.
Catering: dining room, men only;
Cardinal room, mixed, casual dress,
light lunches.
Hotels: Parkstone; Fairways; Golf
View; North Beach.

Q119 Prestwick St Cuthbert
☎(0292) 77101
East Rd, Prestwick, Ayrshire KA9 2SX
Off main Ayr to Prestwick Rd, at
Bellevue Rd.
Parkland course.
18 holes, 6470 yards, S.S.S.71
Designed by Stutt & Co.
Founded 1899
Visitors: welcome weekdays,
weekends if introduced by member.
Green Fee: £15/round, £20/day.
Societies: by arrangement, not
weekends or Bank Holidays.
Catering: lunch, bar lunches, dinner.
Hotels: Carlton; St Nicholas;
Parkstone.

Q120 Prestwick St Nicholas
☎(0292) 77608
Grangemuir Rd, Prestwick, Ayrshire
KA9 1SN
Off A79, from Main St turn into
Grangemuir Rd which runs to sea.
Links course.

18 holes, 5926 yards, S.S.S.68
Designed by C. Hunter.
Founded 1851
Visitors: welcome weekdays.
Green Fee: £18/round, £28/day WD.
Societies: weekdays.
Catering: bar lunch, high tea, dinner.
Hotels: Parkstone; St Ninians; North Beach.

Q121 Ralston
☎(041) 882 1349
Strathmore Ave, Ralston, Paisley, Renfrewshire PE1 3EP
Off main Paisley to Glasgow road.
Parkland course.
18 holes, 6100 yards, S.S.S.69
Visitors: organised parties only.
Green Fee: on application.
Catering: meals served.

Q122 Ranfurly Castle
☎(0505) 612609
Golf Rd, Bridge of Weir, Renfrewshire PA11 3HN
Off M8 at sign for Linwood.
Undulating moorland course.
18 holes, 6284 yards, S.S.S.70
Founded 1889
Visitors: weekdays by introduction.
Green Fee: on application.
Societies: certain Tues only.
Catering: snacks, lunches, high teas.
Hotels: Gryffe Arms.

Q123 Renfrew
☎(041) 886 6692
Blythswood Estate, Inchinnan Rd, Renfrew
Off A8 at Normandy Hotel.
Parkland course.
18 holes, 6818 yards, S.S.S.73
Designed by John Harris.
Founded 1894
Visitors: introduced by member.
Green Fee: £16/round, £25/day.
Societies: welcome by arrangement, max 30.
Catering: full catering.
Hotels: Normandy; Glynehill; Dean Park.

Q124 Rothesay
☎(0700) 503554
Canada Hill, Rothesay, Isle of Bute PA20 7HN
30 minutes by steamer from Wemyss Bay (30 miles from Glasgow).
Undulating parkland course.
18 holes, 5440 yards, S.S.S.67
Designed by James Braid.

Founded 1892
Visitors: welcome, bookings advisable Sat/Sun.
Green Fee: £10/day, £15 WE; £50 weekly.
Societies: by arrangement.
Catering: full catering all week, April-Sept.

Q125 Routenburn
☎(0475) 673230
Largs, Ayrshire KA30 9AH
1 mile N of Largs; 1st major left turn coming into Largs from Greenock.
Seaside hill course.
18 holes, 5650 yards, S.S.S.67
Founded 1914
Visitors: welcome weekdays.
Green Fee: on application.
Societies: welcome weekdays.
Catering: full catering facilities except Thurs.
Hotels: Charleston.

Q126 Royal Troon
☎(0292) 311555 Office, 317578 Club Master, 313281 Pro.
Craigend Rd, Troon, Ayrshire KA10 6EP
3 miles from Prestwick Airport.
Seaside links courses.
Old Course (championship), 18 holes, 6641 yards (6070 metres), S.S.S.73; Portland Course, 18 holes, 6274 yards (5738 metres), S.S.S.71
Designed by Cotton, Pennink, Lawrie & Partners.
Founded 1878
Visitors: Mon to Thurs only with starting time restriction; max h/cap 18; no Ladies on Old Course; letter of intro required.
Green Fee: £65/day; Portland £40/day; only 1 round permitted on Old Course; lunch etc included.
Societies: by arrangement, max 24 persons.
Catering: full restaurant service and bar snacks by arrangement.
Hotels: Marine Highland; Piersland.

Q127 Ruchill
Brassey Street, Maryhill, Glasgow G20
2.5 miles NW of Glasgow off Bearsden road.
Municipal parkland course.
9 holes, 2240 yards, S.S.S.31
Founded 1928
Visitors: welcome.
Green Fee: municipal rates.
Societies: contact Glasgow Parks Dept.

Q128 Sandyhills
☎(041) 778 1179
223 Sandyhills Rd, Glasgow G32 9NA
E side of Glasgow, from Tollcross Rd, left at Killin St and right into Sandyhills Rd.
Parkland course.
18 holes, 6253 yards, S.S.S.70
Founded 1905
Visitors: welcome by arrangement.
Green Fee: on application.
Societies: welcome by arrangement.
Catering: full catering except Mon.

Q129 Shiskine
☎(077 086) 293 Sec, 346 Treasurer
Blackwaterfoot, Isle of Arran KA27 8HA
300 yards off A841 in Blackwaterfoot.
Seaside course.
12 holes, 3000 yards, S.S.S.42
Founded 1896
Visitors: welcome.
Green Fee: on application.
Societies: catered for, write or phone Hon Sec or Hon Treasurer.
Catering: snacks, June-Sept.
Tennis, bowling.
Hotels: Kinloch; Blackwaterfoot; Rock.

Q130 Shotts
☎(0501) 20431
Blairhead, Shotts ML7 5BJ
Off M8 junction 5, B7057 Benhar road for 2 miles.
Undulating moorland course.
18 holes, 6125 yards, S.S.S.70
Designed by James Braid.
Founded 1895
Visitors: unlimited during week.
Green Fee: £12/day WD, £15 WE.
Societies: weekdays only by prior booking.
Catering: full catering April-Oct.
Hotels: Station.

Q131 Skelmorlie
☎(0475) 520152
Skelmorlie, Ayrshire PA17 5ES
1 mile from Wemyss Bay station.
Parkland/moorland course.
13 holes, 5104 yards, S.S.S.65
Designed by James Braid.
Founded 1891
Visitors: welcome except Sat from Mar to Oct.
Green Fee: on application.
Societies: welcome except Sat.
Catering: lunches, dinners and teas served.

Q132 Strathaven
☎(0357) 20539 or 20421
Overton Ave, Glasgow Rd, Strathaven
ML10 6NL
On outskirts of town on A726.
Parkland course.
18 holes, 6226 yards, S.S.S.70
Designed by William Fernie of Troon,
extended to 18 holes by J.R. Stutt.
Founded 1908
Visitors: welcome weekdays.
Green Fee: on application.
Societies: parties on Tues only.
Catering: available all day.
Hotels: Strathaven.

Q133 Strathclyde Park
☎(0698) 66155 Ext 154
Mote Hill, Hamilton, ML3 9XX
Take Hamilton turn off M74 (heading
towards Glasgow), 0.5 mile on to
roundabout, 2nd exit (straight
through), to next roundabout and turn
right into Mote Hill.
Public parkland course.
9 holes, 3147 yards, S.S.S.70
Visitors: booking system; book
same day, phones open 8.45am.
Green Fee: £1.75 for 9 holes.
Catering: bar lunches and dinners.
Driving range.

Q134 Tarbert
☎(0880) 820565
Kilberry Rd, Tarbert, Argyll PA29 6XX
1 mile on A83 to Campbeltown from
Tarbert, turn right onto B8024 for
0.25 mile.
Hilly seaside course.
9 holes, 2230 yards, S.S.S.64
Visitors: welcome with restrictions.
Green Fee: £4 (9 holes), £6 (18
holes), £8/day.
Societies: by arrangement.
Hotels: Stonefield Castle; Tarbert;
West Loch Tarbert.

Q135 Tobermory
c/o Sec, (0688) 2013, 2275
Erray Rd, Tobermory, Isle of Mull
PA75 6PS
A848 to Tobermory, course past
Police Station.
Clifftop heathland course; panoramic
views over Sound of Mull.
9 holes, 4474 metres, S.S.S.64
Designed by David Adams.
Founded 1896
Visitors: welcome.
Green Fee: £7/day payable at
Brown's Shop or Western Isles Hotel.
Societies: welcome.
Hotels: Western Isles.

Q136 Torrance House
☎(03552) 33451
Strathaven Rd, East Kilbride,
Glasgow G75 0QZ
On A726 on outskirts of East Kilbride.
Parkland course.
18 holes, 6640 yards, S.S.S.71
Designed by Hawtree & Sons.
Founded 1969
Visitors: welcome by reservation.
Green Fee: on application.
Catering: meals served.

Q137 Troon Municipal
☎(0292) 312464
Harling Drive, Troon, KA10 6NE
100 yards from railway station.
Links course.
Lochgreen, 18 holes, 6687 yards,
S.S.S.72; Darley, 18 holes, 6327
yards, S.S.S.70; Fullerton, 18 holes,
4784 yards, S.S.S.63
Founded 1905
Visitors: welcome.
Green Fee: on application.
Societies: welcome.
Catering: full catering.
Hotels: Ardnell; South Beach.

Q138 Turnberry Hotel
☎(0655) 31000
Turnberry Hotel, Turnberry, Ayrshire
KA26 9LT
0.25 mile off A77 from Glasgow, 15
miles south of Ayr.
Seaside links courses.
Ailsa, 18 holes, 6408 yards,
S.S.S.71; Arran, 18 holes, 6276
yards, S.S.S.70
Designed by Mackenzie Ross.
Visitors: principally reserved for
residents; non residents must apply
in writing.
Green Fee: on application.
Societies: written applications.
Catering: clubhouse restaurant and
bar open all day.
Wide range of facilities within
Turnberry Hotel and Spa.
Hotels: Turnberry.

Q139 Vale of Leven
☎(0389) 52351
Northfield Rd, Bonfield, Alexandria,
Dunbartonshire G83 9EP.
Turn right from A82 at Bonhill; course
signposted from here.
Moorland course overlooking Loch
Lomond and Ben Lomond.
18 holes, 5962 yards, S.S.S.66
Founded 1907
Visitors: welcome except Sat during
April-Oct.

Green Fee: £6/round, £8.50/day
WD; £8/round, £12.50/day WE.
Societies: welcome except Sat on
application to Sec.
Catering: full bar and catering
facilities except Tues.
Hotels: Balloch; Tullichewan;
Lomond Park; Duck Bay Marina;
Dumbuck; Dumbarton.

Q140 Vaul
☎(08792) 339
Scarinish, Isle of Tiree, PA77 6XH
50 miles west of Oban by ferry; 40
minute flight from Glasgow Airport.
Public seaside course on E coast of
island.
9 holes, 5822 yards, S.S.S.70
Founded 1920
Visitors: welcome; no Sun golf.
Green Fee: £40/annum locals;
£30/annum mainland members;
days, weeks etc on application.
Societies: by arrangement.
Catering: available at nearby Lodge
Hotel.
Hotels: Lodge Hotel (19th)

Q141 West Kilbride
☎(0294) 823911
33-35 Fullerton Drive, Seamill, W
Kilbride, Ayrshire KA23 9HS
On A78 Ardrossan to Largs road at
Seamill.
Seaside/links course.
18 holes, 6247 yards, S.S.S.70
Designed by Tom Morris.
Founded 1893
Visitors: welcome weekdays with
introduction; not Bank Holidays or
weekends.
Green Fee: on application.
Societies: Tues and Thurs.
Catering: bar and lunches, high teas
and dinners.
Hotels: Seamill Hydro; Hospitality
Inn.

Q142 Western Gailes
☎(0294) 311649
Gailes, Irvine, Ayrshire KA11 5AE
5 miles N of Troon on A78.
Links course.
18 holes, 6664 yards, S.S.S.72
Founded 1897
Visitors: welcome Mon, Tues, Wed
and Fri (no Lady visitors on Tues);
advisable to book in advance.
Green Fee: £33/round, £40/day.
Societies: welcome by arrangement
Mon, Tues, Wed, Fri.
Catering: lunches, snacks and high
teas available.

Q143 Westerwood Hotel G & CC

☎(0236) 457171, 725281 Pro shop.
St Andrews Drive, Cumbernauld, G68 0EW
Signposted off A80 13 miles from Glasgow.
Parkland course.
18 holes, 6721 yards, S.S.S.73.
Designed by Seve Ballasteros and Dave Thomas.
Founded May 1989
Visitors: Welcome, no restrictions.
Green Fee: £22.50/round, £35/day WD; £27.50/round, £45/day WE.
Societies: by prior arrangement.
Catering: lunch, dinner and bar snacks available in clubhouse.
Bowls, tennis, croquet, boules, swimming, jacuzzi, gym etc.
Hotels: 49 bed hotel with business and conference facilities. Reduced green fees for residents; golfing packages available.

Q144 Whinhill

☎(0475) 21064
Beith Road, Greenock, Renfrewshire
Just outside Greenock on old Largs road.
Municipal parkland course.
18 holes, 5434 yards, S.S.S.68
Visitors: welcome.
Green Fee: £2.60/round (£1.30 jnrs, 35p OAPs).
Catering: small clubhouse for members only.
Putting green.

Q145 Whitecraigs

☎(041) 639 4530
72 Ayr Rd, Giffnock, Glasgow G46 6SW

7 miles S of Glasgow on A77.
Parkland course.
18 holes, 6230 yards, S.S.S.70
Founded 1905
Visitors: by introduction only.
Green Fee: £23/round (£1 with member).
Societies: Wed only.
Catering: lunches except Mon.
Hotels: Macdonald.

Q146 Whiting Bay

☎(07707) 487
Golf Course Rd, Whiting Bay, Isle of Arran, Strathclyde
8 miles S of Brodick.
Heathland and hilly, levelling out from 4th.
18 holes, 4405 yards, S.S.S.66
Founded 1895
Visitors: welcome, no restrictions.
Green Fee: £6/day.
Societies: on application to Sec.
Catering: bar and catering from Easter to end Oct. Snooker, pool.
Hotels: Cameronia; Grange House; Kiscadale.

Q147 Williamwood

☎(041) 637 1783
Clarkston Rd, Netherlee, Glasgow G44
5 miles S of Glasgow.
Wooded parkland course.
18 holes, 5808 yards, S.S.S.68
Designed by James Braid.
Founded 1906
Visitors: by introduction only.
Green Fee: on application.
Societies: weekdays by arrangement.
Catering: lunch and evening meals.
Hotels: MacDonald; Redhurst.

Q148 Windyhill

☎(041) 942 7157 Pro shop, 942 2349 clubhouse.
Baljaffray Rd, Bearsden, Glasgow G61 4QQ
Take A739 from Glasgow, after 8 miles turn right onto A809, after 1 mile turn left onto A810, club 1 mile on right.
Undulating moorland course.
18 holes, 6254 yards, S.S.S.70
Designed by James Braid.
Founded 1908
Visitors: welcome on weekdays; weekends only with member
Green Fee: day ticket £15.
Societies: only by prior arrangement with Sec.
Catering: full facilities available except Tues.
Hotels: Burnbrae; Black Bull (Milngavie).

Q149 Wishaw

☎(0698) 372869
55 Cleland Rd, Wishaw, Lanarkshire ML2 7PH
15 miles SW of Glasgow, 5 miles from M74 (Motherwell Junction).
Parkland course.
18 holes, 6167 yards, S.S.S.69
Designed by James Braid.
Founded 1897
Visitors: welcome weekdays before 4pm; no visitors on Sat.
Green Fee: £8.50/round, £11.50/day; £18 Sunday.
Societies: welcome weekdays, Sun by arrangement; not Sat.
Catering: lunches, bar snacks, high tea, dinner until 9pm.
Hotels: Wishaw Town.

R

TAYSIDE, CENTRAL REGION, FIFE

St Andrews, Carnoustie, Gleneagles and Blairgowrie — a vivid cross section of the many varied attractions that bring golfers by the thousand every year. Fife itself, quite apart from St Andrews, is as full of good things as a Christmas hamper, the magic carpet ride concentrating on the majestic coastal sweep round past Kirkcaldy to the point near the lovely Balcomie links at Crail and then on still further to the shores of St Andrews Bay.

Burntisland and Kinghorn are the first of note although Leven and Lundin Links start the historians dipping into the archives to remind the modern golfer that he is on hallowed ground. The low boundary fence shared by the two Clubs reflects the days when Leven extended as far as the present clubhouse at Lundin. Later, it found spare land nearer home to the north of the old railway thus allowing Lundin to come into being in 1857.

Now, the railway has ceased to function but the line of the track remains a feature of both courses, a little more forbidding perhaps at Lundin. Scenic landmarks are Largo Bay and the opposite shore of East Lothian but the best view of that is from the 10th green of the Golf House Club, Elie, a course in the best holiday traditions and a notable favourite.

There are good practice facilities at Elie Sports Club where children are welcome, but St Andrews too is well launched in its plans for a permanent driving range as an accompaniment to the new Strathtyrum and revised Balgove courses due to open in 1993. Meanwhile the updated versions of Jubilee and Eden help divert the demands on the Old and New but, before focusing

attention on the other side of the Tay, mention must be made of Scotscraig and Ladybank.

Downfield, home of championships, is the finest of the courses in the immediate vicinity of Dundee but, by now, sights are set on Carnoustie, although not at the expense of by-passing Monifieth or Panmure at Barry which overlap on either side of the railway line to Aberdeen.

Carnoustie's absence from the Open championship rota since 1975, the year of Tom Watson's first victory, is no sign of declining powers. Very much the opposite. It is preparing for the return of the Amateur championship and remains as formidable a challenge as any. And a word for Montrose, which hosted the 1991 British Boys championship, and for Letham Grange near Arbroath. Letham Grange, a relative newcomer, is a worthy addition to a famous area, a soothing contrast to the links lining its coastline.

For overseas visitors who tend to prefer inland golf, Gleneagles is still an automatic favourite, preparing, what is more, for the opening of their new Jack Nicklaus creation. Almost as popular is Blairgowrie at Rosemount in almost as glorious a setting.

King James VI, an island retreat in the centre of the River Tay in the middle of Perth, is a must for romantics and historians while Glenbervie between Falkirk and Stirling is a regular staging post for important events.

Further afield, the charms of Central Region are epitomised by Callander, Crieff, Dalmunzie, Alyth and Edzell, a gentle way of breaking travellers in to the beautiful, rugged highland country to the north.

R1 Aberdour

☎(0383) 860256, 860688
Clubmaster
Seaside Place, Aberdour, Fife KY3
0TX
Right off A92 in Aberdour village
travelling from Inverkeithing; by
coast route to Burntisland.
Parkland/seaside course.
18 holes, 5469 yards, S.S.S.67
Designed by Peter Robertson & Joe
Anderson.
Founded 1896
Visitors: welcome weekdays; casual
visitors phone Pro for tee reservation.
Green Fee: £13/round, £17/day WD.
Societies: visiting clubs by prior
booking with Sec, except Sat.
Catering: by arrangement with
Clubmaster, except Tues.
Hotels: Aberdour.

R2 Aberfeldy

☎(0887) 20535
Taybridge Rd, Aberfeldy, Perthshire
PH15 2BH
10 miles off A9 at Ballinluig.
Parkland course.
9 holes, 2733 yards, S.S.S.67
Visitors: welcome.
Green Fee: on application.
Societies: small society meetings
can be arranged.
Catering: snacks available.
Hotels: Weem; Cruachan;
Breadalbane; Ailean Chraggan;
Station; Balnearn.

R3 Aberfoyle

☎(08772) 493
Braeval, Aberfoyle, Stirling FK8 3RL
1 mile from Aberfoyle on A81 Stirling
road.
Heathland course.
18 holes, 5204 yards, S.S.S.66
Designed by James Braid.
Founded 1890
Green Fee: £12 WD; £15 WE.
Catering: limited catering, full bar.

R4 Alloa

☎(0259) 722745
Schawpark, Sauchie,
Clackmannanshire FK10 3AX
On A908 1 mile N of Alloa; 8 miles E
of Stirling.
Undulating parkland course.
18 holes, 6230 yards, S.S.S.70
Designed by James Braid.
Founded 1891
Visitors: welcome.
Green Fee: £9/round, £16/day WD;
£18 WE.
Societies: catered for on weekdays
only.
Catering: full catering facilities
available.
Snooker
Hotels: Bruce; Royal Oak; Dunmar
House; Claremont Lodge.

R5 Alva

☎(0259) 60431
Beauclerc St, Alva,
Clackmannanshire FK12 5LE
On A91 Stirling-St Andrews road, 7
miles from Stirling.
Undulating course at foot of Ochil
Hills.
9 holes, 2432 yards, S.S.S.64
Founded 1900
Visitors: welcome.
Green Fee: on application.
Catering: bar snacks.
Pool table.
Hotels: Alva Glen; Johnstone Arms.

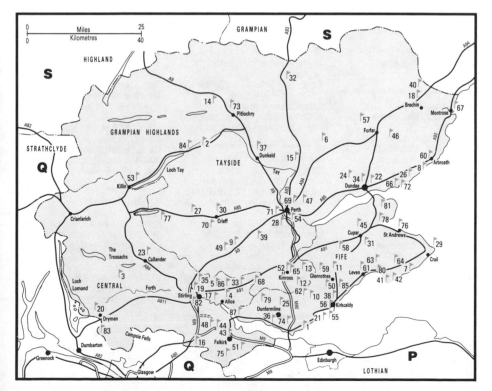

R6 **Alyth**
☎(08283) 2268 Sec and Steward, 2411 Starter/Pro.
Pitcrocknie, Alyth, Perthshire PH11 8JJ
On B954 Alyth to Glenisla road about 0.5 mile from major roundabout on A926 Blairgowrie-Kirriemuir road.
Heathland course.
18 holes, 6226 yards, S.S.S.70
Designed by James Braid.
Founded 1894
Visitors: welcome.
Green Fee: on application.
Societies: welcome by arrangement with Sec.
Catering: full catering facilities.
Hotels: Alyth; Lands of Loyal; Losset Inn.

R7 **Anstruther**
☎(0333) 310956 Clubhouse, (0333) 312283 Sec.
Marsfield, Shore Rd, Anstruther, Fife KY10 3DZ
Turn right off main road at Craw's Nest Hotel.
Seaside course.
9 holes, 4120 yards, S.S.S.63
Founded 1890
Visitors: welcome except on competition days.
Green Fee: £6/day WD, £8/day WE; £3 jnrs.
Catering: snacks and lunch served.
Hotels: Craw's Nest; Royal; Smugglers Inn.

R8 **Arbroath**
☎(0241) 75837 Pro, 72069 clubhouse.
Elliot, Arbroath, Angus
On A92, 1 mile S of Arbroath.
Public seaside links course.
18 holes, 6078 yards, S.S.S.69
Designed by James Braid
Founded 1905
Visitors: unrestricted but should be a member of a golf club.
Green Fee: £10/round, £15/day WD; £20/day WE.
Societies: by arrangement.
Catering: full bar and catering.
Hotels: Best of Scotland Golf Ticket £50 per week 5 local courses.

R9 **Auchterarder**
☎(0764) 62804
Orchil Rd, Auchterarder, Perthshire PH3 1LS
On A9 between Stirling and Perth.
Woodland and heathland course.
18 holes, 5757 yards, S.S.S.68

Designed by Bernard Sayers.
Founded 1892
Visitors: advisable to pre book.
Green Fee: £10/round, £15/day WD; £15/round, £20/day WD.
Societies: must be booked by letter to secretary.
Catering: full catering and bar.

R10 **Auchterderran**
☎(0592) 721579 clubhouse, 720457 sec.
Woodend Rd, Cardenden, Fife KY5 0NH
On main Lochgelly to Glenrothes road at N end of Cardenden.
Public parkland course.
9 holes, 5250 yards, S.S.S.66
Founded 1904
Visitors: welcome.
Green Fee: on application.
Societies: welcome by advance booking.
Catering: bar facilities available.
Hotels: Bowhill; Central.

R11 **Balbirnie Park**
☎(0592) 752006
Balbirnie Park, Markinch, Glenrothes, Fife KY7 6DD
2 miles E of Glenrothes.
Scenic parkland course.
18 holes, 6210 yards, S.S.S.70
Founded 1983
Visitors: unrestricted, but advisable to book beforehand.
Green Fee: £17/round, £24/day WD; £25/round, £30/day WE.
Societies: welcome.
Catering: coffee, lunches, snacks, high teas; dinners by arrangement.

R12 **Ballingry**
☎(0592) 860086
Lochore Meadows Country Park, Crosshill, Ballingry, Fife KY5 8BA
Between Lochgelly and Ballingry, W of M90.
Public parkland course.
9 holes, 6488 yards, S.S.S.71
Founded 1981
Visitors: welcome.
Green Fee: on application.
Societies: welcome by arrangement.
Catering: cafeteria.
Angling, wind surfing, pony trekking.

R13 **Bishopshire**
☎(0592) 780203
Kinnesswood by Kinross, Tayside.
3 miles E of Kinross off M90.
Upland course.

9 holes, 4700 yards, S.S.S.64
Designed by W. Park.
Founded 1903
Visitors: welcome, no restrictions.
Green Fee: £3 WD, £4 WE.
Societies: by arrangement.
Catering: by arrangement.
Hotels: Lomond; Scotlandwell Inn.

R14 **Blair Atholl**
☎(0796) 81407
Blair Atholl, Perthshire PH18 5TG.
On A9 5 miles N of Pitlochry.
Parkland course.
9 holes, 5710 yards, S.S.S.69
Founded 1894.
Visitors: welcome.
Green Fee: £7/day WD, £8/day WE.
Societies: bookings only.
Catering: bar snacks and meals.
Hotels: Atholl Arms.

R15 **Blairgowrie**
☎(0250) 2594, 2622
Rosemount, Blairgowrie, Perthshire PH10 6LG
A93 from Perth.
Moorland course.
Rosemount, 18 holes, 6588 yards, S.S.S.72; Lansdowne, 18 holes, 6895 yards, S.S.S.73; Wee, 9 holes, 2307 yards, S.S.S.32
Designed by James Braid, Thomas & Alliss, Peter Chalmers.
Founded 1889
Visitors: advance booking Mon, Tues, Thur; through starter Wed, Sat, Sun; no parties Wed, Sat, Sun.
Green Fee: £22/round, £33/day; WE £30/round.
Societies: Mon, Tue, Thur; book through (0250) 2622.
Catering: full facilities.
Hotels: Kinloch House; Rosemount Golf; Altamount House.

R16 **Bonnybridge**
☎(0324) 812645
Larbert Rd, Bonnybridge, Stirlingshire
On B816, 3 miles W of Falkirk.
Undulating moorland course.
9 holes, 6060 yards, S.S.S.69
Founded 1925
Visitors: with member only.
Green Fee: on application.
Catering: meals, limited in winter.

R17 **Braehead**
☎(0259) 722078
Cambus, by Alloa
On A907 on Stirling-Alloa road, about 1.5 miles W of Alloa.

Parkland/meadowland course.
18 holes, 6013 yards, S.S.S.69
Founded 1891
Visitors: welcome unrestricted, although advised to telephone starting time.
Green Fee: £10/round, £12/day WD; £15/round, £20/day WE.
Societies: Mon-Fri, prior booking required in writing.
Catering: April-Oct, lunch, high tea 7 days.
Hotels: Royal Oak; Dunmar House.

R18 Brechin
☎(03562) 2383
Trinity, by Brechin, Angus DD9 7PD
Take B966 out of Brechin toward Aberdeen, course is 1 mile from Brechin and is clearly signposted.
Parkland/meadowland course.
18 holes, 5267 yards, S.S.S.66
Designed by James Braid.
Founded 1893
Visitors: welcome at any time; restricted Wed (Ladies Day).
Green Fee: £10.20/round, £15.40/day WD; £12.30/round, £18.40/day WE.
Societies: write to Club Sec.
Catering: full catering and lounge bar refreshments.
Hotels: Northern; Glenesk; Panmure; Central.

R19 Bridge of Allan
☎(0786) 832332
Sunnlaw, Bridge of Allan, Stirling
3 miles N of Stirling, at bridge over River Allan, turn up hill for 1 mile.
Undulating course.
9 holes, 4932 yards, S.S.S.65
Founded 1895
Visitors: welcome weekdays & Sun.
Green Fee: £7 WD, £10 WE.
Catering: bar snacks at weekends and after 7.30pm weekdays.
Hotels: Royal.

R20 Buchanan Castle
☎(0360) 60369 Clubmaster
Drymen, Glasgow
Off A809, 17 miles NW of Glasgow.
Parkland course.
18 holes, 6086 yards, S.S.S.69
Designed by James Braid.
Founded 1936
Visitors: by arrangement (limited).
Green Fee: £18.50/round, £26/day.
Societies: by arrangement, phone Drymen (0360) 60307.
Catering: apply to Clubmaster.
Hotels: Buchanan Highland.

R21 Burntisland
☎(0592) 874093 Manager, 873247
Starter and Pro.
Dodhead, Burntisland, Fife
On B923, 0.5 mile E of Burntisland.
Moorland course.
18 holes, S.S.S.69
Redesigned by James Braid.
Founded 1897
Visitors: welcome; contact Pro for starting time.
Green Fee: on application.
Societies: catered for.
Catering: snacks and meals served.

R22 Caird Park
☎(0382) 453606
Mains Loan, Dundee, DD4 9BX
Via Kingsway to NE of town.
Parkland course.
18 holes, 6303 yards, S.S.S.70
Founded 1926
Visitors: welcome.
Green Fee: on application.
Catering: by arrangement.

R23 Callander
☎(0877) 30090 Clubhouse.
Aveland Rd, Callander, Perthshire FK17 8EN
A84 from Stirling, turn right at Roman Camp Hotel about 0.5 mile from Main St, club signposted.
Parkland course.
18 holes, 5125 yards, S.S.S.66
Designed by Tom Morris.
Founded 1890
Visitors: welcome any time.
Green Fee: £10/round, £15/day WD; £14/round, £19/day WE; jnrs half price.
Societies: welcome any time, contact Sec, phone 10am-1.30pm (0877) 30090, 2.30pm-9pm 30866.
Catering: full bar and catering daily.
Hotels: Abbotsford Lodge; Roman Camp; Dalgair House; The Coppice.

R24 Camperdown Municipal
☎(0382) 623398, 23141 bookings.
Camperdown Park, Dundee, Tayside
Coupar-Angus road, at Kingsway junction.
Championship parkland course.
18 holes, 6305 yards, S.S.S.72
Designed by Eric Brown.
Founded 1959
Visitors: bookings only.
Green Fee: £7.75 day ticket.
Societies: by arrangement.
Catering: bar facilities. Tennis.
Hotels: Swallow.

R25 Canmore
☎(0383) 724969
Venturefair Ave, Dunfermline, Fife
On A823, 1 mile N of Dunfermline.
Undulating parkland course.
18 holes, 5474 yards, S.S.S.66
Founded 1897
Visitors: welcome weekdays, Sat after 4pm.
Green Fee: on application.
Societies: welcome by prio arrangement.
Catering: full catering.

R26 Carnoustie
☎(0241) 53789 reservations, 53249 Starter
Links Parade, Carnoustie, Angus DD7 7JE
On A630, 12 miles E of Dundee.
Seaside course.
Championship, 18 holes, 6936 yards, S.S.S.74; Burnside, 18 holes, 6020 yards, S.S.S.69; Buddon Links, 18 holes, 5872 yards, S.S.S.68
Visitors: welcome with reservation, deposit required; h/cap certs required on Championship Course.
Green Fee: Championship, £31/round, £54/day; Burnside, £12/round, £20/day; Buddon Links, £7/round, £10/day; jnrs half-price; combination, 3-day and weekly tickets available.
Societies: by arrangement.
Catering: available.
Hotels: Brax; Glencoe; Station; Kinloch; Carlogie; Earlston.

R27 Comrie
☎(0764) 70055 clubhouse.
C/o Sec, Donald C. McGlashan, 10 Polinard, Comrie, Perthshire
On A85 6 miles W of Crieff.
Highland course.
9 holes, 5962 yards, S.S.S.69
Founded 1891
Visitors: welcome at all times.
Green Fee: £6 WD, £10 WE.
Societies: by arrangement with Sec.
Catering: coffee, light snacks during summer season.
Hotels: Comrie; Royal.

R28 Craigie Hill
☎(0738) 20829 Sec, 22644 Pro, 24377 Clubhouse
Cherrybank, Perth PH2 0NE
About 1 mile W of Perth, easy access from Stirling-Perth road.
Hilly course.
18 holes, 5739 yards, S.S.S.66
Founded 1911

Visitors: Mon to Fri unlimited; weekends telephone bookings.
Green Fee: on application.
Societies: weekdays and Sun.
Catering: full except Mon.

R29 Crail

☎(0333) 50278 Clubhouse, 50686 Sec, 50960 Pro.
Balcomie Clubhouse, Fifeness, Crail KY10 3XN
11 miles SE of St Andrews on A917.
Seaside links/parkland course.
18 holes, 5720 yards, S.S.S.68
Designed by Tom Morris.
Founded 1786
Visitors: welcomed, restrictions only on main competition days and members priority times.
Green Fee: £13.50/round, £19.50/day WD; £16.50/round, £24.50/day WE.
Societies: entertained as for visitors except 2nd half July and 1st half Aug.
Catering: full quality service.
Hotels: Balcomie Links; Marine (Crail); Craw's Nest (Anstruther).

R30 Crieff

☎(0764) 2909 bookings, 2397 office and catering, 2397 sec.
Perth Rd, Crieff, Perthshire PH7 3LR
From Edinburgh M9 to Dunblane; from Glasgow A80/M80/M9 to Dunblane then A9 for 5km and A822 to Crieff. Take A85 at town centre for 1km, course on left. From Perth A85, course at entry to Crieff on right.
Parkland course.
Ferntower, 18 holes, 6402 yards, S.S.S.71; Dornock, 9 holes, 2386 yards, S.S.S.63
Founded 1891
Visitors: welcome, advance booking advisable, must book for weekends.
Green Fee: Ferntower – £15/round, £25/day WD; £17/round WE.
Dornock – £10/round (18 holes) WD; £11/round (18 holes) WE.
Societies: welcome but must book well in advance.
Catering: full restaurant facilities, advisable to book; bar meals.
Hotels: Crieff Hydro; Murray Park; Arduthie.

R31 Cupar

☎(0334) 53549
Hilltarvit, Cupar
10 miles from St Andrews off A91.
Hillside/parkland course
9 holes, 5300 yards, S.S.S.65
Founded 1855

Visitors: welcome weekdays.
Green Fee: WD, £7/round, £9/day; WE, £9/round, £11/day.
Societies: weekdays and Sun.
Catering: lunches and high teas by arrangement.

R32 Dalmunzie

☎(025 085) 226
Spittal of Glenshee, Blairgowrie, Perthshire PH10 7QG
On A93 Blairgowrie-Braemar road 18 miles N of Blairgowrie, adjacent to Dalmunzie Hotel.
Undulating course.
9 holes, 2035 yards, S.S.S.60
Designed by Alister Mackenzie.
Founded 1922
Visitors: welcome any day.
Green Fee: £5/round (9 holes), £7/day.
Societies: please book, all welcome.
Catering: facilities in hotel.
Hotels: Dalmunzie House.

R33 Dollar

☎(0259) 42400
Brewlands House, Dollar, Clackmannanshire
On A91, 13 miles E of Stirling.
Hillside course.
18 holes, 5144 yards, S.S.S.66
Founded 1890
Visitors: welcome.
Green Fee: £6/round, £9/day WD; £12/day WE.
Societies: by arrangement.
Catering: meals daily except Tues.
Hotels: Castle Campbell.

R34 Downfield

☎(0382) 825595
Turnberry Ave, Dundee DD2 3QP
Turn off Kingsway into A923, 100 yards from roundabout turn right into Harrison Rd, 0.5 mile to clubhouse.
Parkland course.
18 holes, 6899 yards, S.S.S.73
Designed by C.K. Cotton.
Founded 1932
Visitors: weekdays 9.30-11.48am and 2.18-3.48pm; no jeans or T shirts in clubhouse.
Green Fee: £22/round, £33/day.
Societies: accepted at Committee's discretion.
Catering: available, book in advance.
Snooker.

R35 Dunblane New

☎(0786) 823711
Perth Rd, Dunblane FK15 0LJ

On old A9 at Fourways roundabout, 6 miles N of Stirling.
Parkland course.
18 holes, 5863 yards, S.S.S.68
Founded 1923
Visitors: welcome Mon-Fri (advisable to pre-book with Pro).
Green Fee: £15/round, £22/day.
Societies: Mon and Thurs only.
Catering: full bar and restaurant.
Tennis and squash adjacent.
Hotels: Dunblane Hydro; Stirling Arms.

R36 Dunfermline

☎(0383) 723534
Pitfirrane, Crossford, Dunfermline KY12 8QV
2 miles W of Dunfermline on road to Kincardine Bridge, A994.
Parkland course.
18 holes, 6237 yards, S.S.S.70
Designed by J.R. Stutt & Sons.
Founded 1887
Visitors: welcome Mon-Fri before 5pm subject to availability.
Green Fee: £25/day, £15/round.
Societies: welcome Mon-Fri by arrangement.
Catering: bar and restaurant.
Short 9 hole Par 3 course; snooker.
Hotels: Keavil; Pitfirran Arms; The Maltings.

R37 Dunkeld & Birnam

☎(03502) 524, 564 Sec.
Fungarth, Dunkeld, Perthshire PH8 0HY
1 mile N of Dunkeld on A923 Blairgowrie road.
Heathland course.
9 holes, 5264 yards, S.S.S.66
Founded 1892
Visitors: welcome.
Green Fee: on application.
Societies: catered for.
Catering: full facilities.

R38 Dunnikier Park

☎(0592) 261599
Dunnikier Way, Kirkcaldy, Fife KY1 3LP
N boundary of town.
Parkland course.
18 holes, 6601 yards, S.S.S.72
Founded 1963
Visitors: no restrictions.
Green Fee: £7.20/round WD, £9.60/round WE.
Societies: on application to Sec.
Catering: full catering facilities available.
Hotels: Dunnikier House.

39 Dunning
☎(076 484) 398 Treasurer
Rollo Park, Dunning, Perth
Off A9, 9 miles SW of Perth.
Parkland course.
9 holes, 4836 yards, S.S.S.64
Visitors: welcome.
Green Fee: on application.
Societies: by arrangement.
Catering: at Dunning Hotel.

R40 Edzell
☎(03564) 235
High St, Edzell, by Brechin, Angus
DD9 7TF
A94 Forfar-Aberdeen road, turn onto
B966 at end of Brechin by-pass, golf
course on left past arch at entrance
to village.
Undulating moorland course.
18 holes, 6299 yards, S.S.S.70
Founded 1895
Visitors: welcome.
Green Fee: £14/round, £21/day WD;
£18/round, £27/day WE.
Societies: by arrangement with Sec.
Catering: full meal and bar service.
Hotels: Glenesk; Central; Panmure
Arms.

R41 Elie
☎(0333) 330301 Sec, 330327
Clubhouse
Golf House Club, Elie, Leven, Fife KY9
1AS
12 miles from St Andrews on A915, 6
miles from Leven on A917.
Seaside links course.
18 holes, 6241 yards, S.S.S.70
Founded 1875
Visitors: welcome.
Green Fee: £16/round, £24/day WD;
£22/round, £32/day WE.
Societies: by arrangement with Sec;
not June, July, Aug, public holidays
or weekends.
Catering: lunch, soups, sandwiches,
high tea if arranged with Steward.
Hotels: Craw's Nest; Old Manor; Golf.

R42 Elie Sports Club
☎(0333) 330955
Elie, Fife KY9 1AG
10 miles S of St Andrews on A917.
Seaside course.
9 holes, 5800 yards, S.S.S.64
Visitors: welcome.
Green Fee: on application.
Societies: by arrangement.
Catering: meals served.
Tennis, bowling, putting.
Hotels: Victoria; Craw's Nest;
Smugglers Inn.

R43 Falkirk
☎(0324) 611061, 612219
136 Stirling Rd, Falkirk FK2 7YP
1.5 miles W of Falkirk centre on A9.
Parkland course.
18 holes, 6282 yards, S.S.S.69
Founded 1922
Visitors: weekdays only to 4pm; not
Sat/Sun.
Green Fee: £8/round, £15/day.
Societies: not Wed or Sat; £15 WD,
£20 Sun.
Catering: full facilities.
Hotels: Stakis Park; Norwood; Red
Lion.

R44 Falkirk Tryst
☎(0324) 562415
86 Burnhead Rd, Larbert FK5 4BD
3 miles NW of Falkirk on outskirts of
Stenhousemuir, close to A9, 0.75
mile from Larbert Station.
Flat links course.
18 holes, 6053 yards, S.S.S.69
Founded 1885
Visitors: no unintroduced visitors
Sat or Wed.
Green Fee: £8.50/round,
£13.50/day.
Societies: Mon, Tues, Thurs and Fri
only.
Catering: full facilities.
Hotels: Red Lion; Commercial; Park.

R45 Falkland
☎(0337) 57404
The Myre, Falkland, Cupar, Fife KY7
7AA
In The Howe of Fife near to villages of
Freuchie and Auchtermuchty.
Parkland course
9 holes, 5216 yards, S.S.S.65
Founded 1976
Visitors: all welcome.
Green Fee: £6/day WD, £8/day WE.
Societies: by prior arrangement.
Catering: morning coffee, lunch,
high tea available by arrangement;
bar lunchtime and summer evenings
and weekends; restricted in winter.

R46 Forfar
☎(0307) 62120
Cunninghill, Arbroath Rd, by Forfar,
Angus DD8 2RL
1 mile from town on road to Arbroath.
Undulating moorland course.
18 holes, 5497 yards, S.S.S.69
Designed by James Braid.
Founded 1871
Visitors: welcome.
Green Fee: £12/round, £18/day WD;
£20 Sun.

Societies: welcome by arrangement
with Sec.
Catering: meals served.
Hotels: Royal.

R47 Glenalmond
☎(073 888) 270
Glenalmond, Perthshire, Tayside
Moorland course.
9 holes, 2900 yards, S.S.S.68
Founded 1923
Visitors: members only.

R48 Glenbervie
☎(0324) 562605
Stirling Rd, Larbert, Stirlingshire FK5
4SJ
On A9 between Falkirk and Stirling.
Parkland course.
18 holes, 6469 yards, S.S.S.71
Designed by James Braid.
Founded 1932
Visitors: no visitors at weekends.
Green Fee: on application.
Societies: Tues and Thurs.
Catering: lunches, high teas, dinner.
Hotels: Park (Falkirk).

R49 Gleneagles Hotel
☎(07646) 3543
Auchterarder, Perthshire PH3 1NF
Half way between Perth and Stirling
on A9.
Undulating moorland courses.
Kings, 18 holes, 6452 yards,
S.S.S.71; Queens; 18 holes, 5964
yards, S.S.S.69; Glendevon, 18
holes, 5719 yards, S.S.S.68; Princes,
18 holes, 4664 yards, S.S.S.64
Designed by James Braid (Kings and
Queens courses).
Founded 1908
Green Fee: £35/round.
Societies: welcome if resident.
Catering: meals and snacks; 4
restaurants and bars.
9 hole Par 3 course; Country Club;
health spa; clay target shooting
school; equestrian centre;
Hotels: Gleneagles.

R50 Glenrothes
☎(0592) 758686
Golf Course Rd, Glenrothes, Fife KY6
2LA
W end of town 8 miles from M90.
Public, undulating parkland course.
18 holes, 6449 yards, S.S.S.71
Designed by J.R. Stutt.
Founded 1958
Visitors: no restrictions; parties of
12 + to book in advance through Sec.

Green Fee: £7.20/round WD, £9.70/round WE.
Societies: by arrangement with Sec 1 month in advance, min 15 max 40.
Catering: all types of catering available 7 days.
Hotels: Forum; Stakis Albany; Rescobie; Balgedie; Balbirnie.

R51 Grangemouth
☎(0324) 711500
Polmonthill, Polmont, Stirlingshire FK2 0YA
M9 junction 4, follow signpost to Polmont Hill.
Public parkland course.
18 holes, 6,330 yards, S.S.S.71
Designed by Sportwork.
Founded 1973
Visitors: welcome.
Green Fee: WD £6/round, £9/day; WE £8/round £11/day.
Societies: by arrangement.
Catering: meals by arrangement.
Hotels: Inchrya Grange; Lea Park

R52 Green Hotel
☎(0577) 63467 Hotel, 62237 Club
Green Hotel, Kinross KY13 7AS
On M90 between Edinburgh and Perth.
Parkland course.
Red, 18 holes, 6257 yards, S.S.S.70; Blue, 18 holes, 6456 yards, S.S.S.71
Visitors: welcome.
Green Fee: £12/round, £18/day WD; £18/round, £25/day WE.
Societies: by arrangement.
Catering: meals served.
Hotels: Green.

R53 Killin
☎(05672) 312
Killin, Perthshire FK21
On outskirts of village on Aberfeldy road going E.
Parkland course.
9 holes, 2508 yards, S.S.S.65
Designed by John Duncan of Stirling.
Founded 1913
Visitors: welcome all week.
Green Fee: £8/round, £12/day.
Societies: April, May, June, Sept.
Catering: bar, meals and snacks.
Hotels: Bridge of Lochay; Killin; Falls of Dochart.

R54 King James VI
☎(0738) 32460 and 25170
Moncrieffe Island, Perth PH2 8NR
On an island in centre of Perth (River Tay); across footbridge (15 min walk).

Parkland course.
18 holes, 5661 yards, S.S.S.68
Founded 1858
Visitors: welcome; not Sat.
Green Fee: £11.50/round, £17 day WD; £23 day, £11.50 after 4pm Sun.
Societies: by arrangement.
Catering: yes.

R55 Kinghorn
☎(0592) 890345
Macduff Crescent, Kinghorn, Fife KY3 9RE
Off A92 3 miles W of Kirkcaldy (A921).
Municipal undulating links course.
18 holes, 5269 yards, S.S.S.67
Layout recommended by Tom Morris.
Founded 1887
Visitors: welcome, parties by arrangement in writing.
Green Fee: £7 WD, £9.40 WE.
Societies: as for visiting parties.
Catering: full catering by arrangement, snacks at weekends.
Hotels: Kingswood; Longboat.

R56 Kirkcaldy
☎(0592) 260370
Balwearie Rd, Kirkcaldy, Fife KY2 5LT
On A92 at W end of town.
Parkland course.
18 holes, 6004 yards, S.S.S.70
Founded 1904
Visitors: welcome except Sat.
Green Fee: £12/round, £18/day WD; £15/round, £21/day WE.
Societies: any day except Tues, Sat.
Catering: full catering every day.
Hotels: Parkway.

R57 Kirriemuir
☎(0575) 72604
Northmuir, Kirriemuir, Angus
1 mile N of town centre.
Heathland/parkland course.
18 holes, 5591 yards, S.S.S.67
Designed by James Braid.
Founded 1907
Visitors: weekdays only.
Green Fee: £14.50/day, £8/round after 4pm
Societies: can be booked weekdays.
Catering: full catering at clubhouse.
Hotels: Dykehead; Ogilvy Arms; Airlie Arms; Thrums Hotel.

R58 Ladybank
☎(0337) 30814 Sec, 30725 Starter
Annsmuir, Ladybank, Fife KY7 7RA
6 miles W of Cupar on main Kirkcaldy to Dundee road.

Moorland course.
18 holes, 6641 yards, S.S.S.72
Designed by Tom Morris.
Founded 1879
Visitors: at any time (Sat excepted)
Green Fee: on application.
Societies: by arrangement with Sec.
Catering: full catering services.
Hotels: Fernie Castle; Lomond Hills.

R59 Leslie
Balsillie, Leslie, Fife KY6 3EZ
Undulating course.
9 holes, 4940 yards, S.S.S.64
Founded 1898
Visitors: welcome.
Green Fee: on application.
Hotels: Rothes Oak; Station; Greenside.

R60 Letham Grange
☎(024 189) 373
Letham Grange, Colliston, by Arbroath, Angus DD11 4RL
A92 Dundee to Arbroath, at Arbroath take A933 to Brechin, at Colliston (4 miles) turn right, signposted.
Parkland/woodland course.
18 holes, 6789 yards, S.S.S.73
Designed by Donald Steel & G.K. Smith.
Founded 1985
Visitors: welcome.
Green Fee: on application.
Societies: by arrangement.
Catering: bars and restaurants within hotel.
Hotels: Letham Grange.

R61 Leven
☎(0333) 26096
Links Rd, Leven, Fife KY8 4HS
Travel E along Promenade, turn left into Church Rd, turn right into Links Rd, clubhouse at end of road on right.
Seaside course.
18 holes, 6434 yards, S.S.S.71
Founded 1820
Visitors: welcome weekdays but some restrictions at weekends; for parties of 12 or under phone Leven (0333) 21390, over 12 phone 23509.
Green Fee: £16/round, £22/day WD; £20/round, £30/day WE.
Societies: contact Mr B Jackson, Links Secretary, c/o Starters Box, Leven Links, Promenade, Leven, Fife (0333) 23509.
Catering: full meals at any time, bar snacks etc.
Snooker table.
Hotels: Old Manor; Lundin Links; Caledonian.

R62 Lochgelly
☎(0592) 780174
Cartmore Rd, Lochgelly, Fife
On A910 2 miles NE of Cowdenbeath.
Parkland course.
18 holes, 5768 yards, S.S.S.67
Founded 1911
Visitors: welcome.
Green Fee: on application.
Catering: facilities available.

R63 Lundin
☎(0333) 320202, 320051 Pro
Golf Rd, Lundin Links, Fife KY8 6BA
14 mile E of Kirkcaldy, 3 miles from
Leven.
Seaside course.
18 holes, 6377 yards, S.S.S.71
Designed by James Braid.
Founded 1857
Visitors: Mon-Fri 9am-3pm,
booking system operates; Sat only
after 2.30pm.
Green Fee: £16.50/round, £24/day
WD; £20/round Sat.
Catering: during playing season
Mon-Fri.
Hotels: Old Manor, Lundin Links.

R64 Lundin Ladies
☎(0333) 320832, 320022
Woodielea Road, Lundin Links, Fife
KY8 6AR
On N side of A915 in middle of Lundin
Links (100 yards W of Lundin Links
Hotel).
Short, challenging, parkland course.
9 holes, 4730 yards, S.S.S.67 (LGU
criteria)
Designed by James Braid.
Founded 1891
Visitors: welcome; Wed in summer
may be difficult (medal).
Green Fee: £6 WD, £7.50 WE.
Societies: tee booking through Sec
for parties.

R65 Milnathort
☎(0577) 64069
South St, Milnathort, Tayside KY13
2AW
Off M90 1.5 miles N of Kinross.
Parkland course.
9 holes, 5411 yards, S.S.S.68
Founded 1890
Visitors: welcome except on
competition days.
Green Fee: £8/day WD, £12/day WE.
Societies: welcome by prior
arrangement with Hon. Sec.
Catering: meals and snacks
available.
Hotels: Royal; Thistle.

R66 Monifieth
☎(0382) 532767
c/o Sec, J.A.R. Fraser, 64 Strathern
Rd, Broughty Ferry, Dundee DD5 1PH
6/7 miles E of Dundee along A930 to
Monifieth High St; signposted to golf
courses thereafter.
Seaside courses.
Medal, 18 holes, 6657 yards,
S.S.S.72; Ashludie, 18 holes, 5123
yards, S.S.S.66
Visitors: welcome by arrangement
with Starter; Sat after 2pm; Sun after
10am; party bookings through Sec.
Green Fee: Medal, £16/round, £24/
day WD; £17/round, £27/day Sun:
Ashludie, £10/round, £15/day WD;
£11/round, £16.50/day Sun.
Societies: welcome by arrangement
with Sec, subject to weekend
restrictions as above.
Catering: every day.
Hotels: Panmure.

R67 Montrose Links Trust
☎(0674) 72932
Traill Drive, Montrose, Angus DD10
8SW
Off A92 Dundee-Aberdeen road, 1
mile from town centre.
Seaside courses.
Medal, 18 holes, 6443 yards,
S.S.S.71; Broomfield, 18 holes, 4815
yards, S.S.S.66
Founded 1810
Visitors: welcome.
Green Fee: Medal, £16/day, £10/
round WD; £21/day, £13.50/round
WE: Broomfield, £9/day, £6/round
WD; £11.50/day, £9/round WE.
Societies: welcome.
Catering: can be arranged in one of
the member Golf Clubs (Royal Albert
GC, phone (0674) 72376).
Hotels: Park (offers golfing package
holidays); Links; George.

R68 Muckhart
☎(025 981) 423
Drumburn Rd, Muckhart, Dollar,
Clackmannanshire FK14 7JH
Lies between A91 and A823 S of
Muckhart, signposted.
Undulating moorland course.
18 holes, 6192 yards, S.S.S.70
Founded 1908
Visitors: welcome, phone call
advisable at weekends.
Green Fee: £10/round, £15/day WD;
£15/round, £20/day WE.
Societies: daily, contact Clubmaster.
Catering: lunches every day,
evening meals by arrangement.
Hotels: B&B on perimeter of course.

R69 Murrayshall
☎(0738) 51171, 52784 Pro Shop
Scone, Perthshire PH2 7PH
Signposted off A94 Perth/Coupar
Angus, 4 miles from Perth centre.
Parkland course.
18 holes, 6420 yards, S.S.S.71
Designed by J. Hamilton Stutt.
Founded 1981
Visitors: no restrictions.
Green Fee: £22.50/round, £35/day
WD; £27.50/round, £45/day WE.
Societies: welcome by prior
arrangement.
Catering: full clubhouse catering.
Tennis, bowls, croquet.
Hotels: Murrayshall House on course
(award-winning restaurant).

R70 Muthill
☎(0764) 3319 Sec, (076 481) 523
Clubhouse
Peat Rd, Muthill, Crieff PH5 2AD
500 yards off Stirling-Crieff road
A822, signposted at foot of road at W
end of village.
Parkland course.
9 holes, 2371 yards, S.S.S.63
Founded 1935
Visitors: restricted evenings and
club match days.
Green Fee: £7 WD, £10 WE.
Societies: not encouraged.
Hotels: Drummond Arms.

R71 North Inch
☎(0738) 39911 Council, 36481
Starter
c/o Perth & Kinross District Council,
Old Council Chambers, 3 High Street,
Perth PH1 5JU
On open space to N of central Perth,
adjacent to Gannochy Trust Sports
Complex.
Public course, tree- and river-lined
parkland.
18 holes, 5178 yards, S.S.S.65
Tom Morris involved in original
design.
18 holes since 1927
Visitors: pay as you play policy.
Green Fee: up to £5.40 depending
on season/day.
Societies: in summer, tee
occasionally reserved for local clubs.
Catering: adjacent sports complex.

R72 Panmure
☎(0241) 53120
Burnside Road, Barry, Angus DD7 7RT
Off A930, 2 miles W of Carnoustie.
Seaside course.
18 holes, 6317 yards, S.S.S.70

St Andrews

Golfers go to St Andrews as Moslems flock to Mecca, Mormons descend on Salt Lake City and Roman Catholics gather in St Peter's Square. It is as much a shrine as any religious centre, indeed, its symbolic importance grows more not less.

Every golf course in the world owes something to the Old course; whether by accident or design, it embraces nearly all the elements on which sound, traditional golf-course architecture is based. In discussing the qualifications for an architect long ago, Tom Simpson said that, 'Above everything else, he must understand the message of the Old course'.

Some architects have even gone to the lengths of building replicas of some of the holes. Charles Blair Macdonald, a figure of enormous influence in shaping golf in America, repaid his love of St Andrews by building a course on the lines of the old, classic links at The National Golf Links of America on Long Island. Among the holes he built were copies of St Andrews 11th and 17th. Augusta's 4th hole also bears more than a little resemblance to St Andrews' 11th. They are fine holes but, however much of a compliment they may be, the best holes are always those which owe nothing to imitation and everything to Nature.

Modern machinery has simplified golf course architecture in the sense that nothing is now impossible. However it has allowed some architects to drift away from the age-old tenets which St Andrews holds dear. This syndrome is typified by greens in the middle of lakes, huge carries to greens, enormous bunkers shaped like eccentric jig-saw pieces, and railway sleepers by the train load. Television and resort developers are largely to blame for this 'stadium golf'.

Horror-provoking stretches of water, roller-coaster fairways and penal hollows make only the publicity men happy. Golf, even professional golf, is played for pleasure and there is no pleasure in losing ball after ball or feeling that the impossible is being attempted.

However, there are signs that sanity is being restored. The 1986 US Open at Shinnecock Hills brought forth *cris de coeur* from such players as Lee Trevino, Hale Irwin, David Graham and Jack Renner. Shinnecock is one of the oldest courses in the America, the Club in fact, being the first to be 'formalised' in the United States. Everyone liked the course for different reasons. Trevino saw Shinnecock's greatness in the fact that it favoured no particular group of players. Graham liked the idea that it allowed you to hit the ball low with the chance to run the ball on to the green, if you wanted to. It gave the player desirable options, and made a break from the all-or-nothing shots typical of many new courses.

Curtis Strang endorsed this view a year later, following his record breaking 62 over the Old course in the 1987 Dunhill Cup, when he declared 'They should come to St Andrews and be reminded what traditional design is all about'.

Maybe the developments in course architecture in the last few years are part of a passing phase. Fashion exists in golf course architecture just as it does in clothes, motor cars or buildings but golf courses are more permanent. It needs visits to St Andrews to understand that simplicity is the best basic art and that the game is better when the player has to formulate his strategy on the tee, choosing how to play a hole from as many as four or five options.

Often the fairways appear to have no limits but positional play is a vital ingredient at St Andrews. You must always think at least a shot ahead — although St Andrews offers a wide choice of courses, too. The New, the Eden and a Jubilee course, which has recently been substantially upgraded, are splendid foils for the Old. In a few years, there will be a Strathtyrum, a remodelled Balgove and excellent practice facilities which, alas have been lacking for too long.

St Andrews is planning for the future, not just living in the past, but it needs a shrewd mind to understand that what one might term traditional architecture is still the best and St Andrews is still its most faithful standard-bearer.

Founded 1845
Visitors: welcome except Sat.
Green Fee: on application.
Societies: by arrangement.
Catering: snacks served; meals except Mon.
Hotels: Glencoe; Carlogie; Woodlands.

R73 Pitlochry

☎(0796) 2792 Pro and Starter
Golf Course Rd, Pitlochry
A9 to Pilochry, then via Atholl Rd, Larchwood Rd, and Golf Course Rd.
Hill course.
18 holes, 5811 yards, S.S.S.68
Designed by Willie Fernie of Troon, modernised by Cecil Hutchinson.
Founded 1908
Visitors: welcome.
Green Fee: on application.
Societies: welcome by arrangement with Estate Office (0796) 2114.
Catering: meals and snacks served, breakfast and dinner by arrangement with Steward (0796) 2334.

R74 Pitreavie (Dunfermline)

☎(0383) 722591, 723151 Pro.
Queensferry Rd, Dunfermline, Fife KY11 5PR
From A90(M) turn off for Dunfermline to join A823, course half way between Rosyth and Dunfermline on E side of dual carriageway.
Undulating parkland course.
18 holes, 6086 yards, S.S.S.69
Designed by Dr Mackenzie of Leeds.
Founded 1923
Visitors: welcome every day; parties and societies must reserve in advance; small parties can reserve tees through Pro.
Green Fee: £12/round, £18/day WD; £22/day WE (no round tickets at WE).
Societies: must be reserved in advance through Sec.
Catering: full catering facilities, parties to be booked in advance.
Hotels: King Malcolm (Thistle Inns); Pitbauchlie House.

R75 Polmont

☎(0324) 711277
Manuelrigg Maddiston, by Falkirk, Stirlingshire
4 miles S of Falkirk, 1st right after Central Region Fire Brigade HQ.
Undulating parkland course.
9 holes, 3044 yards, S.S.S.69
Founded Old 1904, New 1976
Visitors: welcome, not on Sat.

Green Fee: £4/round WD, £7 Sun; £2.50/round with member.
Societies: by arrangement.
Catering: full catering by arrangement with Sec.
Hotels: Inchyra Grange; Polmont.

R76 St Andrews

☎(0334) 75757 (all courses)
St Andrews Links Management Committee, Pilmour Cottage, St Andrews, Fife KY16 9JA
60 miles N of Edinburgh via A91 to St Andrews; by rail to Leuchars on Edinburgh-Dundee main line.
Public seaside courses.
Catering: available in nearby hotels; temporary membership of St Andrews Golf Club (0334 73107) permits use of clubhouse facilities to male members of properly constituted clubs (£2/day, £10/week).
Hotels: full range in St Andrews from B&B to 4-star international standard.

Old Course
18 holes, 6566 yards, S.S.S.72
Founded circa 1400
Visitors: welcome except Sun; only with letter of introduction or h/cap cert.
Green Fee: on application.
Societies: welcome.

New Course
18 holes, 6604 yards, S.S.S.72
Founded 1896
Visitors: welcome.
Green Fee: on application.
Societies: welcome.

Jubilee Course
18 holes, 6805 yards, S.S.S.72
Founded 1897
Visitors: welcome.
Green Fee: on application.
Societies: welcome.

Eden Course
18 holes, 6400 yards, S.S.S.70
Founded 1914
Visitors: welcome.
Green Fee: on application.
Societies: welcome.

Balgove Course
9 holes
Founded 1974
Visitors: welcome.
Green Fee: on application.
Societies: welcome.

R77 St Fillans

☎(0764) 85312
South Loch Earn Rd, St Fillans, Perthshire PH6 2NG
12 miles W of Crieff on A85 to Crianlarich.
Parkland course.
9 holes, 5268 yards, S.S.S.68
Designed by James Braid.
Founded 1903
Visitors: welcome any day.
Green Fee: £5 (9 holes), £8 (18 holes), £12/day WD; £7 (9 holes), £10 (18 holes), £14/day WE & BH.
Societies: any time except July and Aug (max 16).
Catering: unlicensed, snacks and light meals available.
Hotels: Achray House; Four Seasons; Drummond Arms; Comrie. Weekly holiday tickets, 5 9-hole courses £35.

R78 St Michaels

☎(033 483) 365
Leuchars, St Andrews, Fife
On A919 6 miles from St Andrews and Dundee, at W end of Leuchars village turn over railway bridge about 200 yards out of village.
Undulating parkland course.
9 holes, 5510 yards, S.S.S.68
Founded 1903
Visitors: welcome except Sun before 1pm.
Green Fee: on application.
Societies: welcome except Sun am by prior arrangement with Sec.
Catering: bar and lounge facilities, meals available except Wed.

R79 Saline

☎(0383) 852591
Kinneddar Hill, Saline, Fife KY12 9UN
Exit 4 on M90 travel 7 miles on B914 to Dollar 5 miles NW of Dunfermline.
Hillside course.
9 holes, 5302 yards, S.S.S.66
Founded 1912
Visitors: welcome without restriction except Sats April-Oct.
Green Fee: £7 WD, £10 Sunday.
Societies: weekdays and most Sun.
Catering: bar, snacks all day, full catering by prior arrangement.
Hotels: Saline; Castle Campbell.

R80 Scoonie

☎(0333) 27057
North Links, Leven, Fife KY8 4SP
10 miles SW of St Andrews.
Public flat parkland course.
18 holes, 4967 metres, S.S.S.66
Founded 1951

Visitors: welcome by letter to Sec, except Thurs and Sat.
Green Fee: £3.20 WD (OAPs £0.75), £4.40 WE (OAPs £1.10).
Societies: welcome by appointment, letter to Sec, min 12 max 30.
Catering: bar, snacks and full meals.

R81 Scotscraig
☎(0382) 552515
Golf Rd, Tayport, Fife DD6 9DZ
On B946 3 miles from S end of Tay Road Bridge, turn left 3rd street past petrol station.
Links/seaside course.
18 holes, 6496 yards, S.S.S.71
Founded 1817
Visitors: welcome weekdays and by arrangement at weekends.
Green Fee: on application.
Societies: welcome by arrangement.
Catering: meals served except Tues.
Hotels: Seymour; Pinewoods.

R82 Stirling
☎(0786) 64098
Queens Rd, Stirling FK8 2QY
1 mile W of town centre on A811.
Parkland course.
18 holes, 6400 yards, S.S.S.71
Designed by James Braid/Henry Cotton.
Founded 1869
Visitors: welcome weekdays, weekends on application.
Green Fee: £15.50/round, £21.50/day WD.
Societies: weekdays only.
Catering: full bar and restaurant. Pool table.
Hotels: Garfield; Golden Lion.

R83 Strathendrick
☎(0360) 40582 Sec.
Glasgow Rd, Drymen, Stirlingshire
17 miles NW of Glasgow off A809.
Hilly moorland course.
9 holes, 4962 yards, S.S.S.65
Founded 1901
Visitors: with member only.

R84 Taymouth Castle
☎(08873) 228
Kenmore, by Aberfeldy, Tayside
PH15 2NT
6 miles W of Aberfeldy, large sign by castle gates on right of road.
Fairly flat parkland course.
18 holes, 6066 yards, S.S.S.69
Designed by James Braid.
Founded 1923
Visitors: unlimited, booking required.
Green Fee: on application.
Societies: welcome.
Catering: full catering, bar open all day from 11am.
Hotels: Kenmore; Fortingall; Weem; Coshieville.

R85 Thornton
☎(0592) 771111
Station Rd, Thornton, Fife KY1 4DW
1 mile E of A92 through Thornton.
Parkland course.
18 holes, 6177 yards, S.S.S.69
Founded 1921
Visitors: welcome.
Green Fee: £10/round, £15/day WD; £15/round, £22/day WE.
Societies: catered for.
Catering: lunches, snacks, high teas.
Hotels: Crown; Albany.

R86 Tillicoultry
☎(0259) 50124
Alva Rd, Tillicoultry, FK13 6BL
9 miles E of Stirling on A91.
Undulating meadowland course.
9 holes, 5266 yards, S.S.S.66
Designed by Peter Robertson, Braids Hill G.C. Edinburgh.
Founded 1899
Visitors: welcome weekdays, weekends by arrangement; restrictions on juniors (under 15).
Green Fee: £6/round, £8/day WD; £8/round, £10/day WE.
Societies: by prior arrangement, contact Sec, R. Whitehead, 12 Stalker Ave, Tillicoultry, FK13 6EY, telephone (0259) 50124 or 51337 (home).
Catering: bar meals April-Sept; catering for parties by prior arrangement.
Hotels: Castle Craig.

R87 Tulliallan
☎(0259) 30396
Alloa Rd, Kincardine on Forth, by Alloa
1.5 miles N of Kincardine Bridge on Alloa road, course situated next to Police College.
Parkland course.
18 holes, 5982 yards, S.S.S.69
Founded 1902
Visitors: welcome by arrangement with Pro.
Green Fee: on application.
Societies: welcome by prior arrangement except Sat; weekdays max 40, Sun max 30.
Catering: available, meals and snacks served.

HIGHLANDS, GRAMPIAN

By far the fastest and most convenient road to Inverness is the much improved A9 which has no sooner bade farewell to Perth than it has, it seems, found Aviemore beckoning. The scenery along the way outshines even the postcards and calendars, although it is one journey in Scotland in which golf takes a back seat.

There are one or two courses that might tempt a stopover. Blair Atholl, Pitlochry and, on reaching Aviemore, Boat of Garten, an authentic classic in the short course mould. There has been a course of some sort at Boat of Garten for a hundred years, but it was the handiwork of James Braid which, by extending it to 18 holes, really put it on the map.

But the ardent connoisseur, who has had his card marked properly, will undoubtedly opt for the east coast route starting in Aberdeen and working north round Buchan Ness and then west along the Moray Firth to Inverness.

It will, in fact, be hard getting away from Aberdeen after acquaintance with Royal Aberdeen, with its valleyed fairways between dunes and an awareness that the Club, founded in 1780, is one of the oldest in the world. The nearby Kings Links is one of the country's busiest courses, while Murcar, which rubs shoulders with Royal Aberdeen, has a lot in common with its distinguished neighbour, although a number of holes in the second half occupy a lofty perch that marks a change in character.

A few miles to the north, Cruden Bay represents the model links with mountainous dunes and resplendent views worthy of comparison alongside Turnberry, Tralee and Pebble Beach. In prewar days, it had a luxury hotel, a railway link with the south and a glowing reputation. The hotel and public railway have disappeared but its reputation remains undimmed, an example of ingenuity guiding shotmaking and one or two old-fashioned blind shots that undoubtedly enhance that reputation.

All these courses deserve a long look, but time is often pressing and many good things lie ahead notably Peterhead, Fraserburgh, the Moray Club at Lossiemouth and Nairn, once known freely as the Brighton of the North. As with Cruden Bay, the scenic quality of Moray and Nairn is a major part of their attraction. Nairn opens with a number of holes along the shore but both have housed their championships and left their would-be conquerors suitably contrite and chastened.

Nairn lies close to Inverness Airport, providing easier access from London for those whose sights are set on Dornoch and who haven't the time to indulge in leisurely detours. It would be wrong to say that the aeroplane has been responsible for the discovery of Dornoch because its praises have been sung by many, not least Roger and Joyce Wethered who knew a thing or two about good courses.

However, it is perfectly true to say that the fashion for visiting Dornoch has grown significantly in the last 30 years particularly among Americans curious to see where Donald Ross, the most famous American golf course architect, was born, and what it was about the ancient links that influenced his work so enormously. This is not an attempt to betray the secret, simply a laying of the scent and an assurance that bridges over the Cromarty and Dornoch Firth have shortened the approach from Inverness.

Nor is Dornoch the end of the northern rainbow. It certainly lives up to its star billing but nearby Golspie is decidedly pleasant if less severe and Brora, a creation of James Braid, where the insomniac golfer can play in the famous midnight competition in June, provides the perfect foil for anyone seeking relief from trying to tame Dornoch. Even true lovers of art cannot look at one masterpiece all the time.

S1 Abernethy
☎(047 982) 350
Nethybridge, Inverness-shire
On B970 Grantown-on-Spey/Coylum
Bridge road, 0.25 mile N of
Nethybridge.
Undulating course.
9 holes, 2484 yards, S.S.S.66
Founded 1893
Visitors: welcome.
Green Fee: on application.
Societies: by arrangement.
Catering: meals served.
Hotels: Nethybridge; Mountview;
Heatherbrae.

S2 Aboyne
☎(03398) 86328
Formaston Park, Aboyne, AB3 5HD
Travelling W on A93 from Aberdeen,
take 1st turning on right after
entering village, signposted on A93.
Undulating parkland course.
18 holes, 5330 yards, S.S.S.66
Founded 1883
Visitors: welcome.
Green Fee: on application.
Societies: welcome except Sun.
Catering: full catering service
available April-Oct.
Hotels: Charleston Hotel; Balnacoil
House; Birse Lodge.

S3 Alness
☎(0349) 883877
Ardross Rd, Alness, Ross-shire
On A9 10 miles N of Dingwall.
9 holes, 4718 yards, S.S.S.63
Designed by John Sutherland.
Founded 1904
Visitors: welcome at any time.
Green Fee: on application.
Catering: can be arranged.

S4 Askernish
Lochboisdale, Askernish, South Uist,
Western Isles
5 miles NW of Lochboisdale, ferry
terminal from Oban.
Seaside course.
9 holes, 5371 yards, S.S.S.61
Designed by Tom Morris.
Founded 1891
Visitors: welcome.
Green Fee: £5/day.
Societies: welcome.
Hotels: Borrodale; Lochboisdale.

S5 Auchenblae
☎(05617) 8869
Auchenblae, Laurencekirk,
Kincardineshire AB30 1BU.
2 miles off A94 W of Fordoun.
Parkland course.
9 holes, 2174 yards, S.S.S.30
Visitors: welcome anytime; Wed and
Fri competition nights for members
so restricted 5.30-9pm.
Green Fee: £5 WD, £6 Sat; £6.50
Sun; jnrs and OAPs half-price.
Catering: local shop selling golf
balls, snacks etc.
Hotels: Drumtochty Arms.

S6 Auchmill
☎(0224) 714577
Auchmill, Aberdeen
5 miles N of Aberdeen.
Municipal course.
9 holes, S.S.S.35
Visitors: all welcome.
Green Fee: on application.

S7 Ballater
☎(03397) 55567 Sec, 55658 Pro.
Victoria Rd, Ballater, AB3 5QX
A93 on Deeside, 42 miles W of
Aberdeen, 62 miles from Perth.
Open flat, moorland course.
18 holes, 5638 yards, S.S.S.69
Designed by James Braid.
Founded 1891
Visitors: welcome, book weekends
and certain days during summer.
Green Fee: £12/round, £18/2 rounds
WD; £14/round, £19/2 rounds WE;
jnrs (under 18) half adult rate.
Societies: welcome by arrangement
with Sec.
Catering: full catering.
Putting green, tennis, snooker,
bowls.

S8 Balnagask
☎(0224) 876407, 871286 (Nigg Bay
GC)
St Fitticks Rd, Balnagask, Aberdeen
2 miles SE of city centre.
Public seaside course.
18 holes, 5986 yards, S.S.S.69
Designed by Hawtree & Son.
Founded 1955
Visitors: welcome.
Green Fee: on application.
Societies: by arrangement.
Catering: apply to Council.

S9 Banchory
☎(03302) 2365, 2447 reservations
Kinneskie Rd, Banchory,
Kincardineshire AB31 3TA
18 miles W of Aberdeen, on North
Deeside road; 100 yards SW of
Banchory shopping centre.
Parkland course.
18 holes, 5284 yards, Par 67
Founded 1905
Visitors: welcome, no introduction
necessary.
Green Fee: £15/day WD, £17 WE.
Societies: welcome by prior
arrangement Mon, Tues, Wed, Fri
only.
Catering: full bar and restaurant.
Hotels: Tor-na-coille; Burnett Arms;
Banchory Lodge; Invery House;
Raemoir House.

S10 Boat of Garten
☎(047 983) 282 Golf Shop
Boat of Garten, Inverness-shire PH24
3BQ
5 miles N of Aviemore on old A9 road,
turn right onto B970.
Undulating course, birch tree lined
fairways.
18 holes, 5720 yards, S.S.S.68
Designed by James Braid.
Founded 1898
Visitors: welcome. Starting sheet
used every day.
Green Fee: £12 WD, £15 WE.
Societies: must book in advance.
Catering: facilities available all day.
Hotels: Craigard; Moorfield; Boat.

S11 Bonar Bridge & Ardgay
☎(08632) 750
Market Stance, Migdale Rd, Bonar
Bridge IV24 3EJ
Off A9 travelling N from Inverness.
Moorland course.
9 holes, 2313 yards, S.S.S.63
Founded 1901
Visitors: welcome at all times.
Green Fee: £6/day.
Societies: any weekday by prior
arrangement.
Hotels: Bridge; Caledonian;
Dunromin.

S12 Braemar
☎(03397) 41618
Cluniebank Rd, Braemar, AB3 5XX
Signposted from village of Braemar,
club lies approximately 0.5 mile from
Braemar on Cluniebank.
Parkland/moorland course with River
Clunie running through.
18 holes, 4916 yards, S.S.S.64
Designed by Joe Anderson.
Founded 1902
Visitors: welcome by arrangement
(book 24 hours in advance).
Green Fee: £9/round, £12/day WD;
£12/round, £15/day WE; £40/week.

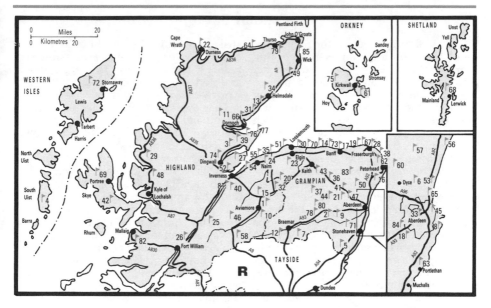

Societies: welcome, prior booking required.
Catering: bar open 11am-11pm (midnight Fri and Sat), lunch, snacks and high teas available to 7pm.
Hotels: Fife Arms; Moorfield; Invercauld Arms.

S13 **Brora**
☎(0408) 21417
Golf Rd, Brora, Sutherland KW9 6QS
75 miles N of Inverness on A9, signposted in middle of village.
Seaside links course.
18 holes, 6110 yards, S.S.S.69
Designed by James Braid.
Founded 1891
Visitors: welcome at any time, restrictions on tournament days.
Green Fee: £13/day; £60/week.
Societies: arranged by written application.
Catering: available June, July, Aug; also available on request from Societies and parties.
Hotels: Links; Royal Marine; Sutherland Arms; Braes; Bay View.

S14 **Buckpool (Buckie)**
☎(0542) 32236
Barhill Rd, Buckie, Banffshire AB5 1DU
Leave A98 signposted Buckpool, course 1 mile at end of road before entering St Peters Rd.

Seaside links course.
18 holes, 6259 yards, S.S.S.70
Founded 1965
Visitors: welcome.
Green Fee: £9/day WD, £12/day WE.
Societies: societies and groups welcome by prior arrangement.
Catering: weekends and daily by prior arrangement.
Hotels: St Andrews; Cluny; Commercial.

S15 **Carrbridge**
☎(047 984) 623 Clubhouse
Carrbridge, Inverness PH23 3AU
About 200 yds from village on A938.
Parkland/moorland course.
9 holes, 2625 yards, S.S.S.66
Founded 1980
Visitors: welcome; Sun limited due to competitions.
Green Fee: £7 WD, £8 WE.
Catering: tea, coffee, light snacks.
Hotels: Dalrachnie Lodge; Carrbridge; Struan House; Cairns.

S16 **Cruden Bay**
☎(0779) 812285
Aulton Rd, Cruden Bay, Peterhead, Aberdeenshire AB42 7NN
23 miles N of Aberdeen on coastal route to Peterhead.
Seaside course.
9 holes, 4710 yards, S.S.S.62;
18 holes, 6370 yards, S.S.S.71

Designed by Tom Morris & Archie Simpson.
Founded 1899
Visitors: not on competition days before 3.30pm; restricted weekends.
Green Fee: £18.50/day, £25 WE.
Societies: on application.
Catering: full bar and restaurant.
Hotels: Kilmarnock Arms; Waterside Inn; Udny Arms; Red House.

S17 **Cullen**
☎(0542) 40685
The Links, Cullen, Buckie, Banffshire
200 yards from A98 on W of Cullen.
Seaside course.
18 holes, 4610 yards, S.S.S.62
Visitors: welcome, time restrictions on application.
Green Fee: £7/day WD, £10/day WE.
Societies: all months except July/August, apply for details.
Catering: bar and catering April-Oct.
Sea swimming, fishing, bowls, tennis, pool, darts etc.
Hotels: Royal Oak; Grant Arms; Seafields Arms; Three Kings Inn; Bayview; Cullen Bay; Moray Golf Rover scheme from Moray Council.

S18 **Deeside**
☎(0224) 867697
Bieldside, Aberdeen
3 miles W of Aberdeen on A93 North Deeside road.

Cruden Bay

Cruden Bay is no place for those who like their golf to be an exercise of dull predictability in a sheltered setting. However, if you are a romantic imbued with a sense of adventure and a belief that the game should be primarily a test of ingenuity and adaptability in which the wind plays a leading role, it is heaven on earth.

Nowhere is the spirit of seaside links better embodied or more faithfully preserved than on a stretch of the Aberdeenshire coastline where the dunes contain a turbulent air and the holes portray an excitement that matches the mood. There are those who will say that some are unfair and old-fashioned but the sign of a great course is one that has stood the test of time. Cruden Bay has certainly done that.

It has neither seen nor needed much adjustment to combat the relentless march of the steel shaft and the modern ball, although there are some elements of the course that have evoked cries for change. Over the 8th, they have had their way but holes such as the 14th and 15th are those on which Cruden Bay's fame is based. Their future is as important as their past.

One landmark which has sadly disappeared is the hotel, an edifice of pink Peterhead granite known as the "Palace in the Sandhills". In terms of position, it rivalled Turnberry, looking down on the links and capturing the coastal splendour at a glance. In pre-war days, when seaside holidays were taken at home, it was fashionable and popular; but at least its disappearance meant that the clubhouse could fill the gap, the old clubhouse remaining as a reminder of an era when its needs were less.

There is an inviting start to the round from an elevated tee that immediately indicates the special nature of the golf and its surroundings, the 2nd and 3rd continuing parallel with the main street — a scene familiar in so many towns or villages in Scotland which are known to the world for their golf. The 3rd is typical of a number of imaginatively shaped greens that may lie hidden from the striker but which lose nothing in terms of challenge or devilment. Professionals who try to reduce golf to a repetitive and sterile dependence on statistics and yardages do it a grave disservice.

They overlook the fun which is paramount and which Cruden Bay offers in abundance but they may wish that the stern demands of the short 4th were not so visible. Beside a picturesque creek and the cottages of Port Ellen, they involve a mighty carry from the back tee and a high premium on being straight.

The course now turns to follow the line of the shore, the 5th tempting with a drive between the dunes, the 6th a par 5 to a heavily defended green and the 7th, a par 4 swinging left to a green in the hills. Par along that little stretch is good going. Some of the original menace of the 8th has been lost by the removal of a hill to fill a hollow and by the realignment of the green of which Tom Simpson, its designer, was justly proud. It is as well that artists do not suffer a desire by people to tamper with their work.

The 9th marks a change in the character of the terrain which, having scaled the hill, plunges down for five holes that are interesting if not remarkable.

The most remarkable and unique part comes with the narrow neck between a mountain and the shore occupied by the 14th and 15th, the artery that reconnects with the main heartland which is impossible to by-pass. A shallow valley, highlighting the drive at the 14th, is vital to hit if the second is to be broached successfully, a towering shot over a marker-post on the top of the ridge which must drop onto, or run down to, a beautiful green nestling in a hollow.

Here, there is no alternative to a blind shot that can be thrilling; nor is there much alternative at the 15th, another blind shot round a stony escarpment of the mountain. It is a little like threading a ball through the eye of a needle, a tall order for the weaker brethren but that helps Cruden Bay stand apart although, by way of maintaining variety, the 17th and 18th are more conventional but certainly not lacking interest.

Parkland course.
18 holes, 5972 yards, S.S.S.69
Founded 1903
Visitors: welcome if member of recognised golf club and with letter of intro from Sec.
Green Fee: £15/day WD, £17/day WE & BH.
Societies: welcome Thurs only by arrangement.
Catering: full facilities.
Hotels: Cults; Bieldside Inn.

S19 Duff House Royal
☎(0261) 812062
The Banyards, Banff AB45 3SX
On A98 entering town from S.
Parkland course.
18 holes, 6161 yards, S.S.S.69
Designed by Dr A. and Major C.A. Mackenzie.
Founded 1909
Visitors: welcome at all times, h/cap cert preferred, tee times restricted at weekends and July/Aug.
Green Fee: £9/round, £12/day WD; £12/round, £15/day WE.
Societies: catered for at all times but weekends fully booked with waiting list.
Catering: full service.
Hotels: Banff Springs; County; Fife Lodge; Highland Haven; Carmelite.

S20 Dufftown
☎(0340) 20325
Tomintoul Road, Dufftown, Banffshire AB55 4BX
1 mile from Dufftown on B9009.
Family course with panoramic views.
18 holes, 5308 yards, S.S.S.67
Founded 1896
Visitors: unrestricted.
Green Fee: £7 WD, £8 WE; £25 weekly.
Societies: welcome 7 days, by arrangement.
Catering: bar, snacks etc.

S21 Dunecht House
☎(0224) 487187
Dunecht, Skene, Aberdeenshire AB3 7AX
B944 to Dunecht, 1st left.
Parkland course.
9 holes, 6270 yards, S.S.S.78
Founded 1925
Visitors: with member only.

S22 Durness
☎(097 181) 364 Sec (home).
Balnakeil, Durness, Sutherland, IV27 4PN
57 miles NW of Lairg on A838.
Public seaside course with daring finishing hole.
9 holes (18 tees), 5545 yards, S.S.S.68
Designed by F. Keith, L. Ross, I. Morrison.
Founded 1988
Visitors: welcome, occasionally restricted Sun am.
Green Fee: £6/day, £24/week.
Societies: any time.
Catering: snacks 12am-5pm, June-Sept.

S23 Elgin
☎(0343) 542338
Hardhillock, Birnie Rd, Elgin, Moray IV30 3SX
On S edge of Elgin, turn right into Birnie Rd from Rothes road going S.
Undulating sandy parkland course.
18 holes, 6401 yards, S.S.S.71
Founded 1906
Visitors: welcome after 9.30am weekdays, 10am weekends; book in advance.
Green Fee: £13/round, £19/day WD; £18.50/round, £26.50/day WE.
Societies: book with Sec.
Catering: full bar and catering available.
Hotels: Eight Acres; Laich Moray; Rothes Glen; St Leonards.

S24 Forres
☎(0309) 72949
Muiryshade, Forres, IV36 0RD
1 mile S of clock tower in town centre, by St Leonards Rd and Edgehill Rd.
Undulating parkland course.
18 holes, 6140 yards, S.S.S.69
Designed by James Braid.
Founded 1889
Visitors: welcome.
Green Fee: £12/day WD, £16 WE.
Societies: welcome by confirmation.
Catering: full facilities all year.
Hotels: Royal; Ramnee; Park.

S25 Fort Augustus
☎(0320) 6460 Sec.
Markethill, Fort Augustus, PH32 4DT
A82, beyond 30mph sign S of village.
Moorland course.
9 holes (18 tees), 5454 yards, S.S.S.68
Designed by Dr Lane.
Founded 1905
Visitors: tickets at clubhouse, minimum restrictions.
Green Fee: on application.
Societies: apply Sec, Glentarff, Fort Augustus.
Catering: self-catering facilities.
Hotels: Lovat Arms; Caledonian; Brae.

S26 Fort William
☎(0397) 704464
North Rd, Torlundy, Fort William PH33 6RD
On A82 Fort William to Inverness road, 2 miles N of Fort William.
Moorland course.
18 holes, 5640 yards, S.S.S.68
Designed by J.R. Stutt.
Founded 1975
Visitors: welcome any time.
Green Fee: on application.
Societies: welcomed.
Catering: full license, bar snacks.

S27 Fortrose & Rosemarkie
☎(0381) 20529, 20733
Ness Rd East, Fortrose, IV10 8SE
On Cromarty road branching off A9 N
out of Inverness, about 16 miles N of
Inverness.
Seaside links course.
18 holes, 5973 yards, S.S.S.69
Re-designed by James Braid.
Founded 1888
Visitors: welcome at all times.
Green Fee: on application.
Societies: catered for if possible on
written application.
Catering: available.
Hotels: Marine; Royal (Fortrose).

S28 Fraserburgh
☎(0346) 28287
Philarth, Fraserburgh AB4 5TL
1 mile E of Fraserburgh, on A92
Aberdeen-Fraserburgh road, turn off
right on road to Cairnbulg.
Undulating seaside course.
18 holes, 6217 yards, S.S.S.70
Designed by James Braid.
Founded 1881
Visitors: welcome, no restrictions.
Green Fee: on application.
Societies: no restrictions weekdays
and most Sun; small parties on Sat
subject to Club commitments.
Catering: bar lunches daily, evening
meals to order.

S29 Gairloch
☎(0445) 2407
Gairloch, Ross-shire IV21 2BE
On main road A832, in Gairloch.
Seaside course.
9 holes, 2093 yards, S.S.S.63
Designed by Captain Burgess.
Founded 1898
Visitors: welcome all week.
Green Fee: £10/day.
Catering: shop with refreshments
during season.

S30 Garmouth & Kingston
☎(034 387) 388
Garmouth, Fochabers, IV32 7LU
Off A96 8 miles E of Elgin.
Seaside course.
18 holes, 5649 yards, S.S.S.67
Founded 1929
Visitors: welcome.
Green Fee: £10/round, £12/day WD;
£14/round, £18/day WE.
Societies: by arrangement with Sec;
deductions for parties over 20.
Catering: by arrangement with Sec.
Hotels: Gordon Arms; Garmouth.

S31 Golspie
☎(0408) 633266
Ferry Rd, Golspie, Sutherland KW10
6ST
First right in Golspie off A9 from
Inverness.
Links/heathland/seaside/
meadowland course.
18 holes, 5836 yards, S.S.S.68
Founded 1889
Visitors: unrestricted.
Green Fee: £12/day.
Societies: welcome subject to tee
reservations for competitions and
tournaments.
Catering: all day during season
(April-Oct).
Hotels: Stags Head; Sutherland
Arms.

S32 Grantown-on-Spey
☎(0479) 2079, 2715 Sec.
Golf Course Rd, Grantown-on-Spey,
Morayshire PH26 3HY
Leave A9 at Aviemore, take A939 to
Grantown, situated at end of town.
Woodland/parkland course.
18 holes, 5715 yards, S.S.S.67
Designed by Willie Park and James
Braid.
Founded 1890
Visitors: welcome, not before 10am
Sat/Sun.
Green Fee: £11/day WD, £14/day
WE.
Societies: by arrangement, not
before 10am Sat/Sun.
Catering: full facilities April-Oct.
Hotels: Grant Arms; Ben Mohr;
Garth; Strathspey.

S33 Hazlehead
☎(0224) 317336 Pro.
Hazlehead Park, Aberdeen
4 miles NW of city centre.
Municipal moorland courses.
18 holes, 6045 yards, S.S.S.68;
18 holes, 6205 yards, S.S.S.70
Visitors: all welcome.
Green Fee: on application.

S34 Helmsdale
☎(04312) 240 Sec.
Golf Rd, Helmsdale, Sutherland, KW8
6JA
Off A9 into village of Helmsdale.
Moorland course.
9 holes, 3650 yards, S.S.S.66
Founded 1905
Visitors: welcome.
Green Fee: £3/day, £10/week.
Societies: welcome.
Hotels: Bridge.

S35 Hopeman
☎(0343) 830578
Hopeman, Moray IV30 2YA
7 miles N of Elgin on B9012.
Seaside links-type course.
18 holes, 5500 yards, S.S.S.67
Designed by J. McKenzie.
Founded 1923
Visitors: unrestricted weekdays,
after 9.30am Sat/Sun.
Green Fee: £10 WD, £15 WE.
Societies: welcome.
Catering: bar and restaurant.
Pool.
Hotels: Station; Neuk.

S36 Huntly
☎(0466) 2643
Cooper Park, Huntly, Aberdeenshire
On A96 0.5 mile from town centre.
Parkland course.
18 holes, 5399 yards, S.S.S.66
Founded 1900
Visitors: welcome except Thurs.
Green Fee: £8/day WD, £10/day WE;
£20 weekly.
Societies: by arrangement with Sec.
Catering: facilities by arrangement.
Hotels: Castle; Huntly; Gordon Arms.

S37 Insch
☎(0464) 20363
Golf Terrace, Insch, Aberdeenshire
28 miles NW of Aberdeen, off A96
Inverness road.
Parkland course with water hazards.
9 holes, 5488 yards, S.S.S.67
Visitors: welcome, no restrictions.
Green Fee: £5 WD, £7 WE, £15/week.
Catering: bar; catering on request.
Snooker, darts.

S38 Inverallochy
☎(03465) 2324
Inverallochy, Nr Fraserburgh,
Grampian
3 miles S of Fraserburgh on B9033.
Seaside links course.
18 holes, 5137 yards, S.S.S.65
Founded 1888
Visitors: welcome except
10.30am-2.30pm Sat.
Green Fee: £5.
Societies: welcome.
Catering: limited. Bowls.
Hotels: Tufted Duck (Fraserburgh).

S39 Invergordon
☎(0349) 852715
King George St, Invergordon,
Ross-shire
Off High St, Invergordon.

RESCOBIE HOTEL & RESTAURANT

Valley Drive, Leslie, Glenrothes, Fife KY6 3BQ

| AA ★★ | RAC ★★ | STB ★★★★ "commended" | Tel: 0592 742143 Fax: 0592 620231 |

Rescobie is a secluded 1920s country house where old-fashioned standards of service and hospitality are maintained.

All 10 rooms have private bath or shower, remote control colour TV, direct dial telephone, tea/coffee, room bar, etc.

The cuisine is renowned locally; the 4 chefs use only fresh produce for their a la carte, table d'hote and vegetarian menus.

The hotel is ideally placed for a golfing holiday: 40 golf courses are within a 40-minute drive; 100 are within 1½ hours.

A special DB&B rate is available for golfers; this includes the arrangement of starting times or a full golfing programme.

Tony and Wendy Hughes-Lewis invite you to be their guest.

Parkland course.
9 holes, 3014 yards, S.S.S.69
Designed by Mr J. Urquhart.
Founded 1940
Visitors: welcome at any time; (Mon and Wed evenings Ladies competitions; Tues and Thurs evenings Men's competitions; all day Sat Men's competitions).
Green Fee: on application.
Societies: by arrangement.
Catering: bar lunches on Sat.
Hotels: Marine; Kincraig.

S40 Inverness
☎(0463) 239882 Sec, 231989 Pro.
Culcabock Rd, Inverness IV2 3XQ
Mile W of A9, near Raigmore Hospital.
Parkland course.
18 holes, 6226 yards, S.S.S.70
Founded 1883
Visitors: welcome, restricted Sat.
Green Fee: £14/round, £18/day WD; £17/round, £20/day WE.
Societies: limited; early booking required; not Sat or Sun.
Catering: full bar facilities; no catering Thurs unless pre-booked. 2 practice areas.
Hotels: Kingsmills; Craigmonie; Caledonian.

S41 Inverurie
☎(0467) 24080
Blackhall Rd, Inverurie, Aberdeenshire
On A96 Aberdeen-Inverness road, off Blackhall Rd.
Wooded parkland course.
18 holes, 5096 yards, S.S.S.65
Designed by G. Smith and J.M. Stutt.
Founded 1923
Visitors: welcome but prior booking on (0467) 20193 advisable.
Green Fee: £8/day WD, £10/day WE.
Societies: welcome by arrangement.
Catering: available daily.
Hotels: Kintore Arms; Gordon Arms; Pittodrie House.

S42 Isle of Skye
☎(0478) 2000
Sconser, Isle of Skye, Inverness
Between Broadford and Portree (on main road).
Seaside course.
9 holes, 4798 yards, S.S.S.63
Designed by Dr F. Deighton.
Founded 1964
Visitors: welcome at all times.
Green Fee: £7/day, £14/3 days, £20/week.
Hotels: Sconser Lodge.

S43 Keith
☎(05422) 2469, 2831 Sec.
Fife-Keith, Keith, Banffshire
0.5 mile off A96 on Dufftown road.
Undulating parkland course.
18 holes, S.S.S.68
Founded 1965
Visitors: welcome.
Green Fee: on application.
Societies: by arrangement.
Catering: by arrangement.
Hotels: Gordon Arms.

S44 Kemnay
☎(0467) 42225
Monymusk Road, Kemnay, Aberdeenshire AB51 9NB
15 mile N of Aberdeen on A96, turn onto B994.
Parkland course.
9 holes, 2751 yards, S.S.S.67
Founded 1908
Visitors: welcome, not Sun before 11am, not Mon, Tues, Thurs evenings.
Green Fee: £8/day WD, £10/day WE.
Societies: welcome by arrangement.
Catering: bar, bar snacks.
Hotels: Park Hill Lodge; Grant Arms (Monymusk)

S45 King's Links
☎(0224) 632269
King's Links, Aberdeen
E of city centre adjacent to Pittodrie
Stadium.
Municipal seaside course
18 holes, 6433 yards, S.S.S.71
Visitors: all welcome.
Green Fee: £4.80/round, jnrs before
5pm £2.40; winter £3.20/round, jnrs
before 5pm £1.80.
Societies: by arrangement.
Catering: by arrangement with
member clubs (Bon Accord (0224)
633464; Caledonian (0224) 632443)
Driving range.

S46 Kingussie
☎(0540) 661600 Sec, 661374
Clubhouse
Gynack Rd, Kingussie,
Inverness-shire PH21 1LR
Leave A9 at N end of village, drive
into village, turn right at Duke of
Gordon Hotel and continue to end of
road.
Hill course.
18 holes, 5555 yards, S.S.S.67
Designed by Vardon & Herd.
Founded 1891
Visitors: unrestricted.
Green Fee: £10/round, £13/day WD;
£12/round, £16/day WE.
Societies: by arrangement.
Catering: available May-Oct.

S47 Kintore
☎(0467) 32631
Balbithan Rd, Kintore, Inverurie,
Aberdeenshire
Off A96, 12 miles N of Aberdeen.
Undulating moorland course.
18 holes, 5985 yards, S.S.S.69
Founded 1911
Visitors: welcome daily except Mon,
Wed and Fri after 4pm.
Green Fee: £8/day WD, £12/day WE.
Societies: welcome.
Catering: if booked in advance.
Hotels: Crown; Torryburn.

S48 Lochcarron
☎(05202) 257 Sec.
Lochcarron, Ross-shire
1 mile E of Lochcarron village.
Seaside/heathland course.
9 holes, 3578 yards, S.S.S.62
Founded 1910
Visitors: welcome except 1-6pm
Sat; club hire.
Green Fee: £5/round.
Hotels: Lochcarron; Rock Villa;
Strathcarron.

S49 Lybster
Main St, Lybster, Caithness KW1 6BL
13 miles S of Wick on A9, turn down
village main street, golf course
entrance opposite football pitch.
Moorland course.
9 holes, 1898 yards, S.S.S.62
Founded 1926
Visitors: welcome, pay before play
in money box provided.
Green Fee: on application.
Societies: any group welcome
anytime except Sat evenings (club
competitions).

S50 McDonald
☎(0358) 20576
Hospital Rd, Ellon, Aberdeenshire
AB4 9AW
Leave Ellon by A948 Auchnagatt road
and take 1st turning on left.
Parkland course.
18 holes, 5986 yards, S.S.S.69
Founded 1927
Visitors: welcome.
Green Fee: on application.
Societies: by arrangement.
Catering: bar 7 days, full catering
Tues-Sun.
Hotels: Buchan; New Inn; Station.

S51 Moray
☎(0343) 812018
Stotfield Rd, Lossiemouth, IV31 6QS
From Elgin on A96 Aberdeen-
Inverness road, travel on A941
Elgin-Lossiemouth road.
Links courses.
Old, 18 holes, 6643 yards, S.S.S.72;
New, 18 holes, 6044 yards, S.S.S.69
Founded 1889
Visitors: welcome; New Course any
time; Old Course, weekdays after
9.30am, weekends after 10am, not
1pm-2pm any day, advance booking
required.
Green Fee: on request.
Societies: reduction of 10% for
parties of 12 or more.
Catering: full during summer,
weekends Oct-Mar.
Hotels: Stotfield; Laverock Bank;
Huntly House; Skerrybrae; Rock
House.

S52 Muir of Ord
☎(0463) 870825
Great Northern Rd, Muir of Ord, Ross
and Cromarty IV6 7SX
15 miles N of Inverness on A862.
Moorland/parkland course.
18 holes, 5129 yards, S.S.S.65
Part designed by James Braid.

Founded 1875
Visitors: welcome unrestricted.
Green Fee: £9 WD, £10 WE.
Societies: welcome, book in
advance.
Catering: bar, snacks, full meals.
Snooker, pool.
Hotels: Ord Arms; Coul House.

S53 Murcar
☎(0224) 704354
Bridge of Don, Aberdeen AB2 8BD
3 miles from Aberdeen on A92,
Fraserburgh road.
Seaside course.
18 holes, 6240 yards, S.S.S.70
Designed by Archie Simpson.
Founded 1909
Visitors: welcome weekdays, h/cap
cert required.
Green Fee: on application.
Societies: catered for weekdays.
Catering: snacks, lunches, dinners.

S54 Nairn
☎(0667) 53208, 56328 fax.
Seabank Rd, Nairn IV12 4HB
1 mile N of A96, W of Nairn, turn off
onto Seabank Rd at church.
Seaside links course.
18 holes, 6722 yards, S.S.S.72
Designed by Tom Morris, James
Braid.
Founded 1887
Visitors: welcome.
Green Fee: on application.
Societies: catered for.
Catering: summer full catering,
winter restricted. Snooker.
Hotels: Golf View; Royal Marine;
Windsor; Newton; Alton Burn.

S55 Nairn Dunbar
☎(0667) 52741
Lochloy Rd, Nairn IV12 5AE
Off A96, 0.5 mile E of town.
Seaside course.
18 holes, 6431 yards, S.S.S.71
Founded 1899
Visitors: welcome.
Green Fee: £15 WD, £20 WE.
Societies: welcome.
Catering: available.
Hotels: Links; Golf View; Windsor.

S56 Newburgh-on-Ythan
☎(03586) 89438
c/o 51 Mavis Bank, Newburgh, Ellon,
Aberdeen AB4 0FB
14 miles N of Aberdeen on Peterhead
road, on entering village of
Newburgh turn right at Ythan Hotel.

Seaside links course.
9 holes, 6404 yards, S.S.S.71
Founded 1888
Visitors: welcome except Tues after 4pm from May to Sept.
Green Fee: £8/day WD, £10/day WE.
Societies: apply to Sec.
Hotels: Ythan; Foveran House; Udny.

S57 Newmachar

☎(06517) 3002
Swailend, Newmachar, Aberdeen AB2 0JN
12 miles N of Aberdeen on A947.
Heathland course.
18 holes, 6313 yards, S.S.S.71
Designed by Dave Thomas
Founded 1990
Visitors: welcome weekdays; h/cap cert required.
Green Fee: £12/round, £18/day WD; £18/round WE.
Societies: weekdays, prior booking.
Catering: full catering and bar.

S58 Newtonmore

☎(05403) 328
Golf Course Rd, Newtonmore, Highland PH20 1AT
Leave A9 2 miles S of Newtonmore, course 150 yds from centre of village.
Moorland/parkland course.
18 holes, 5890 yards, S.S.S.68
Designed by James Braid.
Founded 1893
Visitors: welcome, no restrictions.
Green Fee: £12 WD, £15 WE.
Societies: apply to Sec.
Catering: meals and snacks. Pool.
Hotels: Craigerne; Alvey; Glen; Balavil Sports; Braeriach; Mains; Highland.

S59 Northern

☎(0224) 636440
Golf Rd, Kings Links, Aberdeen
E of city centre.
Municipal seaside course.
18 holes, 6700 yards, S.S.S.69
Visitors: welcome.
Green Fee: on application.
Societies: by arrangement.
Catering: at weekends, by arrangement during week.

S60 Oldmeldrum

☎(06512) 2648
Kirk Brae, Oldmeldrum, AB51 0DJ
18 miles NW of Aberdeen on A947
Banff road; turn 1st right on entering village of Kirk Brae.
Parkland course.

18 holes, 5988 yards, S.S.S.69
Founded 1885 extended 1990
Visitors: phone clubhouse for tee reservation (bar hours).
Green Fee: £10/round/day WD, £12/round/day WE.
Societies: contact Sec via clubhouse.
Catering: by arrangement; licensed bar, snacks available. Practice area.

S61 Orkney

☎(0856) 2457
Grainbank, St Ola, By Kirkwall, Orkney KW15 1RD
0.5 mile W of Kirkwall.
Parkland course.
18 holes, 5406 yards, S.S.S.68
Founded 1889
Visitors: welcome anytime.
Green Fee: £8/day.
Catering: bar evenings and all day at weekends (new clubhouse 1992).
Hotels: Ayre.

S62 Peterhead

☎(0779) 72149
Craigewan Links, Peterhead AB4 6LT
A92 and A975, 30 miles N of Aberdeen.
Seaside links course.
18 holes, 6100 yards, S.S.S.70;
9 holes, 2400 yards, S.S.S.60
Founded 1841
Visitors: welcome any time.
Green Fee: £8/day WD, £12/day WE.
Societies: any day except Sat or tournament days (by appointment, telephone or letter).
Catering: by prior arrangement with Steward.
Hotels: Caledonian; Palace; Waterside.

S63 Portlethen

☎(0224) 782575
Badentoy Rd, Portlethen, Aberdeen AB1 4YA
Alongside A92 6 miles S of Aberdeen.
Parkland course.
18 holes, 6735 yards, S.S.S.72
Designed by Donald Steel
Founded 1981
Visitors: some restrictions weekends; dress, smart but casual.
Green Fee: £8.50/round, £12.50/day WD; £10.50/round, £15.50/day WE.
Societies: by prior arrangement.
Catering: bar 11am-12pm daily, restaurant 12am-2pm and 6-9pm. Snooker.
Hotels: Hillside; Skean Dhu.

S64 Reay

☎(084 781) 288
By Thurso, Caithness KW14 7RE
11 miles W of Thurso.
Most northerly links course on mainland Britain.
18 holes, 5865 yards, S.S.S.68
Founded 1893
Visitors: welcome anytime.
Green Fee: £8/day, £25/week, £45/month.
Societies: not Sat.
Catering: bar; lunch during summer months only.
Hotels: Forss House; Meluich.

S65 Royal Aberdeen

☎(0224) 702571
Balgownie, Bridge of Don, Aberdeen AB2 8AT
2 miles N of Aberdeen on A92, cross River Don, turn right at 1st set of traffic lights, then down Links Rd to course.
Seaside links courses.
18 holes, 4066 yards, S.S.S.60;
18 holes, 6372 yards, S.S.S.71
Designed by Robert Simpson and James Braid.
Founded 1780
Visitors: welcome with letter of intro or h/cap cert; not before 3.30pm Sat.
Green Fee: £23/round WD, £30/round/day WE.
Societies: weekdays and Sun by arrangement.
Catering: full facilities; bar and dining room.
Hotels: Invery House; Udny Arms.

S66 Royal Dornoch

☎(0862) 810219
Golf Rd, Dornoch IV25 3LW
A9 from Inverness, via Tain and Dornoch Bridge.
Links course.
Championship 18 holes, 6581 yards, S.S.S.72; Struie 18 holes (6 from original course), 5500 yards, S.S.S.66
Designed by Tom Morris, John Sutherland, George Duncan.
Founded 1877
Visitors: welcome, tee reservations in advance; h/cap certs (max 24 Men, 35 Ladies) required for Championship course.
Green Fee: on request.
Societies: when requested except July/Aug; early reservations required.
Catering: full facilities except Mon.
Hotels: Burghfield; Castle; Mallin House; Royal Golf.

S67 Royal Tarlair
☎(0261) 32897
Buchan St, Macduff AB4 1TA
On A98 48 miles from Aberdeen.
Seaside links course.
18 holes, 5866 yards, S.S.S.68
Designed by George Smith.
Founded 1923
Visitors: welcome any day.
Green Fee: £8/day WD, £10/day WE.
Societies: by arrangement.
Catering: full catering and bar.
Hotels: Knowes; Highland Haven.

S68 Shetland
☎(059 584) 369
Dale, Shetland
Road N from Lerwick, 3 miles.
Undulating moorland course.
18 holes, 5776 yards, S.S.S.70
Designed by Fraser Middleton
Visitors: welcome.
Green Fee: £5/day.
Societies: by arrangement.
Hotels: Lerwick; Grand; Queens.

S69 Skeabost
☎(047 032) 202
Skeabost Bridge, Isle of Skye IV5
19NP
40 miles from Kyle of Lochalsh.
Parkland course.
9 holes Par 3, 1700 yards, S.S.S.29
Founded 1984
Visitors: welcome; no jeans or
T-shirts, proper golf shoes.
Green Fee: £7.50/day.
Catering: bar and restaurant in hotel
(April-Oct).
Hotels: Skeabost (26 beds).

S70 Spey Bay
☎(0343) 820424
Spey Bay, Fochabers, Moray IV32 7JP
Turn off A96 near Fochabers Bridge,
follow B9104 Spey Bay road to coast.
Links course.
18 holes, 6059 yards, S.S.S.69
Designed by Ben Sayers.
Founded 1907
Visitors: welcome.
Green Fee: £7 Mon-Sat, £8.50 Sun.
Catering: meals and bar all day.
Driving range, tennis, petanque,
putting, caravan site.
Hotels: Spey Bay, golf packages/golf
outings arranged.

S71 Stonehaven
☎(0569) 62124
Cowie, Stonehaven AB3 2RH
On A92 1 mile N of town, new

roundabout at Commodore Hotel,
take second exit on left, pass Leisure
Centre on right.
Seaside/parkland course.
18 holes, 5103 yards, S.S.S.65
Designed by A. Simpson.
Founded 1888
Visitors: welcome except Sat and
Sun forenoons.
Green Fee: on application.
Societies: usually each month (last
Sat).
Catering: full.
Hotels: Commodore; St Leonards;
Heugh; Royal.

S72 Stornoway
☎(0851) 702240
Castle Grounds, Stornoway, Isle of
Lewis PA87 0XP
5 mins walk from town centre, just
within main entrance to castle
grounds.
Parkland/moorland course.
18 holes, 5119 yards, S.S.S.66
Designed by J.R. Stutt.
Founded 1890
Visitors: welcome from Mon to Sat.
Green Fee: £7/round, £10/day,
£30/week, £50/fortnight.
Societies: by arrangement.
Catering: available by arrangement.
Hotels: Caberfeigh; County;
Seaforth.

S73 Strathlene
☎(0542) 31798
Portessie, Buckie, Banffshire AB5
2DJ
On A942, 2 miles E of Buckie
Harbour, from main Banff-Inverness
road, take turning to Strathlene 3
miles E of Buckie road sign.
Undulating moorland/seaside
course.
18 holes, 6180 yards, S.S.S.69
Designed by Alex Smith.
Founded 1877
Visitors: welcome.
Green Fee: on application.
Societies: welcome.
Catering: available 9am-5pm.
Hotels: Commercial.

S74 Strathpeffer Spa
☎(0997) 421219
Strathpeffer, Ross-shire IV14 9AS
5 miles W of Dingwall, 0.25 mile N of
village square (signposted).
Upland course, no sand bunkers.
18 holes, 4792 yards, S.S.S.65
Designed by W. Park.
Founded 1888

Visitors: welcome without
reservation; tee reserved for
members and guests until 10am
Sun.
Green Fee: £10/round, £15/day WD;
£15/round WE.
Societies: by arrangement.
Catering: licensed, meals, snacks;
no catering Mon.
Hotels: Craigdarroch Lodge;
Dunraven Lodge; Holly Lodge;
Richmond; Achilty; all offer package
arrangements.

S75 Stromness
☎(0856) 850772
Ness, Stromness, Orkney K16 3DU
Bordering sea at S end of town.
Parkland course.
18 holes, 4672 yards, S.S.S.64
Founded 1890
Visitors: no restrictions.
Green Fee: £7/day.
Societies: welcome any time.
Catering: bar.
Tennis, pool, darts, bowls.

S76 Tain
☎(0862) 892314
Tain, Ross-shire IV19 1PA
A9 N of Inverness, 0.5 mile from town
centre.
Seaside/parkland course.
18 holes, 6238 yards, S.S.S.70/69
Designed by Tom Morris.
Founded 1890
Visitors: welcome.
Green Fee: on application.
Societies: welcome.
Catering: by arrangement with Club
Steward.
Hotels: Royal; Morangie; Mansfield.

S77 Tarbat
☎(086 287) 236
Portmahomack, Ross-shire IV20 1YQ
B9165 off A9, 7 miles E of Tain.
Seaside links course.
9 holes, 2329 yards, S.S.S.63
Designed by J. Sutherland.
Founded 1910
Visitors: welcome except Sun.
Green Fee: £4/day, £15/week.
Societies: apply to Sec.
Hotels: Castle; Caledonian.

S78 Tarland
☎(03398) 81413
Aberdeen Rd, Tarland, Aboyne,
Aberdeenshire AB3 4YL
On A974, 30 miles W of Aberdeen, 6
miles N of Aboyne.

Parkland course.
9 holes, 5816 yards, S.S.S.68
Designed by Tom Morris.
Founded 1908
Visitors: no restrictions.
Green Fee: £8 WD, £10 WE.
Societies: not weekends.
Catering: June-Sept all day; April, May, Oct by arrangement.
Hotels: Aberdeen Arms; Balnacoil; Commercial; Pannanich Wells.

S79 Thurso
☎(0847) 63807
Newlands of Geise, Thurso, Caithness KW14 7XF
2 miles SW from centre of Thurso on B870.
Parkland course.
18 holes, 5841 yards, S.S.S.69
Designed by W. Stuart.
Founded 1964
Visitors: no restrictions.
Green Fee: on application.
Catering: all day bar, catering all day during summer.
Hotels: Pentland; John O'Groats House; (both offer free golf for residents).

S80 Torphins
☎(03398) 82115
Bog Rd, Torphins, Banchory AB31 4JA
6 miles W of Banchory on A980.
Undulating heathland course.
9 holes, 2317 yards, S.S.S.63
Founded 1896
Visitors: unrestricted except during competitions.
Green Fee: £8/day, £10 WE.
Catering: snacks only.
Hotels: Learney Arms.

S81 Torvean
☎(0463) 225651 (ans. machine), 236648 lounge
Glenurquhart Rd, Inverness
On A82 Fort William road, 1 mile W of city centre, on W of Caledonian Canal.
Municipal parkland course.
18 holes, 5784 yards, S.S.S.68
Founded 1962
Visitors: welcome; contact Starter's office (0463) 237543.
Green Fee: apply to Starter.
Societies: welcome by arrangement with Inverness District Council.
Catering: meals by arrangement.
Hotels: Loch Ness House (50 yards).

S82 Traigh
☎(06875) 220 Sec.
Traig Farm, Traigh, Arisaig, Inverness-shire
3 miles W of Arisaig on A830 Fort William-Mallaig road.
Links course.
9 holes, 2100 yards, S.S.S.64
Visitors: welcome, pay-as-you-play.
Green Fee: £3/day.
Hotels: Cnoc-na-Faire.

S83 Turriff
☎(0888) 62745 Clubhouse, 62982 Sec, 63025 Pro.
Rosehall, Turriff, Aberdeenshire AB53 7BB
On Aberdeen side of town, about 1 mile up Huntly Rd on B9024.
Meadowland/parkland course.
18 holes, 6145 yards, S.S.S.69
Founded 1896
Visitors: welcome with h/cap cert, book with Pro; not before 10am weekends unless with member.

Green Fee: £8/round, £11/day WD; £12/round, £15/day WE.
Societies: by arrangement with Sec.
Catering: by arrangement.
Hotels: Union; Banff Spring.

S84 Westhill
☎(0224) 740159
Westhill Heights, Skene, AB3 6TY
6 miles from Aberdeen on A944 Aberdeen-Alford road, course to N of town overlooking it.
Undulating parkland/moorland course.
18 holes, 5866 yards, S.S.S.69
Designed by Charles Lawrie.
Founded 1977
Visitors: welcome except 4.30-7pm weekdays, not Sat.
Green Fee: £8/round, £11/day WD; £10/round, £13/day WE & BH.
Societies: weekdays and Sun.
Catering: bar; meals by arrangement
Hotels: Westhill Inn.

S85 Wick
☎(0955) 2726
Reiss, Wick, Caithness KW1 4RW
3 miles N of Wick on A9, turn right at signpost, 0.75 mile to clubhouse.
Seaside links course.
18 holes, 5976 yards, S.S.S.69
Designed by McCulloch.
Founded 1870
Visitors: welcome subject to club and open competitions.
Green Fee: on application.
Societies: by arrangement.
Catering: bar, snacks at weekends. Pool.
Hotels: Queens; Nethercliffe; Mackays (free golf for residents); Rosebank; Mercury.

T

NORTHERN IRELAND

Discussion on comparative merits of golf courses is always fierce although rarely conclusive. Golfers are influenced by a multitude of factors from how they played to the condition of the greens and the beauty of the setting. Where the debate surrounds courses that are near neighbours, passions are liable to be even more frenzied but, whilst Royal Portrush and Royal County Down cannot quite be classed as neighbours, they lie roughly equidistant to the north and south of Belfast and as a result tend to split opinion nicely.

This is not the place to fuel the argument as to which is the better but there is not the slightest doubt that both are in the classic mould and nobody should visit Ulster and play one without the other. Few big cities can boast two championship links within such easy reach of its centre.

Royal County Down is at Newcastle, an attractive holiday town nestling in the romantic shadow of the Mountains of Mourne. Mountains make an imposing backcloth to golf anywhere and one is always aware of their brooding presence at Newcastle, sun and cloud casting ever changing patterns and colours. They make the 9th particularly imposing but an equally dominant impression of the course is forged by the massive sand dunes that line so many of the fairways, together with the heather and gorse that magnify and punish errant shots.

They place huge demands on bold, forceful driving, although the varied nature of the shots to the greens gives an important added dimension that increases the regret that circumstances beyond its control have denied Royal County Down more major championships. The British Amateur of 1970 and the Curtis Cup match two years earlier were events enhanced by the quality of its challenge; but the same applies to Royal Portrush — the only Irish Club to have housed the Open Championship — in 1951. It saw Max Faulkner emerge as champion, although his win marked the beginning of a drought where British victories were concerned, which lasted until Tony Jacklin won in 1969.

Portrush also saw the crowning of Catherine Lacoste as British Women's champion, many of the noble holes bringing out the best in a supreme striker. The spectacular part is down by the shore, not far from the Giant's Causeway. Holes entitled Purgatory and Calamity convey the true picture.

But it must not be thought that golf in the Province is confined to Newcastle and Portrush — superb as they are. Lovers of links golf have a splendid example in Portstewart and another in Castlerock — both close to Portrush. Belfast itself is well served, Royal Belfast, with excellent views of the city, and Malone, being perhaps the pick.

There is also Balmoral, home club of the late Fred Daly, Hollywood and Shandon Park, which used to stage the Gallaher's Ulster Open at a time when a young Tony Jacklin was taking his first steps onto the world golfing stage.

Clandeboye and Bangor are towns on the fringe of the Belfast district with splendid courses and I well remember journeys to Lurgen when Frank Pennink was redesigning the course; and a sentimental mention for Warrenpoint near the border with the Republic, the course that raised Ronan Rafferty.

T1 **Ardglass**
☎(0396) 841219, 841755
Castle Place, Ardglass, Co Down
On B176 7 miles from Downpatrick.
Seaside course.
18 holes, 5515 metres, S.S.S.69
Founded 1896
Visitors: welcome.
Green Fee: £10.50 WD, £15.50 WE;
discount if playing with member.
Societies: welcome.
Catering: meals served except Mon.
Hotels: Abbey Lodge; Arms.

T2 **Ballycastle**
☎(026 57) 62536
Cushendall Rd, Ballycastle, Co
Antrim BT54 6QP
About 50 miles along coast road, W
of Larne Harbour.
Undulating seaside course.
18 holes, 5882 yards, S.S.S.69
Founded 1890
Visitors: welcome weekdays.
Green Fee: £10 (£6 with member)
WD, £14 (£8 with member) WE.
Societies: catered for all year except
July/Aug (bookable).

Catering: light snacks available.
Hotels: Antrim Arms; Hillsea; Marine.

T3 **Ballyclare**
☎(09603) 22696, 42352 Bar
25 Springvale Rd, Ballycare, Co
Antrim
14 miles N of Belfast, off Larne road.
Parkland course.
18 holes, 5840 metres, S.S.S.71
Founded 1923
Visitors: welcome, not Sat.
Green Fee: £11/day WD, £15 WE &
BH.
Societies: by arrangement.
Catering: restaurant and snacks.
Snooker, indoor bowls (winter).
Hotels: Chimney Corner; Dunadry
Inn.

T4 **Ballyearl G & LC**
☎(0232) 848287
585 Doagh Rd, Newtownabbey,
Belfast BT36 8RZ
1 mile N of Mossley off B59.
Public parkland course.
9 holes Par 3, 2400 yards

Visitors: welcome.
Green Fee: on application.
Squash, fitness centre, driving range.
Hotels: Chimney Corner.

T5 **Ballymena**
☎(0266) 861487
128 Raceview Rd, Ballymena, Co
Antrim BT42 4HY
2.5 miles E of town on A42 to Brough
Shane and Carnlough.
Heathland/parkland course.
18 holes, 5245 metres, S.S.S.67
Founded 1902
Visitors: welcome weekdays and
Sun; not Sat.
Green Fee: on application.
Societies: recognised golfing
societies by arrangement with Sec.
Catering: available daily.
Hotels: Adair Arms; Tullyglass
House; Leighinmohr; Country House.

T6 **Balmoral**
☎(0232) 381514, 667747 Pro shop
518 Lisburn Rd, Belfast BT9 6GX
2 miles S of Belfast centre; club

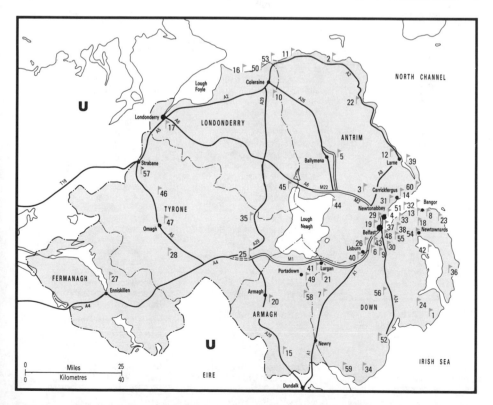

beside King's Hall on Lisburn Rd,
opposite Balmoral Halt station.
Flat parkland course.
18 holes, 5702 metres, S.S.S.70
Founded 1914
Visitors: welcome except Sat.
Green Fee: £11/day WD, £13
Wednesdays; £16.50 WE & BH.
Societies: Mon and Thurs by
arrangement.
Catering: bar (0232 668540);
restaurant (664571). Snooker
Hotels: Conway; Europa; Plaza;
York; Beechlawn.

T7 Banbridge
☎(08206) 62211/62342
Huntly Rd, Banbridge, Co Down BT32
3UR
About 0.5 mile from town along Huntly
Rd, River Bann on right all the way.
Parkland course.
18 holes, 5376 metres, S.S.S.68
Founded 1913
Visitors: welcome most days, Ladies
preference Tues, Men's competitions
Sat.
Green Fee: £7 WD, £12 WE.
Societies: welcome summer
months, green fees £7 WD, £10 Sun.
Catering: arranged on request.
Hotels: Bannville House; Belmont;
Downshire.

T8 Bangor
☎(0247) 270922
Broadway, Bangor, Co Down BT20
4RH
0.75 mile from town centre.
Undulating parkland course.
18 holes, 6372 yards, S.S.S.70
Designed by James Braid.
Founded 1903
Visitors: welcome weekdays;
weekends by prior arrangement.
Green Fee: on application.
Societies: Mon and Wed only by
prior arrangement.
Catering: bar meals available
11.30am-2.30pm and 5.30-7.30pm;
dining room available, contact
caterer (0247) 270483.
Hotels: Royal; Groomsport House;
Crawfordsburn Inn.

T9 Belvoir Park
☎(0232) 491693 office, 641159
catering, 692817 bar, 646714 Pro.
73 Church Rd, Newtownbreda,
Belfast BT8 4AN
About 4 miles from centre of Belfast,
off Ormean Rd which is main road to
Saintfield and Newcastle.

Parkland course.
18 holes, 6276 yards, S.S.S.70
Designed by H.S. Colt.
Founded 1927
Visitors: welcome.
Green Fee: £20 WD except Wed, £25
WE, Wed and Bank Holidays.
Societies: council permits 5 outings
per month April/Sept, 24 or more £15.
Catering: excellent facilities by
Executive Catering.
Snooker
Hotels: Drumkeen; Stormont.

T10 Brown Trout
☎(0265) 868209
209 Agivy Road, Aghadowey, Nr
Coleraine, Co Londonderry
Intersection of the A54 and B66.
Parkland course.
9 holes, 2800 yards, S.S.S.68
Designed by Bill O'Hara Snr.
Founded 1984
Visitors: no restrictions.
Green Fee: £6 WD, £8.50 WE & BH.
Societies: very welcome, inc. Sat.
Catering: all-day catering, à la carte
restaurant.
Horse riding, fishing.
Hotels: Brown Trout Golf and
Country Inn on course.

T11 Bushfoot
☎(026 57) 31317
50 Bushfoot Rd, Portballintrae, Co
Antrim BT57 8RR
4 miles E of Portrush on coast.
Seaside links course.
9 holes, 5572 yards, S.S.S.67
Founded 1890
Visitors: welcome weekdays and
weekends if no club competitions.
Green Fee: on application.
Societies: welcome by arrangement;
£7 WD, £10 WE.
Catering: bar and restaurant.
Snooker room, Pitch & Putt
(summer), functions.
Hotels: Bayview; Beech; Bushmills
Inn; Causeway.

T12 Cairndhu
☎(0574) 583324
192 Coast Rd, Ballygally, Larne, Co
Antrim BT40 2QG
4 miles N of Larne.
Parkland course.
18 holes, 6112 yards, S.S.S.69
Designed by John S.F. Morrison.
Founded 1929
Visitors: welcome except Sat.
Green Fee: men £10 WD, £15 Sun;
ladies £5 WD, £7.50 Sun.

Societies: welcome.
Catering: meals and snacks on
weekdays 5pm-10pm, Sat 11.30am-
8pm, Sun (12.30-6.30pm).
Snooker
Hotels: Ballygally Castle; Halfway
House.

T13 Carnalea
☎(0247) 270368
Station Rd, Bangor, Co Down BT19
1EZ
Adjacent to Carnalea railway station
1.5 miles from Bangor.
Seaside meadowland course.
18 holes, 5548 yards, S.S.S.67
Founded 1927
Visitors: welcome 7 days.
Green Fee: £8 (£6 with member) WD,
£12 (£10 with member) WE & BH.
Societies: weekdays only.
Catering: full catering except Mon.
Hotels: Royal; Crawfordsburn Inn;
Tedworth.

T14 Carrickfergus
☎(09603) 63713 Sec, 62203
Clubhouse
35 North Rd, Carrickfergus, Co
Antrim BT38 8LP
Off A2, 9 miles NE of Belfast.
Parkland/meadowland course.
18 holes, 5752 yards, S.S.S.68
Founded 1926
Visitors: welcome except Sat.
Green Fee: £16 WE; £12 WD.
Societies: Mon and Fri only.
Catering: full facilities.
Hotels: Coast Road; Dobbins Inn;
Glenavana House.

T15 Castleblayney
☎(042) 40197 Sec.
Onomy, Castleblayney, Co
Monaghan, Ulster
Almost in Castleblayney town centre
on Derry-Dublin road.
Parkland course.
9 holes, 2678 yards, S..S.S.66
Founded 1985
Visitors: welcome.
Green Fee: £6/day WD.
Societies: welcome.
Catering: full facilities.
Hotels: Glencarn; Central.

T16 Castlerock
☎(0265) 848215 Members, 848314
Office
65 Circular Rd, Castlerock, Co
Londonderry BT51 4TJ
Off A2, 6 miles W of Coleraine.

Seaside course.
18 holes, 6121 metres, S.S.S.72;
9 holes, 2457 metres, S.S.S.34
Designed by Ben Sayers.
Founded 1901
Visitors: welcome.
Green Fee: £13 (£7 with member)
WD, £25 (£13 with member) WE &
BH.
Societies: weekdays only.
Catering: franchise at club.
Snooker.
Hotels: Golf.

T17 City of Derry
☎(0504) 46369
49 Victoria Rd, Londonderry BT47
2PU
On main Londonderry-Strabane
road, 3 miles from Craigavon Bridge.
Parkland course.
Dunhugh, 9 holes, 4708 yards,
S.S.S.63; Prehen, 18 holes, 6362
yards, S.S.S.71
Founded 1912
Visitors: welcome weekdays before
4.30pm unless with member;
weekends by arrangement with Pro;
Dunhugh course open at all times.
Green Fee: on application.
Societies: catered for on weekdays
and possibly at weekends.
Catering: full facilities available.
Hotels: Everglades (bargain break
packages); Broomhill House; White
Horse Inn; Waterfoot.

T18 Clandeboye
☎(0247) 271767
Tower Rd, Conlig, Newtownards, Co
Down BT23 3PN
Above Conlig village off A21 between
Bangor and Newtonards.
Dufferin, parkland/heathland course;
Ava, parkland/moorland course.
Dufferin, 18 holes, 5915 metres,
S.S.S.72; Ava, 18 holes, 5172
metres, S.S.S.67
Designed by William Rennick
Robinson and Dr Bernard von
Limburger.
Founded 1933
Visitors: welcome weekdays; must
be accompanied by member Sat and
certain times on Sun; (Ladies Day
Thurs).
Green Fee: £12/£11 WD (£8/£7 with
member), £18/£14 WE & BH (£10/£9
with member).
Societies: by arrangement except
Sat, Sun and Thurs.
Catering: available.
Hotels: Royal; Culloden;
Crawfordsburn Inn; Strangford Arms.

T19 Cliftonville
☎(0232) 744158, 746595 Sec and
catering
44 Westland Rd, Belfast BT14 6NH
From centre of Belfast take Antrim
road for about 2 miles, then Cavehill
Rd on left and left again at Fire
Station.
Parkland course.
9 holes, 3120 yards, S.S.S.70
Founded 1911
Visitors: welcome except Sat and
Tues afternoons.
Green Fee: £9 (£5 with member)
WD, £11 (£6 with member) Sun.
Societies: by arrangement with
Council through Hon Sec.
Catering: bar snacks available;
meals by arrangement.
Hotels: Lansdowne Court.

T20 County Armagh
☎(0681) 522501
Demesne, Newry Rd, Armagh, Co
Armagh
Off Newry Rd, 0.25 mile from city
centre.
Parkland course.
18 holes, 6147 yards, S.S.S.69
Founded 1893
Visitors: welcome except
12am-2pm Sat and 12am-3pm Sun.
Green Fee: £9 WD, £12 WE.
Societies: catered for except on Sat.
Catering: full catering facilities
available.
Hotels: Charlemont Arms; Drumsill
House.

T21 Craigavon
☎(0762) 326606
Golf and Ski Centre, Turmoyra Lane,
Silverwood, Lurgan, Craigavon, Co
Armagh
Off M1 from Belfast at A76 exit 10,
500 yards from sliproad take 1st
turning right into Kiln Rd and 1st right
again.
Public parkland course.
18 holes, 6496 yards, Par 72;
9 holes, 1349 yards, Par 3.
Visitors: welcome any time,
advisable to ring in advance at
weekends.
Green Fee: £7.15/round WD,
£10/round WE & BH; reductions for
jnrs and OAPs.
Societies: by arrangement, mainly
Sun, some Sat.
Catering: snacks, bar and restaurant
at Golf & Ski Centre adjacent.
12-hole Pitch & Putt, driving range
and putting green.
Hotels: Silverwood.

T22 Cushendall
☎(0266) 71318
Shore Rd, Cushendall, Ballymena, Co
Antrim BT44 0QQ
Turn right at Curfew Tower in village,
proceed 0.25 mile to Strand.
Seaside/parkland course.
9 holes, 2193 metres, S.S.S.63
Designed by Daniel Delargy.
Founded 1938
Visitors: welcome.
Green Fee: £8/day WD, £10/day WE
& BH.
Societies: weekdays.
Catering: in summer and at
weekends in winter.
Hotels: Thornlea.

T23 Donaghadee
☎(0247) 883624
84 Warren Rd, Donaghadee, Co
Down BT21 0PQ
On A2 18 miles E of Belfast.
Links/parkland course.
18 holes, 5576 metres, S.S.S.69
Founded 1899
Visitors: welcome except Sat
(competition day), booking advisable.
Green Fee: £11.50 WD; £15.50 WE.
Societies: Mon and Wed.
Catering: full facilities.
Snooker.
Hotels: Copelands; Dunallen.

T24 Downpatrick
☎(0396) 615947 office; 612152 club
615244 catering; 615167 golf shop
43 Saul Rd, Downpatrick, Co Down
BT30 6PA
A24 and A7 23 miles SE of Belfast.
Parkland course.
18 holes, 6400 yards, S.S.S.69
Designed by Hawtree & Sons.
Founded 1932
Visitors: welcome, restricted at
weekends.
Green Fee: on application.
Societies: by arrangement.
Catering: full facilities.
Driving range, snooker
Hotels: Denvir's; Abbey Lodge.

T25 Dungannon
☎(08687) 22098, 27338 Office
Springfield Rd, Mullaghmore,
Dungannon, Co Tyrone
0.5 mile out of town on Donaghmore
Rd.
Parkland course.
18 holes, 5818 yards, S.S.S.68
Founded 1890
Visitors: welcome anytime.
Green Fee: £7 WD, £10 WE.

Societies: welcome by arrangement.
Catering: by arrangement.
Hotels: Dunowen; Inn on the Park;
Glengannon Inn.

T26 Dunmurry
☎(0232) 610834
91 Dunmurry Lane, Dunmurry,
Belfast BT17 9JS
Situated between Dunmurry village
and Upper Malone Rd, Belfast.
Parkland course.
18 holes, 5832 yards, S.S.S.68
Designed by T.J. McAuley.
Founded 1905
Visitors: not before 5pm Sat, after
5pm Tues and Thurs.
Green Fee: £11 WD, £15 WE & BH
Societies: not Sat or
11.30am-12.30pm Sun.
Catering: each day except Mon.
Hotels: Conway; Beechlawn.

T27 Enniskillen
☎(0365) 25250
Castle Coole, Enniskillen, Co
Fermanagh
1 mile from Enniskillen.
Parkland course.
18 holes, 5420 metres, S.S.S.70
Designed by Dr Dixon & George
Mawhinney (1st 9), T.J. McAuley
(2nd 9).
Founded 1896
Visitors: unrestricted.
Green Fee: £7.50/day.
Societies: welcome if previous
arrangements made with Sec.
Catering: bar snacks daily, full
catering by prior arrangement.
Hotels: Killyhevlin; Fort Lodge;
Railway.

T28 Fintona
☎(0662) 841480
Ecclesville Demesne, Fintona, Co
Tyrone
9 miles SW of Omagh.
Parkland course.
9 holes, 6251 yards, S.S.S.70
Founded 1896
Visitors: welcome.
Green Fee: on application.
Societies: catered for on weekdays.
Catering: by prior arrangement.

T29 Fortwilliam
☎(0232) 370770
Downview Ave, Belfast B15 4EZ
On A2 3 miles N of Belfast.
Meadowland course.
18 holes, 5796 yards, S.S.S.67

Designed by Mr Buchart.
Founded 1891
Visitors: welcome except Sat.
Green Fee: £12 (£7 with member)
WD, £17 (£9 with member) WE.
Societies: welcome by arrangement
with Sec.
Catering: full service available.
Hotels: Lansdowne Court.

T30 Gilnahirk
☎(0232) 448477
Manns Corner, Upper Bramel Rd,
Gilnahirk, Castlereagh, Belfast
3 miles from Belfast off Ballygowan
road.
Public moorland course.
9 holes, 5398 metres, S.S.S.68
Founded 1984
Visitors: welcome.
Green Fee: £ (9 holes) WD, £3.75
WE.
Putting green.
Hotels: Stormont.

T31 Greenisland
☎(0232) 862236
156 Upper Rd, Grennisland,
Carrickfergus BT38 8RW
About 9 miles N of Belfast.
Meadowland course.
9 holes, 5887 yards, S.S.S.68
Re-designed by H. Middleton.
Founded 1894
Visitors: welcome except Sat.
Green Fee: £8 WD, £12 Sun.
Societies: welcome by arrangement.
Catering: full facilities.
Hotels: Glenavna; Newtown Abbey.

T32 Helen's Bay
☎(0247) 852601
Golf Rd, Helen's Bay, Bangor, Co
Down BT19 1TL
Off A2, 9 miles E of Belfast.
Seaside course.
9 holes, 5176 metres, S.S.S.67
Founded 1896
Visitors: welcome, after 2.15pm
Tues, with member only Sat.
Green Fee: on application.
Societies: Mon, Wed and Fri.
Catering: full facilities.

T33 Holywood
☎(02317) 2138
Nuns Walk, Demesne Rd, Holywood,
Co Down BT18 9DX
On A2 6 miles E of Belfast.
Undulating course.
18 holes, 5885 yards, S.S.S.68
Founded 1904

Visitors: welcome except Sat.
Green Fee: £14.50 WD, £19.25 Sun.
Societies: catered for except Thurs,
Sat and Bank Holidays.
Catering: bar and catering facilities.
Snooker.
Hotels: Culloden.

T34 Kilkeel
☎(06937) 62296
Mourne Park, Kilkeel, Co Down BT34
4LB
3 miles from Kilkeel on Newry road,
signposted.
Parkland course.
9 holes (18 from 1993), 5631
metres, S.S.S.69
Designed by Lord Justice Babbington.
Founded 1948 on present site.
Visitors: welcome at all times.
Green Fee: £10 WD, £12 WE & BH.
Societies: on application.
Catering: full facilities.
Snooker, pool.
Hotels: Kilmorey Arms; Cranfield
House.

T35 Killymoon
☎(06487) 62254, 63762
200 Killymoon Rd, Cookstown, Co
Tyrone BT80 8TW
0.5 mile off A29 on S side of
Cookstown.
Parkland course.
18 holes, 5498 metres, S.S.S.69
Designed by Hugh Adair.
Founded 1889
Visitors: all week except Sat, club
competition day.
Green Fee: £11.50 WD, £15.50 Sun
and Bank Holidays.
Societies: except Thurs and Sat.
Catering: bar, full catering available,
phone 62254.
Hotels: Glenavon.

T36 Kirkistown Castle
☎(02477) 71233, 71353
142 Main Rd, Cloughey, Co Down
BT22 1JA
A20 from Belfast to Kircubbin, follow
signs to Newtownards and
Portaferry, then B173 to Cloughey.
Links course.
18 holes, 6157 yards, S.S.S.70
Designed by B. Polley.
Founded Oct 1902
Visitors: welcome.
Green Fee: on application.
Societies: welcome weekdays,
except Bank Holidays.
Catering: full facilities.
Hotels: The Roadhouse (Cloughey).

T37 **The Knock**
☎(0232) 483251 office, 483825 Pro, 482249 Club, 480519 Catering
Summerfield, Upper Newtownards Rd, Dundonald, Belfast BT16 0QX
Travel E out of Belfast towards Dundonald, course 0.5 mile beyond Stormont Houses of Parliament.
Parkland course.
18 holes, 6407 yards, S.S.S.71
Designed by Colt, McKenzie & Allison.
Founded 1895
Visitors: not Sat unless with member.
Green Fee: £15 WD (£7.50 with member), £20 WE & BH (£10 with member).
Societies: Mon and Thurs.
Catering: full facilities all week. Snooker.
Hotels: Stormont (within 1 mile).

T38 **Knockbracken G & CC**
☎(0232) 792108, 795666
Ballymaconaghy Rd, Knockbracken, Belfast BT8 4SB
Near Four Winds restaurant on SE outskirts of city.
Meadowland course
18 holes, 5312 yards, S.S.S.68
Visitors: welcome but priority tee times for members at weekends.
Green Fee: £9 (£7 with member) WD, £11 (£9 with member) WE; reductions for jnrs.
Societies: by arrangement.
Catering: full bar and restaurant facilities 7 days.
Driving range, putting greens, ski slope.
Hotels: La Mon; Drumkeen.

T39 **Larne**
☎(09603) 82228
54 Ferris Bay Rd, Islandmagee, Larne BT40 3RT
From Belfast, N to Carrickfergus and 6 miles from Whitehead, from Larne S along coast road to Islandmagee.
Seaside course.
9 holes, 6082 yards, S.S.S.69
Designed by Babington.
Founded 1894
Visitors: weekdays; not Sat.
Green Fee: on application.
Societies: open; not Sat.
Catering: available.
Hotels: Magheramorne House.

T40 **Lisburn**
☎(0846) 677216
68 Eglantine Rd, Lisburn, Co Antrim BT27 5RQ
3 miles S of Lisburn, 200 yards from BBC radio transmitter mast.
Meadowland/parkland course.
18 holes, 5708 metres, S.S.S.72
Designed by Hawtree & Sons.
Founded 1905
Visitors: at specified times.
Green Fee: £15 WD, £25 WE.
Societies: Mon, Thurs, Fri.
Catering: 7 days.
Hotels: White Gables (Hillsborough).

T41 **Lurgan**
☎(0762) 322087 Sec/Manager, 325306 Club, 321068 Pro.
The Demesne, Lurgan, Co Armagh BT67 9BN
Centre of Lurgan to Windsor Ave, proceed past castle gates around edge of lake.
Parkland course bordering on Lurgan Park and lakes.
18 holes, 5836 metres, S.S.S.70
Designed by F. Pennink.
Founded 1894
Visitors: welcome except Sat.
Green Fee: £12.50 WD, £15 WE & BH; Ladies £9, students £7.50, under 18 £4.
Societies: on request; weekdays £10, Sun and Bank Holidays £15.
Catering: available except Mon.
Hotels: Silverwood; Carngrove; Seagoe.

T42 **Mahee Island**
☎(0238) 541234
Comber, Newtownards, Co Down, BT23 6ET
Turn left 0.5 mile from Comber on Comber/Killyleagh road, keep bearing left to Mahee Island, 6 miles.
Parkland/seaside course.
9 holes, 5588 yards, S.S.S.67
Founded 1929
Visitors: restricted after 4pm Wed and until 5pm Sat.
Green Fee: £8 WD, £12 WE & BH.
Societies: alternate Sun, weekdays except Mon; apply in writing to Sec.
Catering: by arrangement, no bar. Pool.
Hotels: Balloo House; La Mon House; Strangford Arms.

T43 **Malone**
☎(0232) 612758
240 Upper Malone Rd, Dunmurry, Belfast BT17 9LB
5 miles from Belfast centre, take Upper Malone Rd.
Parkland course.
18 holes, 6433 yards, S.S.S.71
Designed by Fred Hawtree.
Founded 1895
Visitors: welcome except Wed after 2pm and Sat before 5pm.
Green Fee: on application.
Societies: welcome Mon and Thurs.
Catering: full except Sun after 2pm.

T44 **Massereene**
☎(08494) 28096
51 Lough Rd, Antrim
1 mile S of town, 3.5 miles from Aldergrove Airport.
Parkland course.
18 holes, 6614 yards, S.S.S.72
Designed by F.W. Hawtree.
Founded 1895
Visitors: welcome weekdays and weekends, Sat competition day.
Green Fee: on application.
Societies: Tues, Thurs 9-12am and 2-3.30pm; Wed 9-11.30am.
Catering: full facilities.
Hotels: Dunadry; Deerpark.

T45 **Moyola Park**
☎(0648) 68468, 68830 Pro.
Shanemullagh, Castledawson, Magherafelt, Co Londonderry BT45 8DG
Turn right half-way through Castledawson village, along Curran Rd, entrance 400 yards on right.
Parkland course.
18 holes, 6517 yards, S.S.S.71
Designed by Don Patterson.
Founded 1976
Visitors: welcome.
Green Fee: on application.
Societies: welcome at all times by prior arrangement.
Catering: full facilities, phone 68392.
Hotels: The Arches; Moyola Lodge.

T46 **Newtownstewart**
☎(06626) 61466, 61829
38 Golf Course Rd, Newtownstewart, Omagh, Co Tyrone BT78 4HU
2 miles SW of Newtownstewart via B84 Drumquin road.
Parkland course.
18 holes, 5468 metres, S.S.S.69
Designed by Frank Pennink.
Founded 1914
Visitors: welcome but advance booking advisable.
Green Fee: £6 WD, £8 WE & BH.
Societies: by prior arrangement.
Catering: bar open normal hours, meals by arrangement. Snooker.
Hotels: Hunting Lodge; Royal Arms; Silver Birch; Knocknamoe; Fir Trees Lodge.

Royal Portrush and Royal County Down

Old Tom Morris's achievement in laying out Royal County Down at a cost not to exceed £4.00 is part of golf's folklore and represented remarkably good value for money even in those far off days. However, not much of his original work survives in the modern version of a links that many now regard as perhaps the mightiest of them all.

If you are lucky enough to play golf on either of Northern Ireland's two great courses, Royal County Down and Royal Portrush, somebody, sooner or later, is bound to fuel the debate about which is the better.

Rather like being asked to decide whether Bobby Jones was superior to Ben Hogan, or Jack Hobbs a better batsman than Don Bradman, it is a provocative question, but one fact upon which nearly everyone is agreed is that both rank among the 10 best courses in Great Britain and Eire, and no self-respecting golfer visiting those parts for the first time should play the one and not the other.

Although the approach to Portrush along the coast road from Antrim can be spectacularly beautiful, one reason for giving County Down at Newcastle the edge is because its setting under the shadow of the Mountains of Mourne is so majestic and inspiring that nobody could fail to be moved by it. There is something special about playing against a backcloth of mountains, but even if you denied Newcastle the splendour of its distant views, the avenues forged by the fairways between high sandhills clad with gorse, would still be most beguiling.

The quiet seaside town of Newcastle lies on a narrow strip of dune country on the edge of Dundrum Bay, its fine, natural features combining to present the severest of championship tests in which there is a big demand on long, straight driving, and no end of challenging strokes onto the well protected greens.

It is sad that Ulster's problems have denied it more championship status following its staging of the Curtis Cup in 1968 and the British Amateur Championship, won for the third successive year by Michael Bonallack, in 1970.

The first three holes along the shore make a stern beginning; then comes a long short hole from a high tee across the gorse and a classic par 4, the 5th doglegging round the hills. More holes linger in the mind notably the 9th which, following a blind drive, unveils the full panoply of the setting: it is one of the most photographed pictures in golf. The inward half continues the challenging trend, the least blemish being severely punished.

Not that Portrush offers any more relief. It, too, lies in the mist of some natural golfing country, north of Belfast, and, with the wind blowing in from the Atlantic and the rough in full bloom, good scoring is no light matter.

Bernard Darwin, on seeing it for the first time, wrote that its designer, Harry Colt, had built himself a monument more enduring than brass and it is certainly a thorough examination of a golfer's skill. The 5th, with its green by the water's edge looking away towards the giant's causeway, is particularly appealing, along with the magnificent one-shot 6th that follows. Then, later on, there are holes aptly termed "calamity corner" and "purgatory" and all the time, to lend a historical note the reminder that in 1951 Max Faulkner won the Open Championship on the only occasion in which it ventured outside Scotland or England. Similarly, in 1960, Joe Carr, perhaps the best known and most loved figure in all Ireland, stood 10 up and 10 to play in the final of the Amateur Championship.

These were the supreme moments of the lives of two players who, in their respective worlds, provided more colour and entertainment than any of their contemporaries. For them, Royal Portrush must have a warm place in their hearts, and no wonder.

T47 Omagh

☎(0662) 243160, 241442
83A Dublin Rd, Omagh, Co Tyrone
BT78 1HQ
On A5 on outskirts of Omagh.
Parkland course.
18 holes, 5208 metres, S.S.S.68
Founded 1910
Visitors: welcome any day except
Tues and Sat.
Green Fee: £7/day WD, £10/day WE
& BH; £2 reduction with member.
Societies: welcome weekdays.
Catering: available for societies.
Snooker.
Hotels: Royal Arms.

T48 Ormeau

☎(0232) 641069, 640700, 640999
50 Park Rd, Belfast BT7 2FX
2 miles city centre on Ravenhill Rd.
Parkland course.
9 holes, 2653 yards, S.S.S.65
Founded 1893
Visitors: welcome weekdays and
Sun.
Green Fee: on application.
Societies: Thurs and Sun on
application.
Catering: bar and restaurant
facilities. Snooker.
Hotels: Drumkeen House.

T49 Portadown

☎(0762) 355356
192 Gilford Rd, Portadown,
Craigavon, Co Armagh BT63 5LF
On A59 2 miles SE of Portadown,
entrance 400 yards beyond Metal
Box factory on right.
Parkland course.
18 holes, 5621 metres, S.S.S.70
Founded 1900
Visitors: welcome except Tues, Sat.
Green Fee: £12 (men), £10 (women)
WD; £15 (men), £12 (women) WE &
BH.
Societies: details on request.
Catering: bar daily, restaurant
except Mon. Squash.
Hotels: Seagoe; Carn.

T50 Portstewart

☎(026583) 2015, 3839
117 Strand Rd, Portstewart, Co
Londonderry BT55 7PG
4 miles W of Portrush.
Links course.
Strand, 18 holes, 6714 yards,
S.S.S.72; Town, 18 holes, 4733
yards, S.S.S.62; Blue, 9 holes, 2662
yards, Par 32
Founded 1894

Visitors: weekdays on application.
Green Fee: Strand, £16 (£8 with
member) WD, £22 (£10 with member)
WE & BH; Town, £6 WD, £9 WE & BH.
Societies: welcome weekdays,
must book by phone.
Catering: every day.
Hotels: Edgewater.

T51 Royal Belfast

☎(0232) 428165
Station Rd, Craigavad, Holywood, Co
Down BT19 0BP
2 miles E of Holywood on A2.
Parkland course.
18 holes, 5963 yards, S.S.S.69
Designed by H.C. Colt, redesigned
(1988) Donald Steel.
Founded 1881
Visitors: except Thurs and Sat
before 4.30pm, by introduction or
letter from home club.
Green Fee: £20/round WD,
£25/round WE & BH.
Societies: by arrangement.
Catering: full facilities
Hotels: Culloden.

T52 Royal County Down

☎(03967) 23314, 26281 fax.
Newcastle, Co Down BT33 0AN
From Belfast take A24 to Carryduff,
A7 to Ballynahinch and A2 to
Newcastle, about 30 miles.
Links course.
18 holes, 6968 yards, S.S.S.73
Designed by Tom Morris Snr.
Founded 1898
Visitors: Mon, Tues, Thurs, Fri;
h/cap cert required.
Green Fee: summer, £35 WD, £40
WE & BH; winter, £25 WD, £30 WE &
BH.
Societies: by arrangement only.
Catering: Centenary Room open
Mon-Fri, April-Sept.
Hotels: Slieve Donard; Burrendale.

T53 Royal Portrush

☎(0265) 822311, 823139 fax.
Bushmills Rd, Portrush, Co Antrim
BT56 8JQ
1 mile from Portrush town off A1.
Seaside links course.
Valley, 18 holes, 6273 yards,
S.S.S.70; Dunluce, 18 holes, 6784
yards, S.S.S.73
Designed by H.S. Colt.
Founded 1888
Visitors: welcome Mon, Tues, Thurs,
Fri am, Sun after 10am.
Green Fee: Dunluce, £25 WD, £30
WE; Valley, £12 WD, £16 WE.

Societies: catered for; on Dunluce
Mon, Tues, Thurs, Fri am, Sun
10.30-11.30am; on Valley every day
except Sat/Sun am.
Catering: full catering daily, snacks,
high tea and à la carte.
Hotels: Bayview (Portballatrae);
Magherabuoy House.

T54 Scrabo

☎(0247) 812355 Sec, 817848 Pro.
233 Scrabo Rd, Newtownards, Co
Down BT23 4SL
Off A20 10 miles E of Belfast; near
Scrabo Tower.
Hilly parkland course.
18 holes, 5699 metres, S.S.S.71
Founded 1907
Visitors: welcome weekdays except
Wed.
Green Fee: £10 WD, £15 WE.
Societies: any day except Sat, not
during June.
Catering: full bar and restaurant
facilities.
Snooker.
Hotels: Strangford Arms; George; La
Monde.

T55 Shandon Park

☎(0232) 793730
73 Shandon Park, Belfast BT5 6NY
3 miles from city centre via Knock
dual carriageway.
Parkland course.
18 holes, 6252 yards, S.S.S.70
Founded 1926
Visitors: welcome weekdays.
Green Fee: £14 (£7 with member)
WD, £18 (£9 with member) WE.
Societies: Mon and Fri only by
arrangement.
Catering: meals and snacks served.
Hotels: Stormont; Drumkeen.

T56 Spa

☎(0238) 562365
20 Grove Rd, Ballynahinch, Co Down
BT24 8PN
A24, 1 mile from Ballynahinch, exit at
sign for Spa or Dromara.
Parkland course.
18 holes, 5938 metres, S.S.S.70
Founded 1907
Visitors: welcome.
Green Fee: on application.
Societies: Mon-Thurs and some
Sun; 1st tee 10.30-11.45am.
Catering: bar; meals by
arrangement.
Snooker, pool, bowls.
Hotels: Millbrook Lodge; White
Horse.

T57 Strabane

☎(0504) 382271, 382007
Ballycolman, Strabane, Co Tyrone
BT82 9PH
1 mile from Strabane on Dublin road
beside church and three schools.
Parkland course.
18 holes, 5865 yards, S.S.S.69
Designed by Eddie Hackett.
Founded 1909
Visitors: welcome.
Green Fee: on application.
Societies: apply to Sec.
Catering: by arrangement.
Hotels: Fir Trees Lodge.

T58 Tandragee

☎(0762) 841272 office, 840727
Club
Market Hill Rd, Tandragee, Co
Armagh BT62 2ER
From Portadown in Newry direction;
take right to Market Hill/Clare Glen in
Tandragee, course 200 yards on right.
Parkland course.

18 holes, 5519 metres, S.S.S.69
Designed by F. Hawtree.
Founded 1920
Visitors: weekdays before 4pm.
Green Fee: £9 WD, £12 WE & BH.
Societies: by arrangement.
Catering: bar 7 days, catering
12.30-9pm except Mon.
Hotels: Seagoe; Gosford House;
Cam Grove.

T59 Warrenpoint

☎(06937) 73695
Lower Dromore Rd, Warrenpoint, Co
Down BT34 3LN
5 miles from Newry on main
Warrenpoint road.
Parkland course.
18 holes, 5626 metres, S.S.S.70
Founded 1893
Visitors: by appointment.
Green Fee: on application.
Societies: by prior arrangement.
Catering: full facilities. Snooker.
Hotels: Carlingford Bay.

T60 Whitehead

☎(09603) 53631 Sec, 53792
Clubhouse
McCrae's Brae, Whitehead, Co
Antrim BT38 9NZ
Take turning into Whitehead off main
Carrickfergus-Larne road to
Islandmagee road, signposted at
bottom of McCrae's Brae to club.
Undulating parkland course.
18 holes, 6426 yards, S.S.S.71
Founded 1904
Visitors: welcome any day except
Sat.
Green Fee: £10 WD, £9 parties of 25
plus; £15 Sun and BH, £14 parties of
25 plus.
Societies: before 4.30pm Mon to
Thur, before 3.30pm Fri;
10.30-12am Sun; not Sat.
Catering: by arrangement with
Steward.
Hotels: Magheramorne House.

U

EIRE

The first lesson that has to be learned about golf in Ireland is that, in order to derive the greatest benefit, it is better not to be in too much of a hurry. Settle in to the pace of life. Don't plan an impossible itinerary. Travel can be slow and golfing destinations remote but that is undoubtedly part of their attraction and you will soon adapt.

This certainly applies to the coastal sweep that begins in Dublin and ends in Galway, a journey that incorporates many wonderful courses, particularly out west where giant dunes, lonely beaches and wild winds lend an accompaniment to the play that is quite uplifting. Ballybunion, Lahinch, Tralee and Waterville are fit for giants, places that pose the ultimate in challenge although beguiling enough to soften failure.

For those arriving at Shannon Airport, the decision is whether to head north or south of the great estuary which runs into Limerick. Greater by far is the number of courses to the south-west but Lahinch, called the St Andrews of Ireland because of its discovery by officers of the Black Watch, is as fine an example of links golf as could be imagined.

Ballybunion's Old course is an undoubted monument that has brought deserved fame to the little seaside town. It involves a little more climbing than on other links, but some of the high spots enhance the spectacular views. Herbert Warren Wind, the American writer, puts it on an exalted pinnacle but fiercer debate involves the New course whose design and construction led to the building of a newly positioned clubhouse.

Nearby Tralee, the work of Arnold Palmer, is a course of two parts, a front 9 of more open land and a back 9 dominated by majestic dune country involving many demanding strokes.

Some of the greens on the outward half enjoy settings on the edge of the sea which are captivating if the wind is not severe. But the beauty of the settings is a recurring theme all over the south-west of Ireland, and it certainly applies to Waterville, the inspiration of a local man, J.A. Mulcahy.

I never think the golf at Killarney quite matches the surroundings but that is splitting hairs. It may be because Killarney is inland and my leanings are more seaside, but there are other inland delights such as Little Island, Cork, and Carlow, set in a lovely old deer park.

On the east coast, Baltray represents as fine a tract of natural terrain as exists in a country renowned for its great courses. Like most links, Baltray rarely plays the same way two days running.

The Irish course which has seen more great events than any other is Portmarnock, a few miles south of Baltray. Many Irish Opens, the Canada Cup, British Amateur and last year's Walker Cup, head the impressive list, a tribute to the formidable nature of Portmarnock as a test of golf.

Royal Dublin, older than Portmarnock, is another noble links and a word for Sutton, the 9-hole course famous for its association with Joe Carr. It stands on Cush Point looking across the narrow estuary to Portmarnock where Carr was born. It is such a short, compact little course that it used to be said that if Carr shouted "Fore", everybody ducked; but if it is enchantment that you want, the Island at Malahide offers the perfect retreat among its lonely dunes.

Many of Dublin's other courses are more parkland in character, but out on the west coast the feature of the courses is again one of grandeur and beauty. Connermara, Donegal, Rosapenna and Westport are the main attractions, and there are few lovelier spots where the game is played than County Sligo at Rosses Point, home of the late Cecil Ewing, another giant of Irish golf. Last year, the Club housed the Home Internationals, a wonderfully friendly environment for a unique gathering.

U1 Abbeyleix
☎(0502) 31450
Abbeyleix, Co Laois
Within 0.5 mile of Main St on
Stradbally Rd.
Parkland course.
9 holes, 5680 yards, S.S.S.68
Visitors: welcome.
Green Fee: £5 WD, £6 WE.
Societies: usually on Sat.
Catering: by arrangement for
societies.
Hotels: Hibernian; Killeshin,
Montague (Portlaoise).

U2 Achill Island
☎(098) 43202
Keel, Achill, Co Mayo
Via Castlebar or Westport.
Public seaside course.
9 holes, 2723 yards, S.S.S.66
Designed by P. Skerrit.
Founded 1951
Visitors: welcome.
Green Fee: £3/round, £15/week.
Societies: monthly (approx).
Hotels: Achill Sound; Wavecrest;
Atlantic; Gray's; McDowell's;
Slievemore; Achill Head; Clew Bay.

U3 Adare Manor
☎(061) 86204
Adare, Co Limerick
10 miles from Limerick city on main
Killarney road.
Parkland course.
9 holes, 5700 yards, S.S.S.67
Founded 1900
Visitors: welcome weekdays up to
4.30pm, other times with member or
by prior arrangement.
Green Fee: on application.
Societies: on club notice board;
book well in advance.
Catering: limited to chicken, fish etc
in basket; sandwiches, tea, coffee
etc available.
Hotels: Dunranen Arms; Woodlands.

U4 Ardee
☎(041) 53227/56283
Town Parks, Ardee, Co Louth
0.25 mile N of town on Mullinstown
Road.
Parkland course.
18 holes, 6046 yards, S.S.S.69
Designed by Eddie Hackett.
Founded 1911
Visitors: welcome any time Mon-Fri.
Green Fee: £12.
Societies: Mon-Sat.
Catering: available at all times.
Hotels: Gables B&B; Nuremore.

U5 Arklow
☎(0402) 32401
Abbeylands, Arklow, Co Wicklow
0.5 mile from Arklow town centre.
Seaside course.
18 holes, 5963 yards, S.S.S.68
Designed by Hawtree & Taylor.
Founded 1927
Visitors: welcome except Sun.
Green Fee: on application.
Societies: welcome except Sun.
Catering: by arrangement.
Hotels: Arklow Bay; Royal; Hoynes.

U6 Athenry
☎(091) 94466
Palmerstown, Oranmore, Co Galway
5 miles from Athenry on Galway-
Dublin route N6 at junction with
Athenry road.
Parkland course.
18 holes, 6100 yards, S.S.S.69
Designed by Eddie Hackett
Founded 1902
Visitors: welcome Mon-Sat.
Green Fee: £10.
Societies: welcome if booked in
advance.
Catering: by arrangement.

U7 Athlone
☎(0902) 92073/92235
Hodson Bay, Athlone
3 miles from Athlone on Roscommon
road on shores of Lough Ree.
Undulating parkland course.
18 holes, 5529 yards, S.S.S.68
Designed by Fred Hawtree.
Founded 1892
Visitors: welcome weekdays, by
arrangement on Sat and Bank
Holidays.
Green Fee: £10
Societies: weekdays only.
Catering: bar and restaurant.
Snooker.
Hotels: Hodson Bay; Prince of Wales;
Royal Hoey; Shamrock Lodge;
Newpark.

U8 Athy
☎(0507) 31729
Geraldine, Athy, Co Kildare
On T6, 2 miles N of Athy
Undulating parkland course.
9 holes, 3079 yards, S.S.S.69
Founded 1906
Visitors: welcome weekdays.
Green Fee: on application.
Societies: catered for Sat am.
Catering: by arrangement with Club
Steward; ring after 7.30pm.
Hotels: Leinster Arms; Kilkea Castle.

U9 Balbriggan
☎(01) 412173, 412229
Sec/Manager
Blackhall, Balbriggan, Co Dublin
0.5 mile S of town on main Belfast-
Dublin road, 17 miles from Dublin.
Parkland course.
18 holes, 5881 metres, S.S.S.71
Designed by R. Stilwell/J. Paramour
Founded 1945
Visitors: welcome weekdays.
Green Fee: £12 WD, £15 WE & BH.
Societies: weekdays.
Catering: full restaurant facilities.
Hotels: Holmpatrick House;
Skerries; Old Well; Julianstown.

U10 Ballina
☎(096) 21050
Mossgrove, Shanaghy, Ballina, Co
Mayo
On outskirts of town on road to
Bonniconlon.
Inland, undulating course.
9 holes, 5700 yards, S.S.S.67
Designed by Eddie Hackett.
Founded 1910
Visitors: welcome.
Green Fee: £7 daily.
Societies: by arrangement with Sec
or Steward.
Catering: bar meals by
arrangement.
Hotels: Downhill; American; Bartra
House.

U11 Ballinamore
☎(078) 44346
Creevy, Ballinamore, Co Leitrim
1 mile from town centre, sign at
bridge.
Moorland/parkland course.
9 holes, 5680 yards, S.S.S.67
Founded 1939
Visitors: welcome at all times except
some Sun.
Green Fee: £5/day.
Societies: welcome by
arrangement.
Catering: bar, coffee, soup and
sandwiches available.
Hotels: Slieve an larainn;
Commercial; McAllisters.

U12 Ballinascorney
☎(01) 512516
Bohernabreena, Tallaght, Dublin 24
10 miles SW of Dublin.
18 holes, 5464 yards, S.S.S.67
Founded 1971
Visitors: welcome weekdays.
Green Fee: £10 WD.
Catering: bar.

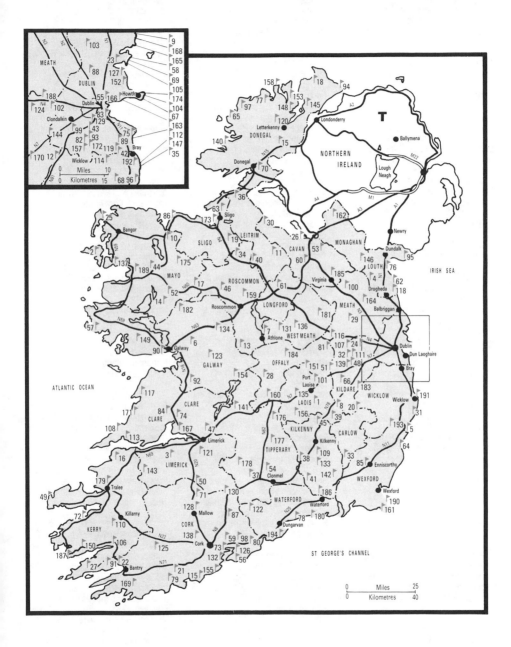

U13 **Ballinasloe**
☎(0905) 42126
Rossgloss, Ballinasloe, Co Galway
Turn left opposite Garbally College
gates on Ballinasloe-Portumna road,
1 mile from there.
Parkland/meadowland course.
18 holes, 6445 yards, S.S.S.70
Designed by Eddie Hackett.
Founded 1894
Visitors: welcome 7 days except
major competitions on Sun.
Green Fee: £10/day.
Societies: welcome 7 days.
Catering: bar and full catering.
Hotels: Haydens; Lerridges Country.

U14 **Ballinrobe**
☎(092) 41448
Castlebar Road, Ballinrobe, Co Mayo
30 miles from Galway, 30 miles from
Knock Airport.
Public parkland course set amid
beautiful scenery.
9 holes, 5790 yards, S.S.S.68
Founded 1905
Visitors: welcome all week except
Tues after 5pm and Sun during
competitions.
Green Fee: £6/day, £18/week.
Societies: welcome weekdays.
Catering: bar and restaurant; good
food also at Red Door restaurant and
several pubs. Fishing in some of the
best lakes in Ireland.
Hotels: Lakeland; Valkenberg.

U15 **Ballybofey & Stranorlar**
☎(074) 31093
Stranorlar, Ballybofey, Co Donegal
14 miles from Strabane, signposted
on Strabane-Balleybofey main road.
Parkland course.
18 holes, 5922 yards, S.S.S.69
Designed by P.C. Carr.
Founded 1958
Visitors: welcome all times except
major competitions; check with B.
Duffy Steward.
Green Fee: on application.
Societies: by arrangement with Sec
or Steward.
Catering: bar facilities; snacks and
meals by arrangement.
Hotels: Kee's; Jackson's.

U16 **Ballybunion**
☎(068) 27146
Sandhill Rd, Ballybunion, Co Kerry
Seaside course.
Old, 18 holes, 6542 yards, S.S.S.72;
New, 18 holes, 6477 yards, S.S.S.72

Founded 1896
Visitors: welcome.
Green Fee: on application.
Societies: welcome.
Catering: snacks and meals served.

U17 **Ballyhaunis**
☎(0907) 30014, 30013 Hon Sec
J.G. Forde (30143 home)
Coolnaha, Ballyhaunis, Co Mayo
2 miles N of Ballyhaunis on Sligo
road, 6 miles from Horan
International Airport; on main rail line
from Dublin; main bus routes
Galway/Derry, Dublin/Westport.
Undulating course.
18 holes, 5801 yards, S.S.S.68
Founded 1929
Visitors: welcome; Ladies Day
Thurs, Club competitions on Sun.
Green Fee: £5/day.
Societies: catered for by Ladies
Committee; contact Hon Sec 1-2
weeks in advance.
Catering: Lady Captain and Ladies
Committee, on notification.
Fishing, shooting, clay pigeon shoot,
snooker, bridge etc.
Hotels: Central; Manor House;
Westway; Orina; International; also
local B&B.

U18 **Ballyliffin**
☎(077) 76119
Ballyliffin, Carndonagh P.O., Co
Donegal
8 miles from Buncrana, 6 miles from
Carndonagh.
Seaside links course.
18 holes, 6384 yards, S.S.S.72
Founded 1947
Visitors: welcome.
Green Fee: on application, £7 WD,
£10 WE.
Societies: welcome by booking; £6
weekdays, £10 weekends.
Catering: bar, snacks and meals
during summer (or by arrangement).
Hotels: Strand; Ballyliffin; (free golf
for residents).

U19 **Ballymote**
☎(071) 83460
Carrigans, Ballymote, Co Sligo
1 mile N of Ballymote.
Parkland course.
9 holes, 2576 yards, S.S.S.66
Founded 1966
Visitors: welcome at any time.
Green Fee: £3/day.
Catering: available at Corrann
Restaurant.
Hotels: Castle.

U20 **Baltinglass**
☎(0508) 81350
Baltinglass, Co Wicklow
40 miles S of Dublin.
Parkland course.
9 holes, 6070 yards, S.S.S.69
Designed by Dr. W.G. Lyons, Hugh
Dark and Col. Mitchell.
Founded 1928
Visitors: welcome.
Green Fee: on application.
Societies: 3 outings allowed per
month.
Catering: meals by arrangement.

U21 **Bandon**
☎(023) 41111, 42224
Castlebernard, Bandon, Co Cork
1.5 miles W of Bandon town, 15
miles from Cork Airport.
Parkland course.
18 holes, 5496 yards, S.S.S.69
Founded 1909
Visitors: welcome weekdays and
weekends.
Green Fee: £12 WD, £15 WE.
Societies: welcome weekdays.
Catering: full facilities.
Tennis.
Hotels: Munster Arms.

U22 **Bantry Park**
☎(027) 50372
Donemark, Bantry, Co Cork
1 mile from Bantry on Glengariff
road.
9 holes, 6436 yards, S.S.S.70
Founded 1975
Visitors: welcome; club handicap
required.
Green Fee: £10/day.
Societies: apply in writing.
Catering: bar, snacks, lunches.
Hotels: West Lodge, Bantry Bay, Sea
View, Reendesert, Dromkeal; all
have special arrangements with
club.

U23 **Beaverstown**
☎(01) 436439
Beaverstown, Donabate, Co Dublin
24km (15 miles) N of Dublin, 5km N
of Dublin Airport.
Parkland course.
18 holes, 5855 metres, S.S.S.71
Founded 1985
Visitors: welcome weekdays, with
member at weekends.
Green Fee: £12 WD, £16 WE & BH.
Societies: by prior arrangement.
Catering: bar, restaurant, snacks,
lunches, evening meals.
Snooker.

U24 Beech Park

☎(01) 580522, 580100
Johnstown, Rathcoole, Co Dublin
2 miles from Rathcoole village on
Kilteel road.
Parkland course.
18 holes, 5730 metres, S.S.S.70
Designed by Eddie Hackett.
Founded 1983
Visitors: welcome on Mon, Thurs,
Fri, subject to course availability.
Green Fee: £13 (£6 with member).
Societies: by arrangement with
Sec/Manager.
Catering: full bar and catering.
Snooker.
Hotels: Greenisle; Ambassador.

U25 Belmullet

☎(097) 81266
Belmullet, Co Mayo
Turn right at Binghaustown Church.
Seaside links course.
9 holes, 2857 yards, S.S.S.67
Founded 1923
Visitors: welcome.
Green Fee: on application.
Hotels: Western Strands.

U26 Belturbet

☎(049) 22210
Erne Hill, Belturbet, Co Cavan
0.5 mile on Cavan road from
Belturbet, on left.
Parkland course.
9 holes, 5230 yards, S.S.S.65
Founded 1950
Visitors: welcome at all times.
Green Fee: £5/day.
Societies: most welcome at all times
by appointment with Sec.
Catering: full catering on request.
Snooker.
Hotels: Seven Horseshoes; Slieve
Russell.

U27 Berehaven

☎(027) 70469
Millcove, Castletownbere, Co Cork
On main Glengariff-Castletownbere
road, 3 miles before Castletownbere.
Public seaside course.
9 holes, 2257 metres, S.S.S.66
Founded 1902
Visitors: welcome.
Green Fee: £7.
Tennis, swimming, fishing, sailing.

U28 Birr

☎(0509) 20082
Glenns, Birr, Co Offaly
2 miles from Birr on road to Banager.
Undulating parkland course.
18 holes, 6262 yards, S.S.S.70
Founded 1893
Visitors: welcome, check on Sun.
Green Fee: on application.
Societies: every day except Sun.
Catering: by arrangement except
Tues.
Hotels: County Arms, Doolys (Birr);
Shannon (Banager).

U29 The Black Bush

☎(01) 250021
Thomastown, Dunshaughlin, Co
Meath
0.5 mile E of Dunshaughlin on
Ratoath road.
Parkland course, panoramic views.
18 holes, 7000 yards, S.S.S.73;
9 holes, 3400 yards, S.S.S.71
Designed by Robert Brown.
Founded 1988
Visitors: welcome, 9 hole course
any time; 18 hole course weekdays,
check for availability weekends.
Green Fee: £10/day WD, £12 WE; 9
hole course £5/day.
Societies: welcome weekdays.
Catering: bar and restaurant
11am-11pm daily.
Driving range.
Hotels: Gaulstown House.

U30 Blacklion

☎(072) 53024
Toam, Blacklion, Co Cavan, via Sligo
W on A4 from Enniskillen to Sligo; E
on N16 from Sligo to Enniskillen.
Parkland course.
9 holes, S.S.S.69
Designed by E. Hackett.
Founded 1962
Visitors: welcome except on
President's/Captain's days etc.
Green Fee: £5 WD, £7 Sun; £4 WD,
£5 Sun with member.
Societies: by arrangement.
Catering: bar, bar snacks, meals by
arrangement. Fishing.
Hotels: guest houses in Blacklion,
Belcoo and Florencecourt.

U31 Blainroe

☎(0404) 68168
Blainroe, Co Wicklow
3 miles S of Wicklow town on coast
road.
Seaside course.
18 holes, 6681 yards, S.S.S.72
Designed by Hawtree & Sons.
Founded 1978
Visitors: ring for times.
Green Fee: £14 WD, £19 WE.

Societies: catered for 7 days.
Catering: lunch, dinner and bar food.
Hotels: Arklow Bay; Grand.

U32 Bodenstown

☎(045) 97096
Bodenstown, Sallins, Co Kildare
5 miles N of Naas via N7 and R407.
Championship course.
Old Course, 18 holes, 6132 metres,
S.S.S.72; New Course, 18 holes,
5278 metres, S.S.S.71
Founded 1983
Visitors: welcome; members only on
Old Course weekends.
Green Fee: £8/round WD, £6/round
WE (New Course only).
Societies: by arrangement.
Catering: full facilities.
Hotels: Ambassador (Kill).

U33 Borris

☎(0503) 73143
Deer Park, Borris, Co Carlow
Drive S from Carlow via
Begenalstown; drive E from Kilkenny
via Gowran and Goresbridge.
Parkland course.
9 holes, 6041 yards, S.S.S.69
Visitors: welcome weekdays and
with member on Sun.
Green Fee: on application.
Societies: catered for on weekdays
and Sat am between 10am and 12am.
Catering: catering available for
societies by arrangement.
Hotels: New Park; Springhill;
Clubhouse; Hotel Kilkenny; Royal;
Seven Oaks.

U34 Boyle

☎(079) 62594
Boyle, Co Roscommon
1.5 miles from Boyle on Roscommon
road.
Undulating parkland course.
9 holes, 5450 yards, S.S.S.66
Designed by Eddie Hackett.
Founded 1911
Visitors: welcome.
Green Fee: £6, family £12.
Societies: welcome.
Catering: bar facilities and snacks.
Hotels: Royal; Forest Park.

U35 Bray

☎(01) 862484 Sec, 862092 Public
Ravenswell Rd, Bray, Co Wicklow
L29 from Dublin, turn left at bridge
entering town.
Parkland course.
9 holes, 2866 metres, S.S.S.70

Founded 1897
Visitors: welcome weekdays except Mon.
Green Fee: on application.
Societies: societies affiliated to Golfing Union catered for.
Catering: limited catering available.

U36 Bundoran
☎(072) 41302
Bundoran, Co Donegal
32 miles W of Enniskillen, 25 miles N of Sligo.
Links/parkland course.
Championship 18 holes, 5785 metres, S.S.S.71
Designed by Harry Vardon.
Founded 1894
Visitors: welcome at all times, book in advance.
Green Fee: £10/day, £12 WE.
Societies: welcome but advance booking required, £9 20 or more.
Catering: snacks only, meals in hotel.
Hotels: Great Northern on course; Holyrood; Imperial; Maghery; Atlantic.

U37 Cahir Park
☎(052) 41474
Kilcommon, Cahir, Co Tipperary.
1 mile S of Cahir on Clogheen road.
Parkland course.
9 holes, 5696 metres, S.S.S.69
Designed by Eddie Hackett.
Founded 1965
Visitors: welcome; advisable to check at weekends.
Green Fee: £7.
Societies: catered for on Sat.
Catering: bar; group meals at 3 days notice.
Hotels: Cahir House; Castle Court; Kilcoran Lodge.

U38 Callan
☎(056) 25136
Geraldine, Callan, Co Kilkenny
10 miles S of Kilkenny, 0.5 mile from Callan.
Parkland course.
9 holes, 6258 yards, S.S.S.70
Designed by Des Smyth.
Founded 1929
Visitors: welcome.
Green Fee: £7 (£5 with member).
Societies: welcome weekdays and Sat am.
Catering: bar daily, food by arrangement.
Hotels: Somers; Newpark; Hotel Kilkenny; Club House.

U39 Carlow
☎(0503) 31695 office, 40065 fax.
Deerpark, Dublin Rd, Carlow, Co Carlow
1 mile from Carlow station, take Naas road from Dublin (52 miles).
Undulating parkland course.
18 holes, 5844 metres, S.S.S.70
Designed by Tom Simpson.
Founded 1899
Visitors: welcome.
Green Fee: £13 WD, £17 WE.
Societies: welcome weekdays or Sat am.
Catering: full catering available.
Hotels: Seven Oaks; Royal.

U40 Carrick-on-Shannon
☎(079) 67015
Woodbrook, Carrick-on-Shannon, Co Roscommon.
3 miles W of Carrick on N4 route.
Parkland course.
9 holes, 5545 yards, S.S.S.68
Designed by E. Hackett.
Founded 1910
Visitors: welcome at all times.
Green Fee: £6/day.
Societies: on request to Sec.
Catering: bar facilities and snacks, catering on request.
Hotels: County.

U41 Carrick-on-Suir
☎(051) 40047
Garravoone, Co Tipperary
Approx 2 miles from Carrick-on-Suir on main road to Dungarvan; signposted on right side of road.
Undulating parkland course.
9 holes, 5948 yards, S.S.S.68
Designed by Edward Hackett.
Founded 1939
Visitors: welcome except Sun.
Green Fee: £10.
Societies: welcome except Sun.
Catering: available by advance booking.
Hotels: Carraig; Cedarfield House.

U42 Carrickmines
☎(01) 955972
Carrickmines, Dublin 18
T43, 7 miles S of Dublin, left at Sandyford.
Heathland course.
9 holes, 6078 yards, S.S.S.69
Founded 1905
Visitors: welcome weekdays and with member on Sat; also Sun and Bank Holidays.
Green Fee: £15 WD, £18 WE & BH.
Catering: very limited.

U43 Castle
☎(01) 904207
Woodside Drive, Rathfarnham, Dublin 14
From city turn left after Terenure and 2nd right.
Parkland course.
18 holes, 6240 yards, S.S.S.69
Designed by H.S. Colt.
Founded 1913
Visitors: welcome weekdays.
Green Fee: £25.
Societies: applications considered.
Catering: full lunch and dinner.
Hotels: Orwell Lodge.

U44 Castlebar
☎(094) 21649
Rocklands, Castlebar, Co Mayo
1.25 miles from town centre.
Parkland course.
18 holes, 6109 yards, S.S.S.69
Founded 1910
Visitors: welcome weekdays.
Green Fee: on application.
Societies: welcome.
Catering: catering available with 3 hours notice.
Hotels: Welcome Inn; Breaffy House; Travellers Friend; Imperial.

U45 Castlecomer
☎(056) 41139
Drumgoole, Castlecomer, Co Kilkenny
On N7 10 miles N of Kilkenny.
Parkland course.
9 holes, 6450 yards, S.S.S.71
Designed by Pat Ruddy.
Founded 1935
Visitors: welcome Mon to Sat, book in advance.
Green Fee: £10 WD, £12 WE & BH.
Societies: Mon-Sat.
Catering: snacks; lunches to order.
Hotels: Newpark (Kilkenny).

U46 Castlerea
☎(0907) 20068
Clonalis, Castlerea, Co Roscommon
On main Dublin-Castlebar road, course just outside town on Castlebar side.
Parkland course.
9 holes, 4974 yards, S.S.S.66
Founded 1905
Visitors: welcome.
Green Fee: on application.
Societies: welcome by prior arrangement.
Catering: available by arrangement for societies.
Hotels: Don Arms; Tullys.

U47 Castletroy
☎(061) 335261, 335753 Sec.
Castletroy, Limerick
3 miles from Limerick city on Dublin
road, turn right at signpost in
Castletroy, course 300 yards on left.
Parkland course.
18 holes, 6340 yards, S.S.S.71
Founded 1937
Visitors: weekdays unlimited,
weekends with member only.
Green Fee: £20 (£12 with member).
Societies: Mon, Wed, Fri by
arrangement.
Catering: full catering service.
Hotels: Two Mile Inn; Castletroy
Park; Royal George.

U48 Castlewarden G & CC
☎(01) 589254
Castlewarden, Kill, Co Kildare
Off Naas dual carriageway between
Newlands Cross and Naas.
18 holes, Par 73
Founded 1990
Visitors: welcome weekdays.
Green Fee: £10 weekdays.
Societies: apply to Sec.
Catering: bar, snacks, lunches,
dinners.

U49 Ceann Sibéal (Dingle)
☎(066) 56255
Ballyferriter, Co Kerry
Follow Ballyferriter signs from
Dingle, turn right 0.5 mile after
Ballyferriter.
Seaside links course.
18 holes, 6440 yards, S.S.S.71
Designed by Eddie Hackett.
Founded 1924
Visitors: welcome at all times.
Green Fee: £15.
Societies: welcome, prior booking.
Catering: at adjacent hotel.
Sea fishing.
Hotels: Granville; Ostan Golf Dun an
Oir; Benners, Skel Ig (Dingle)

U50 Charleville
☎(063) 81257 office, 81274
members
Ardmore, Charleville, Co Cork
About 35 miles from Cork, 25 miles
from Limerick; course 2 miles on
Charleville-Kanturk road.
Parkland course.
18 holes, 6430 yards, S.S.S.70
Founded 29 July 1941
Visitors: welcome weekdays.
Green Fee: £10/day.
Societies: any day except Sun.
Catering: bar and restaurant.

U51 Cill Dara
☎(045) 21433
Kildare, Co Kildare
1 mile E of Kildare.
Moorland course.
9 holes, 6196 yards, S.S.S.66
Visitors: welcome.
Green Fee: on application.
Societies: meals served by
arrangement.

U52 Claremorris
☎(094) 71527
Rushbrook, Castlemaggaret,
Claremorris, Co Mayo
On Galway road from Claremorris,
1.5 miles from town.
Parkland course.
9 holes, 5898 yards, S.S.S.69
Founded 1927
Visitors: welcome, no restrictions.
Green Fee: on application.
Societies: catered for on weekdays.
Catering: by arrangement.
Swimming, squash, snooker in
Claremorris town.
Hotels: Dalton Inn; Western.

U53 Clones
☎(047) 56017
Hilton Park, Clones, Co Monaghan
3 miles S of Clones towards
Scotshouse.
Parkland course.
9 holes, 5788 yards, S.S.S.68
Founded 1913
Visitors: welcome, restricted Sun.
Green Fee: £6.
Societies: welcome, except Sun.
Catering: available at all times.
Hotels: Creighton; Hibernian;
Lennard Arms; White Horse,
Cootehill.

U54 Clonmel
☎(052) 21138, 24050 Sec.
Lyreanearla, Mountain Rd, Clonmel,
Co Tipperary
On road to Comeragh Mountains, 2
miles SE of Clonmel.
Parkland course.
18 holes, 5806 metres, S.S.S.71
Designed by Eddie Hackett.
Founded 1911
Visitors: phone Sec for details.
Green Fee: £10 WD, £12 WE.
Societies: welcome by prior
arrangement.
Catering: full catering facilities
available.
Snooker, pool, table tennis.
Hotels: Hotel Minella; Clonmel Arms;
Hearns; Knocklofty.

U55 Clontarf
☎(01) 331892 office, 331877 Pro,
331520 bar
Donnycarney House, Malahide Rd,
Dublin 3
NE of city centre, proceed for 2.5
miles from city centre via North
Strand and Fairview to Lower
Malahide Road.
Parkland course.
18 holes, 5459 metres, S.S.S.68
Founded 1912
Visitors: welcome weekdays, check
with Sec re times.
Green Fee: £18.
Societies: Tues and Fri.
Catering: full facilities.
Bowling green.
Hotels: Skylon; Hollybrook; Marine.

U56 Cobh
☎(021) 812399
Ballywilliam, Cobh, Co Cork
1 mile E of Cobh.
Parkland course.
9 holes, 4366 metres, S.S.S.63
Designed by Eddie Hackett.
Founded 1987
Visitors: welcome, booking at
weekends.
Green Fee: £6/day WD, £7/day WE.
Societies: welcome Mon-Sat.
Catering: bar, snacks.
Hotels: Commodore (free golf).

U57 Connemara
☎(095) 23502, 23662 fax.
Ballyconneely, Clifden, Co Galway
9 miles S of Clifden.
Seaside course.
18 holes, 6620 metres, S.S.S.75
(Championship)
Designed by Eddie Hackett.
Founded 1973
Visitors: welcome; must have h/cap
cert.
Green Fee: May-Sept £16, Mar, April
and Oct £14, Nov-Feb £10.
Societies: welcome; special rate £9
(min 20) Oct-May.
Catering: bar and à la carte
restaurant. Banqueting for 100.
Hotels: Allbeyglen Castle; Rockglen
Manor; Clifden Bay.

U58 Corballis
☎(01) 436583
Dunabate, Co Dublin
Off main Dublin-Belfast road.
Public seaside links course.
18 holes, 4543 metres (4971 yards),
S.S.S.64
Founded 1971

Visitors: welcome, golf clubs for each player, no other restrictions.
Green Fee: £6 WD, £7 WE & BH.
Societies: welcome by arrangement except Sun.
Catering: no bar, limited facilities. Pool.
Hotels: Dunes; Swords.

U59 **Cork**
☎(021) 353451, 353410 fax.
Little Island, Cork, Co Cork
5 miles E of Cork on N25.
Championship parkland course.
18 holes, 6115 metres, S.S.S.72
Designed by Alister Mackenzie.
Founded 1888
Visitors: welcome, advisable to ring in advance.
Green Fee: £20/day WD, £22 WE, (£7.50 with member).
Societies: apply to Sec/Manager.
Catering: full catering facilities.
Hotels: Silver Springs; Ashbourne House; John Barleycorn; Commodore; Metropole.

U60 **County Cavan**
☎(049) 31283
Arnmore House, Drumelis, Cavan, Co Cavan
1 mile from Cavan town on Killeshandra road.
Parkland course.
18 holes, 6030 yards, S.S.S.69
Founded 1894
Visitors: welcome 7 days per week, restricted days Wed and Sun.
Green Fee: £9/day (£5 with member).
Societies: Mon-Fri preferred.
Catering: full catering.
Snooker.
Hotels: Kilmore; Farnham Arms.

U61 **County Longford**
☎(043) 46310
Glack, Longford
Off Dublin to Sligo road (N4) E of town, signposted.
Undulating course.
18 holes, 6028 yards, S.S.S.68
Designed by E. Hackett.
Founded 1894
Visitors: welcome.
Green Fee: on application.
Societies: welcome by arrangement.
Catering: meals served.

U62 **County Louth**
☎(041) 22329
Baltray, Drogheda, Co Louth

4 miles NE of Drogheda, take road along N bank of River Boyne to Baltray village.
Seaside links course.
18 holes, 6763 yards, S.S.S.72
Designed by Tom Simpson.
Founded 1892
Visitors: on request, not Tues.
Green Fee: on application.
Societies: on application.
Catering: full facilities.
Tennis, snooker.
Hotels: Glenside; Neptune.

U63 **County Sligo**
☎(071) 77186, 77134, 77460 fax.
Rosses Point, Co Sligo
5 miles W of Sligo, signposted Rosses Point.
Seaside links championship course.
18 holes, 6003 metres, S.S.S.72
Designed by Colt & Alison.
Founded 1894
Visitors: welcome, booking advised.
Green Fee: £20/round.
Societies: by arrangement.
Catering: full facilities.
Hotels: Yeats Country; Ballincar House; Sligo Park; Sligo Great Southern.

U64 **Courtown**
☎(055) 25166
Kiltennel, Gorey, Co Wexford
3 miles from Gorey off Dublin-Rosslare road.
Parkland course.
18 holes, 6398 yards, S.S.S.70
Designed by Harris & Associates.
Founded 1936
Visitors: welcome except on major competition days.
Green Fee: £11 WD, £15 WE.
Societies: by prior arrangement except June-Aug.
Catering: snacks and full catering.
Hotels: Bayview; Marlfield House.

U65 **Cruit Island**
☎(075) 43296
Kincasslagh, Co Donegal
6 miles N of Dungloe.
Scenic seaside links course.
9 holes, 4833 metres, S.S.S.66
Founded 1985
Visitors: welcome.
Green Fee: £7/day; July/Aug £8/day; family and weekly rates.
Societies: welcome.
Catering: bar and snacks weekends; daily in summer.
Hotels: through Donegal Leisure Breaks, golf incl. (phone 075 42167).

U66 **Curragh**
☎(045) 41714, 41238
Curragh, Co Kildare
3 miles S of Newbridge, 28 miles SW of Dublin.
Parkland course.
18 holes, 6001 metres, S.S.S.71
Designed by David Ritchie (1852).
Founded 1883
Visitors: weekdays only; required to contact Sec before attending.
Green Fee: £12/round WD, £15/round BH.
Societies: weekdays, limited number of weekends; apply to Sec in advance.
Catering: full facilities.
Hotels: Hotel Keadeen; Lumville House.

U67 **Deer Park Hotel**
☎(01) 322624
Deer Park Hotel, Howth, Co Dublin
9 miles E of city centre via Fairview, Clontarf and Sutton; 3rd turn right after Sutton Cross.
Public parkland courses.
18 holes, 6647 yards; 9 holes, 3130 yards; 12 holes Par 3, 1810 yards.
Designed by Fred Hawtree.
Founded 1973
Visitors: welcome all week; weekends expect delays.
Green Fee: £7.75.
Societies: welcome weekdays.
Catering: full facilities, lounge, snack bar, restaurant.
Snooker, function room.
Hotels: Deer Park Hotel on site; golfing specials available.

U68 **Delgany**
☎(01) 287 4536
Delgany, Co Wicklow
Adjacent to village of Delgany off main road to Wexford.
Parkland course.
18 holes, 5454 metres, S.S.S.69
Founded 1908
Visitors: welcome except competition days.
Green Fee: on application.
Societies: welcome.
Catering: full catering facilities.
Hotels: Wicklow Arms; Glenview.

U69 **Donabate**
☎(01) 436346, 436001
Donabate, Balcarrick Co Dublin
Take 1st right 1 mile N of Swords on Dublin to Belfast road.
Parkland course.
18 holes, 5679 metres, S.S.S.69

County Louth

There are certain courses throughout Britain and Ireland where a sense of expectancy reaches a peak at a specific point near journey's end; when turning off the main road at Wadebridge for St Enodoc, for instance, or when a long drive nears its end along the only road to Southerness, a superb links on the Solway Firth, which in 1985 hosted the Scottish Amateur for the first time.

A similar sense of anticipation accompanies the last lap to Brancaster which takes you past the church and down through the marsh lined by tall rushes; and there is a less glamorous approach beyond the level crossing to the Royal Cinque Ports Golf Club at Deal. The twisty conclusion to the journey to Rye is another example. But there can be few sights as thrilling as the links of County Louth at Baltray at last coming into view.

It is a fine, challenging course in the traditional mould of dunes, undoubtedly one of my favourites and one whose rating within Ireland is not as high as it should be. It is worthy of the best, full of variety and contrast with always the magnificence of its distant views.

Although there have been modifications, one or two made necessary by moving the clubhouse some years ago, there is still an authentic touch of Tom Simpson about it that bears the unmistakable mark of quality. If I had to exemplify it, I would point to the long 3rd which, after a reasonably straight forward drive, reveals hidden talents once the brow of dunes has been scaled. Beautifully natural humps and hollows make careful placing of the second shot essential and, for those attempting to get home in two, there is only a narrow path between salvation and ruin. An attractive small green is not easy to hit.

The curving 1st and testing 2nd make a nice introduction but the 4th, a short par 4, offers some relief before the first of four first class short holes. The 5th and 7th, sandwiched around another fine par 5, demand well-controlled, truly hit iron shots while the 8th and 9th are no easy 4s.

A sense of space becomes more apparent on the second half which, having begun with a hole alongside the clubhouse, works its way towards the sea by means of the dogleg par 5 11th. It is then that a special character is lent by the 12th, 13th and 14th which, from a combination of factors, comprise a notable trio. They emphasise the merit of great par 4s, not perhaps daunting in terms of yardage but rewarding in the satisfaction they give by being played properly, as they must be if they are to yield a par or a birdie.

Changes to the course have resulted in two short holes in the last four but the 16th is appealing and the 18th the last of five par 5s.

Baltray, as the course is more conveniently called after the local fishing village, has a championship cloak without a doubt and it also has its less forbidding side which makes it so popular for a day out.

Harry Bradshaw's winning aggregate of 291 in the 1947 Irish Professional championship tells a tale or two about its full blown potential. It is also rare among Irish clubs in having two legendary Irish women golfers as members. Val Reddan, as Clarrie Tiernan, won the Irish title twice and was also the first Irish woman to play in the Curtis Cup. After the war, she was confronted by her new local rival Philomena Garvey in the final of the Irish, not, as would have been most appropriate, at Baltray, but at Lahinch. After the longest final, Garvey won at the 39th, the first of her 15 victories.

Continuing the feminine influence, Mrs Josephine Connolly founded the East of Ireland Men's championship played annually at Baltray, an event by which Irish golfers set great store. It can claim father and son winners in Joe and Roddy Carr, but when you speak of the course you speak of distinction. Its list of champions is no more than it deserves.

Visitors: welcome.
Green Fee: on application.
Societies: welcome by arrangement.
Catering: meals served.

U70 Donegal
☎(073) 34054
Murvagh, Ballintra, Co Donegal
About 6 miles S of Donegal via N15.
Seaside links course.
18 holes, 6867 yards, S.S.S.73
Designed by Eddie Hackett.
Founded 1960, opened 1973
Visitors: welcome, no restrictions.
Green Fee: £10/day.
Societies: catered for daily.
Catering: bar and restaurant; buffet.
Snooker.
Hotels: Sand House, special 3-day
mid-week golfing breaks.

U71 Doneraile
☎(022) 24137
Doneraile, Co Cork
Off T11, 28 miles N of Cork, 9 miles
from Mallow.
Parkland course.
9 holes, 5528 yards, S.S.S.66
Visitors: welcome.
Green Fee: on application.
Societies: welcome.
Catering: meals served.

U72 Dooks
☎(066) 68205
Glenbeigh, Co Kerry
4 miles W of Killonglin, at bridge
between Killonglin and Glenbeigh.
Seaside course.
18 holes, 6021 yards, S.S.S.68
Designed by Eddie Hackett.
Founded 1889
Visitors: welcome, check at
weekends; h/cap cert required.
Green Fee: £14/day.
Societies: welcome.
Catering: restaurant facilities.
Hotels: Glenbeigh; Towers; Bianconi
Inn; Canagh Lodge; Mount Brandon;
And na Si; Castlerosse.

U73 Douglas
☎(021) 891086, 895297
Sec/Manager
Douglas, Cork
Within 3 miles of Cork city, 0.5 mile
beyond Douglas village.
Parkland course.
18 holes, 5294 metres, S.S.S.68
Founded 1910
Visitors: welcome, with reservation
at weekends.

Green Fee: on application.
Societies: by arrangement before
start of season.
Catering: snacks and meals served.

U74 Dromoland Castle
☎(061) 368444, 368144
Newmarket-on-Fergus, Co Clare
On Limerick-Galway road, 1.5 miles
through Newmarket-on-Fergus.
Public parkland course.
18 holes, 6098 yards, S.S.S.71
Designed by Whittaker (USA).
Founded 1964
Visitors: welcome.
Green Fee: £18/day WD, £20 WE.
Societies: welcome, fees negotiable.
Catering: available.
Tennis, banqueting.
Hotels: Dromoland Castle.

U75 Dun Laoghaire
☎(01) 280 3916
Eglinton Park, Tivoli Rd, Dun
Laoghaire, Co Dublin
7 miles from Dublin, 0.5 mile from
Dun Laoghaire centre and ferry port.
Parkland course.
18 holes, 5478 metres, S.S.S.69
Founded 1910
Visitors: Mon, Tues, Wed am, Fri;
reserved for members 12.30-2pm.
Green Fee: £20.
Societies: Tues and Fri by prior
booking only.
Catering: full service during season.
Hotels: Royal Marine; Fitzpatricks
Castle; Hotel Victor.

U76 Dundalk
☎(042) 21731 Office, 22102 Pro,
21379 Members.
Blackrock, Dundalk, Co Louth
Off T1 3 miles S of Dundalk on
Dundalk Bay.
Parkland course.
18 holes, 6740 yards, S.S.S.72
Designed by Thomas & Allis.
Founded 1905
Visitors: welcome except Sun.
Green Fee: on application.
Societies: welcome; booking
essential.
Catering: dinners, snacks every day.
Hotels: Fairways; Imperial;
Ballymascanlon; Derryhale;
Carrickdale; Lorne.

U77 Dunfanaghy
☎(074) 36335
Dunfanaghy, Letterkenny, Co
Donegal

On main Letterkenny-Dunfanaghy
road 0.5 mile E of Dunfanaghy.
Public seaside links course.
18 holes, 5066 metres, S.S.S.66
Founded 1906
Visitors: welcome except Sun.
Green Fee: £7 WD, £8 WE.
Societies: by arrangement.
Catering: bar, snacks.
Hotels: Arnold's; Shandon; Carrig
Rua; Port-na-blagh.

U78 Dungarvan
☎(058) 41605
Ballinacourty, Dungarvan, Co
Waterford
About 3 miles E of Dungarvan, from
Dungarvan take coast road to
Tramore, 1st right turn leads to club.
Meadowland course.
9 holes, 5615 metres, S.S.S.69
Founded 1924
Visitors: Mon-Fri.
Green Fee: £10/day.
Societies: Mon-Fri, apply in advance.
Hotels: Clonea Strand; Gold Coast
Holiday Homes at entrance to club.

U79 Dunmore
☎(023) 33352
Dunmore House, Muckross,
Clonakilty, Co Cork
3 miles from Clonakilty, signposted.
Hilly open course.
9 holes, 4464 yards, S.S.S.61
Designed by E. Hackett.
Founded 1967
Visitors: welcome any time.
Green Fee: on application.
Societies: welcome by arrangement.
Catering: bar and restaurant
facilities in Dunmore House.
Hotels: Dunmore House (free golf).

U80 East Cork
☎(021) 631687
Gortacrue, Midleton, Co Cork
On main Cork to Waterford road 10
miles E of Cork city, turn left at
roundabout in Middleton,
signposted, about 1.5 miles.
Parkland course.
18 holes, 4874 yards, S.S.S.69
Designed by Edward Hackett.
Founded 1970
Visitors: welcome except Sun am.
Green Fee: on application.
Societies: phone for details.
Catering: lunch served except Sun.
Snooker, riding etc, details on
request.
Hotels: Commodore, Garryvoes (golf
packages); Middleton Park.

U81 Edenderry

☎(0405) 31072
Kishavanny, Edenderry, Co Offaly
1 mile before town on road from
Dublin; turn right just before River
Boyne, clubhouse 0.5 mile on left.
Public parkland/moorland course,
quick drying.
9 holes, 5531 metres, S.S.S.69;
further 9 holes under construction.
Founded 1947
Visitors: restricted Thurs and
weekends; apply for details.
Green Fee: £5/day WD, £6/day WE.
Societies: on application except Sun
and Thurs.
Catering: bar, good quality catering
by arrangement.

U82 Edmondstown

☎(01) 932461 Club, 931082 Sec,
941049 Pro, 933205 restaurant
Rathfarnham, Dublin 16
T42 S of Dublin, Rathfarnham 1 mile.
Parkland course.
18 holes, 5663 metres, S.S.S.69
Designed by Eddie Hackett.
Founded 1944
Visitors: welcome, dress code in
operation.
Green Fee: £18 WD, £22 WE by
arrangement.
Societies: Mon, Thurs, Fri, Sat, to
11.30am.
Catering: full facilities.
Snooker.

U83 Elm Park

☎(01) 693438, 693014 or 694505
Nutley Lane, Donnybrook, Dublin 4
2 miles from city centre beside
Montrose television studios and St
Vincents Hospital.
Parkland course.
18 holes, 5422 metres, S.S.S.68
Designed by Fred Davies.
Founded 1927
Visitors: welcome but phone in
advance.
Green Fee: on application.
Societies: catered for Tues only.
Catering: full facilities.

U84 Ennis

☎(065) 24074 Office, 20690 Pro.
Drumbiggle, Ennis, Co Clare
1 mile W of N18 Limerick-Galway at
Ennis.
Gently rolling parkland course.
18 holes, 5316 metres, S.S.S.68
Founded 1907
Visitors: welcome; not before 12am
Sun; please book in advance.

Green Fee: £14.
Societies: not Sun.
Catering: bar, excellent daylong
catering.
Snooker.
Hotels: Auburn Lodge; Queens; West
County; Old Ground; (concessionary
green fee scheme).

U85 Enniscorthy

☎(054) 33191, 33135
Knockmarshal, Enniscorthy, Co
Wexford
1.5 miles from town on New Ross
road.
Parkland course.
18 holes, 5382 metres, S.S.S.70
Designed by E. Hackett.
Founded 1924
Visitors: welcome except Tues
(Ladies Day); prior arrangement at
weekends.
Green Fee: on application.
Societies: most welcome.
Catering: full catering.
Snooker.
Hotels: Murphy Floods.

U86 Enniscrone

☎(096) 36297, 36657
Enniscrone, Co Sligo
8 miles N of Ballina, 0.5 mile from
Enniscrone.
Seaside course.
18 holes, 6487 yards, S.S.S.72
Designed by E. Hackett.
Founded 1918
Visitors: weekdays unrestricted,
phone for weekend times.
Green Fee: April-Oct £15/day,
husband and wife £20/day.
Societies: welcome if arranged in
advance, phone (096) 36335.
Catering: bar and restaurant
facilities, order before play.
Hotels: Atlantic, Benbulben, Castle
Arms, (Enniscrone); Downhill,
Imperial, Beleek Castle, (Ballina).

U87 Fermoy

☎(025) 31472
Fermoy, Co Cork
2 miles from Fermoy off Cork-Dublin
road.
Undulating course.
18 holes, 5550 yards, S.S.S.70
Designed by Commander Harris.
Founded 1892
Visitors: welcome weekdays.
Green Fee: £12 WD, £15 WE.
Societies: weekdays and Sat am.
Catering: snacks served.
Hotels: Grand.

U88 Forrest Little

☎(01) 401763 or 401183
Forest Little, Cloghran, Co Dublin
0.5 mile beyond Dublin Airport on
Dublin-Belfast road, take 1st left.
Parkland course.
18 holes, 5865 metres, S.S.S.70
Designed by Fred Hawtree.
Founded 1940
Visitors: welcome weekdays.
Green Fee: on application.
Societies: Mon and Thurs pm.
Catering: snacks always available; à
la carte menu from 5pm daily.
Hotels: Dublin Airport; Hawthorn.

U89 Foxrock

☎(01) 289 3992, 2895668
Torquay Rd, Dublin 18
6 miles from Dublin; right off T7 just
past Stillergan on to Leopardstown
Rd, then left into Torquay Rd.
Parkland course.
9 holes, 5439 metres, S.S.S.69
Founded 1893
Visitors: welcome Mon, Wed am,
Thurs, Fri; Sun only with member.
Green Fee: on application.
Societies: Mon and Thurs.
Catering: soup, sandwiches, coffee.

U90 Galway

☎(091) 23038 Pro, 21827 Catering,
22169 Sec/Manager
Blackrock, Salthill, Galway
On L100 2 miles W of Galway.
Seaside course.
18 holes, 5828 metres, S.S.S.70
Founded 1895
Visitors: not Sun, limited Tues, Sat.
Green Fee: on application.
Societies: accepted, advance
booking (green fees £10).
Catering: full facilities.

U91 Glengarriff

☎(027) 63150
Glengarriff, Co Cork
On T65, 55 miles W of Cork.
Seaside course.
9 holes, 2042 metres, S.S.S.62
Founded 1936
Visitors: welcome.
Green Fee: on application.
Societies: special rates for societies.

U92 Gort

☎(091) 31336
Laughty Shaughnessy, Gort, Co
Galway
24 miles S of Galway on Gort to
Tubber road.

Parkland course.
9 holes, 5174 metres, S.S.S.67
Designed by Matt Hackett
Founded 1924
Visitors: welcome all week except
Wed evenings and Sun am.
Green Fee: £6/day.
Societies: apply to Hon Sec.
Catering: snacks April-Sept.
Hotels: Sullivans Royal; Glynn's;
O'Gradey's Rest.

U93 Grange
☎(01) 932832, 932889 or 935800
(locker room)
Grange Rd, Rathfarnham, Dublin 16
7 miles S from city centre, near
Rathfarnham village.
Parkland course.
18 holes, 5517 yards, S.S.S.69
Designed by James Braid.
Founded 1910
Visitors: welcome weekdays except
Tues and Wed afternoons.
Green Fee: on application.
Societies: welcome Mon and Thurs.
Catering: full facilities.
Hotels: Marlay.

U94 Greencastle
☎(077) 81013
Greencastle, Moville, Co Donegal
On L85 23 miles NE of Londonderry
through Moville.
Public seaside course.
18 holes, 5118 metres, S.S.S.67
Designed by Eddie Hackett (new 9
holes).
Founded 1892
Visitors: welcome.
Green Fee: £8 WD (£6 with member),
£12 WE & BH (£8 with member).
Societies: by arrangement.
Catering: bar and catering facilities.
Hotels: Font; McNamaras; Foyle.

U95 Greenore
☎(042) 73229
Greenore, Co Louth
From Belfast, take 1st left on
Dundalk road out of Newry to Omeath
and Carlingford, course 2 miles on
from Carlingford; from Dublin,
through Drogheda, take 1st right on
Newry road out of Dundalk, then 15
miles to Greenore.
Wooded seaside course.
18 holes, 6506 yards, S.S.S.71
Designed by Eddie Hackett.
Founded 1896
Visitors: welcome weekdays and
most weekends; advisable to phone
Sec at weekends.

Green Fee: £8 WD, £12 WE & BH.
Societies: welcome any day.
Catering: daily.
Hotels: Ballymascanlon; McKevitts
Village; Park; Grand Central.

U96 Greystones
☎(01) 287 6624
Greystones, Co Wicklow
20 miles S of Dublin, off main
Dublin-Wexford road.
Parkland course.
18 holes, 5401 metres, S.S.S.68
Founded 1895
Visitors: Mon, Tues, Fri am.
Green Fee: £16 WD, £20 WE.
Societies: Mon, Tues, Fri.
Catering: full catering.
Snooker.
Hotels: La Touche; Royal (Bray).

U97 Gweedore
☎(075) 31140
Derrybeg, Letterkenny, Co Donegal
L82 from Letterkenny or T72 from
Donegal.
Seaside course.
18 holes, 6873 yards, S.S.S.73
Designed by Eddie Hackett.
Founded 1923
Visitors: always welcome,
reasonable rates, excellent service.
Green Fee: on application.
Societies: catered for weekends.
Catering: lunch served at weekends.

U98 Harbour Point
☎(021) 353094
Little Island, Cork, Co Cork
6 miles by road to E of Cork centre.
Undulating parkland championship
course overlooking harbour; 2
natural loops of 9.
18 holes, 6800 yards, S.S.S.72
Designed by Paddy Merrigan.
Founded June 1991
Visitors: welcome any time.
Green Fee: £20/round.
Societies: welcome by prior
arrangement.
Catering: full facilities.
Driving range.

U99 Hazel Grove
☎(01) 520911
Mt Seskin Rd, Jobstown, Tallaght,
Dublin 24
On Blessington road, 2.5 miles from
Tallaght.
Parkland course.
9 holes, 5030 metres, S.S.S.67;
extending to 18 holes.

Designed by Jim Byrne.
Founded 1988
Visitors: welcome Mon, Wed, Fri;
not after 12am Tues, not after 11am
Sat, not Sun; Thurs Ladies' Day.
Green Fee: £8/day (£6 with member)
WD, £12/day (£8 wih member) WE.
Societies: by arrangement max 50
(Sat am max 40).
Catering: bar, function room (140);
catering by arrangement.
Large practice area.

U100 Headfort
☎(046) 40146
Kells, Co Meath
0.25 mile from Kells on main
Kells-Dublin road.
Parkland course.
18 holes, 6393 yards, S.S.S.70
Founded 1930
Visitors: welcome Mon, Wed, Thurs,
Fri; limited weekends.
Green Fee: £10 WD, £15 WE & BH.
Societies: weekday mornings only
(except Tues); limited number of Sat
mornings.
Catering: bar snacks, other by prior
arrangement.
Hotels: Headfort Arms.

U101 Heath
☎(0502) 46533
The Heath, Portlaoise, Co Laois
4 miles NE of Portlaoise, just off main
Dublin to Cork/Limerick road.
Heathland course.
18 holes, 5721 metres, S.S.S.70
Founded 1930
Visitors: welcome; by arrangement
with Hon Sec at weekends.
Green Fee: £8 WD, £12 WE.
Societies: welcome by arrangement
with Sec.
Catering: full facilities available by
arrangement with Steward.
Driving range.
Hotels: Killeshin; Montague;
Regency.

U102 Hermitage
☎(01) 626 8491, 626 5049
Lucan, Co Dublin
T3 W from Dublin, 1 mile from Lucan.
18 holes, 6034 metres, S.S.S.71
(Championship)
Founded 1905
Visitors: welcome Mon, Thurs, Fri
most mornings.
Green Fee: on application.
Societies: weekdays.
Catering: every day.
Hotels: Ashling; Spa; Springfield.

U103 Hollywood

☎(01) 433406, 433113 after hours
Hollywood, Ballyboughal, Co Dublin
12 miles N of Dublin city off
Dublin/Belfast road.
Public parkland course with
all-weather elevated greens.
18 holes, 7146 yards, S.S.S.72
Designed by Mel Flanagan.
Founded 1990
Visitors: welcome any time.
Green Fee: £7 WD, £10 WE.
Societies: booking necessary.
Catering: bar, restaurant.
Hotels: Trust House Forte (Dublin
Airport); Grand (Malahide); Skylon
(Drumcondra).

U104 Howth

☎(01) 323055
Carrickbrack Rd, Sutton, Dublin
9.5 miles NE of city centre, 1.5 miles
from Sutton Cross towards Howth
summit.
Heathland course.
18 holes, 5618 metres, S.S.S.69
Designed by James Braid.
Founded 1916
Visitors: welcome weekdays.
Green Fee: £15 WD only.
Societies: weekdays except Wed.
Catering: snacks and bar service.
Hotels: Marine; Howth Lodge.

U105 Island

☎(01) 436104 Public, 436205
Office, 436462 Sec/Manager
Corballis, Donabate, Co Dublin
From Dublin leave T1 approx 1 mile
beyond Swords at Donabate
signpost, then L91 for 3 miles and
turn right at sign.
Seaside course.
18 holes, 6053 metres, S.S.S.72
Designed by F. Hawtree & Eddie
Hackett.
Founded 1890
Visitors: weekdays.
Green Fee: £21 WD.
Societies: Mon, Tues, Fri.
Catering: available.
Hotels: Grand; The Dunes.

U106 Kenmare

☎(064) 41291
Kenmare, Co Kerry
On T65, 20 miles S of Killarney, 100
yards out of town.
Parkland course.
9 holes, 2410 yards, S.S.S.63
Designed by Eddie Hackett.
Founded 1903
Visitors: welcome, no restrictions.

Green Fee: £10.
Societies: apply to Sec.
Catering: bar, snacks on request.
Hotels: Park; Sheen Falls Lodge;
Kenmare Bay.

U107 Kildare Hotel & CC

☎(01) 627311
Straffan, Co Kildare
22 miles from Dublin city centre via
N7 Naas dual carriageway, or
Lucan/Celbridge route.
Parkland course.
18 holes.
Designed by Arnold Palmer.
Founded 1991
Visitors: booking essential.
Green Fee: £75/round, £110/day.
Societies: by arrangement.
Catering: bar, restaurant, snack bar.
Indoor and outdoor tennis, river and
lake fishing, exercise centre, croquet.
Hotels: Hotel on site.

U108 Kilkee

☎(065) 56048
East End, Kilkee, Co Clare
Within 400 metres of town.
Meadowland course.
9 holes, 6185 yards, S.S.S.69
Designed by McAllister.
Founded 1892
Visitors: welcome.
Green Fee: £12/day.
Societies: May, June and from
mid-Aug to end of Sept.
Catering: snacks always available;
meals for societies by arrangement.
Hotels: Strand; Victoria; Stella Maris;
Bay View.

U109 Kilkenny

☎(056) 22125
Glendine, Kilkenny, Co Kilkenny
2 miles N of town off Castlecomer Rd.
Parkland course.
18 holes, 6400 yards, S.S.S.70
Founded 1896
Visitors: welcome, few restrictions.
Green Fee: £12 WD, £15 WE & BH.
Societies: mostly Sat mornings.
Catering: at clubhouse.
Snooker, pool.
Hotels: Newpark; Hotel Kilkenny;
Springhill.

U110 Killarney

☎(064) 31034, 31242, 33899
Mahoney's Point, Killarney, Co Kerry
3 miles W of Killarney on Killorglin
road.
Parkland/lakeside courses.

Killeen, 18 holes, 7122 yards,
S.S.S.73; Mahony's Point, 18 holes,
6734 yards, S.S.S.71
Designed by Eddie Hackett and Dr W.
Sullivan (Killeen), Sir Guy Campbell
(Mahony's).
Founded 1893
Visitors: welcome, h/cap cert
required.
Green Fee: on application.
Societies: at all times.
Catering: all day every day.
Hotels: green fee discounts at
numerous local hotels.

U111 Killeen (Four Lakes)

☎(045) 66003
Kill, Co Kildare
N7 to Kill village, turn right off
carriageway heading for Straffan, left
at next junction, 2 miles on left.
Parkland course.
18 holes, 5445 yards, S.S.S.66
Founded 1986
Visitors: welcome all week.
Green Fee: £8 WD, £10 WE.
Societies: welcome.
Catering: full bar and catering.
Hotels: Green Isle; Ambassador.

U112 Killiney

☎(01) 285 1983
Ballinclea Rd, Killiney, Co Dublin
3 miles from Dun Laoghaire centre.
Parkland course.
9 holes, 5626 metres, S.S.S.69
Founded 1903
Visitors: welcome; not Thurs, Sat,
Sun am.
Green Fee: £15 WD, £18 WE.
Societies: few, by invitation.
Catering: snacks at all times,
catering by arrangement.

U113 Kilrush

☎(065) 51138
Parknamoney, Kilrush, Co Clare
On main road into town from Ennis.
Parkland course.
9 holes, 2793 yards, S.S.S.67
Founded 1934
Visitors: welcome.
Green Fee: on application.
Societies: welcome by arrangement.
Catering: bar facilities only.

U114 Kilternan G & CC

☎(01) 955542, 955559
Kilternan Hotei, Enniskerry Road, Co
Dublin
10 miles S of Dublin centre.
Hilly course.

18 holes, 5413 yards, S.S.S.66
Founded 1977
Visitors: welcome weekdays and pm weekends; restricted Mon (Ladies).
Green Fee: £12 WD, £15 WE.
Societies: by arrangement.
Catering: full facilities. Extensive leisure and health facilities.
Hotels: own hotel on site; special packages for individuals and societies.

U115 **Kinsale**
☎(021) 772197
Ringenane, Belgooly, Co Cork
On main Cork-Kinsale road, 2 miles short of Kinsale signposted on left, 10 miles from Cork Airport.
Parkland course.
9 holes, 5332 yards, S.S.S.68
Founded 1912
Visitors: welcome weekdays.
Green Fee: £10/day WD.
Societies: welcome by appointment, £8 per player.
Catering: bar and full catering.
Hotels: Trident, Actons, Blue Hand, (reduced green fees for residents).

U116 **Knockanally G & CC**
☎(045) 69322
Donadea, North Kildare
3 miles off main Dublin-Galway road between Kilcock and Enfield.
Parkland course.
18 holes, 6484 yards, S.S.S.72
Designed by Noel Lyons.
Founded 1985
Visitors: welcome, no restrictions.
Green Fee: £13 WD, £16 WE & BH.
Societies: every day.
Catering: full facilities.

U117 **Lahinch**
☎(065) 81003
Lahinch, Co Clare
34 miles from Shannon Airport.
Seaside courses.
Old, 18 holes, 6123 metres, S.S.S.73; Castle, 18 holes, 4786 metres, S.S.S.67
Designed by Tom Morris, revised by Dr A. MacKenzie; Castle Course, Commander J.D. Harris.
Founded 1892
Visitors: welcome weekdays; weekends except from 9-10am and 1-2pm Sat; 9-10.30am and 1-2pm Sun.
Green Fee: on application.
Societies: Old, Mon-Sat; Castle, every day.

Catering: full facilities.
Hotels: Aberdeen Arms; Sancta Maria; Liscannor Golf; Atlantic; Claremont; Falls.

U118 **Laytown & Bettystown**
☎(041) 27170, 27563 locker room
Bettystown, Co Meath
On L125 off T1, 26 miles N of Dublin, 4 miles from Drogheda.
Seaside links course.
18 holes, 5652 metres, S.S.S.69
Founded 1909
Visitors: welcome weekdays.
Green Fee: £13 WD, £18 WE.
Societies: most days; every effort made.
Catering: full bar and restaurant.
Hotels: Neptune; Boyne Valley; Rosnaree; Mosney Holiday Centre.

U119 **Leopardstown Golf Centre**
☎(01) 289 5341
Foxrock, Dublin 18
5 miles S of Dublin.
Public parkland course.
9 holes.
Visitors: welcome.
Green Fee: £5 WD (£4 ladies before 12am), £7 WE.
Societies: Sun am only.
Catering: café, restaurant. Driving range.
Hotels: Fitzpatricks Castle.

U120 **Letterkenny**
☎(074) 21150, 24319 Sec.
Barnhill, Letterkenny, Co Donegal
On T72, 2 miles N of Letterkenny.
18 holes, 6299 yards, S.S.S.69
Designed by E. Hackett
Visitors: welcome.
Green Fee: on application.
Societies: welcome.
Catering: snacks served, meals by arrangement.

U121 **Limerick**
☎(061) 414083
Ballyclough, Limerick
Take Fedamore road S of city.
Parkland course.
18 holes, 6483 yards, S.S.S.71
Founded 1891
Visitors: welcome before 4pm Mon, Wed, Thurs, Fri; not weekends.
Green Fee: £20/day.
Societies: Mon, Wed, and Fri am.
Catering: full facilities.
Hotels: Woodfield House.

U122 **Lismore**
☎(058) 54026
Lismore, Co Waterford
0.5 mile from Lismore on Killarney road.
Parkland course.
9 holes, 5127 metres, S.S.S.67
Designed by Eddie Hackett.
Founded 1965
Visitors: welcome all days, some Sun reserved.
Green Fee: £7/day.
Societies: welcome all days except Sun.
Catering: prior booking needed.
Hotels: Lismore; Ballyraeter House.

U123 **Loughrea**
☎(091) 41049
Loughrea, Co Galway
On L11, 1 mile N of Loughrea.
Meadowland course.
9 holes, 5578 yards, S.S.S.67
Designed by Eddie Hackett.
Founded 1924
Visitors: unrestricted.
Green Fee: £10/day.
Societies: welcome.
Catering: by prior arrangement.
Hotels: O'Deas; Meadow Court.

U124 **Lucan**
☎(01) 628 2106, 628 0246
Celbridge Rd, Lucan, Co Dublin
Take Galway road from Dublin, turn left at traffic lights after passing through village of Lucan, club is on left of road 0.5 mile towards Celbridge.
Parkland course.
18 holes, 6000 yards, S.S.S.71
Founded 1897
Visitors: weekdays only to 3pm.
Green Fee: on application.
Societies: Mon and Tues, special rates for 20 and over.
Catering: full services.

U125 **Macroom**
☎(026) 41072
Lackaduv, Macroom, Co Cork
In Macroom town, 25 miles W of Cork on N22 Killarney road.
Parkland course.
9 holes, 5469 metres, S.S.S.68
Founded 1924
Visitors: welcome except specified weekends, phone to check.
Green Fee: £8/day.
Societies: £100 per hour (for 20).
Catering: full catering.
Hotels: Castle, Victoria; (free golf for residents).

U126 **Mahon**
☎(021) 362480
Blackrock, Co Cork
2 miles SE of Cork on Douglas road.
Municipal course.
18 holes, Par 67
Visitors: welcome weekdays,
advance booking weekends.
Green Fee: £6.50 WD, £7.50 WE &
BH.
Catering: bar, snacks, lunch, dinner
by arrangement.

U127 **Malahide**
☎(01) 461611
Beechwood, The Grange, Malahide,
Co Dublin
1 mile off coast road at Portmarnock,
15 mins by taxi from Dublin Airport.
Parkland course.
3 x 9 holes, 3 courses with
S.S.S.70/70/71
Designed by Eddie Hackett.
Founded 1892 (new course 1991).
Visitors: jacket and tie after 7.30pm.
Green Fee: on application.
Societies: on application.
Catering: full bar and restaurant.
Snooker.
Hotels: Grand; Grove.

U128 **Mallow**
☎(022) 21145, 42501 answering
service
Ballyellis, Mallow, Co Cork
1 mile from town on Killavullen road.
Public parkland course.
18 holes, 5874 metres, S.S.S.71
Designed by Commander J.D. Harris.
Founded 1947
Visitors: weekdays except Tues
(Ladies), weekends members only.
Green Fee: £10/round WD, £12 WE.
Societies: prior booking, not Sun.
Catering: bar and restaurant.
Tennis, squash, snooker.
Hotels: Longueville House; Central;
Hibernian; Springport Hall.

U129 **Milltown**
☎(01) 976090
Lower Churchtown Rd, Dublin 14
3 miles S of city centre, via Ranelagh
village.
Parkland course.
18 holes, 5703 metres, S.S.S.69
Founded 1907
Visitors: welcome except Tues, Wed
pm and Sat.
Green Fee: on application.
Societies: by arrangement.
Catering: lunch and dinner served.
Hotels: Orwell Lodge; Montrose.

U130 **Mitchelstown**
☎(025) 24072
Mitchelstown, Co Cork
1 mile from Mitchelstown off N1
Dublin to Cork road.
Parkland course.
9 holes, 5057 metres, S.S.S.67
Designed by Eddie Hackett.
Founded 1908
Visitors: welcome.
Green Fee: £8.
Societies: welcome except Sun.
Catering: on request for societies.
Hotels: Clongibbon House; Firgrove.

U131 **Moate**
☎(0902) 81271
Moate, Co Westmeath
On T4, 8 miles E of Athlone.
Parkland course.
9 holes, 5348 yards, S.S.S.66
Founded 1942
Visitors: welcome.
Green Fee: on application.
Societies: catered for.
Catering: meals by arrangement.

U132 **Monkstown**
☎(021) 841376 Manager
Parkgariffe, Monkstown, Co Cork
On L68 7 miles S of Cork.
Parkland course.
18 holes, 5669 metres, S.S.S.69
Founded 1908
Visitors: welcome except Tues.
Green Fee: £15 WD, £16 WE.
Societies: welcome, £14.
Catering: full meals all day.

U133 **Mount Juliet G & CC**
☎(056) 24725
Thomastown, Co Kilkenny
1 mile from Thomastown on main
Dublin-Waterford road.
Parkland course.
18 holes, 7142 yards, Par 72; 3 hole
Teaching Academy
Designed by Jack Nicklaus.
Founded 1991
Visitors: welcome every day, please
book in advance.
Green Fee: on application.
Societies: daily, book in advance.
Catering: full bar and restaurant.
Driving range, riding, fishing, clay
shooting, archery, tennis.
Hotels: Mount Juliet House.

U134 **Mountbellew**
☎(0905) 79259
Shankhill, Mountbellew, Co Galway
On T4, 28 miles E of Galway

Undulating meadowland course.
9 holes, 5649 yards, S.S.S.66
Founded 1927
Visitors: welcome.
Green Fee: on application.
Societies: by arrangement with Sec.
Catering: teas, soup, sandwiches,
full meals on notification.

U135 **Mountrath**
☎(0502) 32558
Knockinina, Mountrath, Co Laois
1.5 miles on Limerick side of
Mountrath off Dublin-Limerick road.
Undulating parkland course.
9 holes, 5300 yards, S.S.S.66
Founded 1929
Visitors: welcome.
Green Fee: £5/day.
Societies: contact Sec.
Catering: on request for outings etc.
Hotels: Killeshin; Leix County.

U136 **Mullingar**
☎(044) 48366, 48629
Belvedere, Mullingar, Co Westmeath
3 miles from Mullingar on Tullamore
road.
Parkland course.
18 holes, 6450 yards, S.S.S.71
Designed by James Braid.
Founded 1937
Visitors: welcome, no restrictions.
Green Fee: on application.
Societies: welcome by arrangement.
Catering: full bar and restaurant
facilities.
Hotels: Bloomfield House; Greville
Arms.

U137 **Mulrany**
☎(098) 36262 (day)
Mulrany, Westport, Co Mayo
N59, 10 miles W of Newport.
Undulating seaside links.
9 holes, 6383 yards, S.S.S.69
Founded 1896
Visitors: welcome.
Green Fee: on application.
Societies: welcome.
Catering: at Mulrany Bay Hotel.
Hotels: Mulrany Bay; Newport
House; Achill Sound.

U138 **Muskerry**
☎(021) 385297 Sec, 385104 Pro.
Carrickrohane, Co Cork
7 miles W of city centre, near Blarney
village.
Parkland course.
18 holes, 5786 metres, S.S.S.70
Founded 1897

Visitors: welcome weekdays except Wed pm, Thurs before 12.30pm, Fri after 5pm; advisable to phone.
Green Fee: on application.
Societies: as for visitors.
Catering: snacks available; meals by arrangement before play.
Hotels: Christys; Blarney Park.

U139 Naas
☎(045) 97509
Kerdiffstown, Naas, Co Kildare
On road between Johnstown and Sallins.
Parkland course.
18, 5792 metres, S.S.S.70
Designed by Arthur Spring.
Founded 1896
Visitors: Mon, Wed, Fri and Sat.
Green Fee: £10 WD, £12 WE & BH.
Societies: Mon, Wed, Fri, Sat am.
Catering: bar; meals by arangement.
Snooker.
Hotels: Harbour View; Town House; Ambassador.

U140 Narin & Portnoo
☎(075) 45107
Portnoo, Co Donegal
From Donegal via Ardara, then 6 miles N.
Seaside course.
18 holes, 5976 yards, S.S.S.68
Founded 1930
Visitors: welcome, restricted July/Aug.
Green Fee: £10 WD, £12 WE.
Societies: by arrangement.
Catering: bar and light snacks.
Snooker.
Hotels: Nesbitt Arms; Highlands.

U141 Nenagh
☎(067) 31476, 33242 Pro.
Beechwood, Nenagh, Co Tipperary
4 miles from Nenagh, signposted.
Inland course.
18 holes, 5181 metres, S.S.S.67
Designed by E. Hackett.
Founded 1917
Visitors: welcome every day except Sat am or Sun; open all year.
Green Fee: on application.
Societies: Sat 10am-12.30pm.
Catering: full facilities.
22-acre practice ground.

U142 New Ross
☎(051) 21433
Tinneanny, New Ross, Co Wexford
From town centre take Waterford Rd, right at Albatros factory, c. 1 mile.

Parkland course.
9 holes, 6133 yards, S.S.S.69
Founded 1904
Visitors: welcome except Sun if there is a competition.
Green Fee: on application.
Societies: by arrangement.
Catering: snacks always available, meals by arrangement.

U143 Newcastle West
☎(069) 62105
Newcastle West, Co Limerick
1 mile from town on Cork road.
Meadowland course.
9 holes, 5400 yards, S.S.S.65
Visitors: welcome.
Green Fee: on application.
Societies: by arrangement.

U144 Newlands
☎(01) 593157 Sec/office, 592903 bar
Clondalkin, Dublin 22
6 miles from city centre on main southern Cork road.
Parkland course.
18 holes, 5696 metres, S.S.S.70
Designed by James Braid.
Founded 1926
Visitors: welcome weekdays.
Green Fee: £20 (£7 with member).
Societies: welcome weekdays.
Catering: full facilities.
Hotels: Green Isle.

U145 North West
☎(077) 61027
Lisfannon, Fahan, Co Donegal
2 miles S of Buncrana.
Seaside links course.
18 holes, 6203 yards, S.S.S.69
Founded 1891
Visitors: welcome, no restrictions.
Green Fee: £8 WD, £13 WE.
Societies: weekdays, weekends in summer.
Catering: bar and restaurant weekends, weekdays on request.
Hotels: White Strand; Roneragh House; Lake of Shadows.

U146 Nuremore
☎(042) 61438
Carrickmacross, Co Monaghan
On main Dublin-Derry road, c. 1 mile from Carrickmacross on Dublin side.
Parkland course.
9 holes, 5466 metres, S.S.S.69
Designed by Eddie Dunne.
Founded 1964
Visitors: welcome.

Green Fee: on application.
Societies: catered for by prior arrangement through hotel.
Catering: meals and snacks at hotel.

U147 Old Conna
☎(01) 282 6055
Ferndale Road, Bray, Co Dublin
12 miles from Dublin city.
18 holes, Par 72
Visitors: welcome Mon, Thurs, Fri.
Green Fee: £15 WD.
Catering: bar, snacks, lunch, dinner.

U148 Otway
Rathmullan, Co Donegal
On W shore of Loch Swilly.
Seaside course.
9 holes, 4134 yards, S.S.S.60
Visitors: welcome.
Green Fee: on application.

U149 Oughterard
☎(091) 82131
Oughterard, Co Galway
1 mile from Oughterard on Galway road, 15 miles from Galway.
Parkland course amid hills and lakes.
18 holes, 6256 metres, S.S.S.69
Founded 1973
Visitors: welcome.
Green Fee: £12 WD, £15 WE & BH.
Catering: bar, snacks, lunch, dinner.

U150 Parknasilla
☎(064) 45233
Parknasilla, Sneem, Co Kerry
2 miles E of Sneem on Ring of Kerry road.
Undulating seaside course.
9 holes, 4894 yards, S.S.S.65
Founded 1976
Visitors: welcome.
Green Fee: £10.
Hotels: Parknasilla Great Southern

U151 Portarlington
☎(0502) 23115
Garryhinch, Portarlington, Co Offaly
3 miles from Portarlington on Mountmellick road.
Tree-lined parkland course.
18 holes, 5598 yards, S.S.S.66
Founded 1908
Visitors: welcome.
Green Fee: £6 WD, £8 WE & BH.
Societies: welcome except Sun.
Catering: bar and restaurant.
Snooker.
Hotels: East End (for special breaks phone 23225); Hazel; Montague.

U152 Portmarnock
☎(01) 323082 Office, 323050 Bar,
323183 Caddymaster, 324617 fax.
Portmarnock, Co Dublin
From Dublin along coast road to
Baldoyle, on to Portmarnock, right at
Jet Garage, 1 mile up private road.
Seaside course.
3 x 9 holes; Green, 18 holes, 6064
yards, S.S.S.73; White, 18 holes,
6276 yards, S.S.S.74; Yellow, 18
holes, 6489 yards, S.S.S.75
Designed by W.G. Pickeman &
George Ross.
Founded 1894
Visitors: welcome (no Ladies
weekends or Bank Holidays).
Green Fee: £35 (Men), £15 (Ladies);
£45 (men) WE.
Societies: by arrangement, max 50.
Catering: full facilities.
Hotels: Grand; Marine.

U153 Portsalon
☎(074) 74002, 59108
Portsalon, Co Donegal
L78 from Letterkenny.
Seaside course.
18 holes, 5522 yards, S.S.S.67
Visitors: welcome.
Green Fee: on application.

U154 Portumna
☎(0509) 41059
Woodford Rd, Portumna, Co Galway
1.5 miles from Portumna on
Woodford road.
Parkland course.
18 holes, 5205 metres, S.S.S.69
Founded 1913
Visitors: welcome.
Green Fee: £10 WD, £12 WE.
Societies: by arrangement.
Catering: light refreshments, dinner
by arrangement.
Hotels: Westpark; Clonwyn House;
Portland House.

U155 Raffeen Creek
☎(021) 378430
Ringaskiddy, Co Cork
1 mile from Ringaskiddy (Cork)
Ferryport.
Seaside/parkland course with water.
9 holes, 5800 yards, S.S.S.68
Designed by Eddie Hackett.
Founded 1989
Visitors: unrestricted weekdays,
afternoons at weekends.
Green Fee: £11.
Societies: by arrangement.
Catering: bar food.
Snooker.

U156 Rathdowney
☎(0505) 46170
Rathdowney, Portlaoise
Take N7 to Abbeyleix, turn left for
Rathdowney, follow signposts from
square in Rathdowney.
Meadowland course.
9 holes, S.S.S.69
Designed by Eddie Hackett.
Founded 1931
Visitors: welcome.
Green Fee: on application.
Societies: by arrangement.
Catering: by arrangement with Hon
Sec giving one week notice.
Hotels: Central; Leix County.

U157 Rathfarnham
☎(01) 931201
Newtown, Rathfarnham, Dublin 16
2 miles from Rathfarnham village.
Parkland course.
9 holes, 3173 yards, S.S.S.70
Designed by John Jacobs.
Founded 1899
Visitors: not Tues and Sat.
Green Fee: £14 (£8 with member).
Societies: weekdays.
Catering: lunch and dinners by
arrangement with Club Steward.
Hotels: Marley Park.

U158 Rosapenna
☎(074) 55301
Rosapenna, Downings, Co Donegal
25 miles N of Letterkenny.
Championship links course.
18 holes, 6271 yards, S.S.S.71
Designed by Tom Morris (1893),
re-designed by Braid & Vardon
(1906)
Visitors: welcome.
Green Fee: £12 WD, £15 WE & BH.
Catering: available at Rosapenna
Hotel.
Hotels: Rosapenna; Carrigart.

U159 Roscommon
☎(0903) 26382
Mote Park, Roscommon, Co
Roscommon
On T15, 95 miles W of Dublin, 0.5
mile from Roscommon town.
Public parkland course.
9 holes, 5784 metres, S.S.S.70
Founded: 1903
Visitors: welcome.
Green Fee: £8/day, £40/week.
Societies: on request by
arrangement.
Catering: bar and limited restaurant
facilities.
Hotels: Royal; Abbey.

U160 Roscrea
☎(0505) 21130
Derryvale, Roscrea, Co Tipperary
2 miles E of Roscrea on N7 Dublin rd.
Public parkland course.
18 holes, 6283 yards, S.S.S.71
Designed by A. Spring.
Founded 1891
Visitors: no restrictions.
Green Fee: £10/day.
Societies: by appointment.
Catering: bar and restaurant.
Snooker.
Hotels: Racket Hall; Pathe; Leix
County.

U161 Rosslare
☎(053) 32370
Rosslare Strand, Co Wexford
In Rosslare Strand village.
Seaside links course.
18 holes, 6564 yards, S.S.S.71
Founded 1908
Visitors: members of golf clubs
welcome.
Green Fee: £15 WD, £20 WE.
Societies: welcome off season.
Catering: bar and restaurant.
Snooker.
Hotels: Kellys Strand; Cedars;
Burrow Park, (4-day packages).

U162 Rossmore
☎(047) 81316
Rossmore Park, Monaghan
About 2 miles from Monaghan on
Cootehill road.
Undulating parkland course.
9 holes, 6000 yards, S.S.S.68
Designed by Des Smyth Golf Design.
Founded 1916
Visitors: welcome; check by phone
at weekends.
Green Fee: £8 WD, £10 WE & BH.
Societies: catered for.
Catering: full facilities 7 days.
Snooker, bridge club.
Hotels: Hillgrove; Four Seasons;
Westenra; Glencarn.

U163 Royal Dublin
☎(01) 336346 Sec/Manager,
337153 Club, 336504 fax.
Bull Island, Dollymount, Dublin 3
4 miles NE of city centre on coast
road to Howth.
Seaside links course.
18 holes, 6858 yards, S.S.S.73
Designed by H.S. Colt.
Founded 1885
Visitors: welcome weekdays;
weekends and Bank Holidays by
arrangement with Sec/Manager.

Green Fee: £35/day WD, £45 WE.
Societies: weekdays except Wed.
Catering: full service.
Hotels: Marine; Howth Lodge.

U164 Royal Tara
☎(046) 25244, 25508
Bellinter, Navan, Co Meath
30 miles N of Dublin off N3.
Public parkland course.
18 holes, 5757 yards, S.S.S.70;
9 holes, 3184 yards, S.S.S.35
Designed by Des Smyth Golf Design.
Founded 1923
Visitors: welcome by arrangement.
Green Fee: £12 WD, £15 WE & BH.
Societies: Mon, Thurs, Fri, Sat by arrangement.
Catering: full facilities.

U165 Rush
☎(01) 437548, 438177 Office
Rush, Co Dublin
Dublin to Belfast road, turn right at Blakes Cross.
Seaside links course.
9 holes, 5598 metres, S.S.S.69
Founded 1943
Visitors: preferably not Wed, Thurs, Sat, Sun and Bank Holidays.
Green Fee: on application.
Societies: catered for.
Catering: full facilities.
Hotels: Argyle Lodge B&B.

U166 St Annes
☎(01) 332797 Club, 336471 Sec.
North Bull Island, Dollymount, Dublin 5
4 miles NE of Dublin off coast road to Howth.
Seaside course.
18 holes, 5660 metres, S.S.S.69
Designed by Eddie Hackett
Founded 1921
Visitors: no restrictions except competitions; prior enquiry advised.
Green Fee: £15 WD, £20 WE & BH.
Societies: on application.
Catering: by arrangement.

U167 Shannon
☎(061) 61020
Shannon Airport, Co Clare
0.5 mile from Airport terminal.
Woodland/parkland course.
18 holes, 6854 yards, S.S.S.73
Founded 1966
Visitors: welcome weekdays.
Green Fee: £18 WD, £20 WE.
Societies: by arrangement.
Catering: bar, snacks, lunch, dinner.

U168 Skerries
☎(01) 491567, 491204
Hacketstown, Skerries, Co Dublin
Take Belfast road N out of Dublin, past Airport and Swords, fork right for Lusk and Skerries after end of Swords by-pass.
Undulating parkland course.
18 holes, 6174 metres, S.S.S.72
Founded 1906
Visitors: welcome.
Green Fee: £15 (£7 with member) WD, £18 (£8 with member) WE.
Societies: welcome Mon, Thurs and Fri.
Catering: full facilities.
Snooker.
Hotels: Pier House; Anna Villa.

U169 Skibbereen
☎(028) 21227
Skibbereen, Co Cork
Off T65, 47 miles SW of Cork.
Moorland course.
9 holes, 5890 yards, S.S.S.67
Visitors: welcome.
Green Fee: on application.
Societies: welcome.

U170 Slade Valley
☎(01) 582207, 582183, 582739
Lynch Park, Brittas, Co Dublin
Off N1 Dublin to Naas road.
Undulating course.
18 holes, 5337 metres, S.S.S.68
Designed by W.D. Sullivan and D. O'Brien.
Founded 1971
Visitors: welcome by arrangement with Sec.
Green Fee: on application.
Societies: welcome on application to Sec.
Catering: meals at weekends, also Tues and Wed during summer.
Hotels: Green Isle; Downshire House.

U171 Spanish Point
☎(065) 84198
Spanish Point, Miltown Malbay, Co Clare
2 miles from Milton Malbay, 8 miles from Lahinch.
Seaside course.
9 holes, 3470 metres, S.S.S.58
Founded 1896
Visitors: welcome.
Green Fee: £8/day.
Societies: welcome except Sun.
Catering: only on special occasions; light snacks at bar (eg sandwiches).
Hotels: Central.

U172 Stackstown
☎(01) 942338, 941993
Kellystown Rd, Rathfarnham, Dublin 16
8 miles S of Dublin via N81 and R115.
Hilly course with panoramic views.
18 holes, 5925 metres, S.S.S.72
Founded 1975
Visitors: unrestricted weekdays.
Green Fee: £12 WD, £15 WE & BH.
Societies: by arrangement.
Catering: bar, snacks, lunch, dinner.

U173 Strandhill
☎(071) 68188
Strandhill, Co Sligo
5 miles W of Sligo city, 1 mile from Strandhill Airport; situated in resort of Strandhill, well signposted.
Seaside links course.
18 holes, 5950 yards, S.S.S.69
Founded 1931
Visitors: welcome weekdays and most weekends.
Green Fee: on application.
Societies: welcome, group rates available.
Catering: snacks available, meals by arrangement.
Hotels: Ocean View; Southern; Silver Swan; Yeats Country Ryan; Sligo Park.

U174 Sutton
☎(01) 323013
Cush Point, Sutton, Dublin 13
7 miles NE of city centre.
Seaside links course.
9 holes, 5522 yards, S.S.S.67
Designed by Donald Steel.
Founded 1890
Visitors: welcome except competition days (Tues and Sat).
Green Fee: on application.
Societies: welcome by arrangement only.
Catering: by arrangement only.
Hotels: Marine; Howth Lodge; Royal Howth.

U175 Swinford
☎(094) 51378
Brabazon Park, Swinford, Co Mayo
Beside town, opposite Western Health Board complex.
Parkland course.
9 holes, 2950 yards, S.S.S.68
Founded 1922
Visitors: welcome.
Green Fee: £5/day, £25/week.
Societies: enquiries welcome.
Catering: by arrangement.
Hotels: O'Connors; Westway.

U176 Templemore
☎(0504) 31400, 31720 Sec.
Manna South, Templemore, Co
Tipperary
0.5 mile from town centre beside the
Thurles road.
Parkland course.
9 holes, 5112 metres, S.S.S.67
Founded 1972
Visitors: no restrictions except on
special event days.
Green Fee: £5/day.
Societies: by appointment with Hon
Sec.
Catering: no bar, light refreshments
on request, catering at Polly's Pub,
Templemore Arms, Richmond House.

U177 Thurles
☎(0504) 21983
Turtulla, Thurles, Co Tipperary
1 mile S of Thurles on Cork road.
Parkland course.
18 holes, 6300 yards, S.S.S.70
Founded 1911
Visitors: welcome weekdays and
weekends except Sun.
Green Fee: on application.
Societies: catered for on weekdays
and Sat.
Catering: full facilities.

U178 Tipperary
☎(062) 51119
Rathanny, Tipperary
1 mile from town on Glen of Aherlow
road.
Parkland course.
9 holes, 5805 metres, S.S.S.70
Founded 1896
Visitors: welcome weekdays, Sun
by prior arrangement.
Green Fee: £8/day.
Societies: welcome by arrangement.
Catering: bar, snacks.
Hotels: Glen; Royal; Aherlow House.

U179 Tralee
☎(066) 36379
West Barrow, Ardfert, Co Kerry
From Tralee through villages of Spa
and Churchill to Barrow.
Links course.
18 holes, 5961 metres, S.S.S.71
Designed by Arnold Palmer Design.
Founded 1904
Visitors: welcome Mon to Sat by
arrangement with Sec.
Green Fee: £22 WD, £30 WE.
Societies: weekdays; 10% discount
for 20 or more.
Catering: full facilities.
Hotels: Mount Brandon; Grand.

U180 Tramore
☎(051) 86170
Newtown Hill, Tramore, Co Waterford
Via Waterford, 1 mile beyond
Tramore.
Parkland course.
18 holes, 6660 yards, S.S.S.71
Designed by Tibbett (1936/7)
Founded 1894
Visitors: welcome.
Green Fee: on application.
Societies: welcome by prior
arrangement.
Catering: meals served except Mon.
Hotels: Majestic; Grand; Sea View.

U181 Trim
☎(046) 31463
Newtownmoynagh, Trim, Co Meath
3 miles from Trim on Trim/Longwood
road.
Parkland course.
18 holes, 6720 yards, S.S.S.72
Designed by Eddie Hackett.
Founded 1898
Visitors: welcome weekdays,
restrictions Thurs, Sat, Sun.
Green Fee: on application.
Societies: Mon-Sat inc., enquiries
welcome.
Catering: full bar and catering
facilities.
Hotels: Wellington Court (Trim);
Harry's (Kinnegad); Wells (Enfield).

U182 Tuam
☎(093) 24354
Barnacurragh, Tuam, Co Galway
1.5 miles from town on the Athenry
road which is off Dublin road.
Parkland course.
18 holes, 6321 yards, S.S.S.70
Founded around 1910
Visitors: welcome weekdays.
Green Fee: on application.
Societies: catered for on weekdays
and Sat by arrangement.
Catering: snacks available.

U183 Tulfarris Hotel & CC
☎(045) 64574
Blessington, Co Wicklow
Turn left 6 miles from Blessington off
N81.
9 holes, 5612 metres, S.S.S.69
Designed by Eddie Hackett.
Founded 1987
Visitors: welcome; limited Sun.
Green Fee: £12 WD, £15 WE & BH.
Societies: weelcome by prior
arrangement.
Catering: restaurant, bar, bar
snacks.

Banqueting, conference centre,
tennis, indoor swimming pool, gym,
snooker.
Hotels: Tulfarris Hotel & CC, special
golfing packages on request.

U184 Tullamore
☎(0506) 21439
Brookfield, Tullamore, Co Offaly
2.5 miles from town centre on Kinnity
road.
Parkland course.
18 holes, 6314 yards, S.S.S.70
Designed by James Braid.
Founded 1896
Visitors: welcome except during
club competitions on Sun.
Green Fee: on application.
Societies: weekdays and Sat.
Catering: by prior arrangement.
Hotels: Phoenix Arms.

U185 Virginia
☎(049) 47235
Virginia, Co Cavan
50 miles N of Dublin on main
Cavan-Dublin road, within Park
Hotel, by Lough Ramor.
Meadowland course.
9 holes, 4139 metres, S.S.S.62
Founded 1946
Visitors: welcome.
Green Fee: £8/day.
Catering: in Park hotel.
Hotels: Park.

U186 Waterford
☎(051) 76748
Newrath, Waterford
0.25 mile from city centre.
Parkland course.
18 holes, 6237 yards, S.S.S.69
Designed by Cecil Barcroft and Willie
Park.
Founded 1912
Visitors: welcome weekdays.
Green Fee: £12 WD, £15 WE.
Societies: catered for weekdays.
Catering: full facilities available.
Hotels: Ardree; Bridge; Granville;
Dooleys; Tower.

U187 Waterville
☎(0667) 4102, 4545, 4482 fax.
Waterville, Co Kerry
N70 to Waterville, then coastal road
for 1 mile W of town.
Seaside links course.
18 holes, 7184 yards, S.S.S.74
Designed by E. Hackett.
Founded 1970
Visitors: welcome.

Green Fee: £30/round, £40 two rounds.
Societies: group rates available, 7 days.
Catering: snacks, full meals.
Hotels: Waterville Lake; Butlers Arms; Bay View; Strand; Villa Maria.

U188 Westmanstown
☎(01) 205817
Clonsilla, Dublin 15
Coming from Dublin to Lucan village turn right and follow sign for Clonsilla, course on right.
Flat parkland course.
18 holes, 5819 metres, S.S.S.70
Designed by Eddie Hackett.
Founded 1989
Visitors: welcome Mon-Fri.
Green Fee: £10.
Societies: by prior arrangement.
Catering: available when clubhouse completed.
Hotels: Spa (Lucan).

U189 Westport
☎(098) 25113, 27070
Carrowholly, Westport, Co Mayo
2 miles from Westport, continue for 0.5 mile on Newport road then left.
Parkland course.
18 holes, 7606 yards, S.S.S.71
Designed by Hawtree & Son.
Founded 1973 (present course)
Visitors: welcome.
Green Fee: April-Sept, £15 WD, £18 WE & BH; Oct-March, £12 WD, £15 WE & BH.
Societies: welcome; special rates by arrangement.

Catering: lounge bar; snacks and meals in dining room.
Hotels: Railway; Clewbay; Central; Castlecourt; Woods; Hotel Westport.

U190 Wexford
☎(053) 42238
Mulgannon, Wexford
Within 0.5 mile of town.
Parkland course.
18 holes, 6100 yards, S.S.S.69
Designed by J. Hamilton Stutt & Co.
Founded 1961
Visitors: welcome; timesheets at weekends.
Green Fee: £12 WD, £15 WE.
Societies: welcome by booking.
Catering: bar facilities.
Hotels: Talbot; Whites; Kelly's Strand; Cedars.

U191 Wicklow
☎(0404) 67379
Dunbur Rd, Wicklow, Co Wicklow
On L29 32 miles from Dublin.
Seaside course.
9 holes, 2633 yards, S.S.S.67
Founded 1904
Visitors: welcome weekdays.
Green Fee: on application.
Catering: meals served except Tues.

U192 Woodbrook
☎(01) 282 4799
Dublin Rd, Bray, Co Wicklow
11 miles S of Dublin centre on N11.
Parkland course.
18 holes, 6540 yards, S.S.S.71
Founded 1921

Visitors: by arrangement.
Green Fee: £25 WD, £35 WE & BH.
Societies: Mon, Thurs, Fri by arrangement.
Catering: bar, snacks, dinner, à la carte.
Hotels: Royal; Victor; Killiney Castle.

U193 Woodenbridge
☎(0402) 35202
Woodenbridge, Avoca, Co Wicklow
50 miles S of Dublin on route N11 to Arklow; 4 miles from Arklow.
Parkland course.
9 holes, 6104 yards, S.S.S.68
Founded 1884
Visitors: welcome except Thurs and Sat.
Green Fee: £12 WD, £15 Sun.
Societies: weekdays by arrangement.
Catering: lunches and evenings meals except Mon.
Hotels: Woodenbridge; Valley; Vale View.

U194 Youghal
☎(024) 92787
Knockaverry, Youghal, Co Cork
Overlooking Youghal town and bay.
Meadowland course.
18 holes, 6206 yards, S.S.S.69
Designed by Commander Harris.
Founded 1898
Visitors: welcome.
Green Fee: on application.
Societies: welcome.
Catering: full bar and restaurant facilities in new clubhouse.
Hotels: Hilltop; Devonshire Arms.

DRIVING RANGES

The arrangement of driving ranges and other golfing facilities in this section is based on the county groups used in the main part of the Guide (see the map on p7). Entries are numbered sequentially, from 1 to 273, and each number is prefixed with the letter corresponding to the county group within which it falls, from A (Devon and Cornwall) to U (Eire). Within each group, entries are listed alphabetically.

A1 Central Park Golf Course
☎(0752) 509391
Central Park, Plymouth, Devon
9 hole pitch & putt course. **Open:**
9am-dusk. **Charges:** £1.50; £1 deposit;
£1 with own clubs.

A1 Central Park Golf Course
☎(0752) 509391
Central Park, Plymouth, Devon
9 hole pitch & putt course. **Open:**
9am-dusk. **Charges:** £1.50; £1 deposit;
£1 with own clubs.

A2 Cornwall Golf Centre
☎(0208) 77588
Clifton Park, Carminow Cross, Bodmin
8 covered, floodlit bays. **Open:** Mon-Fri
10.30am-9.30pm; Sat 10am-1pm; Sun
10am-5.30pm. **Charges:** £1.50/60
(£1.15 members).

A3 Dinnaton
☎(0752) 892512, 892452
Dinnaton Sporting and Country Club,
Ivybridge, Devon PL21 9HU
6 covered, floodlit bays (max 12 players).
Charges: £1.50/50.
9 hole course (see A17).

A4 Fingle Glen
☎(0647) 61817
Fingle Glen Golf and Leisure Complex,
Tedbourne St Mary, Nr Exeter, Devon
8 covered, floodlit bays. **Open:** winter
Mon-Fri 9am-9.30, Sat 9am-5.30pm,
Sun 9am-6.30pm; summer Mon-Fri
8am-9.30pm, Sat 8am-5.30, Sun
8am-6.30. **Charges:** £1.50/45-50.
9 hole course (see A23).

A5 Ilfracombe & Woolacombe GR
☎(0271) 866222
Woolacombe Rd, Ilfracombe, EX34 7HF
12 covered bays; 6 open bays. **Open:**
June/July/August 8am-8pm; winter ring
to check. **Charges:** £2/50.

A6 Killiow
☎(0872) 70246
Killiow, Kea, Nr Truro, Cornwall TR3 6AG
8 covered, floodlit bays. **Open:** Mon-Fri
9.30am-9pm; Sat/Sun 9.30am-4.30pm.
Charges: £1.25/50.
18 hole course (see A30).

A7 Les Mielles Golf Centre (Western Golf Range)
☎(0534) 82787
The Mount, Valde la Mare, St Ouens,
Jersey
30 open bays. **Open:** Dawn-dusk.
Charges: on application.
12 hole course (see A33).

A8 Libbaton
☎(0769) 60269, 60167 Pro.
High Bickington, Umberleigh, N Devon
EX37 9BS
Covered, floodlit bays. **Open:** 8am-dusk.
Charges: £1.50/50.
18 hole course (see A34).

A9 Meads Farm GDR
☎(08403) 303
On A38, Poundstock, Nr Bude, Cornwall
EX23 0EE
10 open bays; 6 indoor floodlit bays.
Open: Oct-Easter, closed Mon, Tues-Fri
10am-9pm; Sat/Sun 10am-5pm;
summer 9am-9pm daily. **Charges:**
£1.75/50; club hire 50p.

A10 Merlin GDR
☎(0841) 540222
Mawganporth, Newquay, Cornwall TR8
4AD
6 covered, floodlit bays. **Open:** summer
8am-10pm; winter 8am-6/7pm.
Charges: £1.20/50.
9 hole course (see A38).

A11 Newton Abbot GR
☎(0626) 64885
The Racecourse, Newton Abbot, Devon
TQ12 3AF
10 open, 10 grass bays. **Open:** winter
9.30am-dusk; summer
9.30am-7.30pm; closed on race days.
Charges: £1.50/40; £2/40 best balls.

A12 Otter Valley Golf Centre
☎(0404) 86266
Upottery, Honiton, Devon EX14 9QP
Private golf school; lage practice
grounds, indoor and outdoor facilities.
Open: daily. **Charges:** £5/day.

A13 Radnor Golf Centre
☎(0209) 211059
Radnor Rd, Redruth, Cornwall TR16 5EL
12 covered, floodlit bays; 6 open bays.
Open: Mon-Fri 8.30am-9pm; winter
Sat/Sun 8.30am-5pm; summer Sat/Sun
8.30am-6pm. **Charges:** £1.30/50.
9 hole Par 3 course (see A47).

A14 Thorn Park GR
☎(0395) 579564

Salcombe Regis, Sidmouth, Devon EX10
0JH
9 covered, floodlit bays. **Open:** winter
10am-7.30pm; summer 10am-dusk.
Charges: £1.60/50+.

A15 Torbay Golf Centre
☎(0803) 528728
Grange Rd, Clennan Valley, Goodrington,
Paignton TQ4 7JY
26 covered, floodlit bays. 9 hole Par 3
pitch & putt course. **Open:** Mon-Fri
12am-8pm; Sat/Sun 10am-6pm.
Charges: £1.90/50; £2.20 9 holes;
£3.20 18 holes.

A16 Willingcott Golf & Country Club
☎(0271) 870070, 870077
Woolacombe, N Devon EX34 7HN
6-10 covered, floodlit bays opening
Autumn 1992. **Open:** phone to check.
Charges: on application.
Golf course (see A73).

B17 Bournemouth GDR
☎(0202) 593131
Parley Green Lane, Hurn, Christchurch,
Dorset
15 covered, floodlit bays. 6 hole Par 23
starter course. **Open:** Mon-Fri
9am-9pm; Sat/Sun 7am-8pm. **Charges:**
£1.50/50.

B18 Bowood G & CC
☎(0249) 822228, 822218 fax
Calne, Wilts SN11 9PQ
10 covered, floodlit bays; 8 open bays.
3 Academy holes (2 Par 3, 1 Par 4)
(£5/hour). **Open:** summer 8am-9.30pm;
winter 8am-4.30pm. **Charges:** £3/50.
Golf course (see B5).

B19 Broome Manor DR
☎(0793) 532403
Piper's Way, Swindon, Wilts SN3 1RG
29 covered, floodlit bays; 5 two-tier
bays. **Open:** Mon-Fri 8am-9pm; Sat/Sun
7am-9pm. **Charges:** £2.55/large;
£1.80/med; £1/small.
18 and 9 hole courses (see B12).

B20 Cheddar Valley GDR
☎(0934) 742727
Penstone, Lyppiatt Lane, Cheddar,
Somerset BS27 3QT
10 covered, floodlit bays; 5 open bays.
Open: 7 days 9am-9pm. **Charges:**
£2/basket.

B21 Crane Valley GR
☎(0202) 814088
West Farm, Romford, Verwood, Dorset
BH31 6LE
12 covered bays. **Open:** dawn-dusk.
Charges: £2/75.
27 hole course (see B20).

B22 East Dorset
☎(0929) 472272
Hyde, Wareham, Dorset BH20 7NT
12 covered, floodlit bays; 10 open bays.
Open: Mon-Fri 10am-10pm; Sat/Sun
10am-6pm. **Charges:** £2/bucket.
18 hole course (see B23).

B23 Farrington Golf Club
☎(0761) 241274
Marsh Lane, Farrington Gurney, Bristol
BS18 5TS
18 covered bays; 40 open bays. **Open:**
dawn-dusk. **Charges:** £2/50.
Golf course (see B27).

B24 Halstock DR
☎(0935) 891689
Common Lane, Halstock, Nr Yeovil,
Somerset BA22 9SF
10 covered, floodlit bays. **Open:**
8am-7.30pm. **Charges:** £1.65/50;
£1.85/50 floodlit.
18 hole course (see B30).

B25 Iford Bridge GR (Christchurch)
☎(0202) 473817
Iford Bridge Sports Centre, Barrack Rd,
Iford, Christchurch, Dorset
13 open bays. **Open:** dawn-dusk.
Charges: £1.60/50; £3/100.
9 hole course (see B35).

B26 Long Sutton GR
☎(0458) 241017
Long Load, Nr Langport, Somerset TA10
9JU
Open range. **Open:** 8am – dusk. **Charges:**
£2/60.
18 hole course (see B42).

B27 Mendip Spring
☎(0934) 853337
Honey Hall Lane, Congresbury, Avon BS19
5JT
15 covered, floodlit bays. **Open:** winter
8am-8pm; summer 8am-10pm. **Charges:**
£4/100; £2.50/45.
Golf course (see B47).

B28 Oaksey Park Golf & Leisure Complex
☎(06667) 7995
Oaksey, Nr Malmesbury, Wilts SN16 9SB
6 covered, floodlit bays. **Open:**
dawn-dusk. **Charges:** £2/55.
Golf course (see B53).

B29 Solent Meads
☎(0202) 420795
Rolls Drive, Nr Hengistbury Head,
Bournemouth, Dorset
10 open bays. **Open:** 8am-dusk. **Charges:**
£1.70/50; £1/25.
18 hole course (see B64).

B30 Stockwood Vale
☎(0272) 866505
Stockwood Lane, Keynsham, Avon BS18
2ER
12 covered bays; 4 open bays. **Open:**
Mon-Fri 8am-dusk; Sat/Sun
7.30am-dusk. **Charges:** £2.50/75.
9 hole course (see B65).

B31 Swingrite Golf Centre
☎(0823) 442600
Haydon Lane, Holway, Taunton, Somerset
TA3 5AB
12 covered, floodlit bays; 5 open bays.
Open: 7 days 9am-9pm. **Charges:**
£2.30/60; £1.80/60 juniors, unemployed,
retired, disabled; Happy hours.

B32 Thoulston Park
☎(0373) 832825
Chapmanslade, Nr Westbury, Wilts BA13
4AQ
20 covered, floodlit bays; 4 open bays.
Open: Mon-Sat 8am-9.30pm; Sun
8am-6.30pm. **Charges:** £2/50; £3/100.
18 hole course (see B70).

B33 Wessex Golf Centre
☎(0305) 784737
Radipole Lane, Weymouth, Dorset
20 open bays. **Open:** 10am-dusk.
Charges: £1.85/bucket.
9 hole course (see B74).

B34 Wingfield GDR
☎(0225) 776365
Wingfield Rd, Trowbridge, Wilts BA14 9LW
28 covered, floodlit bays. **Open:** Mon-Sat
9.30am-9.30pm; Sun 9.30am-6pm.
Charges: £2/50; £3/100.

B35 Wrag Barn G & CC
☎(0793) 764533 Sec, 766027 Pro.
Shrivenham Road, Sevenhampton, Nr
Highworth, Wilts SN6 7QA
6 open mats. **Open:** 8am-dusk. **Charges:**
£1.50/50; £3/100.
18 hole course (see B82).

C36 Aldershaw
☎(0424) 870898
Sedlescombe, E Sussex TN33 0SD
24 covered, floodlit bays. **Open:**
10am-10pm. **Charges:** £1/36.
18 hole course (see C1).

C37 Basingstoke Golf Centre
☎(0256) 50054
Worting Rd, West Ham, Basingstoke,
Hants RG23 0TY
24 covered, floodlit bays. **Open:**
8.30am-9.30pm. **Charges:** £3.70/120.
9 hole course (see C12).

C38 Bishopswood GR
☎(0734) 815213
Bishopswood Lane, Tadley, Basingstoke,
Hants RG26 6AT
11 covered, floodlit bays. **Open:** Mon-Fri
8am-9pm; Sat/Sun 8am-7pm. **Charges:**
£1.50/45; £2.80/90.
9 hole course (see C13).

C39 Botley Park Hotel
☎(0489) 780888
Winchester Rd, Boorley Green, Botley,
Hants SO3 2UA
12 open bays. **Open:** 7 days 8am-dusk.
Charges: £1/40.
18 hole course (see C16).

C40 Chichester Golf Centre
☎(0243) 533833
Hoe Farm, Hunston, Chichester, W Sussex
PO20 6AX
27 covered, floodlit bays. **Open:**
7am-9pm. **Charges:** £2.50/60; £1/20 (2
piece balls).
18 and 9 hole courses (see C21).

C41 Fairway GDR
☎(0293) 521706
Horsham Rd, Pease Pottage, Crawley, W
Sussex RH11 8AL
16 covered, floodlit bays; 15 open, floodlit
bays. **Open:** 9am-10pm. **Charges:**
£2.30/60; £3.80/120.
9 hole course (see C38).

C42 Hastings
☎(0424) 852981
Battle Rd, St Leonards-on-Sea, E Sussex
TN37 7AB
14 covered, floodlit bays; 9 hole pitch &
putt. **Open:** 9.30am-9.30pm. **Charges:**
£1.20/bucket before 5pm; 80p/bucket
after 5pm.
18 hole course (see C49).

C43 Horam Park DR
☎(04353) 3477, (04353) 3677 fax
Chiddingley Rd, Horam, E Sussex TN21 0JJ
15 covered, floodlit bays; pitch & putt
course. **Open:** 9am-10pm. **Charges:**
£2/45.
9 hole course (see C56).

C44 Moors Valley Golf Centre
☎(0425) 479776
Moors Valley Country Park, Horton Rd, Nr
Ringwood, Hants
14 covered, floodlit bays. **Open:**
8am-9.30pm (except Christmas).
Charges: £1.55/50.
Golf course (see C66).

C45 Old Thorns DR
☎(0428) 724555
Longmoor Rd, Liphook, Hants GU30 7PE
4 covered bays. **Open:** 8am-dusk.
Charges: £2.50/bucket.
Golf course (see C70).

C46 Osiers Farm
☎(0798) 44097
London Road, Petworth, W Sussex GU28
9LX
6 open bays. **Open:** dawn-dusk. **Charges:**
£3/120; £2/60.
9 hole course (see C72).

C47 Portsmouth Golf Centre
☎(0705) 664549
Eastern Rd, Portsmouth, Hants PO3 6QB
25 covered, floodlit bays. **Open:** summer
Mon-Fri 8am-9pm, Sat/Sun 8am-8pm;
winter Mon-Fri 8am-9pm, Sat/Sun
7am-6pm. **Charges:** £1.80/50;
£3.20/100.
18 hole course (see C46).

C48 Slinfold Park
☎(0403) 791154
Stane St, Slinfold, Horsham, W. Sussex
RH13 7RE.
14 covered, floodlit bays. **Open:**
10am-10pm. **Charges:** £3.50/96 approx.
18 and 9 hole courses (see C92).

C49 Southampton GR
☎(0703) 733166
Manor Farm, Botley Rd, Chilworth,
Southampton, Hants SO1 7JE
34 covered, floodlit bays. **Open:** Mon-Fri
8am-8pm; Sat/Sun 8am-6pm. **Charges:**
£1.25/50.   9 hole course (see C94).

C50 Tilgate Forest
☎(0293) 530103
Titmus Drive, Tilgate, Crawley, RH10 5EY
30 floodlit bays. **Charges:** on application.
18 and 9 hole courses (see C100).

C51 West Chiltington GC
☎(0798) 813574 Sec, 812115 Pro shop,
Broadford Bridge Rd, W Chiltington, W
Sussex, RH20 2YA
8 open bays; 5 covered bays. **Open:**
7.30am-dusk. **Charges:** £2/bucket.
18 and 9 hole courses (see C105).

C52 Winchester GDR
☎(0962) 842948
Bar End, Winchester, Hants
15 bays (some covered). **Open:** Mon-Fri
10.30am-7.30pm; Sat/Sun
10am-5.30pm. **Charges:** Standard £1.40
small, £2 large; Top £1.80 small, £3 large.

D53 Beverley Park GR
☎(081) 949 9200
Beverley Way, New Maldon, KT3 4PH
60, 2 tier, covered, floodlit bays. **Open:**
Mon-Fri 9.30-10pm; Sat/Sun 9am-10pm.
Charges: £1.80/basket.

D54 Broadwater Park
☎(0483) 429955
Guildford Road, Farncombe, Nr
Godalming, Surrey GU7 3BU
16 covered, floodlit bays. **Open:**
8am-10pm. **Charges:** £2/55.   9 hole Par
3 course (see D15).

D55 Chatham Golf Centre
☎(0634) 848925
Street End Rd, Chatham, Kent ME5 0BG
30 covered, floodlit bays. **Open:** 7 days
10am-10pm. **Charges:** £1.80/50.

D56 Chessington Golf Centre
☎(081) 391 0948
Garrison Lane, Chessington, KT9 2LW
18 covered, floodlit bays. **Open:** Mon-Fri
9am-10pm; Sat/Sun 9am-9pm. **Charges:**
£1/bucket.   9 hole course (see D22).

D57 Croydon GDR
☎(081) 656 1690
175 Long Lane, Addiscombe, Croydon
CR0 7TE.
24 covered, floodlit bays. **Open:** Mon-Fri
10am-10pm; Sat/Sun 10am-9pm.
Charges: £1.70/40; £3.05/80;
£3.90/110.

D58 Edenbridge G & CC
☎(0732) 865097
Crouch House Rd, Edenbridge, TN8 5LQ
13 covered, floodlit bays. **Open:** Mon-Fri
8am-8.30pm; Sat/Sun 8am-7.30pm.
Charges: £1.90/bucket.   18 hole and
beginners courses (see D42).

D59 Fairmile DR
☎(0932) 864419
Portsmouth Rd, Cobham, Surrey
24 covered floodlit bays. **Open:** Mon-Fri
10am-10pm; Sat/Sun 9am-9pm.
Charges: £1.75 medium; £2.75 large;
3.75 extra large.

D60 Herne Bay GDR
☎(0227) 742742
Bullockstone Rd, Herne Bay, Kent CT6 7TL
20 covered, floodlit bays. **Open:** 7 days
9am-10pm. **Charges:** £3 large; £2 small.

D61 Hoebridge Golf Centre
☎(0483) 722611
Old Woking Rd, Old Woking, GU22 8JH
25 covered, floodlit bays. **Open:**
7.30am-10pm. **Charges:** £2/50; £3/75;
£3.75/100.
18 and 9 hole courses (see D60).

D62 Langley Park DR
☎(0622) 863163
Langley Park, Sutton Rd, Langley,
Maidstone, Kent ME17 3NQ
25 covered, floodlit bays. **Open:** 7 days
10am-9pm. **Charges:** £1.25/39.

D63 Lingfield Park
☎(0342) 834602
Racecourse Road, Lingfield, RH7 6PQ
10 open bays. **Open:** dawn-dusk.
Charges: £2/40; £3/80; £4/120.
18 hole course (see D74).

D64 Oak Park
☎(0252) 850880
Oak Park, Heath Lane, Crondall, Nr
Farnham, Surrey GU10 5PB
16 covered, floodlit bays. **Open:** summer
7.30am-9.30pm; winter 8.30am-6.30pm.
Charges: £1.50/28; £2.50/50.
18 hole course (see D86).

D65 Oaks Sports Centre
☎(081) 643 8363
Woodmansterne Rd, Carshalton, SM5 4AN
16 covered, floodlit bays. **Open:**
9am-10pm. **Charges:** £1/35.
18 and 9 hole courses (see D87).

D66 Oast Golf Centre
☎(0795) 473527
West Tonge Farm, Church Rd, Tonge, Kent
ME9 9AR
18 covered, floodlit bays; 10 grass bays.
Open: 7 days 10am-10pm. **Charges:**
£1/35.

D67 Pachesham Park
☎(0372) 843453
Oaklawn Rd, Leatherhead, Surrey KT22
0BT.
30 covered, floodlit bays. **Open:** Mon-Fri
8am-10pm; Sat/Sun 8am-8.30pm.
Charges: £2/bucket (60).
9 hole course (see D88).

D68 Princes Golf Club
☎(0304) 611118, 613797 Pro shop
Sandwich Bay, Sandwich, Kent CT13 9QB
Off grass. **Open:** 8am-dusk. **Charges:**
£2/small; £3/large.
18 hole course (see D90).

D69 Richmond GR
☎(081) 940 5570
Chertsey Rd, Richmond, Surrey TW9 2SS
23 covered, floodlit bays. **Open:** Mon-Fri
9.30am-9.30pm; Sat/Sun 9am-5pm.
Charges: £1.50/small; £2.20/large.

D70 Ruxley Park Golf Centre
☎(0689) 871490
Sandy Lane, St Paul's Cray, Orpington,
Kent BR5 3HY
25 covered, floodlit bays. **Open:**
9am-10pm. **Charges:** £2.50/50;
£4.30/100.
18 hole course (see D105).

**D71 Sandown Park Golf
Centre**
☎(0372) 463340/465921
More Lane, Esher, Surrey KT10 8AN
33 covered, floodlit bays. **Open:** Mon-Fri
10am-10pm; Sat/Sun 10am-9pm.
Charges: £2/70.
9 hole course (see D108).

D72 Sandwich GDR
☎(0304) 612812
Ash Rd, Sandwich, Kent CT13 9XX
9 covered, floodlit bays. **Open:** 7 days
10am-10pm. **Charges:** £2.50 large;
£1.25 small.

D73 Silvermere DR
☎(0932) 867275
Redhill Rd, Cobham, Surrey KT11 1EF
34 covered, floodlit bays. **Open:** Mon-Fri
8.30am-10pm; Sat/Sun 8.30am-8.30pm.
Charges: £3/90; £2/55.
18 hole course (see D117).

D74 Swanley Golf Centre
☎(0322) 669201
Beechenlea Lane, Swanley, Kent BR8 8DR
18 open bays; 18 covered, floodlit bays.
Open: 7 days 9am-9.30pm. **Charges:**
£2.50 small; £4 large.

D75 Upchurch River Valley
☎(0634) 379592
Oak Lane, Upchurch, Sittingbourne, Kent
ME9 7AY
16 covered, floodlit bays. **Open:** Mon-Fri
7am-9pm; Sat/Sun 6am-8pm. **Charges:**
£1/30.
18 and 9 hole courses (see D129).

D76 Windlemere DR
☎(0276) 858727
Windlesham Rd, West End, Woking,
Surrey GU24 9QL
12 covered, floodlit bays. **Open:**
dawn-10pm. **Charges:** £2.30/50.
9 hole course (see D145).

**E77 Belhus Park Leisure
Complex**
☎(0708) 852248
Belhus Park, South Ockendon, Essex
RM15 4PX
11 covered, floodlit bays. **Open:** Mon
10am-10pm; Tues-Fri 9am-10pm; Sat
8am-6pm; Sun 8am-8pm. **Charges:**
£1.90/50; £2.80/100.
18 hole course (see E12).

E78 **Belvedere GR**
☎(0268) 286612, 522828
Hardings Elms Rd, Crays Hill, Billericay,
Essex CM11 2UH
26 astro turf mats. **Open:** Mon-Fri
10am-10pm; Sat/Sun 10am-9pm.
Charges: £2/50.

E79 **Brentwood Park**
☎(0277) 211994
Brentwood Park, Warley Gap, Brentwood,
Essex CM13 3LG
22 covered, floodlit bays. **Open:**
9am-10pm. **Charges:** £2.50/50;
£3.50/100.

E80 **Bunsay Downs Golf Club**
☎(0245 41) 2648/2369
Little Baddow Rd, Woodham Walter, Nr
Maldon, Essex CM9 6RW
4 indoor bays. **Open:** 7am-9.30pm.
Charges: £1/basket.
9 hole course (see E24).

E81 **Bushey GR**
☎(081) 950 2283, 950 2215 Pro shop
High Street, Bushey, Herts WD2 1BJ
30 covered, floodlit bays. **Open:**
9am-9pm. **Charges:** £2/60.
9 hole course (see E27).

E82 **Castle Point GR**
☎(0268) 510830
Somness Avenue, Canvey Island, Essex
SS8 9FG
18 covered, floodlit bays. **Open:** Mon-Fri
dawn-9.30pm; Sat/Sun dawn-8.30pm.
Charges: £1/bucket.
18 hole course (see E31).

E83 **Chingford GR**
☎(081) 529 2409
Waltham Way, Chingford, London E4 8AQ
23 covered, floodlit bays. **Open:**
9.30am-10pm. **Charges:** £1.35/40;
£1.70/60; £2.40/100.

E84 **Colchester Golf range**
☎(0206) 230974
Old Ipswich Road, Ardleigh, Colchester,
Essex
12 covered, floodlit bays; 2 open bays.
Open: Mon-Fri 10am-9pm; Sat/Sun
10am-5pm. **Charges:** £1.25/30;
£1.75/50.

E85 **Ealing GR**
☎(081) 845 4967
Rowdell Road, Northolt, Middlesex UB5
36 covered, floodlit bays; 4 open bays.
Open: 10am-10.30pm. **Charges:** £1/28.

E86 **Earls Colne G & LC**
☎(0787) 224466
Earls Colne, Nr Colchester, Essex CO6 2NS
20 covered, floodlit bays. **Open:**
9am-9pm. **Charges:** £1.75/50.
9 and 18 hole courses (see E45).

E87 **Elstree GR**
☎(081) 953 6115 Sec, 207 5680 Pro.
Watling St, Elstree, Herts WD6 3AA
45 covered, floodlit bays; 15 open bays.
Open: 7am-10pm. **Charges:** £2/basket.
18 hole course (see E48).

E88 **Fairlop Waters GR**
☎(081) 500 9911
Forest Rd, Barkingside, Ilford, IG6 3JA
36 covered, floodlit bays. **Open:**
9am-10pm. **Charges:** £2.40/70;
£1.50/40.
18 and 9 hole courses (see E50).

E89 **Fairways GR**
☎(081) 531 5126
Walthamstow Avenue, N Circular Rd,
London E4 8TA
31 covered, floodlit bays. **Open:** Mon-Fri
10am-10pm; Sat/Sun 9am-9pm.
Charges: £2/bucket (60).

E90 **The Family Golf Centre**
☎(0462) 482929
Jack's Hill, Graveley, Herts SG4 7EQ
25 covered, floodlit bays; 12 open, floodlit
bays. **Open:** 7am-10pm. **Charges:** £1/25;
£2/60 2 piece balls.
9 and 18 hole courses (see E51).

E91 **Gosling Sports Park**
☎(0707) 331056
Stanborough Rd, Welwyn Garden City,
Herts AL8 6XE
24 covered floodlit bays. **Open:** Mon-Fri
10am-10pm; Sat/Sun 9am-8pm.
Charges: £1.80/48 non members;
£1.55/48 members.

E92 **Hockley GR**
☎(0702) 207218/201008
Aldermans Hill, Hockley, Nr
Southend-on-Sea, Essex
16 covered, floodlit bays. **Open:**
9am-9pm. **Charges:** £1/bucket.

E93 **Kingsway Golf Centre**
☎(0763) 262727
Cambridge Rd, Melbourn, Royston, Herts
SG8 6EY.
40 floodlit bays. **Open:** winter Mon-Fri
9am-10pm, Sat/Sun 8am-8pm; summer
Mon-Fri 9am-10.30pm, Sat/Sun
8am-10.30pm. **Charges:** £1/42, 2 piece
balls.
9 hole, Par 3 pitch & putt; 9 hole course
(see E81).

E94 **Langdon Hills**
☎(0268) 548061 office, 548444 Pro.
Lower Dunton Rd, Bulpham, RM14 3TY.
22 covered, floodlit bays. **Open:** Mon-Fri
7.30am-10pm; Sat/Sun 7am-9.30pm.
Charges: £2/basket.
18 and 9 hole courses (see E84).

E95 **Leigh GDR**
☎(0702) 710586
Leigh Marshes, Leigh-on-Sea, Essex
18 covered, floodlit bays. **Open:**
10am-9.30pm (not Christmas). **Charges:**
£1.50/50.

E96 **Little Hay Golf Complex**
☎(0442) 833798
Box Lane, Bovingdon, Hemel Hempstead,
Herts HP3 0DQ
23 covered, floodlit bays; 9 hole pitch &
putt. **Open:** Mon-Fri 10am-10om; Sat/Sun
10am-9pm. **Charges:** £1.25/50.
18 hole course (see E86).

E97 **London Golf Centre**
☎(081) 842 0442
Ruislip Rd, Northolt, Middx UB5 6QZ
20 covered, floodlit bays. **Open:**
dawn-10.15pm. **Charges:** £2/70-80;
£1/30-35. 9 hole course (see E87).

E98 **Picketts Lock GR**
☎(081) 803 3611
Picketts Lock Lane, Edmonton, London N9
20 covered, floodlit bays. **Open:** Mon-Fri
10am-9pm; Sat/Sun 9am-8pm. **Charges:**
£2/75. 9 hole course (see E102).

E99 **Ruislip GR**
☎(0895) 638081
Ickenham Rd, Ruislip, Middlesex HA4 7DQ
30 covered, floodlit bays; 10 open, floodlit
bays. **Open:** 9am-10pm. **Charges:** £1/32;
£2/64. 18 hole course (see E114).

E100 **Stevenage GR**
☎(0438) 880424
Aston Lane, Aston, Stevenage, SG2 7EL
24 covered, floodlit bays. **Open:**
7.30am-10pm. **Charges:** £1.60/50.
18 hole course (see E121).

E101 **Tiptree GDR**
☎(0621) 819374
Newbridge Road, Tiptree, Essex CO5 0HS.
14 covered, floodlit bays. **Open:** Mon-Fri
10am-9pm; Sat/Sun 10am-6pm.
Charges: £1.50/50.

E102 **Top Meadow**
☎(0708) 852239
Fen Lane, North Ockendon, Essex RM14
3PR.
12 covered, floodlit bays. **Open:** Mon-Sat
dusk-10pm; Sun members only. **Charges:**
£1.50/bucket. 9 hole course (18 from
Oct 1992) (see E131).

E103 **Towerlands GR**
☎(0376) 26802
Panfield Rd, Braintree, Essex CM7 5BJ
6 open bays. **Open:** dawn-dusk (phone to
check). **Charges:** £1.25/50; £2.50/100.
9 hole course (see E132).

E104 **Warren Park Golf
Centre**
☎(081) 597 1120, 590 5457 Fax
Whalebone Lane North, Chadwell Heath,
Romford, Essex RM6 6SB
27 covered, floodlit bays. **Open:** Mon-Fri
9am-10pm; Sat 9am-9pm; Sun
9am-10pm. **Charges:** £1.50/35;
£2.50/75; 3.30/110.

E105 **Watford GDR**
☎(0923) 675560
Sheepcot Lane, Garston, Watford, Herts
20 covered, floodlit bays. **Open:**
9am-10pm. **Charges:** £1/35 approx.

E106 **Whitehill Golf Centre**
☎(0920) 438495
Dane End, Ware, Herts SG12 0JS
24 covered, floodlit bays. **Open:**
Mon/Wed/Thurs/Fri dawn-10pm; Tues
10am-10pm; Sat/Sun dawn-dusk.
Charges: £2.50/80-90; £1.30/40-45.
18 hole course (see E146).

E107 Woodham Mortimer GR
☎(0245) 222276
Burnham Road, Woodham Mortimer,
Maldon, Essex CM9 6SR
15 covered, floodlit bays; 8 open bays; 9
hole pitch & putt. **Open:** Mon-Fri
10am-9pm; winter Sat/Sun 9am-5pm;
summer Sat 9am-7pm, Sun 9am-8pm.
Charges: £2.40/60; £3/100; £3.50/150;
Pitch & Putt (18 holes) £2.50 adult, £1
child.

F108 Braywick GR
☎(0628) 76910
Braywick Rd, Maidenhead, Berks SL6 1DH
45 bays (grass and mats). **Open:** Spring
9am-4pm; summer 9am-9.15pm;
Autumn 9am-6pm. **Charges:** £1.90/50;
£3.50/100.

F109 Colnbrook GDR
☎(0753) 682670
Galleymead Rd, Old Bath Rd, Colnbrook,
Slough SL3 0EN
14 covered, floodlit bays; 10 open bays.
Open: 7 days 9.30am-10.30pm.
Charges: £1/bucket.

F110 Drayton Park GC
☎(0235) 550607
Steventon Road, Drayton, Oxfordshire
OX14 2RR.
22 covered, floodlit bays; 9 hole pitch &
putt. **Open:** 9am-9pm. **Charges:** £2/45;
£3/75.
18 hole course (autumn 1992) (see F23).

F111 Hawthorn Hill
☎(0628) 75588 bookings, 26035 shop
Drift Rd, Hawthorn Hill, Nr Maidenhead,
Berks SL6 3ST
32 covered, floodlit bays. **Open:**
8am-10pm. **Charges:** £2.30/bucket.
18 hole course (see F33).

F112 Heathfield GDR
☎(0869) 50626
Heathfield G & CC, Bletchingdon,
Oxfordshire
12 floodlit bays; 25 grass tees. **Open:**
10am-9pm all year. **Charges:** £3/100.
27 hole course in preparation.

F113 Hillside Farm GDR
☎(0295) 720361
Bloxham, Banbury, Oxon OX15 4PF
15 covered bays. **Open:** 7 days winter
8am-dusk; summer 8am-8pm. **Charges:**
£1/40; £3/160.

F114 Lavender Park Golf Centre
☎(0344) 884074, 886096 Pro shop
Swinley Rd, Ascot, Berks SL5 8BD
30 covered, floodlit bays. **Open:**
10am-10pm. **Charges:** £1.90/small,
£3/large. 9 hole course (see F39).

F115 Oxford Golf Centre
☎(0865) 721592
Binsey Lane, Botley, Oxford OX2 0EX
19 covered, floodlit bays; 8 open bays.
Open: 7 days 10am-9pm. **Charges:**
£2.80/90; £1.80/50.

F116 Sindlesham GR
☎(0734) 788494
Mole Rd, Sindlesham, Berks RG11 5DJ
24 covered, floodlit bays. **Open:** 7 days
7am-10.30pm. **Charges:** £1/bucket.

F117 Wavenden Golf Centre
☎(0908) 281811
Lower End Road, Wavendon, Milton
Keynes MK17 8DA
30 floodlit bays. **Open:** 8am-10pm.
Charges: £2.75/large; £1.50/small.
18 and 9 hole courses (see F57).

F118 Windmill Hill Golf Complex
☎(0908) 378623
The New Clubhouse, Tattenhoe Lane,
Bletchley, Milton Keynes, Bucks MK3 7RB
24 covered, floodlit bays; 3 open bays.
Open: Mon-Fri 8am-9pm; Sat/Sun
8am-8pm. **Charges:** £1.45/45; £2.70/90.
18 hole course (see F62).

F119 Woodcote GDR
☎(0491) 681188
Reading Rd, Woodcote, Reading, RG8 0RB
12 covered, floodlit bays. **Open:** 7 days
8am-8pm. **Charges:** £1.50/57.

F120 Wycombe Golf Centre
☎(0494) 473946
8 Marlborough Estate, West Wycombe
Road, High Wycombe, Bucks HP11 2LB
PGA approved indoor centre. **Open:**
Mon-Fri 10am-8pm; Sat 10am-6pm; Sun
10am-4pm summer/10am-1pm winter.
Charges: lessons £15; video (incl tape)
£25; full analysis (incl print out) £25.

F121 Wycombe Heights GC
☎(0494) 816686
Rayners Ave, Loudwater, High Wycombe,
Bucks HP10 9SW
24 covered, floodlit bays. **Open:** winter
7.30am-10pm; summer 4am-11pm.
Charges: £2/bucket.
2 18 hole courses (see F65).

G122 Abbotsley
☎(0480) 215153, 74000
Eynesbury Hardwicke, St Neots, PE19 4XN
20 covered, floodlit bays. **Open:**
8am-10pm. **Charges:** £2/80.
18 hole course (see G1).

G123 Blaby GR
☎(0533) 784804
Lutterworth Road, Blaby, Leics LE8 3DP
27 covered, floodlit bays; 10 open, floodlit
bays. **Open:** winter, Mon-Fri 8am-10pm,
Sat/Sun 7am-9pm; summer, Mon-Fri
7am-10pm, Sat/Sun 6am-9pm. **Charges:**
£1.80/45; jnrs/OAPs £1/45; 2 baskets get
1 free; special discount if buy passes.
9 hole course (see G7)

G124 Charnwood Golf Centre
☎(0509) 610022
Derby Road Sports Ground,
Loughborough, Leics LE11 0SS
24 covered, floodlit bays. **Open:** 8am-12
midnight. **Charges:** £1.80/60.
9 hole pitch & putt (£1.50)

G125 Collingtree Park
☎(0604) 700000, (0604) 702600
Windingbrook Lane, Northhampton NN4
0XN
16 covered, floodlit bays. **Open:**
(members only) winter 8am-8pm;
summer 7.30am-8pm. **Charges:**
£1.50/bucket (2 piece balls).
18 hole course (see G13).

G126 Daventry District Council Pitch & Putt
☎(0327) 71100 ext 413
Lodge Rd, Daventry, Northants
9 hole pitch & putt course. **Open:**
May-Sept Tues-Fri 12am-dusk;
Sat/Sun/BH 10am-dusk; school hols 7
days 10am-dusk. **Charges:** adults £1.10;
children/concessions 65p; off peak 70p.

G127 Delapre Park Golf Complex
☎(0604) 764036/763957
Eagle Drive, Nene Valley Way,
Northampton NN4 0DU
36 open bays; 44 covered, floodlit bays;
pitch & putt. **Open:** 10am-10pm.
Charges: £1/30.
18 hole course (see G17).

G128 Golf Link
☎(0530) 36591
Snibston Heritage Centre, Ashby Rd,
Coalville, Leics LE6 2LN
20 covered, floodlit. **Open:** winter Mon-Fri
10am-9.30pm, Sat 9am-6pm, Sun
9am-7pm; summer Mon-Fri 10am-10pm,
Sat/Sun 9am-10pm. **Charges:** £2/75-80.
9 hole Par 3 (WD £2.50 9 hole, £3.50 18
hole; WE £3 9 hole, £4 18 hole).

G129 Hellidon Lakes GR
☎(0327) 62550
Hellidon, Nr Daventry, Northants NN11 6LN
8 covered bays. **Open:** 7 days 8am-dusk.
Charges: £2/60 (members); £2.50/60
(non members).
18 hole course (see G26).

G130 Hemingford GC
☎(0480) 492939
Rideaway, Hemingford Abbots,
Huntingdon PE18 9HQ
30 covered, floodlit bays. **Open:** Mon-Fri
10am-10pm; Sat/Sun 9am-9pm.
Charges: £2.70/95; £1.65/45.
9 hole course (see G27).

G131 Ivinghoe GR
☎(0296) 662720
Cheddington Rd, Ivinghoe, Nr Leighton
Buzzard, Beds LU7 9DY
33 covered, floodlit bays. **Open:** winter
Mon-Fri 10am-9pm, Sat/Sun 10am-8pm;
summer Mon-Fri 10am-9pm, Sat/Sun
10am-7pm. **Open:** 10am-4pm WD
£1.50/large (c.80), £0.75 small; WE and
evenings £1.80/large, £0.90 small.

G132 Lakeside Lodge
☎(0487) 740540 Sec, 741541 Pro.
Fen Road, Pidley, Huntingdon, PE17 3DD
Open summer 1992. **Charges:** £1.20/50.
18 hole course, 9 hole Par 3 course (see
G36).

G133 Langton International Golf
☎(085) 884 374
Langton Hall, Leicestershire LE16 7TY.
12 covered, floodlit bays. **Charges:** on application. 18 hole course (see G37).

G134 Leicestershire Forest
☎(0455) 824800
Maltfield Lane, Botcheston, Leics LE9 9FJ
22 floodlit bays. **Open:** all day every day.
Charges: £2/70.
18 hole course (see G39).

G135 Mowsbury Golf & Squash Complex
☎(0234) 216374 shop, 771493 course
Kimbolton Rd, Bedford, MK41 8DQ
14 covered, floodlit bays. **Open:**
9am-10pm. **Charges:** £1.80/basket.
18 hole course (see G50).

G136 Range Inn GR
☎(0533) 664400
Melton Rd, Leicester LE4 0HQ
24 covered, floodlit bays. **Open:**
9am-10pm. **Charges:** £1.55/large;
£1.20/small.

G137 Stockwood Park GR
☎(0582) 413704
Stockwood Park, London Rd, Luton, LU1 4L
20 covered, floodlit bays; 9 hole pitch & putt. **Open:** Mon-Fri 7am-10pm; Sat/Sun 7am-6pm. **Charges:** £1.50/50;
£2.20/100. 18 hole course (see G71).

G138 Tilsworth
☎(0525) 210721/2
Dunstable Rd, Tilsworth, Leighton Buzzard, Beds
30 covered, floodlit bays. **Open:**
10am-10pm. **Charges:** £2/100;
£1.25/50. 9 hole course (see G73).

G139 Whaddon Golf Centre
☎(0223) 207325
Church St, Whaddon, Nr Royston, Cambs SG8 5RX.
14 covered, floodlit bays; 7 open bays.
Open: Mon-Fri 8am-9pm; Sat/Sun 8am-dusk. **Charges:** £1/50; £2/100.
9 hole course (see H51).

G140 Whetstone GR
☎(0533) 861424
Cambridge Rd, Cosby, Leicester LE9 5SH
20 turf bays. **Open:** dawn-dusk. **Charges:**
£1.60/80. 18 hole course (see G78).

H141 Bawburgh
☎(0603) 746390, 742323 Pro.
Long Lane, Bawburgh, Norwich, Norfolk NR9 3LX
14 covered bays; fairweather grass tees.
Charges: on application.
9 hole course (see H4).

H142 Browston Hall DR
☎(0493) 603511
Browston Green, Great Yarmouth, Norfolk NR31 9DW
26 floodlit bays; 9 hole pitch & putt. **Open:**
8am-10pm. **Charges:** £1/44; £2/88.

H143 Eagles GR
☎(0553) 827147
39 School Rd, Tilney All Saints, Kings Lynn, Norfolk PE34 4RS
20 floodlit bays (some covered). **Open:**
winter Mon-Fri 8am-9pm; Sat/Sun 8am-6.30pm; summer 7 days 8am-9pm;.
Charges: £1.90/50; £3/100.
9 hole course (see H11).

H144 Fynn Valley Golf Centre
☎(0473) 785463
Witnesham, Ipswich, Suffolk IP6 9JA
10 covered, floodlit bays; 13 open bays.
Open: summer Mon-Fri 7am-9.30pm;
Sat/Sun 7am-7pm; winter Mon-Fri 8am-9.30pm; Sat-Sun 7.30am-6pm.
Charges: £2.20/100; £1.50/50.
9 hole course (see H18).

H145 Middleton Hall GC
☎(0553) 841800
Hall Orchards, Middleton, Nr Kings Lynn, Norfolk PE32 1RH.
8 covered, floodlit bays. **Open:** 8am-dusk.
Charges: £2.50/basket (non members).
9 hole course (see H29).

H146 St Helena
☎(0986) 875567, 874565 fax
Bramfield Rd, Halesworth, IP19 9XA
10 covered, floodlit bays; 8 open bays.
Open: 8am-9pm. **Charges:** £1.10/50;
£1.60/100.
18 and 9 hole courses (see H40).

H147 Silfield Village P&P
☎(0953) 603508
Silfield St, Silfield, Wymondham, Norfolk
18 hole P&P (58-118 yards); 9 raised greens, 9 flat; water and bunkers. **Open:**
March-Oct 7 days 9am-dusk; Oct-March Fri/Sat/Sun only 9am-dusk. **Charges:**
Mon-Sat £3.50 (under 16s £1.50);
Mon-Fri 9am-4pm OAPs £2,50; Sun £4.

H148 Sprowston Park DR
☎(0603) 410657 Sec, 415557 Pro
Wroxham Rd, Sprowston, Norwich, Norfolk NR7 8RP
27 covered, floodlit bays. **Open:**
8am-10pm. **Charges:** £1/small; £2/large.
18 hole course (see H43).

H149 Wensum Valley GR
☎(0603) 261012
Beech Ave, Taverham, Norwich, NR8 6HP
6 open bays. **Open:** 7am-dusk. **Charges:**
£2/80. 9 hole course (see H50).

I150 Abbey Park DR
☎(0527) 63918
Dagnell End Rd, Redditch, Worcs B98 7BD
12 covered bays. **Open:** dawn-dusk.
Charges: £1.25/50; £2.25/100.
18 hole course (see I1).

I151 Bromsgrove Golf Centre
☎(0527) 575886
Stratford Road, Bromsgrove, B60 1LD
41 covered, floodlit bays. **Open:** Mon-Fri 10am-10pm; Sat/Sun 10am-6pm.
Charges: £2.20/100; £1.45/50;
£1.10/35. 9 hole course (see I8).

I152 City of Coventry
☎(0203) 543141
Brandon Lane, Brandon, Coventry CV8 3GQ
11 covered, floodlit bays. **Open:** Mon-Fri 8am-8.30pm; Sat/Sun 8am-dusk.
Charges: £1.20/40; £2/80.
18 hole course (see I13).

I153 Four Ashes Golf Centre
☎(0564) 779055
Four Ashes Rd, Dorridge, Solihull, B93 8NQ
28 covered, floodlit. **Open:** Mon-Fri 10am-10pm; Sat/Sun 10am-6pm.
Charges: £2.10/90; £1.20/45.

I154 Gloucester Hotel & CC
☎(0452) 415242
Robinswood Hill, Matson Lane, Gloucester
12 floodlit bays. **Open:** 10am-9pm.
Charges: £1/30. 18 hole course (see I30).

I155 Halesowen GR
☎(021) 550 2920
Quarry Lane, Halesowen, B63 4PB.
14 open bays. **Open:** 9.30am-dusk.
Charges: £1.40/50; £2.50/100.

I156 Hereford GDR
☎(0432) 263310
Roman Road, Bobblestock, Hereford
10 covered, floodlit bays; 6 open bays.
Open: winter: Mon/Fri 10am-4pm, Tues-Thurs 10am-8pm, Sat/Sun 9am-5pm;
summer: Mon/Fri 10am-5pm; Tues-Thurs 10am-9pm; Sat/Sun 9am-6pm. **Charges:**
£1.50/50.

I157 John Reay Golf Centre
☎(020333) 3920, 8071, 3405
Sandpits Lane, Keresley, Coventry CV7 8NJ
30 covered, floodlit bays. **Open:** Mon-Fri 9am-10pm; Sat/Sun 9.30am-6pm.
Charges: £1/45.

I158 Lea Marston Hotel & LC
☎(0675) 470468
Haunch Lane, Lea Marston, B76 0BY
32 covered, floodlit bays. **Open:** winter 10am-9.30pm; summer 9am-9.30pm.
Charges: £2.20/bucket.
9 hole course (see I49).

I159 MJM Golf Driving Range
☎(052 785) 7129
Brickyard Lane, Studley, B78 7EE.
14 covered, floodlit bays; 6 open, floodlit bays. **Open:** Mon-Fri 10am-9pm; Sat/Sun 10am-6pm. **Charges:** £1.25/50;
£1.85/90; £2.75/150.

I160 Ombersley
☎(0905) 620747
Bishops Wood Road, Lineholt, Ombersley, Droitwich, Worcs WR9 0LE
40 open bays. **Open:** Mon-Fri 8am-dusk;
Sat/Sun 7am-dusk. **Charges:** £1.40/40.
18 hole course (see I67).

I161 Purley Chase
☎(0203) 393118, 395348
Ridge Lane, Nr Nuneaton, N Warwicks CV10 0RB
13 covered, floodlit bays. **Open:**
7am-10pm. **Charges:** £1.25/bucket.
18 hole course (see I70).

I162 **Sapey Golf**
☎(08867) 288/567
Upper Sapey, Nr Worcester, WR6 6XT
6 open bays. **Open:** Mon-Fri 8am-8pm;
Sat/Sun 8am-4pm. **Charges:** £1.25/50;
£2.25/100. 18 hole course (see I77).

I163 **Stratford Oaks**
☎(0789) 731571
Warwickshire Academy of Golf, Bearley
Rd, Snitterfield, Stratford-upon-Avon,
Warwicks CV37 0EZ
26 covered, floodlit bays. **Open:**
7.30am-10pm. **Charges:** £2/80.
18 hole course (see I83).

I164 **Thornbury**
Bristol Rd, Thornbury, Avon
25 covered, floodlit bays opening summer
1992. **Open:** all day every day. **Charges:**
on application.

I165 **The Vale**
☎(038682) 781, 520 Pro shop
Hill Furze Rd, Bishampton, Pershore,
Worcs WR10 2LZ.
20 open bays. **Open:** dawn-dusk.
Charges: £1.50/50; £2.50/100 2 piece
balls. 18 and 9 hole courses (see I91).

I166 **Warwick Golf Centre**
☎(0926) 494316
The Racecourse, Warwick CV34 6HW
28 covered, floodlit bays. **Open:** Mon-Fri
9.30am-9pm; winter Sat/Sun 9.30am-
6pm; summer Sat/Sun 9.30am-4pm.
Charges: £2.20/90; £1.90/60; £1.20/30.
9 hole course (see I94).

I167 **Whitelakes Golf Centre**
☎(0564) 824460
Tilehouse Lane, Wythall, Solihull
15 covered, floodlit bays. **Open:**
8am-9pm. **Charges:** 70p/small;
£1.30/large; £2/ex large.
9 hole Par 3 course.

I168 **Worcester GR**
☎(0905) 421213
Weir Lane, Lower Wick, Worcester WR2
4AY
26 covered, floodlit bays; 9 hole pitch &
putt. **Open:** Mon-Fri 10am-8.45pm;
Sat/Sun 10am-5.30pm. **Charges:**
80p/25; £1.50/45; £3/90.

J169 **Bannel GR**
☎(0244) 544639
Chester Rd, Penymynydd, Nr Chester,
Clwyd CH4 0EN
10 covered, floodlit bays; 3 open bays.
Open: summer Mon-Fri 10am-8.30pm,
Sat/Sun 9.30am-6.30pm; winter Mon-Fri
10am-8.30pm, Sat/Sun 9.30am-4.30pm.
Charges: £1.75/50.

J170 **Caerleon GDR**
☎(0633) 420342
Broadway, Caerleon, Newport, Gwent NP6
1AY
12 covered, floodlit bays; 3 open bays.
Open: dawn-9.30pm. **Charges:**
£1.75/large; £1.25/small.
9 hole course (see J22).

J171 **Clarach GDR**
☎(0970) 828923
Clarach, Aberystwyth, Dyfed SY23 3DT
20 covered, floodlit bays. **Open:** summer
9am-10pm; winter 9am-9pm. **Charges:**
£1/26; £2/52.

J172 **Dewstow**
☎(0291) 430444
Caerwent, Newport, Gwent NP6 4AH
26 floodlit bays. **Open:** 9am-9.30pm.
Charges: £1/55. 18 holes (see J38).

J173 **Kinmel Park GC**
☎(0745) 833548
Bodelwyddan, Clwyd, N Wales LL18 5SR
24 covered, floodlit bays; golf school bay.
Open: summer 7 days 10am-10pm;
winter Mon-Fri 10am-10pm, Sat
10am-6pm, Sun 10am-10pm. **Charges:**
£1.50/50; £2.50/100. 9 hole nursery
course, night time golf (see J53).

J174 **Mayfield GR**
☎(0437) 890308
Clareston Hall, Freystrop, Haverfordwest
12 covered, floodlit bays. **Open:** Mon-Fri
10am-9.30pm; Sat/Sun winter
10am-8pm, summer 10am-9.30pm.
Charges: £2.50/80; £1.25/40.

J175 **Mid Wales Golf Centre**
☎(0686) 688303
Caersws, Nr Newtown, Powys
12 covered, floodlit bays; 4 open bays.
Open: Mon-Fri 10am-9pm; Sat/Sun
10am-6pm. **Charges:** £2/75; £1.20/35.
9 hole Par 3 course (see J68).

J176 **Mountain Lakes GR**
☎(0222) 886666
Blaengwynlais, Caerphilly, Mid-Glam
20 covered, floodlit bays. **Open:**
8am-9.30pm. **Charges:** £1/40-50.
18 hole course (see J29).

J177 **North Wales GR**
☎(0745) 730803
Llanerch Park, St Asaph, Clwyd LL17 0BD
14 covered, floodlit bays. **Open:** summer 7
days 10am-9pm; winter Mon-Fri
10am-9pm, Sat/Sun 10am-5pm.
Charges: £1/36; £1.50/54; £2.50/90;
£3/108. 9 hole course (see J81).

J178 **Oakdale**
☎(0495) 220044
Llwynon Lane, Oakdale, Gwent NP2 0NF
18 covered, floodlit bays; 2 open bays.
Open: 7 days 9.30am-9.30pm. **Charges:**
£1.30/48. 9 hole course (see J36).

J179 **Peterstone G & CC**
☎(0633) 680009
Peterstone, Wentlooge, Cardiff CF3 8TM.
40 covered, floodlit bays. **Open:**
dawn-10pm. **Charges:** on application.
18 hole course (see J90).

J180 **South Wales GR**
☎(0446) 742434
101 Port Rd East, Barry, S Glam CF6 7PX
16 covered, floodlit bays. **Open:** Mon-Fri
9am-8pm, Sat/Sun 9am-6pm. **Charges:**
£1.75/70, £3/140. 9 hole course.

J181 **Talywain GDR**
☎(0495) 774960
Old Bucks Level, Talywain, Pontypool,
Gwent NP4 7UQ
20 covered, floodlit bays. **Open:** Mon-Fri
8am-9pm; Sat/Sun 8am-8pm. **Charges:**
£1/40/50.

J182 **Tregroes DR**
☎(0348) 872316
Fishguard, Dyfed, SA65 9QF
6 covered bays. **Open:** 10am-dusk.
Charges: £1/50.

J183 **Welsh Border Golf
Complex**
☎(0743) 884247
Bulthy Farm, Bulthy, Middletown, Nr
Welshpool SY21 8ER
10 covered, floodlit bays. **Open:** Mon-Fri
7.30am-9.30pm; Sat/Sun
8.30am-7.30pm. **Charges:** £1.50/35;
£2/75; £2.50/100.
9 hole course (see J124).

K184 **Alvaston Hall Golf
Centre**
☎(0270) 610019
Alvaston Hall, Middlewich Rd, Nantwich,
Cheshire CW5 6PD.
16 covered, floodlit bays. **Open:**
9am-9pm. **Charges:** £1/34; £2/68 (2
piece balls).
9 hole Par 3 golf course.

K185 **Cranford GDR**
☎(061) 432 8242
Harwood Rd, off Didsbury Rd, Heaton
Mersey, Stockport, Cheshire SK4 3AW
30 covered, floodlit bays; 2 open, floodlit
bays. **Open:** 10.30am-10pm. **Charges:**
£2.30/50.

K186 **Craythorne Golf Centre**
☎(0283) 64329
Craythorne Rd, Stretton, Burton-on-Trent,
Staffs DE13 0AZ
14 covered, floodlit bays. **Open:** Mon-Sat
9am-9pm; Sun 9am-dusk. **Charges:**
£1.50/bucket.
18 and 9 hole courses (see K32).

K187 **Croft Golf Centre**
☎(0925) 763741
Cross Lane, Croft, Cheshire WA3 7AW
20 floodlit bays. **Open:** winter Mon-Thurs
9am-9pm, Fri-Sun 9am-7pm; summer
9am-9pm. **Charges:** £1/35.

K188 **Fishley Park GR**
☎(0922) 685279
Fishley Lane, Pelsall, Walsall, WS3 5AE.
16 covered, floodlit bays; 9 hole pitch &
putt. **Open:** 9am-9pm. **Charges:**
£1.10/40; £1.70/75; £2.35/125.

K189 **Hartford GR**
☎(0606) 871162
Burrows Hill, Hartford, Northwich,
Cheshire CW9 3AA
30 covered, floodlit bays. **Open:** Sun-Fri
10am-9pm; Sat 10am-7pm. **Charges:**
£1.50/45; £3/100.
9 hole course.

K190 **Keele Golf Centre**
☎(0782) 717417
Municipal Golf Course, Keele Road,
Newcastle-under-Lyme, Staffs ST5 5AB
26 covered, floodlit bays. **Open:**
9am-10pm. **Charges:** £2.60/60; £3/95.
18 hole course (see K83).

K191 **Ketley Golf & Squash Centre**
☎(0952) 251618
Holyhead Road, Ketley, Telford, TF3 1ED
12 covered, floodlit bays. **Open:** winter
Mon-Fri 10am-2pm, 4pm-10pm; Sat/Sun
3pm-10pm; summer Mon-Fri
11.30am-2.30pm, 5.30pm-10pm;
Sat/Sun 7pm-10pm. **Charges:**
£2.65/120; £2.25/80.
6 hole Par 3 course £2.15.

K192 **Perton Park Golf Centre**
☎(0902) 380103
Wrottesley Park Road, Perton,
Wolverhampton, WV6 7HL
12 covered bays; 6 open bays. **Open:**
8am-dusk. **Charges:** £2/bucket.
18 hole course (see K93).

K193 **Sandfield GDR**
☎(0244) 301752
Ince Lane, Bridge Trafford, Nr Chester,
Cheshire CH2 4JR.
18 covered, floodlit bays; 3 open bays.
Open: Mon-Fri 10am-9pm; Sat/Sun
10am-6pm. **Charges:** £1.60/50;
£2.80/100.
9 hole course opening summer 1992.

K194 **Sedgley Golf Centre**
☎(0902) 880503
Sandyfields Rd, Sedgeley, Dudley DY3 3DL
6 open bays; 10 covered, floodlit bays.
Open: Mon-Fri 9.30am-9pm; Sat/Sun
9am-5pm. **Charges:** £1.80/large;
£1/small.
9 hole course (see K110).

K195 **Seedy Mill GDR**
☎(0543) 417333
Elm Hurst, Lichfield, Staffs WS13 8HE
26 covered, floodlit bays. **Open:**
8am-9pm. **Charges:** £1/35.
9 hole Par 3 pitch & putt course; 18 hole
course (see K111).

K196 **Shrewsbury**
Telford Way, Shrewsbury, Shropshire.
28 covered, floodlit bays. **Open:**
10am-9pm. **Charges:** £2/70 approx.

K197 **Shrigley Hall Hotel**
☎(0625) 575755 Office, 575626 Pro.
Shrigley Park, Pott Shrigley, Nr
Macclesfield, Cheshire SK10 5SB
Due to open 1992, phone for details.
Pitch & putt; 18 hole course (see K115).

K198 **Swindon**
☎(0902) 897031
Bridgnorth Rd, Swindon, Dudley, DY3 4PU
20 covered, floodlit bays; 7 open bays.
Open: Mon-Fri 9am-9pm; Sat/Sun
8.15am-5.30pm. **Charges:** £1.40/45;
£2.20/95; £3.50/135.
18 and 9 hole courses (see K121).

K199 **Three Hammers**
☎(0902) 790428
Old Stafford Rd, Coven, Staffs WV10 7PP
23 covered, floodlit bays. **Open:** Mon-Fri
10am-10pm; Sat 9.30am-9pm; Sun
8.30am-9pm. **Charges:** £1/30.
18 hole course Par 3 (see K124).

K200 **Wirral Golf and Drive Centre**
☎(051) 677 6606
Tarran Way, Moreton, Wirral, L46 4TP
20 covered, floodlit bays. **Open:**
9.30am-9pm. **Charges:** £1/30; £2/60.

L201 **Belton Woods Hotel**
☎(0476) 593200
Belton, Nr Grantham, Lincs NG32 2LN
24 covered, floodlit bays. **Open:**
7am-9.30pm. **Charges:** £2/72.
9 hole and 2 18 hole courses (see L7).

L202 **Carlton Forum GR**
☎(0602) 612949
Foxhill Road, Carlton, Nottingham
28 covered, floodlit bays. **Open:** Mon
12-10pm; Tues-Sun 9.30am-10pm.
Charges: £1.80 off peak; £2.05 peak;
£1.55 Sat/Sun after 5.30pm.

L203 **Cotgrave Place G & CC**
☎(0602) 334686
Stragglethorpe, Nottingham NG12 3HB.
10 covered, floodlit bays. **Open:**
dawn-dusk. **Charges:** £2/80.
27 hole course (see L25).

L204 **The Elms GR**
☎(0754) 881230
Croft, Nr Wainfleet, Skegness, Lincs
20 covered, floodlit bays. **Open:** Mon-Fri
10am-10pm; Sat/Sun 9am-10pm.
Charges: £1.50/50.   6 hole course.

L205 **Four Seasons GC**
☎(0335) 60006
Hall Lane, Brailsford, Ashbourne, Derby
15 floodlit bays. **Open:** dawn-10pm.
Charges: £2/60.

L206 **Gainsborough**
☎(0427) 613088
Thonock, Gainsborough, Lincs DN21 1PZ
20 covered, floodlit bays. **Open:** Mon-Fri
8am-9pm; Sat/Sun 8am-dusk. **Charges:**
£1/44.
18 hole course (see L31).

L207 **Gedney Hill**
☎(0406) 330922
West Drove, Gedney Hill, Nr Holbeach,
Lincs PE12 0NT
10 open bays. **Open:** dawn-dusk.
Charges: £1/35.
18 hole course (see L32).

L208 **Golf Driving Range**
☎(0472) 698131
Mini Golf House, Kings Rd, Cleethorpes
8 covered, floodlit bays; open grass area.
Open: 10am-8pm. **Charges:**
£1.20/basket.
9 hole pitch & putt (£1/round, 50p club
hire).

L209 **Grange Park GR**
☎(0724) 764478
Butterwick Rd, Messingham, Scunthorpe
20 covered, floodlit bays. **Open:** Mon-Fri
9am-9.30pm; Sat/Sun 9am-8.30pm.
Charges: £1.25/50.
9 hole course (see L34).

L210 **Horncastle**
☎(0507) 526800
West Ashby, Horncastle, Lincs LN9 5PP
25 covered, floodlit bays. **Open:**
9am-10pm. **Charges:** £2.50/bucket.
18 hole course (see L37).

L211 **Horsley Lodge**
☎(0332) 780838
Horsley Lodge, Smalley Mill Road, Horsley,
Derbys DE2 5BL
10 covered, floodlit bays. **Open:**
8am-10pm. **Charges:** £1.50/50.
18 hole course (see L38).

L212 **Lenton Lane GDR**
☎(0602) 862179
Lenton Lane, Nottingham
21 floodlit bays. **Open:** 7 days Mon-Fri
10am-10pm; Sat/Sun 10am-7pm.
Charges: £2/80.   9 hole pitch & putt £2
(£1.50); 18 hole pitch & putt £3 (£2).

L213 **Lincoln GR**
☎(0602) 653545
Washingborough Rd, Washingborough,
Lincoln
25 covered, floodlit bays. **Open:** Mon-Fri
10am-8.30pm; Sat/Sun 10am-8pm.
Charges: £1.30/small; £1.60/med;
£1.85/large.   9 hole Par 3 course.

L214 **Millfield Golf Complex**
☎(042771) 255
Laughterton, Nr Torksey, Lincoln LN1 2LB.
10 covered, floodlit bays. **Open:**
8am-9pm. **Charges:** £2/large bucket.
18 and 9 hole course (see L57).

L215 **Oakmere Park**
☎(0602) 653545
Oaks Lane, Oxton, Nr Southwell, Notts
30 covered, floodlit bays. **Open:**
7.30am-9.30pm. **Charges:** £2/94.
18 hole and 9 hole courses (see L63).

L216 **Ramsdale Park**
Oxton Rd, Calverton, Notts.
25 covered, floodlit bays opening end May
1992. **Open:** all day every day. **Charges:**
on application.
18 hole course (see L68).

M217 **Bardsley Park GC**
☎(061) 627 2463
Knott Lanes, Bardsley, Oldham, OL8 3JD
17 covered, floodlit bays. **Open:** Mon-Fri
10am-9pm; Sat/Sun 9am-6pm. **Charges:**
£2.20/46.

M218 **Beacon Park DR**
☎(0695) 622700
Beacon Lane, Dalton, Up Holland, Wigan,
Lancs WN8 7RU
24 covered, floodlit bays. **Open:**
8am-9.30pm. **Charges:** £2/64.
18 hole course (see M11).

M219 **Blackburn GDR**
☎(0254) 581996
Queens Park Playing Fields, Haslingden
Rd, Blackburn, Lancs BB2 3HJ
27 covered, floodlit bays. **Open:** Mon-Fri
10am-9pm; Sat/Sun 9am-8pm. **Charges:**
£1/33; £1.65/55.

M220 **Bowlee GDR**
☎(061) 653 1603
Heywood Old Rd, Middleton, Manchester
16 covered, floodlit bays. **Open:** winter
Mon-Fri 10am-7.30pm, Sat/Sun 9am-
4.30pm; summer Mon-Fri 10am-8.30pm,
Sat/Sun 9am-4.30pm. **Charges:** £2.25/60

M221 **Castle Hawk DR**
☎(0706) 40841
Chadwick Lane, Castleton, Rochdale
16 bays. **Open:** Mon-Fri 10am-8pm;
Sat/Sun 8.30am-5pm. **Charges:** £2/60;
£3/100.   18 hole course (see M29).

M222 **Drivers Indoor Golf DR**
☎(0253) 893150
Breck Rd, Poulton-le-Fylde, FY7 7HJ.
4 indoor bays. **Open:** 8am-9pm. **Charges:**
on application.   9 hole course.

M223 **Euxton Park GR**
☎(02572) 261601
Euxton Lane, Chorley, Nr Preston, Lancs
30 covered, floodlit bays; 10 open bays;
10 grass bays. **Open:** Mon-Fri
10am-9.15pm; Sat/Sun 9am-7.15pm.
Charges: £1.75/50; £1.25 jnrs.

M224 **Fore'Long GDR**
☎(0228) 49583
Carlisle Racecourse, Durdar, Carlisle
6 covered, floodlit bays. **Open:** closed Mon
and race days; Tues-Fri 10am-8pm;
Sat/Sun 10am-4pm. **Charges:**
£1.10/small; £1.40/large.

M225 **Formby GR**
☎(07048) 75952
Moss Side, Formby, Merseyside L37 0AF
14 covered, floodlit bays; 7 open bays.
Open: winter Mon-Fri 9.30am-8.30pm;
Sat/Sun 9.30am-5.30pm; summer Mon-
Fri 9.30am-9.30pm; Sat/Sun 9.30am-
8.30pm. **Charges:** £1.30/45; £2.60/90.

M226 **Kearsley DR**
☎(0204) 75726
Moss Lane, Kearsley, Bolton, BL4 8SF
10 covered, floodlit bays; 15 open grass
bays. **Open:** Mon-Fri 11am-10pm;
Sat/Sun 11am-5pm. **Charges:** £1.20/25;
£2.40/50.   9 hole pitch & putt.

M227 **Leisure Lakes GDR**
☎(0772) 815842
Tabby Nook, Mere Brow, Tarleton, PR4 6LA
20 covered, floodlit bays. **Open:**
9am-9pm. **Charges:** £1.50/50.

M228 **Manchester**
☎(061) 643 3202
Hopwood Cottage, Rochdale Rd,
Middleton, Manchester M24 2QP
4 covered bays. **Open:** dawn-dusk.
Charges: £1.50/basket.
18 hole course (see M91).

M229 **Newby Grange**
☎(0228) 573645
Newby Grange, Carlisle, Cumbria.
16 covered, floodlit bays. **Open:**
8am-9pm. **Charges:** £2.50/bucket.
18 hole course (see M97).

M230 **Phoenix GDR**
☎(0253) 854846
Fleetwood Rd, Norbreck, Blackpool
27 covered/open, floodlit bays. **Open:**
Mon-Thurs 9am-9pm; Fri/Sat/Sun
9am-7pm. **Charges:** £1.50/bucket.
9 hole Par 3 golf course.

M231 **Preston GDR**
☎(0772) 861827
Preston Grasshoppers, Lightfoot Lane,
Fulwood, Preston, Lancs PR4 0AE.
23 covered, floodlit bays. **Open:** winter,
Mon-Fri 9.30am-9pm; Sun 9am-12pm;
summer, Mon-Fri 9.30am-9pm, Sat/Sun
9am-6pm. **Charges:** £1.75/45; £3.50/105

M232 **Solway Village GC**
☎(06973) 32544
Silloth-on-Solway, Cumbria CA5 4QQ
10 covered, floodlit bays; 10 open, floodlit
bays. **Open:** summer 9am-9pm; winter
9am-dusk. **Charges:** £1/40.
9 hole course (see M127).

N233 **Arnold Palmer GR**
☎(0742) 361195
Bradway Rd, Bradway, Sheffield S17 4QU.
23 covered, floodlit bays. **Open:**
9am-9pm. **Charges:** £2/65; £2.50/85;
£3.50/120.

N234 **Austerfield Park DR**
☎(0302) 710841
Cross Lane, Austerfield, Bawtry, DN10 6RF
10 covered, floodlit bays. **Open:** Mon-Fri
8am-9pm; Sat/Sun 9am-6pm. **Charges:**
£1.40/basket.   18 hole course (see N5).

N235 **Bradley Park DR**
☎(0484) 539988
Bradley Rd, Huddersfield, HD2 1PZ
14 covered, floodlit bays. **Open:** summer
9am-9.30pm; March-Oct Mon-Fri
9am-9.30, Sat/Sun 9am-7pm. **Charges:**
£2/72; £1/36; 50p/18.
18 and 9 hole courses (see N17).

N236 **Forest Park**
☎(0904) 400425
Stockton on Forest, York, YO3 9UW
7 open bays. **Open:** 8am-dusk. **Charges:**
£1.50/45.   18 hole course (see N45).

N237 **Hull Golf Centre**
☎(0482) 492720
National Avenue, Hull, HU5 4JB
23 covered, floodlit bays. **Open:** Mon-Fri
9.30am-9pm; Sat/Sun 9.30am-7.30pm.
Charges: £1/40; £2/90.   9 hole P&P.

N238 **Little Houghton GR**
☎(0226) 751775
Chappel Lane, Little Houghton, Nr
Barnsley, S73 2BD
17 covered, floodlit bays. **Open:** Mon-Fri
10am-9pm; Sat/Sun 9.30am-6pm.

Charges: range balls £1.30/50;
£2.50/100; two piece balls £1.60/50;
£3/100.
18 hole course opening 1992 (see N114).

N239 **Oulton Park**
Oulton, Leeds 26.
24 covered, floodlit bays. **Open:**
9am-dusk. **Charges:** £1.50/40; £2/60.
18 hole course (see N93).

N240 **Phoenix DR**
☎(0709) 364669
Grange Lane, Brinsworth, Rotherham
20 covered, floodlit bays. **Open:**
9am-9pm. **Charges:** £1.50/50;
£2.50/100.

N241 **Scotton GDR**
☎(0423) 868943
Low Moor Lane, Scotton/Lingerfield, Nr
Knaresborough, W Yorks HG5 9HZ
14 covered bays. **Open:** 10am-dusk.
Charges: £2/basket.

N242 **York GDR**
☎(0904) 690421
Wigginton Road, Wigginton, York YO3 3RJ
20 covered, floodlit bays. **Open:** 7 days
10am-5pm; 7pm-10pm. **Charges:**
£1.50/40; £1.80/60; 2.30/80.

O243 **Aycliffe GDR**
☎(0325) 310820
School Lane, Newton Aycliffe, Durham
18 covered, floodlit bays. **Open:** Mon-Fri
10am-9pm; Sat/Sun 10am-7pm.
Charges: £1.80/large basket;
£1.55/small.   9 hole course (see O6).

O244 **Gosforth Park Complex**
☎(091) 236 4480
High Gosforth Park, Newcastle-upon-Tyne
30 covered, floodlit bays. **Open:**
8am-10pm. **Charges:** £1.50/75.
18 hole course; 9 hole P&P (see O51).

O245 **Knotty Hill GC**
☎(0740) 20320
Sedgefield, Stockton-on-Tees, TS21 2BB.
14 covered, floodlit bays; 14 open bays.
Open: 8am-10pm. **Charges:** £2/small;
£3/large.   18 hole course (see O41).

O246 **Middlesbrough
Municipal DR**
☎(0642) 315533
Ladgate Lane, Middlesborough, TS5 7YZ
20 floodlit bays. **Open:** 9am-9pm.
Charges: £1.95/large; £1/small.
18 hole course (see O44).

O247 **Roseberry Grange**
☎(091 370) 0660 Shop, 2047 office.
Grange Villa, Chester-Le-Street, DH2 3NF.
18 covered, floodlit bays. **Open:** Mon-Fri
8am-9pm; Sat/Sun 7am-9pm. **Charges:**
£1.10/50.   18 hole course (see O55).

O248 **Slaley Hall**
☎(0434) 673691/673350
Slaley, Hexham, N'umberland NE47 0BY.
30 covered, floodlit bays. **Open:**
dawn-dusk.   18 hole course (see O63).

O249 Washington GR
☎(091) 417 2626
Stone Cellar Rd, Usworth, Washington,
Tyne & Wear NE37 1PH
21 covered, floodlit bays. **Open:**
9.30am-10pm. **Charges:** £1.30/50.
9 hole P&P; 18 hole course (see O74).

P250 Polkemmet DR
☎(0501) 43905
Park Centre, Polkemmet Country Park,
Whitburn, Bathgate, W Lothian EH47 0AD
15 floodlit bays. **Charges:** summer
£2/100, £1.20/50; winter £1.40/100,
85p/50; jnrs/OAPs/unemployed discounts.
9 hole course (see P63).

P251 Port Royal GR
☎(031) 333 4377
Ingliston, Edinburgh, Midlothian EH28 8TR
24 covered, floodlit bays. **Open:**
10am-10pm. **Charges:** £1.35/50.
9 hole pitch & putt.

Q252 Auchenharvie DR
☎(0294) 603103
Moorpark Rd West, Brewery Park,
Stevenston, Ayrshire KA20 3HU
18 covered, floodlit bays. **Open:** winter
Mon-Fri 8.30am-8.30pm, Sat/Sun
8.30am-4.30pm; summer Mon-Fri
8.30am-8.30pm, Sat/Sun
8.30am-5.30pm. **Charges:** £1.20/50;
£2.20/100.　9 hole course (see Q5).

Q253 Brunston Castle DR
Dailly, Nr Girvan, Ayrshire
8 covered, floodlit bays. **Charges:** on
application.　18 hole course (see Q22).

Q254 Clydeway Golf Centre
☎(041) 641 8899
Blantyre Farm Rd, Uddingston, Glasgow
25 covered, floodlit bays. **Open:** summer
Mon-Fri 10am-9pm, Sat/Sun 10am-8pm;
winter Mon-Fri 10am-8.30pm, Sat/Sun
10am-8.30pm. **Charges:** £1.50/60.

Q255 Coatbridge GR
☎(0236) 428975
Townhead Rd, Coatbridge, Lanark
18 covered, floodlit bays. **Open:**
8am-10pm. **Charges:** on application.
18 hole course (see Q39).

Q256 Deaconsbank
☎(041) 638 7044
Stewarton Rd, Thornliebank, Glasgow G46
15 covered, floodlit bays. **Open:** Mon-Fri
10am-8.30pm; Sat/Sun 10am-7.30pm.
Charges: £1.75/50; £2.25/75;
£2.75/100.　18 hole course (see Q50).

Q257 Normandy GR
☎(041) 886 7477
Inchinnan Road, Renfrew, Strathclyde
5 open bays; 20 covered, floodlit bays.
Open: 9.30am-10pm. **Charges:** £1/40
(coin operated).

Q258 Prestwick GR
☎(0292) 79849
Monkton Road, Prestwick, Ayrshire KA9
20 covered, floodlit bays. **Open:** Mon-Fri
9am-9pm; Sat 9am-6pm; Sun 9am-8pm.
Charges: 80p/35.

Q259 Strathclyde Park GR
☎(0698) 286505
Mote Hill, Hamilton, Lanarkshire ML3 9XX
24 covered, floodlit bays. **Open:** winter
10am-9pm; summer 10am-9.30pm.
Charges: £2.70/large; £2.20/small.
9 hole course (see Q133).

R260 Glenrothes GDR
☎(0592) 775374
Stenton Rd, Glenrothes, Fife
20 covered, floodlit bays. **Open:** Mon-Fri
10am-9pm; Sat/Sun 10am-6pm.
Charges: £1.25/50.
18 hole golf couse (see R50).

R261 Middlebank GDR
☎(0821) 670317/670335
Middlebank, Errol, Tayside PH2 7SX.
14 covered, floodlit bays. **Open:**
9am-9pm. **Charges:** £1.40/50.

S262 Fairways Leisure Park
☎(0463) 713335
Castle Heather, Inverness IV1 2AA
22 covered, floodlit bays. **Open:**
9am-10.30pm. **Charges:** 85p/24.
9 hole pitch & putt (£2, Jnr £1.50).

T263 Ballyearl Golf Centre
☎(0232) 848287
585 Doagh Rd, Newtownabbey, Belfast
27 covered, floodlit bays. **Open:**
9am-9.30pm. **Charges:** on application.
9 hole course (see T4).

T264 Ballymena GDR
☎(0266) 40654
Warden Street, Ballymena, Co Antrim
7 covered, floodlit bays. **Open:** Oct-April
Mon-Fri 12-3pm, 6.30-9pm; Sat 12-4pm;
May-Sept Mon-Fri 12-9pm; Sat
10.30am-5pm. **Charges:** £1.30/50;
£2.15/100; £3/150; groups (min 6) by
arrangement £1 per person incl club hire.

T265 Craigavon
☎(0762) 326606
Golf and Ski Centre, Turmoyra Lane,
Silverwood, Lurgan, Co Armagh
8 covered, floodlit bays. **Open:** Mon-Fri
9am-9pm; Sat/Sun 9am-4pm. **Charges:**
£1.55/bucket.　12 hole pitch & putt; 18
and 9 hole courses (see T21).

T266 Downpatrick GR
☎(0396) 613558
86 Ardglass Rd, Downpatrick, Co Down
24 covered, floodlit bays. **Open:**
9am-9pm. **Charges:** £2/85; £1.25/45.
18 hole course (see T24).

T267 Knockbracken G & CC
☎(0232) 792108, 795666
Ballymaconaghy Rd, Knockbracken,
Belfast BT8 4SB.
40 covered, floodlit bays. **Open:**
9am-11pm. **Charges:** from 70p to £2.50.
18 hole course (see T38).

T268 Newry and Mourne GC
☎(06937) 73247
45 Milltown Street, Burren, Warrenpoint,
Co Down BT34 3RJ
10 covered, floodlit bays; grass facilities.
Open: Mon-Fri 10am-10pm; Sat/Sun
10am-8pm. **Charges:** £1/50; £1.50/80;
£2/120.

U269 The Black Bush DR
☎(01) 250021
Thomastown, Dunshaughlin, Co Meath
6 covered, floodlit bays. **Open:**
dawn-dusk. **Charges:** £1/35.
18 and 9 hole course (see U29).

U270 Harbour Point
☎(021) 353094
Little Island, Cork, Co Cork
21 covered, floodlit bays. **Open:**
9am-10pm approx. **Charges:** £2.75/100.
18 hole course (see U98).

U271 The Heath DR
☎(0502) 46533
The Heath, Portlaoise, Co Laois
10 covered, floodlit bays. **Open:**
9am-10pm. **Charges:** £1.50/75; 50p/25.
18 hole course (see U101).

U272 Leopardstown GC
☎(01) 289 5341
Foxrock, Dublin 18
33 covered, floodlit bays; 25 open bays.
Open: summer 9.30am-10pm; winter
9.30am-9.15pm. **Charges:** £2/small
bucket; £2.50/medium; £3/large; £4/extra
large.　9 hole course (see U119).

U273 Mount Juliet G & CC
☎(056) 24725
Thomastown, Co Kilkenny
Open: all day, every day. **Charges:** on
application.
18 hole course (see U133).

INDEX